Recent Progress in

HORMONE RESEARCH

The Proceedings of the Laurentian Hormone Conference

VOLUME 41

RECENT PROGRESS IN
HORMONE RESEARCH

Proceedings of the
1984 Laurentian Hormone Conference

Edited by
ROY O. GREEP

VOLUME 41

PROGRAM COMMITTEE

G. D. Aurbach
J. D. Baxter
J. C. Beck
H. Friesen
R. O. Greep
P. A. Kelly

I. A. Kourides
A. R. Means
J. E. Rall
N. E. Schwartz
J. L. Vaitukaitis
W. Vale

ACADEMIC PRESS, INC.
(Harcourt Brace Jovanovich, Publishers)

Orlando   San Diego   New York   London
Toronto   Montreal   Sydney   Tokyo

ACADEMIC PRESS, INC.
Orlando, Florida 32887

United Kingdom Edition published by
ACADEMIC PRESS INC. (LONDON) LTD.
24–28 Oval Road, London NW1 7DX

LIBRARY OF CONGRESS CATALOG CARD NUMBER: Med. 47-38

ISBN 0–12–571141–7

PRINTED IN THE UNITED STATES OF AMERICA

85 86 87 88   9 8 7 6 5 4 3 2 1

CONTENTS

v

LIST OF CONTRIBUTORS AND DISSCUSSANTS

J. Abramowitz
R. N. Anderson
D. R. Aquilano
G. D. Aurbach
C. W. Bardin
K. L. Barker
E. Battenberg
J. D. Baxter
N. Ben-Jonathan
H. A. Bern
L. Birnbaumer
F. E. Bloom
A. Borofsky
D. D. Brandon
G. Callard
I. Callard
G. T. Campbell
M. G. Caron
R. A. Cerione
M. C. Chang
T. Chen
G. P. Chrousos
J. Cidlowski
J. H. Clark
J. Codina
S. Cohen
R. B. Constant
W. F. Crowley
C. N. d'Arville
D. Dluzen
O. V. Dominguez
P. Donahoe
R. Edgren
R. M. Evans
C. E. Farin
A. Ferron
M. Filicori
T. A. Fitz
H. M. Fraser
J. Fryer
M. C. Gershengorn
N. Gesundheit
G. Gibori
K. A. Gregerson
H. Grotjan

P. F. Hall
W. Hansel
J. D. Hildebrandt
J. A. Holt
K. B. Horwitz
R. Iyengar
L. Joshi
D. Keefe
P. Kelly
K. Kim
M. A. Kirschner
E. Knobil
Y. Kobayashi
D. T. Krieger
B. A. Larson
W. Leavitt
K. Lederis
R. J. Lefkowitz
D. A. Leong
H. A. Levey
R. Levine
D. W. Lincoln
G. A. Lincoln
M. B. Lipsett
B. A. Littlefield
D. L. Loriaux
K. L. MacCannell
J. A. Magner
J. R. Mancillas
G. B. Martin
R. Mattera
S. M. McCann
A. S. McNeilly
J. Meites
M. M. Menezes-Ferreira
R. J. Milner
C. Monder
R. Moudgal
T. G. Muldoon
C. S. Nicoll
R. S. Nishioka
G. D. Niswender
R. Osathanondh
A. H. Payne
D. Pearson

ix

P. Petrick
P. G. Quinn
M. H. J. Raj
V. D. Ramirez
C. S. S. Rani
J. Rivier
J. Robbins
F. J. Rojas
C. Ronin
M. C. Rosenfeld
K. Ryan
N. A. Samaan
N. F. Santoro
H. R. Sawyer
R. H. Schwall
N. Schwartz
S. M. Sedlacek
A. Segaloff
M. Selmanoff
G. Siggins
M. S. Smith
D. I. Spratt

J. Stalvey
B. S. Stannard
K. Sterling
R. L. Stouffer
T. Sunyer
J. G. Sutcliffe
L. Swanson
T. Taylor
E. Terasawa
M. O. Thorner
M. Tomita
J. L. Vaitukaitis
J. D. Veldhuis
D. L. Vogel
M. R. Walters
L. L. Wei
B. D. Weintraub
J. Weisz
P. Wise
K. L. Wong
N. Woo

PREFACE

This volume, as are all the others of *Recent Progress in Hormone Research,* is based on the proceedings of a Laurentian Hormone Conference. This one was held in late August 1984 at the Homestead in Hot Springs, Virginia.

Comprehensive coverage of progress in this very broad area of biomedical science was not intended, instead the aim was to select areas currently under intensive investigation. They are explored in great depth in papers by leading authorities, and are followed by penetrating and critical discussions.

The present volume reexamines at the molecular level the hormone–receptor interactions and the subsequent series of intracellular events that have provided many important new insights made possible by recent methodological advances and improved instrumentation. First, the biosynthesis, secretion, metabolism, and mechanism of action of the steroid hormones are examined anew with strikingly rewarding results. In like manner the mechanisms of action of TSH and TRH are revealed at a level of sophistication hitherto undreamed of. On another front, the molecular characterization of a brain specific mRNA represents a great step forward in understanding the interaction of hormones and cortical neurons. Additionally, important clarification of the factors affecting changes in frequency and amplitude of GnRH pulses and the resulting functional consequences in various mammals including humans with disorders of fertility are reported in great detail. Topping off these fundamental advances are two reports on the biological heritage of mammalian endocrinology. These detail the structure and activities of urotensin I and urotensin II as derived from the urophysis of a variety of fishes and tested in both the lower vertebrates and mammals.

Headlong advances on all these fronts, including perhaps foremost of all the interspecies transfer of genes that control the secretion of specific hormones, open fantastic vistas of effective therapeutic achievements that surely lie ahead. The reading of these triumphs in our understanding of the role of hormones as chemical communicators in the total neurophysiology of the living organism will attest that the future of hormone research has never before loomed so bright.

I take this opportunity to thank Drs. Geula Gibori, Christopher Longcope, Wendell W. Leavitt, Paul A. Kelly, Dorothy T. Krieger, Samuel M. McCann, Ian P. Callard, and Jacob Robbins for their skillful service in chairing the several sessions. I also wish to express to Lucy Felicissimo and Linda Carsagnini our appreciation for their speedy transcribing of the taped discussions. To our Executive Secretary, Martha Devin I am deeply grateful for her effective handling of the multitudinous affairs that help to make this annual Conference and the published proceedings a successful enterprise. To the staff of Academic Press goes my praise and gratitude for their devoted attention to detail that yields such a satisfying publication.

Roy O. Greep

Trophic Stimulation of Steroidogenesis: In Search of the Elusive Trigger[1]

PETER F. HALL

*Worcester Foundation for Experimental Biology,
Shrewsbury, Massachusetts*

It is a great honor to be asked to deliver the Gregory Pincus Memorial Lecture. My contact with Gregory Pincus was entirely indirect, but for me it was certainly significant. I heard him deliver a characteristically flamboyant lecture on adrenal steroidogenesis at the Royal Society of Medicine, London, in 1954. In the course of this presentation, he suggested that ACTH stimulates steroid synthesis at some early point in the pathway—probably before pregnenolone. It was the first time I had cause to consider the idea that a hormone could stimulate specific steps in a biosynthetic pathway. As things turned out, I came to work at the Foundation which Pincus helped to create but by that time he was no longer alive, so that I was destined never to meet him.

When my time came to start a laboratory, I considered the problem of the mechanism by which LH stimulates steroidogenesis in rabbit testis. It seemed to me useful to break this question into two experimentally more manageable questions: namely, which step(s) in the pathway is(are) stimulated by the hormone and how are these steps stimulated, i.e., what is the molecular basis of stimulation? At Pittsburgh, I met Seymour Koritz who was working with ACTH and we decided to join forces. We suspected that LH and ACTH probably act by the same, or similar mechanisms, and that we could use adrenal, testis, and corpus luteum as the needs of our experiments dictated, because each tissue offers certain advantages. The question of where stimulation is exerted was approached by incubating tissue with radioactively labeled substrates with and without the trophic hormone added *in vitro,* to measure the production of radioactive steroid hormone (Fig. 1). With [7α-³H] cholesterol as substrate, the trophic hormones stimulated incorporation of ³H into the end-products of the steroidogenic pathway. When we used [³H]pregnenolone as substrate, we noticed two differences: conversion was an order of

---

[1] The Gregory Pincus Memorial Lecture.

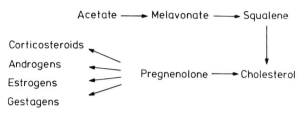

FIG. 1.   The steroidogenic pathway.

magnitude greater and the trophic hormone was without effect on this conversion (1–4). The conclusion seemed inescapable that both trophic hormones in all three tissues stimulate steroid synthesis beyond cholesterol and before pregnenolone; in short, it is the side-chain cleavage of cholesterol that is stimulated. We found no evidence of stimulation before cholesterol although we could not exclude the possibility that under some conditions the synthesis of cholesterol from acetate could be accelerated by the trophic hormone. These studies confirmed the earlier work of Stone and Hechter with the perfused adrenal (5).

I.   Within the Mitochondrion

The fact that the side-chain cleavage system is confined to mitochondria made the source of energy for side-chain cleavage a subject of considerable interest. It was found that in beef adrenal the side-chain cleavage reaction can use reversed electron transport and transhydrogenation as a source of reducing equivalents in the form of NADPH for the cleavage reaction (6, 7). Moreover mitochondrial malic enzyme, which was suggested as a source of NADPH for 11β-hydroxylation (8), could not account for the greater consumption of NADPH required for side-chain cleavage. As it turned out this information did not reveal how ACTH regulated the rate of production of pregnenolone; no evidence was found to suggest that ACTH or cyclic AMP increased the production of NADPH by the adrenal. Purification of the side-chain cleavage enzyme from beef adrenal revealed important properties of the enzyme (9): the stoichiometry of the reaction (10), the involvement of heme in the cleavage of the 20,22 bond (11) and aggregation of the enzyme to an active form composed of 16 subunits (9). However these findings did not clarify the mechanism of action of ACTH.

At this point it was decided to make use of an adrenal cell tumor line developed by Sato and co-workers (12) and studied in detail by Kowal (13)—the so-called Y-1 cell. This cell line has been shown to respond to ACTH and cyclic AMP even better than normal adrenal (13) and monolayer cultures offer advantages for some of the experimental approaches to be described. The tumor cell line does not synthesize the usual cortico-

TABLE I

Production of Pregnenolone by Isolated
Mitochondria from Y-1 Cells[a]

Additions to cells	Pregnenolone (nmol/min/mg protein)
—	32.1 ± 2.9
ACTH	29.9 ± 3.3
db cyclic AMP	30.6 ± 2.4

[a] Y-1 cells were incubated for 30 minutes with the additions shown. Mitochondria were prepared and incubated for 20 minutes at 30°C. Pregnenolone was extracted from mitochondria plus incubation medium and measured by radioimmunoassay (14).

steroid hormones but steroidogenic activity can be measured by determining the rate of production of 20α-dihydroprogesterone (14). The use of Y-1 cells soon brought two important findings: (1) It was decided to use this system to test directly the hypothesis that ACTH stimulates side-chain cleavage of cholesterol by isolating mitochondria from cells incubated with and without ACTH to measure the rate of production of pregnenolone by the isolated mitochondria. To our disappointment, no difference could be detected between the production of pregnenolone by the two groups of mitochondria (Table I) (14). This experiment has been repeated by more than 8 workers in my laboratory with the same result. Moreover addition of cholesterol to the isolated mitochondria did not influence the outcome of such experiments. These negative observations cast doubt on the cherished hypothesis that ACTH stimulates side-chain cleavage of cholesterol.

(2) When Y-1 cells were incubated with radioactive amino acids with and without ACTH, we observed, by gel electrophoresis of mitochondrial extracts, two labeled proteins of molecular weights of 27,000 and 13,000 (15) (Fig. 2). With the aid of inhibitors of the synthesis of protein and RNA (including chloramphenicol), we concluded that these proteins are made on stable mRNA (Fig. 2) by cytoplasmic ribosomes and transported to mitochondria (15).

II. Source of Mitochondrial Cholesterol

Although the first of these two observations (failure to stimulate mitochondrial production of pregnenolone) was disturbing, it was consistent with the findings of Garren and co-workers who found that cycloheximide inhibits the response to ACTH at some step before side-chain cleavage (16). When cholesterol (as opposed to acetate) is the source of the steroids

PETER F. HALL

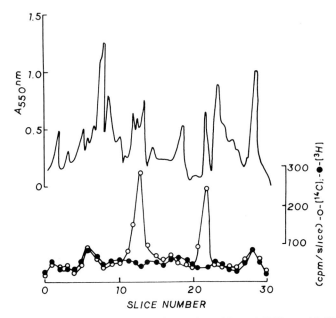

FIG. 2.   Y-1 cells were incubated with [³H]leucine without ACTH or with [¹⁴C]leucine
with ACTH for 1 hour. Mitochondrial protein from the cells incubated with the two isotopes
was analyzed by disc gel electrophoresis with sodium dodecyl sulfate. Gels were examined
by densitometry and then sliced for double-label counting by liquid scintillation spectrometry. The tracing of A_{550} was from control cells; that from treated cells was superimposable.

produced by the adrenal, the only steps before side-chain cleavage are
those associated with the movement of cholesterol to and within mitochondria. Garren *et al.,* on the basis of studies *in vivo,* made the prescient
suggestion that ACTH stimulates transfer of cholesterol to mitochondria
(16). This idea could explain our failure to find increase in the production
of pregnenolone by isolated mitochondria from cells stimulated by
ACTH—by removing the mitochondria from a continuing supply of cholesterol in the cytoplasm, we prevented the mitochondrial enzyme system
from expressing the stimulating influence of ACTH (14). To test this
hypothesis we inhibited side-chain cleavage by incubating the cells with
aminoglutethimide, and incubated the cells with and without ACTH. Under these conditions, steroidogenic cholesterol should accumulate in mitochondria and would be available for side-chain cleavage when the inhibitor was removed. After various periods of time mitochondria were
prepared in the presence of the inhibitor, were washed to remove the
inhibitor, and then incubated in buffered medium for measurement of the
production of pregnenolone. The result was clear: production of preneno-

FIG. 3. Y-1 cells were incubated with aminoglutethimide (0.76 mM) with and without ACTH for 30 minutes. Mitochondria were prepared in buffered sucrose containing the same concentration of the inhibitor. The mitochondria were washed to remove inhibitor and then incubated in a medium containing malate (10 mM) and cyanoketone (20 μM). The production of pregnenolone was measured after incubation for the times shown (14). Cyanoketone was used to prevent further metabolism of pregnenolone.

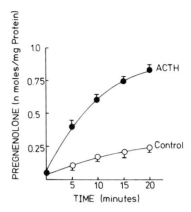

lone was greater with mitochondria from cells treated with ACTH than those from unstimulated cells (Fig. 3) (14). The contrast with the observations made without the inhibitor (Table I) was striking.

It was clearly important to demonstrate that this additional pregnenolone came from greater levels of cholesterol which reached the mitochondria under the influence of ACTH. For this purpose the experiment with aminoglutethimide was repeated with the inhibitor present during the preparation of mitochondria. The mitochondria were then extracted with ether to measure the content of cholesterol. No difference was seen between the concentration of cholesterol (per mg of mitochondrial protein) in mitochondria from stimulated or unstimulated cells. However, when cholesterol was measured in the inner mitochondrial membrane, levels were greater in the organelles from stimulated cells (Fig. 4). These find-

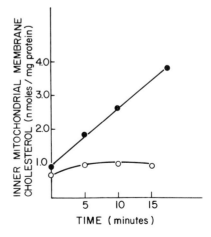

FIG. 4. Cholesterol transport to inner mitochondrial membrane. Y-1 cells were incubated with aminoglutethimide (0.76 mM), with and without ACTH for the times shown. Following incubation, inner mitochondrial membrane was prepared and the content of cholesterol in the membrane was measured by gas/liquid chromatography.

ings supported the view expressed by Garren *et al.* (16) that ACTH promotes the delivery of cholesterol to mitochondria. Although it is difficult
to find other examples of such a mechanism for stimulating the activity of
an enzyme, the circumstances for the side-chain cleavage system are
unusual in that the substrate must be transported to the enzyme from one
compartment in the cell to another.

The two proteins synthesized under the influence of ACTH could be
detected in mitochondria within 5 minutes of exposure to the hormone
(Fig. 5). Moreover, the synthesis of these proteins was inhibited by puro-
mycin and cycloheximide but not by actinomycin D (15). The concentration of cycloheximide required to produce 50% inhibition of the responses
to ACTH and cyclic AMP was approximately the same for steroidogenesis and for incorporation of [³H]tyrosine into mitochondrial protein (Fig.
6) (14). Evidently ACTH and cyclic AMP promote synthesis of two proteins on cytoplasmic ribosomes; these proteins move to mitochondria and
are associated with the increased production of pregnenolone resulting
from the actions of the two stimulating agents (ACTH and cyclic AMP). It
was tempting to relate these new proteins to the transport of cholesterol
to mitochondria. Certainly these observations raised the question of how
the adrenal cell transports cholesterol from cytoplasm to mitochondria in
a regulated manner.

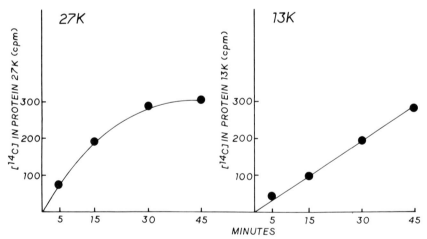

FIG. 5. Mitochondrial proteins synthesized under the influence of ACTH. Mitochondrial proteins were prepared from Y-1 cells incubated with [¹⁴C]leucine and ACTH as
described under Fig. 2. Proteins were isolated after incubation of the cells for the times
shown and separated by electrophoresis on polyacrylamide with sodium dodecyl sulfate. ¹⁴C
was measured in two proteins of molecular weights 27,000 and 13,000.

III. Mechanism of Cholesterol Transport

At this time the family of cytochalasins was introduced into cell biology as inhibitors of microfilaments (17). Could microfilaments be involved in directing the motion of molecules through the cytoplasm? These structures provide vectors within the cell and they are potentially contractile. Moreover a striking characteristic of the responses of Y-1 cells to ACTH and cyclic AMP is a change in shape from flat to round (18). This change must surely involve signifcant reorganization of the cytoskeleton of the cell. Cytochalasin B was soon found to inhibit the steroidogenic responses to ACTH and cyclic AMP and, in particular, the increased transport of cholesterol to mitochondria which these substances produce

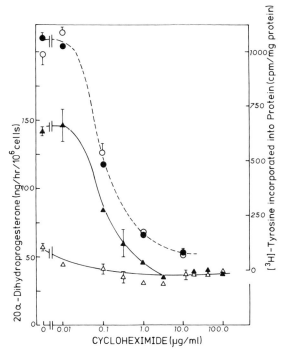

FIG. 6.   Protein synthesis and steroidogenesis in Y-1 cells. In one series of dishes containing Y-1 cells the response to ACTH was measured by determining the production of 20α-dihydroprogesterone by the cells. In a second series of dishes, incorporation of [³H]tyrosine (0.5 nmol; 20 μCi/dish) into Y-1 cell protein was determined by incubating cells with this amino acid for 60 minutes. The effect of increasing concentrations of cycloheximide was examined on both of these functions (response to ACTH and protein synthesis). Protein synthesis: (○) control; (●) ACTH (86 mU/ml). Steroid production: (△) control; (▲) ACTH (86 mU/ml). From Nakamura *et al.* (15).

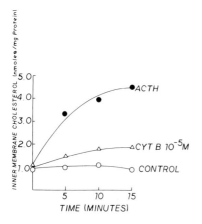

FIG. 7. Effect of cytochalasin B on the transport of cholesterol to mitochondria. Y-1 cells were incubated with aminoglutethimide (0.76 mM) with and without ACTH for the times shown. Mitochondria were isolated and inner membrane was then prepared from these organelles. These procedures were all performed in buffered medium containing the same concentration of aminoglutethimide. The inner membrane was extracted with ether and the cholesterol content of the membrane was measured by gas/liquid chromatography.

(Fig. 7) (19). A determined search for actions of cytochalsin, other than those associated with actin, proved negative (20). Moreover four members of the cytochalasin family (B, D, E, and reduced B) were examined to determine the concentrations required to inhibit steroidogenic responses to ACTH and cyclic AMP, rounding of the cells and binding of cytochalasins to actin purified from Y-1 cells. The concentrations of cytochalasin required to produce half-maximal effects showed a striking correlation for each of the various cytochalasins (Table II) (21). That is, although the potencies of these agents vary over two orders of magnitude,

TABLE II
Potency Ratios of Cytochalasins[a]

| Cyto-chalasin | ACTH | | db C'AMP | | Rounding of cells | Actin Polymerization |
	20α-DHP	Cholest ↓ Mito	20α-DHP	Cholest ↓ Mito		
E	100	98	96	102	104	106
D	9.2	10.3	11.2	10.3	11.1	10.4
B	1.8	2.1	2.0	1.6	1.4	1.3
H₂B	1.0	1.0	1.0	1.0	1.0	1.0

[a] Values represent relative concentrations of the 4 cytochalasins required to give half-maximal effects: inhibition of the stimulation by ACTH and cyclic AMP of the production of 20α-dihydroprogesterone (20α-DHP); inhibition of the effects of these agents on the transport of cholesterol to mitochondria; rounding of Y-1 cells caused by cytochalasins and inhibition of the polymerization of purified Y-1 cell actin. Polymerization was caused by addition of Mg^{2+} (1 mM). Details are given in Hall *et al.* (21). Values are expressed relative to the first effect of cytochalasin E as 100. 20α-DHP, 20α-Dihydroprogesterone; Cholest → mito, transport of cholesterol to mitochondria.

the concentrations of a given cytochalasin required to inhibit the steroidogenic responses, to cause rounding and to inhibit polymerization of actin
were similar for a given cytochalasin. These findings pointed to a close
relationship between inhibition of steroidogenic responses and binding of
cytochalasins to actin. These effects of cytochalasin B were confirmed in
other laboratories (23, 24). Nevertheless, cytochalasins have effects on
various cells that cannot be attributed to binding to actin (22). The hypothesis that the cytoskeleton is involved in the responses to ACTH and cyclic
AMP, rested on shaky ground without a more specific inhibitor.

In 1975, Gabbiani and co-workers reported the isolation of anti-actin
antibodies from the sera of patients suffering from hepatitis (25–27). The
antibodies were purified by affinity chromatography using skeletal muscle
actin as the ligand (25–27). The purified antibodies were carefully characterized and shown to be monospecific (25–27). At about this time reports
had begun to appear concerning the transfer of macromolecules from lipid
vesicles to the cytoplasm of various cells (28). It was decided to incorporate anti-actin antibodies into liposomes and to fuse the liposomes with
Y-1 cells before measuring the responses of these cells to ACTH or cyclic
AMP. It can be seen from Fig. 8 that the antibody injected into the cells in

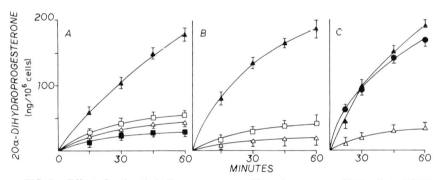

FIG. 8.   Effect of anti-actin in liposomes on steroidogenic response of Y-1 cells to ACTH
(A) or Bt$_2$cAMP (B). Y-1 cells were incubated for 1 hour with liposomes containing buffer or
buffer plus anti-actin (a total dose of 50 μg of antibody protein/dish of cells) (first incubation). Medium was removed, cells were washed, and fresh medium containing albumin/
saline (control) or ACTH (86 mU/ml), or Bt$_2$cAMP (2 mM), but no liposomes (second
incubation), was added. Incubation was continued for various periods of time. The reaction
was stopped and production of 20α-dihydroprogesterone was measured by radioimmunoassay. (C) Effect of adding liposomes containing buffer only on the response to ACTH. Values
show means and ranges for duplicate determinations. ($\triangle$) Liposomes with buffer; no ACTH
or Bt$_2$cAMP. ($\blacktriangle$) Liposomes with buffer; ACTH or Bt$_2$cAMP. ($\square$) Liposomes with anti-
actin; ACTH or Bt$_2$cAMP. ($\blacksquare$) Liposomes with anti-actin; no ACTH or Bt$_2$cAMP. ($\bullet$) No
liposomes; ACTH. In these symbols, the additions for the first incubation are shown to the
left of the semicolon and those for the second incubation, to the right. In (C) values for no
liposomes and no ACTH are so similar to those for liposomes and no ACTH that they have
been omitted for the sake of clarity. From Hall *et al.* (29).

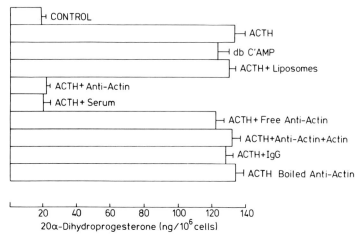

FIG. 9. Production of 20α-dihydroprogesterone by Y-1 cells fused with liposomes containing buffer or anti-actin antibodies dissolved in buffer. Cells were incubated for 1 hour with liposomes containing buffer or anti-actin and other antibodies as indicated (first incubation). Cells were washed and incubated (second incubation) with ACTH or db cyclic AMP as shown. In two bars (fourth and seventh from the top), only a single incubation was performed as described below. At the end of the second incubation (30 minutes) or the first incubation when no second incubation as performed, production of 20α-dihydroprogesterone was measured. Control: no additions. ACTH and db cyclic AMP: liposomes containing buffer; ACTH or db cyclic AMP in second incubation. ACTH + liposomes: liposomes containing buffer, ACTH added in solution. No second incubation. ACTH + anti-actin and ACTH + serum: liposomes containing anti-actin or patients' serum; ACTH in second incubation. ACTH + free anti-actin: ACTH and anti-actin added in solution. No second incubation. ACTH + anti-actin + actin: anti-actin was mixed with 4-fold molar excess of muscle actin before incorporation into liposomes; ACTH in second incubation. Bottom two bars: normal human IgG or boiled anti-actin were incorporated into liposomes; ACTH in second incubation. Bars show means and ranges for duplicate determinations.

this way inhibits the subsequent responses to both ACTH and cyclic AMP. Figure 8C also shows that fusing Y-1 cells with liposomes containing buffer but no antibody was without effect on the subsequent response to ACTH (29). Figure 9 shows important controls. Addition of liposomes containing buffer does not inhibit the response to ACTH added at the same time. Addition of antibodies in aqueous solution (no liposomes) causes little inhibition. Again, when anti-actin is mixed with a 4-fold molar excess of the antigen, i.e., muscle actin, and this mixture is incorporated into liposomes, no inhibition of the action of ACTH is observed (29). Normal human IgG and boiled anti-actin were also without effect (Fig. 9). It seems clear that the effect of anti-actin is specific and that the antibody is acting as the result of its ability to bind actin. Anti-actin

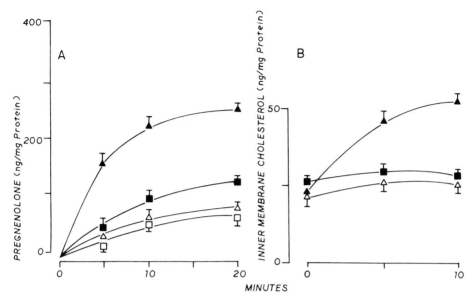

FIG. 10.   Effect of anti-actin antibodies on mitochondrial responses to ACTH. (A) Production of pregnenolone by isolated mitochondria. Y-1 cells were incubated with liposomes containing buffer (△,▲), or buffer plus antibody (□,■). After 1 hour cells were washed and incubated with aminoglutethimide with ACTH (▲,■) or without ACTH (△,□). Mitochondria were prepared, washed, and incubated to determine production of pregnenolone. (B) After incubation with liposomes containing buffer (△,▲) or buffer plus anti-actin (■), the content of cholesterol in the inner mitochondrial membrane was measured as described in Hall *et al.* (29). During the second incubation, ACTH was added (▲,■) or saline was used in control cells (△). From Hall *et al.* (29).

injected into Y-1 cells from liposomes also inhibits the effects of ACTH and cyclic AMP on the transport of cholesterol to mitochondria and on the production of pregnenolone by isolated mitochondria after removing the inhibitor (aminoglutethimide) (Fig. 10) (29).

The experiments with anti-actin left little doubt that actin is involved in the response of Y-1 cells to ACTH because of the high specificity of the antibody (29). However, these studies showed at least three serious limitations, namely (1) it is not possible to determine how much anti-actin is injected into the cell, (2) the mechanism by which the antibody acts is unknown, and (3) because it is necessary to use inner mitochondrial membrane, it is not possible to distinguish an effect of ACTH on transport of cholesterol to mitochondria as opposed to an effect within mitochondria (outer to inner membrane). The first limitation arises from the fact that the liposomes cannot be removed from the cells after fusion and no doubt anti-actin will remain in the liposomes. Any attempt to measure ^{125}I-labeled anti-actin would not distinguish the labeled protein in the cells from that remaining in the liposomes. The second problem arises from the heterogeneity of polyclonal antibodies; it is possible to consider numerous mechanisms by which the combination of actin with anti-actin could affect the function of actin. Therefore the antibody gives no indication of *how* actin is altered in response to ACTH. These limitations were overcome by changing both the inhibitor and the method of injection.

The enzyme DNase is well known as an inhibitor of the polymerization of actin (30). It binds monomeric or G-actin in a one-to-one complex and prevents polymerization of the actin (30, 31). As the result of turnover, this will lead to depolymerization of F-actin. DNase does not bind to F-actin except at very high concentrations (30) that could not be attained by injection of the enzyme into Y-1 cells. In the meantime, red cell ghosts had gained favor as vehicles for the introduction of macromolecules into cells (32). One advantage of this system is that following fusion, the ghosts can be destroyed by lysis with ammonium chloride (33); in this way the remaining extracellular material can be removed from the culture dishes. By labeling the protein with ^{125}I it is then possible to determine how much protein has been injected into the cells.

The method of red cell loading is illustrated in Fig. 11. Cells are swollen in hypotonic buffer which damages the cell membrane and allows equilibration between the cytoplasm and the contents of the ghosts. Restoring isotonicity allows the membrane to repair itself as the original shape of the

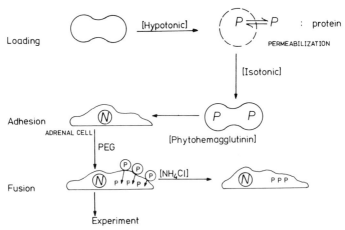

FIG. 11.   Diagram showing steps in loading red cells and fusion of the ghosts with Y-1 cells. After fusion the cells can be used for measurement of steroid synthesis with the fused red cells present or the red cells can be subjected to lysis with ammonium chloride.

cell is restored. The protein in question is trapped in the ghost. Fusion is encouraged by attaching ghosts to Y-1 cells via the lectin phytohemagglutinin. Fusion with polyethylene glycol permits exchange between the contents of the ghosts and that of the cells. Ghosts can be removed by lysis and numerous control studies revealed that neither the presence of fused cells nor treatment with dilute ammonium chloride affected either the subsequent production of steroid, the response to ACTH, or cell division.

Figure 12 shows that loading of Y-1 cells with DNase can be measured accurately and the amount of DNase injected per cell can be controlled since the number of molecules of DNase loaded per adrenal cell shows a linear relationship to the number of red cells added (A) and to the concentration of DNase in the loading solution (B).

Loading Y-1 cells with DNase inhibits the steroidogenic responses to ACTH and cyclic AMP (Fig. 13). Inhibition is dose-dependent with half-

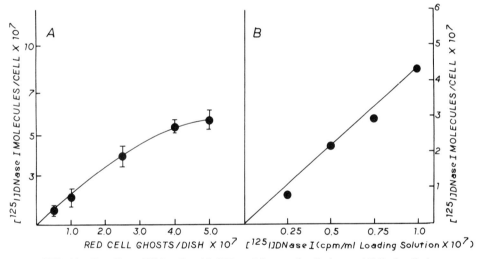

FIG. 12. Loading of Y-1 cells with DNase I from red cell ghosts. (A) Red cell ghosts were loaded with [^{125}I]DNase I (10^6 cpm/mg protein). Red cells, in the numbers shown on the abscissa, were fused with Y-1 cells at approximately 80% confluence (i.e., 80% of the number of cells per dish at confluence: 2×10^6 for a 35-mm dish). Following fusion, red cells were subjected to lysis by ammonium chloride. Y-1 cells were washed and removed from the plates by incubation with EDTA. An aliquot of the cells was counted in a hemocytometer. The remaining cells were collected by centrifugation and dissolved in NaOH. The content of ^{125}I was determined in the NaOH solution. The values shown are means and ranges for duplicate determinations. (B) Studies performed in which concentration of [^{125}I]DNase I in the solution used to load the ghosts was varied. The number of ghosts added to the Y-1 cells was constant (2.5×10^7 per plate). The ordinate shows the number of molecules of DNase I per cell. From Osawa *et al.* (71).

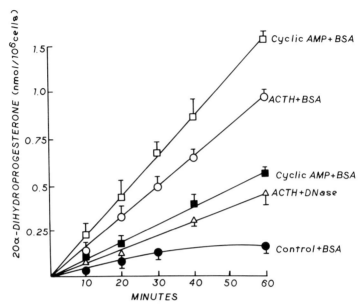

FIG. 13.   Influence of DNase I on steroidogenesis by Y-1 cells. Y-1 cells were fused with red cell ghosts containing bovine serum albumin (BSA) or DNase I. Twelve hours after fusion, cells were washed, fresh medium was added, and the production of 20α-dihydroprogesterone was measured at the times shown. Values are means and ranges of duplicate determinations. The concentrations of ACTH and dibutyryl cyclic AMP used were 86 mU/ml and 1 mM (final concentration), respectively. The loading solutions were prepared with albumin or DNase I at a concentration of 2 mg/ml. From Osawa *et al.* (71).

maximal inhibition at 3×10^7 molecules of DNase per cell (Fig. 14). It was then necessary to relate this value to the number of molecules of G-actin in the Y-1 cell. When the amount of actin per cell was measured by three independent methods, values shown in Table III were obtained. The two methods based upon binding by DNase gave consistent results (30, 34). Less reliance can be placed upon the method using SDS–gel electrophoresis because the separation of the G and F forms of actin in this method is based upon a somewhat arbitrary centrifugation and because densitometry of overlapping peaks is less accurate than measurement of DNase activity by means of a spectrophotometer (35). It appears that the number of molecules of DNase per cell that is required to inhibit the response to ACTH by 50% is approximately twice the number of molecules of G-actin per cell. Presumably, DNase has inhibited polymerization of G-actin and promoted depolymerization of F-actin and has thereby interfered with the redistribution of actin necessary for the response to ACTH. We observed also that loading with DNase also inhibits the response to ACTH

FIG. 14.   Influence of concentration of DNase I on the steroidogenic response to ACTH. Y-1 cells were fused with red cell ghosts containing BSA or DNase I. Numbers in parentheses refer to the number of red cells added to one plate of Y-1 cells. Twelve hours later cells were washed, fresh medium was added, and steroid production was measured after 60 minutes incubation. Bars represent means and ranges for duplicate determinations. The concentration of ACTH used was 86 mU/ml and the loading solution contained DNase I at a concentration of 2 mg/ml. From Osawa *et al.* (71).

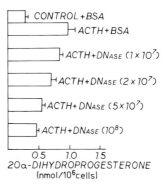

as judged by transport of cholesterol to the inner mitochondrial membrane (Fig. 15).

IV.   Apparent Contradictions

During the course of these studies three important observations were reported from other laboratories in which the action of ACTH was under investigation. At first sight these findings appeared to be inconsistent with our own studies:

1. One group reported increased mitochondrial cholesterol with ACTH and aminoglutethimide when *total* mitochondrial cholesterol was measured in rat adrenal (36).

2. A second group reported increased production of pregnenolone by isolated mitochondria following treatment with ACTH, without the use of aminoglutethimide (37).

TABLE III

Content of Actin (G and F) in Y-1 Adrenal Tumor Cells[a]

Methods (reference)	Actin molecules/cell $\times$ 10[7][b]		
	Total	G	F
DNase (30)	2.0 ± 0.5	1.5 ± 0.3	0.5 ± 0.1
Anti-DNase (34)	1.9 ± 0.4	1.3 ± 0.2	0.6 ± 0.1
SDS gels (35)	1.2	0.8	0.4

[a] G-actin was determined in Y-1 cell homogenate. Samples of homogenate were then treated with guanadinium Cl to depolymerize all actin and the total actin was then determined as G-actin. Values for F-actin were obtained by subtraction.

[b] Means and ranges for duplicate determinations.

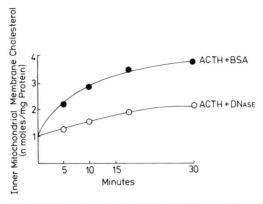

FIG. 15.   The effect of DNase I on the stimulation of cholesterol transport in Y-1 cells by ACTH. Large dishes of Y-1 cells (4 × 10⁷ cells per dish) were fused with red blood cells containing bovine serum albumin (BSA) or DNase. Twelve hours later, cells were washed and incubated with medium containing aminoglutethimide (final concentration 0.76 mM) and ACTH (80 mU/ml) for the times shown. Thereafter inner mitochondrial membrane was prepared and the cholesterol content was determined. From Osawa *et al.* (71).

3. Another group reported the occurrence of a so-called type I spectral shift in mitochondria from rats stimulated by ether stress. This signal was taken as evidence of increased loading of the side-chain cleavage enzyme with substrate, i.e., cholesterol (38). This conclusion is based on the fact that all forms of cytochrome P-450 show a shift in the Soret peak (Type I spectral shift), when the substrate binds to the enzyme. This shift allows the amount of enzyme–substrate complex to be measured accurately (39) and since measurements can be made by difference (enzyme plus substrate in one cuvette and enzyme without substrate in the second), values can be obtained with turbid suspensions, e.g., whole mitochondria. These findings suggested that ACTH promotes loading of P-450 with cholesterol, i.e., movement of cholesterol within the mitochondrion. With time, these apparent differences were resolved.

Careful and repeated measurement of mitochondrial cholesterol in Y-1 cells incubated with aminoglutethimide, with and without ACTH failed to reveal any difference due to the action of the trophic hormone. This is not surprising because the amount of pregnenolone formed is always small compared to the amount of cholesterol in mitochondria: one is looking for a small difference between two large numbers. Moreover the preparation of mitochondria by sedimentation is at best a semiquantitative procedure. By contrast, the cholesterol content of the inner mitochondrial membrane clearly reflects the action of ACTH because the content of cholesterol is

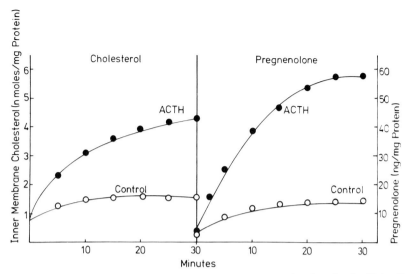

FIG. 16.   The effect of anaerobiosis on cholesterol transport in adrenal cells. Y-1 cells were incubated with and without ACTH under anaerobic conditions for 20 minutes. Mitochondria were prepared under anaerobic conditions for measurement of inner membrane cholesterol (left) or for incubation under aerobic conditions to measure production of pregnenolone (right).

considerably lower (per mg protein) than that of whole mitochondria (Fig. 4). The second and third observations were explained by the experiments of Bell and Harding (40). The blood flow to the adrenal is extremely high (41), second only to that of the carotid body. Unless special care is taken, adrenocortical mitochondria are usually prepared under anaerobic conditions because the gland is abruptly separated from this vigorous blood flow. Since oxygen is necessary for side-chain cleavage, anaerobiosis inhibits the conversion of cholesterol to pregnenolone and would therefore have the same effect as aminoglutethimide. When care is taken to maintain oxygenation of mitochondria, the spectral signal reported by Jefcoate and Orme-Johnson in rat adrenals was not observed by Bell and Harding (40). Moreover such a signal is not seen in mitochondria from Y-1 cells (unpublished). That anaerobiosis acts like aminoglutethimide in its effect on adrenal mitochondria was then demonstrated directly (14). When Y-1 cells were incubated under anaerobic conditions for 20 minutes with and without ACTH and mitochondria are prepared anaerobically, the inner mitochondrial membrane showed higher levels of cholesterol when the organelles are prepared from cells treated with ACTH than those from unstimulated cells (Fig. 16, left). If, on the other hand, mitochondria prepared anaerobically are incubated with buffer containing oxygen, production of pregnenolone is greater from mitochondria prepared from cells incubated with ACTH than those from unstimulated cells (Fig. 16, right). Clearly the system behaves with anaerobiosis much as it does with aminoglutethimide and for the same reason, i.e., both agents reversibly inhibit side-chain cleavage. Cholesterol accumulates because of this inhibition and no doubt some of the accumulated cholesterol exists as an enzyme–substrate complex.

If the type I spectral shift does indicate the amount of enzyme–substrate complex in mitochondria, this signal might well be expected to increase when the side-chain cleavage enzyme is inhibited. Since ACTH stimulates the mobilizaton of cholesterol from the cytoplasm and transfer of this substrate to mitochondria, the amount of enzyme–substrate complex, and hence the magnitude of the type I shift, would be expected to increase. Such considerations could also explain increased production of pregnenolone by mitochondria without inhibition of side-chain cleavage by aminoglutethimide before the mitochondria are prepared. Anaerobiosis, produced either inadvertantly during preparation of mitochondria, or deliberately by incubating Y-1 cells without oxygen, will inhibit side-chain cleavage. ACTH will promote transport of cholesterol to mitochondria and the greater amount of inner membrane cholesterol will produce more enzyme–substrate complex and hence a greater type I spectral shift. Moreover, this greater loading of the enzyme will result in greater production of pregnenolone when oxygen is restored to the anaerobic mitochondria. Y-1 cells do not become anaerobic as easily as rat adrenal, partly because they exist as individual cells without a blood supply, and perhaps partly because of conditions existing in monolayer cultures in which oxygen tension is higher than *in vivo*. All of these observations can be explained by an action of ACTH on the transport of cholesterol to mitochondria, within mitochondria or both:

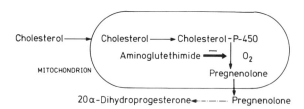

Finally it should be pointed out that the type I spectral shift is not entirely specific for substrate binding because the spin state of the heme iron, which is responsible for this shift, is influenced by such factors as pH and ionic strength (42) and perhaps by unknown factors.

V. Role of Ca^{2+}

It has been known for many years that ACTH does not stimulate steroidogenesis in a Ca^{2+}-free medium (43). This seems hardly surprising. What is less clear is the question of whether the second messenger (cyclic AMP) requires Ca^{2+} to stimulate the intracellular responses to ACTH because, like other peptide hormone receptors, the ACTH receptor requires Ca^{2+} if it is to stimulate production of cyclic AMP. Some evidence favors the view that cyclic AMP requires Ca^{2+} to stimulate production of steroids in the adrenal (44, 45). Exposure of adrenal cells to EGTA prevents the response to dibutyryl cyclic AMP but this may mean nothing more than the obvious fact that Ca^{2+} is *required* for the cell response—it does not necessarily indicate a direct and specific role for Ca^{2+} in the response to cyclic AMP. The introduction of Ca^{2+} ionophores, all of which exert nonspecific effects in whole cells, added nothing but confusion to the problem (46). Since Ca^{2+} is involved in so many biological responses, an agent capable of removing intracellular barriers to the movement of Ca^{2+} is likely to alter so many cellular functions that interpretation of the findings is certain to be difficult (46).

The discovery made during the 1970s, that many of the effects of Ca^{2+} are mediated by the Ca^{2+}-binding protein calmodulin (47, 48), opened new possibilities for exploring the role of Ca^{2+} in steroidogenesis. Moreover the availability of trifluoperazine and other inhibitors of calmodulin suggested a simple exploratory approach to the question of whether or not calmodulin is involved in the responses to ACTH and cyclic AMP. Indeed trifluoperazine inhibits the steroidogenic responses to ACTH and cyclic AMP with half-maximal inhibition at 15 μM (49) (Fig. 17). This value is in the range required for inhibition of the effect of calmodulin on purified phosphodiesterase (50) and is well below the concentration required to produce toxic effects in Y-1 cells (49). Trifluoroperazine sulfoxide, a derivative that is inactive as an inhibitor of calmodulin, is without effect on the response to ACTH (Fig. 17). Moreover trifluoperazine also inhibits the stimulation of the transport of cholesterol to mitochondria produced by ACTH and cyclic AMP (49). Unfortunately inhibitors are seldom specific in whole cells and trifluoperazine is no exception (51, 52). Clearly more direct evidence was required to support the case for the involvement of calmodulin in the regulation of steroid synthesis. Once again, injection of protein into cells from liposomes provided a useful experimental approach.

When calmodulin is introduced into Y-1 cells, it produces a modest increase in steroid synthesis and Ca^{2+} alone is without effect (Fig. 18). When the calmodulin is dialyzed against EGTA to remove bound Ca^{2+}, it

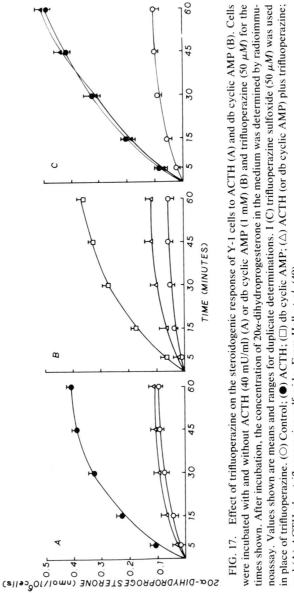

FIG. 17. Effect of trifluoperazine on the steroidogenic response of Y-1 cells to ACTH (A) and db cyclic AMP (B). Cells were incubated with and without ACTH (40 mU/ml) (A) or db cyclic AMP (1 mM) (B) and trifluoperazine (50 μM) for the times shown. After incubation, the concentration of 20α-dihydroprogesterone in the medium was determined by radioimmunoassay. I (C) trifluoperazine sulfoxide (50 μM) was used in place of trifluoperazine. (○) Control; (●) ACTH; (□) db cyclic AMP; (△) ACTH (or db cyclic AMP) plus trifluoperazine; and (▲) ACTH plus trifluoperazine sulfoxide. From Hall *et al.* (49).

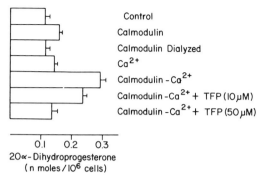

Control
Calmodulin
Calmodulin Dialyzed
Ca^{2+}
Calmodulin-Ca^{2+}
Calmodulin-Ca^{2+} + TFP (10 μM)
Calmodulin-Ca^{2+} + TFP (50 μM)

0.1   0.2   0.3
20α-Dihydroprogesterone
(n moles / 10^6 cells)

FIG. 18. The influence of calmodulin and Ca^{2+} on steroidogenesis by Y-1 cells. Cells were incubated for 60 minutes with liposomes containing buffer (control) or buffer plus the additions shown. Liposomes were prepared as described in Hall *et al.* (49). Following incubation, medium was removed, cells were washed twice with PBS at 0°C, and fresh medium was added with or without trifluoroperazine. Incubation was continued for 30 minutes and 20α-dihydroprogesterone was measured in samples of medium. Dialyzed calmodulin refers to calmodulin extensively dialyzed against EGTA (1 mM). Trifluoperazine was added to the medium "free," i.e., not in liposomes. The values shown represent means and ranges for duplicate determinations. From Hall *et al.* (49).

loses this ability to stimulate steroid synthesis (Fig. 18) (49). The most effective stimulus is calmodulin saturated with Ca^{2+}; stimulation in this case is inhibited by trifluoperazine (Fig. 18). Ca^{2+}-calmodulin also stimulates transport of cholesterol to mitochondria (Fig. 19); this stimulation is inhibited by trifluoperazine (49). Addition of liposomes containing Ca^{2+}-

FIG. 19. The influence of camodulin with calcium on the accumulation of cholesterol in the inner mitochondrial membrane. Y-1 cells were incubated with liposomes containing buffer (control) or buffer with calmodulin and Ca^{2+} (200 μl/ dish) as described in Hall *et al.* (49). The incubation medium contained aminoglutethimide (0.76 mM) and trifluoperazine (50 μM) where indicated. After incubation for the times shown, inner mitochondrial membrane was prepared and the cholesterol content was measured. (○) Liposomes with buffer; (●) liposomes with calmodulin-Ca^{2+}; (△) liposomes with calmodulin-Ca^{2+} and trifluoperazine. From Hall *et al.* (49).

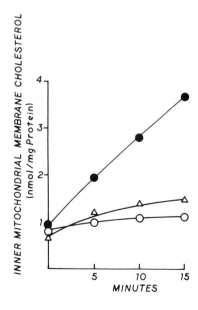

INNER MITOCHONDRIAL MEMBRANE CHOLESTEROL
(nmol / mg Protein)

MINUTES

calmodulin to mitochondria from Y-1 cells is without effect on the production of pregnenolone (49). These provocative findings indicate that calmodulin is involved in the mechanism of action of ACTH and cyclic AMP and in particular that Ca^{2+}-calmodulin is necessary for the increase in the transport of cholesterol to mitochondria produced by these stimulating agents. It was suggested that the unstimulated adrenal cell contains Ca^{2+} and calmodulin distributed in such a way that the calmodulin was, at least partly, depleted of the necessary complement of Ca^{2+}. By flooding the cell with exogenous calmodulin-Ca^{2+}, the protein saturated with Ca^{2+} reached that part of the cell in which it is required to stimulate steroid synthesis, i.e., transport of cholesterol. Presumably, ACTH is capable of redistributing Ca^{2+} or calmodulin or both.

VI. Supply of Cholesterol to the Cell

These studies point to the transport of cholesterol within the cell as a site of action of ACTH in the acute stimulation of the synthesis of steroids by adrenocortical cells. The classical experiments of Long, reported in this series of publications 40 years ago, showed that ACTH causes depletion of adrenal cholesterol—a response that could be used to measure ACTH (53). Long showed that within 6 hours of a single intraperitoneal injection of ACTH more than half of the total adrenal cholesterol is depleted (53). Since the whole adrenal presumably includes much cholesterol that is not involved in steroid synthesis (cholesterol in the medulla, membrane cholesterol, etc.) this represents severe depletion of that cholesterol which serves as the substrate for steroid biosynthesis. Péron and Koritz later showed that *in vitro* the disappearance of adrenal cholesterol could be accounted for, mole for mole, as steroid products (54). Following major abdominal surgery, plasma levels of corticosteroids may remain high for several days (55) so that the adrenal cortex must make some provision for additional cholesterol to maintain increased steroid biosynthesis for long periods of time. It appears that most of the steroidogenic cholesterol used by the adrenal comes from plasma (56). No doubt the adrenal cells can make some cholesterol from acetate (57). Nevertheless, these observations raise the question of whether or not the adrenal can increase uptake of cholesterol from plasma and promote synthesis of cholesterol from acetate at rates sufficient to replenish supplies for use in the steroidogenic pathway during prolonged stimulation. It was pointed out above that ACTH does not appear to stimulate the conversion of acetate to cholesterol. These considerations drew attention to cholesterol transport into the cell as a possible site of action of ACTH.

To approach this question we began by measuring the uptake of [3H]cholesterol by adrenal cells incubated without and with ACTH only to find no net transport of labeled cholesterol with or without ACTH—only exchange of labeled cholesterol for unlabeled cellular cholesterol (20). This finding is in agreement with reports concerning other cells and with the idea that cells obtain cholesterol from plasma not as free cholesterol but from lipoproteins (58). Uptake of LDL-cholesterol ester can be measured by incubating Y-1 cells for 2 days in medium containing serum from which lipoprotein has been removed by centrifugation: this procedure enhances the activity of LDL receptors in Y-1 cells as in fibroblasts (58, 59). The cells are then washed and incubated with LDL prepared from human plasma. The LDL can be labeled either in the protein moiety with ^{125}I or by stripping and reconstituting LDL particles with [3H]cholesteryl linoleate to replace the endogenous unlabeled ester. Following incubation, cells are washed to remove any loosely bound surface radioactivity and are then dissolved in sodium hydroxide to measure cellular ^{125}I or [3]H. It was found that ACTH increases the uptake of LDL-cholesteryl linoleate in this system (Fig. 20) (60). Moreover surface (receptor-bound)-LDL can be discharged by incubating the cells with heparin SO_4 before dissolving the cells in NaOH (59, 60). Such measurements revealed that ACTH specifically stimulates internalization as opposed to surface binding of LDL (Fig. 21). The internalized LDL can be found in a number of cell fractions including a lysosomal or light mitochondrial fraction from Y-1 cells (Fig. 22) (60). Again, if side-chain cleavage is inhibited by aminoglutethimide, free or unesterified cholesterol accumulates in the

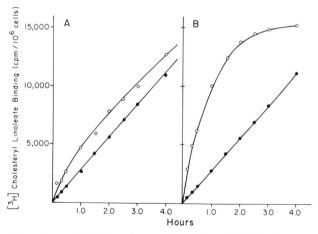

FIG. 20. The effect of ACTH on the specific binding of [3H]cholesteryl linoleate-low density lipoprotein complex by Y-1 cells. The methods used follow the standard protocol described in reference 60. Cells were incubated for the times shown with [3H]cholesteryl linoleate LDL (10 pmol; 1.0×10^5 cpm; 7 μg protein) without (A) or with ACTH (86 mU/ml) (B). In each case companion flasks were incubated with a 500-fold excess of unlabeled LDL (●). Specific binding is calculated as the difference between values without (○) and those with excess unlabeled LDL. From Hall and Nakamura (60).

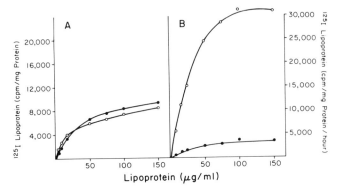

FIG. 21. Surface binding and cellular uptake (internalization) of ^{125}I-labeled low-density lipoprotein by Y-1 cells without (●) and with (○) ACTH (86 mU/ml). (A) Surface-bound lipoprotein was measured as ^{125}I released into the medium by heparin. In (B) [125]I remaining with the cells after treatment with heparin was measured by dissolving cells in NaOH and counting an aliquot of the solution by liquid scintillation spectrometry to determine the amount of internalized LDL. From Hall and Nakamura (60).

inner mitochondrial membrane and accumulation is greater when cells have been treated with ACTH (Fig. 23). Moreover ^{3}H from LDL-[^{3}H]cholesteryl linoleate can be found in 20α-dihydroprogesterone released by the cells into the medium (60). The incorporation of ^{3}H from LDL-[^{3}H]cholesteryl linoleate into 20α-dihydroprogesterone is increased by ACTH (Fig. 24). Incorporation of ^{3}H from LDL-[^{3}H]cholesteryl linoleate into 20α-dihydroprogesterone can be inhibited by chloroquin (an inhibitor of lysosomal activity) and by aminoglutethimide (inhibition of side-chain cleavage). When chloroquin is used as an inhibitor, [^{3}H]cholesteryl linoleate

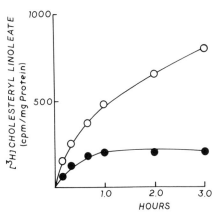

FIG. 22. [^{3}H]Cholesteryl linoleate in light mitochondria of Y-1 cells. Following incubation of cells with [^{3}H]cholesteryl linoleate low-density lipoprotein (10 pmol; 1.0 × 10[5] cpm; 7 μg of protein) without (●) and with ACTH (○) (86 mU/ml) for the times shown, cells were homogenized, and subcellular fractions were prepared by differential centrifugation (60). The fractions were extracted with ether and [^{3}H]cholesteryl linoleate was isolated and measured by liquid scintillation spectrometry. Values are shown for cholesteryl linoleate in light mitochondria from stimulated and unstimulated cells. From Hall and Nakamura (60).

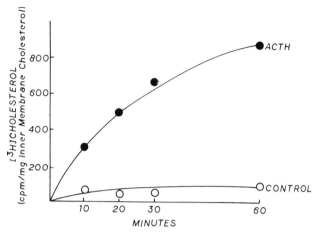

FIG. 23. Effect of ACTH on transport of [³H]cholesterol from LDL-[³H]cholesteryl linoleate to inner mitochondrial membrane. Y-1 cells were incubated with LDL-[³H]cholesteryl linoleate and aminoglutethimide (0.76 mM), with and without ACTH for the times shown. Following incubation mitochondria were prepared. Inner mitochondrial [³H]cholesterol was measured by liquid scintillation spectroscopy.

accumulates in lysosomes (light mitochondrial fraction). When aminoglutethimide is used, [³H]cholesterol accumulates in the inner mitochondrial membrane (60).

Evidently, the adrenal cell binds and internalizes lipoprotein by means of a specific receptor. Endocytosis is followed by transport to lysosomes where the ester is cleaved and thereafter free (unesterified) cholesterol is taken to the mitochondrion to enter the steroidogenic pathway. This last step, i.e., transport of cholesterol to the inner mitochondrial membrane, is the step that was discussed earlier, i.e., the step stimulated by ACTH in

FIG. 24. Conversion of [³H]cholesteryl linoleate to 20α-[³H]dihydroprogesterone by Y-1 cells incubated with [³H]cholesteryl linoleate low-density lipoprotein with and without ACTH. Y-1 cells were incubated with [³H]cholesteryl linoleate low-density lipoprotein (25 pmol; 2.5 × 10⁵ cpm of cholesterol linoleate and 18.8 µg of protein/ml), without (●) and with (○) ACTH (86 mU/ml). Samples of medium were taken at the times indicated and 20α-[³H]dihydroprogesterone was isolated and measured by liquid scintillation. Values are means and ranges for duplicate determinations. From Hall and Nakamura (60).

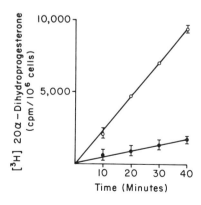

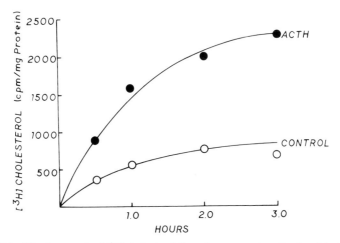

FIG. 25. The transport of [³H]cholesterol from lysosomes to mitochondria. Y-1 cells were incubated with LDL-[³H]cholesteryl linoleate and chloroquin for 3 hours to allow [³H]cholesteryl linoleate to accumulate in lysosomes. Cells were then washed and incubated with heparin sulfate to discharge bound LDL followed by incubation with aminoglutethimide with and without ACTH. At the times shown, inner mitochondrial membrane was prepared and [³H]cholesterol was measured in extracts of these membranes.

which actin, Ca^{2+}, and calmodulin are involved. It therefore became important to demonstrate that this step is stimulated by ACTH when the cholesterol enters the pathway via LDL. When lysosomes are labeled with [³H]cholesteryl linoleate by inhibiting lysosomal enzymes with chloroquin as described above, it is possible to measure transport of [³H]cholesterol from lysosomes to the inner mitochondrial membrane by removing the chloroquin block, washing the cells, and incubating with fresh medium containing aminoglutethimide. When the transport of [³H]cholesterol is measured in this way, treatment of the cells with ACTH during the final incubation shows that ACTH stimulates this transport step (Fig. 25) as expected from the studies with endogenous cholesterol (Fig. 4).

Since internalization of LDL particles in liver is known to involve the cytoskeleton (61), it was of interest to study the effect of cytochalasin B on the internalization of LDL-[³H]cholesteryl linoleate in Y-1 cells. It can be seen from Fig. 26 that the effect of ACTH on this process is inhibited by cytochalasin B. It is tempting to conclude that internalization involves microfilaments. Unfortunately the use of more specific inhibitors has not so far been possible because fusion of red cell ghosts with Y-1 cells complicates the measurement of the binding of LDL to surface receptors. It is probable that internalization involves microfilaments but confirmation of this probability must await confirmation. It would be interesting to learn whether or not the cytoskeletal responses to ACTH resulted both in

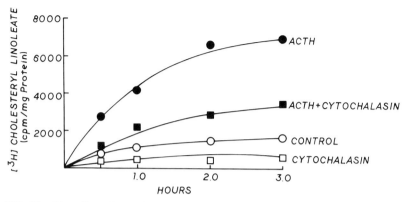

FIG. 26.   The effect of cytochalasin on the internalization of LDL-cholesteryl linoleate by Y-1 cells. Cells were incubated with LDL-[³H]cholesteryl linoleate for various periods of time. The cells were washed, treated with heparin sulfate, and then dissolved in NaOH to measure content of ³H.

increased internalization of LDL particles and increased transport of cholesterol to mitochondria.

VII.   ACTH and Adrenal Steroidogenesis *in Vivo*

These findings point to the supply of cholesterol to the side-chain cleavage enzyme as one important factor in the regulation of steroidogenesis by ACTH and cyclic AMP. Acute responses to these agents involve rapid mobilization of cholesterol from depots in the cytoplasm. In these depots cholesterol may be present as cholesterol esters and if the adrenal cell resembles fibroblasts in this respect (58) the ester may be largely oleate; this has not so far been demonstrated directly. This stimulation involves activation of an esterase which liberates free cholesterol (62). The transport of this cholesterol to the inner mitochondrial membrane occurs by a mechanism that involves actin, Ca^{2+}, and calmodulin, but apparently not microtubules (63). Moreover this step is stimulated by ACTH and cyclic AMP (60). A second system to supply cholesterol for steroidogenesis is available by internalization of LDL from plasma. Presumably this mechanism, which is also stimulated by ACTH and cyclic AMP, serves to maintain intracellular stores of cholesterol. This response to ACTH appears to be slower than mobilization from internal stores (29, 60). Presumably this second source of cholesterol becomes especially important during chronic stimulation by ACTH when internal stores may be depleted. It should be noticed that this pathway involves deesterification in lysosomes, and reesterification probably to a different fatty acid (oleate as opposed to linoleate) and finally deesterification a second time. Moreover although special importance attaches to the LDL pathway under conditions of chronic stimulation, it is this same pathway that normally maintains the appropriate levels of intracellular cholesterol ester that are used under basal conditions and during bursts of acute stimulation. The pathway of synthesis *de novo* from acetate would then be useful when external levels of LDL-cholesteryl linoleate are inadequate. If this view is correct the acetate pathway is presumably seldom extensively used since shortage of LDL-cholesterol probably occurs rarely *in vivo* apart from conditions of chronic stimulation of the adrenal. It should be added that all of these responses to ACTH, including internalization of LDL, are also seen in response to cyclic AMP (60).

VIII.   Conclusion

As so often happens in biology, new clues bring new questions. We have no idea how the cytoskeleton facilitates transport of cholesterol. Microfilaments might serve as guides or tracks for the passage of molecules through the cell. Microfilaments can alter the viscosity of the cytoplasm (64). Changes in viscosity could regulate the rates of intracellular movement. Microfilaments may incorporate myosin and become contractile (65). Shortening could bring organelles and other structures closer together within the cytoplasm. Alternate contraction and relaxation of the cytoskeleton could have the effect of stirring the cytoplasm and promote contact between cytoplasmic components. Bound water associated with the cytoskeleton (66) could facilitate molecular interactions. Certainly actin and microfilaments may be associated with individual enzymes and with biochemical pathways (67). The observations described above can be summarized diagrammatically (Fig. 27).

Clearly, new approaches to the functions of the cytoskeleton must be devised to decide between these and other possibilities. We have recently discovered that the cytoskeleton of Y-1 cells possesses a tightly bound cyclic AMP-dependent protein kinase that phosphorylates a number of specific cytoskeletal proteins (71). No doubt these changes are important in the cytoskeletal responses to ACTH.

Meanwhile progress with other equally important aspects of the response to ACTH continues in a number of laboratories. The demonstration of carrier proteins for cholesterol and its biosynthetic precursors by Scallen and co-workers represents an important achievement (68). The isolation of a low-molecular-weight peptide capable of stimulating mitochondrial side-chain cleavage has been reported by Pedersen and Brownie (69). It seems likely that investigation of this protein will provide new insight into the mechanism of action of ACTH. The important discovery that the step in the transport pathway that is inhibited by cyclo-

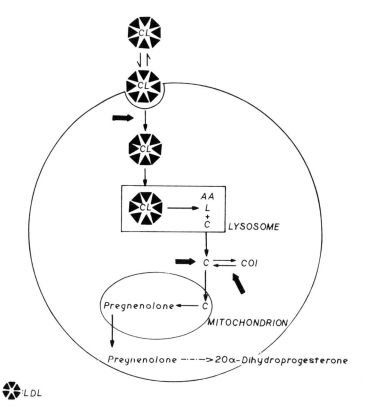

FIG. 27. Sources of cholesterol for the synthesis of adrenal steroids. CL, cholesteryl linoleate; C, cholesterol; COl, cholesteryl oleate; thick arrows, stimulated by ACTH and cAMP; AA, amino acids.

heximide is one associated with intramitochondrial transport of cholesterol has been reported by Privale and coworkers (70). These findings focus attention on the inner mitochondrial membrane in which the important action takes place.

ACKNOWLEDGMENTS

This work was supported by grants from the National Institutes of Health (AM32236, AM28113, HD16525, and CA29497).

REFERENCES

1. Karaboyas, G. C., and Koritz, S. B. (1965). *Biochemistry* **4,** 462.
2. Hall, P. F., and Koritz, S. B. (1965). *Biochemistry* **4,** 1037.
3. Hall, P. F. (1966). *Endocrinology* **78,** 690.
4. Hall, P. F., and Young, D. G. (1968). *Endocrinology* **82,** 559.

5. Stone, D., and Hechter, O. (1954). *Arch. Biochem. Biophys.* **51**, 457.
6. Hall, P. F. (1967). *Biochemistry* **6**, 2974.
7. Hall, P. F. (1972). *Biochemistry* **11**, 2891.
8. Simpson, E. R., and Estabrook, R. W. (1969). *Arch. Biochem. Biophys.* **129**, 384.
9. Shikita, M., and Hall, P. F. (1973). *J. Biol. Chem.* **248**, 5598.
10. Shikita, M., and Hall, P. F. (1974). *Proc. Natl. Acad. Sci. U.S.A.* **71**, 1441–1445.
11. Hall, P. F., Lee Lewes, J., and Lipson, E. D. (1975). *J. Biol. Chem.* **250**, 2283.
12. Buonassisi, V., Sato, G., and Cohen, A. I. (1962). *Proc. Natl. Acad. Sci. U.S.A.* **48**, 1184.
13. Kowal, J. (1979). *Recent Prog. Horm. Res.* **26**, 623.
14. Nakamura, M., Watanuki, M., Tilley, B., and Hall, P. F. (1980). *J. Endocrinol.* **84**, 179.
15. Nakamura, M., Watanuki, M., and Hall, P. F. (1978). *Mol. Cell. Endocrinol.* **12**, 209.
16. Garren, L. D., Gill, G. N., Masui, H., and Walton, G. M. (1971). *Recent Prog. Horm. Res.* **27**, 433.
17. Wessels, N. K., Spooner, B. S., Ash, J. F., Bradley, M. O., Luduena, M. A., Taylor, E. L., Wrenn, J. T., and Yamada, K. M. (1971). *Science* **171**, 135.
18. Yasumura, Y. (1968). *Am. Zool.* **8**, 285.
19. Mrotek, J. J., and Hall, P. F. (1975). *Biochem. Biophys. Res. Commun.* **64**, 891.
20. Mrotek, J. J., and Hall, P. F. (1977). *Biochemistry* **16**, 3177.
21. Hall, P. F., Nakamura, M., and Mrotek, J. J. (1981). *Biochim. Biophys. Acta* **676**, 338.
22. Estensen, R. D., Rosenberg, M., and Sheridan, I. D. (1971). *Science* **173**, 356.
23. Crivello, J. F., and Jefcoate, C. R. (1978). *Biochim. Biophys. Acta* **542**, 315.
24. Mattson, P., and Kowal, J. (1982). *Endocrinology* **111**, 1632.
25. Gabbiani, G., Charponnier, C., and Kohler, L. (1977). *Clin. Exp. Immunol.* **27**, 278.
26. Gabbiani, G., Charponnier, C., and Luscher, E. F. (1975). *Proc. Soc. Exp. Biol. Med.* **149**, 618.
27. Gabbiani, G., Charponnier, C., Zumbe, A., and Vassalli, P. (1977). *Nature (London)* **269**, 697.
28. Papahadjopoulos, D., Poste, G., and Mayhew, E. (1974). *Biochim. Biophys. Acta* **363**, 404.
29. Hall, P. F., Charponnier, C., Nakamura, M., and Gabbiani, G. (1979). *J. Biol. Chem.* **254**, 9080.
30. Blickstad, I., Markey, F., Carlsson, L., Persson, T., and Lindberg, U. (1978). *Cell* **15**, 935–943.
31. MacLean-Fletcher, S., and Pollard T. (1980). *Cell* **20**, 329.
32. Schlegel, R. A., and Reichsteiner, M. C. (1975). *Cell* **5**, 371.
33. Kaltoft, K., Zeuthen, J., Engback, F., Piper, P. W., and Celis, J. E. (1976). *Proc. Natl. Acad. Sci. U.S.A.* **73**, 2793.
34. Snabes, M. C., Boyd, A. E., Pardue, R. L., and Bryan, J. (1981). *J. Biol. Chem.* **256**, 6291.
35. Rubin, R. W., Warren, R. H., Lukeman, D. S., and Clements, E. (1978). *J. Cell Biol.* **78**, 28.
36. Mahaffee, D., Reitz, R. C., and Ney, R. L. (1974). *J. Biol. Chem.* **249**, 227.
37. Hirschfield, I. N., and Koritz, S. B. (1965). *Biochim. Biophys. Acta* **111**, 313.
38. Jefcoate, C. R., and Orme-Johnson, W. H. (1975). *J. Biol. Chem.* **250**, 4671.
39. Remmer, H., Schenkman, J., Estabrook, R. W., Sasame, H., Gillette, J., Narasimhulu, S., Cooper, D. Y., and Rosenthal, O. (1966). *Mol. Pharmacol.* **2**, 187.
40. Bell, J. J., and Harding. B. (1974). *Biochim. Biophys. Acta* **348**, 285.
41. Coupland, R. E. (1975). *Handb. Physiol.* **VI**, 283.

42. Sligar, F. G. (1976). *Biochemistry* **15**, 5399.
43. Birmingham, M. K., Elliot, F. H., and Valere, P. H. L. (1953). *Endocrinology* **53**, 687.
44. Kuo, T. H., Ou, C. T., and Tchen, T. T. (1965). *Biochem. Biophys. Res. Commun.* **65**, 190.
45. Lefkowitz, R. J., Roth, J., and Pastan, I. (1970). *Nature (London)* **228**, 864.
46. Nakamura, M., and Hall, P. F. (1978). *Biochim. Biophys. Acta* **542**, 330.
47. Cheung, W. Y. (1980). *Science* **207**, 19.
48. Means, A. R., and Dedman, J. R. (1980). *Nature (London)* **285**, 73.
49. Hall, P. F., Osawa, S., and Thomason, C. L. (1981). *J. Cell Biol.* **90**, 402.
50. Weiss, B., Fertel, B., Tichn, R., and Uzunov, P. (1974). *Mol. Pharmacol.* **10**, 615.
51. Roufogalis, B. D. (1982). *Calcium Cell Funct.* **3**, 130–159.
52. Weiss, B., Prozialeck, W. C., and Wallace, T. (1982). *Biochem. Pharmacol.* **31**, 2217.
53. Long, C. N. H. (1945). *Recent Prog. Horm. Res.* **1**, 99.
54. Péron, F., and Koritz, S. B. (1960). *J. Biol. Chem.* **235**, 1625.
55. Moore, F. D. (1957). *Recent Prog. Horm. Res.* **13**, 511.
56. Borkowski, A. J., Levin, S., and Delacroix, C. (1970). *J. Appl. Physiol.* **28**, 42.
57. Hechter, O., Solomon, M. M., Zaffaroni, A., and Pincus, G. (1953). *Arch. Biochem. Biophys.* **46**, 201.
58. Brown, M. S., and Goldstein, J. L. (1976). *Science* **191**, 150.
59. Goldstein, J. L., Basu, S. K., Brunschede, G. Y., and Brown, M. S. (1976). *Cell* **7**, 85.
60. Hall, P. F., and Nakamura, M. (1979). *J. Biol. Chem.* **254**, 12547–12554.
61. Ostlund, R. E., Pfleger, B., and Schonfeld, G. (1979). *J. Clin. Invest.* **63**, 75.
62. Beckett, G. J., and Boyd, G. S. (1977). *Eur. J. Biochem.* **72**, 223.
63. Mrotek, J. J., and Hall, P. F. (1978). *Gen. Pharmacol.* **9**, 269–273.
64. Taylor, D. L., and Condeelis, J. S. (1979). *Int. Rev. Cytol.* **56**, 57.
65. Lebowitz, E. A., and Cooke, R. (1978). *J. Biol. Chem.* **253**, 5443.
66. Clegg, J. S. (1982). *Cold Spring Harbor Symp. Quant. Biol.* **46**, 23.
67. Westrin, H., and Backman, L. (1983). *Eur. J. Biochem.* **136**, 407.
68. Chanderbhan, R., Noland, B. J., Scallen, T. J., and Vahouny, C. V. (1982). *J. Biol. Chem.* **257**, 8928.
69. Pedersen, R. C., and Brownie, A. C. (1983). *Proc. Natl. Acad. Sci. U.S.A.* **80**, 1882.
70. Privale, C. T., Crivello, J. F., and Jefcoate, C. R. (1983). *Proc. Natl. Acad. Sci. U.S.A.* **80**, 702.
71. Osawa, S., Betz, G., and Hall, P. F. (1984). *J. Cell Biol.* (submitted).

DISCUSSION

O. V. Dominguez: Why did you select the 20α reduced progesterone as an indicator of steroid formation from cholesterol, instead of progesterone itself? Since you were working with mitochondria and the 3β-hydroxysteroid dehydrogenase is located in microsoma, I would think that pregnenolone could be a better indicator for the steroid formation from cholesterol in mitochondrial preparations. As far as the entire adrenal cell, in response to ACTH, a final corticoid could be also used as an indicator.

P. F. Hall: Yes. The Y-1 cell, during propagation in the laboratory underwent two mutations and as a result of these mutations, it has acquired a new enzyme, (20α-hydroxysteroid dehydrogenase) and it has lost another enzyme (steroid 21-hydroxylase), so it does not produce normal corticosteroids. 20α-Dihydroprogesterone is representative of a family of steroids which the Y-1 cell produces. We have found over many years that production of this steroid reflects total steroid production by the cells. Moreover, it is very easy to measure by a sensitive RIA.

G. Gibori: How physiological are results obtained with the Y-1 cells?

P. F. Hall: I should point out that all of the conclusions presented have been confirmed in rat adrenal cells. The Y-1 cell has long been used as a model for the normal adrenal cell— it responds in every way that we can tell exactly like the adrenal cell, except that it responds rather better to ACTH and cyclic AMP in the normal cell, making it very convenient for certain studies. The responses in the cytoskeleton are much easier to study in the Y-1 cell because they're much more extensive but you can see similar changes when normal adrenal cells are treated with ACTH so that we have every reason to suppose that what we see in the Y-1 cell reflects what happens in the normal adrenal.

D. R. Aquilano: I would like to know if the transporter of pregnenolone from mitochondria to microsomes and that of testosterone, for example in the Leydig cell, to the membrane also involves microfilaments and calcium?

P. F. Hall: Our results would suggest that it doesn't. The conversion of pregnenolone to 20α-dihydroprogesterone is not inhibited by inhibitors of microfilaments. The mechanism of the transport of pregnenolone is not known. There have been suggestions that the smooth endoplasmic reticulum can actually touch mitochondria, so that there might be direct transfer of pregnenolone from mitrochondria to microsomes.

C. S. Nicoll: Would you comment on the role of lipid inclusion granules in the process that you described? Are microfilaments involved in bringing them into contact with the mitochondria?

P. F. Hall: You are presumably referring to the characteristic lipid-containing vesicles that are depleted with ACTH. It is our view that those droplets are indeed the source of most of the steroidogenic cholesterol if not all of it. The cholesterol that is being mobilized to the mitochondria is stored as cholesteryl oleate which must first be cleaved by an esterase. There are electron micrographic studies by other workers that suggest a role for what is called a "docking" of lipid droplets, that is, the lipid vesicles gather around mitochondria, under the influence of ACTH. It may be that this is the process that the microfilaments are accelerating.

K. Sterling: I wanted to ask a question about the intriguing shape change from flat to spherical, as to how long this requires before it occurs; and second, with regard to the three important features you observed in the mitochondria of these Y-1 cells, do you know whether or not they were accompanied by enhanced mitochondrial oxidative phosphorylation and whether that was obligatory?

P. F. Hall: Now the shape change first: it begins within 2 or 3 minutes, and different cells respond at different rates; there is, in fact, a normal distribution curve. The rounding reaches a maximum within 20 minutes; although every batch of cells is a little different, these are average figures. After 30 minutes, rounding begins to reverse; after 1 hour the cells are pretty much back to their original shape. I might point out in this connection that if the cells are forced to grow in a rounded condition, e.g., by growing them on polyHEMA (a charged surface), you can force the cells to grow in a round shape instead of being flat. Steroidogenesis is accelerated in the unstimulated state, so that this rounding has something to do with the reorganization of the organelles to a configuration that promotes steroidogenesis. In answer to the second question, many studies were performed during the 1960s in a number of laboratories and no evidence was found to show that ACTH alters the production of NADPH, which is the final common pathway for the electrons used by the enzyme. Oxidative phosphorylation is not demonstrably affected by ACTH, nor any other mitochondrial function related to electron transport.

G. D. Aurbach: The observation about calcium-stimulated increases in cholesterol transport is rather intriguing in that frequently calcium-mediated kinase phenomenon is exerted in opposite directions to those of cyclic AMP-mediated phenomena. Here is an example where both pathways seem to perform a similar task. Did you observe similar changes in protein phosphorylation with calmodulin? Did you get any effects with phorbol esters?

P. F. Hall: Calcium-calmodulin introduced into adrenal cells does promote phosphorylation of proteins, but they are entirely different proteins from those phosphorylated under the influence of cylic AMP. How these two responses are integrated we don't know at this time. Phorbol esters do stimulate steroidogenesis and there is a Ca^{2+}-dependent and phospholipid-dependent protein kinase seen, which phosphorylates yet another group of proteins. This protein kinase C is particularly active with membrane protein, and, as reported for other cells, the protein kinase C, seen under the influence of ACTH, moves very rapidly to the cell membrane—it goes from 20% in the membrane to 80% in the membrane within 5 minutes of exposure to ACTH.

A. H. Payne: In the studies on the uptake of LDL, were these cells kept in culture for 2 days in the presence of ACTH?

P. F. Hall: No, the cells are kept for 2 days without any LDL; in other words, in medium containing serum from which the LDL has been removed. That simply has the effect of sharpening the avidity of the LDL receptors and this in turn makes the measurements much easier. You can do those experiments without removing LDL but the data are much harder to analyze because uptake of LDL is less.

A. H. Payne: You said that you could see the effect of increase in internalization as early as 5 minutes?

P. F. Hall: That is correct.

T. Chen: I have a question about one receptor that you have not addressed, but I think you have done some work (Borland *et al., Endocrinology* **114**, 240, 1984). This is the receptor for growth factors, since growth factor receptors like EGF or IGF have been shown in a lot of the steroidogenic cell types, and the action of these factors in general is inhibitory, also since the concentration of the growth factors is very high in the serum. Would you speculate how these growth factors regulate steroidogenesis under physiologic conditions?

P. F. Hall: Let me say that I have done no work on receptors for growth factors. EGF in particular did not alter the steroidogenic responses to ACTH in our hands. In fact, many of our experiments have been done in defined medium from which EGF would be absent.

S. Cohen: I can see how LH and ACTH would break off a 6 carbon chain to give you a pregnenolone; does FSH break off an 8 carbon chain to give you an androgen?

P. F. Hall: To my knowledge there is no evidence that FSH does break off an 8 carbon chain although it does stimulate the production of estrogens in concert with other hormones. Perhaps somebody in the audience is better equipped to answer that question that I am.

O. V. Dominguez: Peter, you did not mention some of your earlier work in relation to the steroid sulfates and I was wondering, if you have found similar results using cholesterol sulfate, how they compare with those that you presented today?

P. F. Hall: The side-chain cleavage enzyme, either pure or in mitochondria, will cleave cholesterol esters to give the corresponding pregnenolone ester. Rather surprisingly the presence of an ester at the other end of the molecule from the side-chain does not seem to interfere very much with the interaction of cholesterol with the enzyme. Like other esters, cholesterol sulfate can be cleaved by this same enzyme system. However, very little cholesterol sulfate is used by any mammalian system, except by the fetal adrenal and by malignant adrenal cells.

O. V. Dominguez: I have just a comment with respect to that. I remember a good number of papers that have been published in the last 5 to 8 years in which it is reported that pregnenolone sulfate and dehydroepiandrosterone sulfate are present in the steroid-producing tissue at higher levels than their corresponding free compounds. Several people have worked on that.

One wonders about these sulfates that are present in a greater concentration than the free. This is why I was wondering about the origin of those sulfates. Are they originated from cholesterol sulfate?

P. F. Hall: All I can say is that those pathways, to the best of my knowledge, are most readily seen in fetal and malignant tissues and during pregnancy. It is true that in adrenal cancer you do find a heavy emphasis on the sulfate pathway and the fetus shows the same. I have no idea why that should be so. Cholesterol sulfate, of course, is a bile salt for animals such as the shark and it apparently has evolved as a kind of intestinal detergent. Adult mammalian organisms appear to rely on free cholesterol.

B. F. Rice: I have 2 widely different questions for you Dr. Hall. It seems to me that about 20 years ago there was a very lively discussion at this meeting about whether or not there was an early action of the steroidogenic trophic hormones ACTH or LH on adrenal or corpus luteum in terms of acetate incorporation and early steps—that is question 1. Question 2 is really sort of a clinical question; those of us in clinical medicine often see a syndrome that is referred to as lupoid hepatitis and these are women with chronic hepatitis and as you described have this anti-actin antibody but they are not infrequently associated with polycystic ovary disease and an ovulation and until tonight I had always fairly well concluded that these were really two separate entities that occurred by coincidence in the same patient and I just wondered whether you might have any observations on this.

P. F. Hall: In answer to the first question, your memory is quite correct, it must have been about 20 years since a lot of interest was shown at the Laurentian Conference in the early steps of steroidogenesis and in the possibility that the trophic hormone stimulated steps before cholesterol. Interest seems to have been lost in that controversy with the increasing emphasis on the LDL pathway and on the general recognition that cholesterol per se from outside the steroidogenic cells is a major source of the steroid hormones. However, on chronic treatment with LH some increase in the amounts of the enzymes involved in the biosynthesis of cholesterol does occur. To the best of my knowledge there is no evidence for an acute effect of either ACTH or LH on the steps before cholesterol so that it may be a type of hyperplasia or a long-term growth effect.

With regard to the second question, I don't believe that anti-actin circulating in the plasma does anything to inhibit steroidogenesis. It probably doesn't get into adrenal or ovarian cells. We have to use special methods to get anti-actin into cells and normally *in vivo* one wouldn't expect that to occur, so I think you are still right in suggesting that the two phenomena are probably two separate entities.

J. Weisz: This is a question I am sharing with Dr. Papkoff. How would you fit into your schema for ACTH's action on steroidogenesis the classical bioassay endpoint of ascorbic acid depletion? This occurs in adrenal cells in response to ACTH as it does in luteal cells in response to LH. And the response is a very rapid one. In the new quantitative cytochemical bioassays, ascorbic acid depletion is seen within seconds of exposing to ACTH adrenal cortical cells in cyrostat sections of the adrenal gland. Could it be that there are responses relevant to steroidogenesis that occur on different time scales? Specifically, the response that you have discussed may represent a relatively late one. It may be a response in anticipation that the stress may not go away or return and reflect the need to replenish the precursor stores.

P. F. Hall: I showed a slide by C. N. H. Long and some of you may know that slide, it's been altered to remove ascorbic acid values. The reason I have removed these values is that I have been so frequently asked that question, that I thought I could avoid it by removing the data. As far as I am aware, there is no more known today about the ascorbic acid depletion than there was in Long's day 20 years ago. However, it has been proposed that the adrenal is a storehouse for ascorbic acid and you are probably aware that during stress ascorbic acid is mobilized and has distant effects notably on the pancreas. Therefore, the depletion of adrenal ascorbic acid may in fact be unrelated to steroidogenesis. This is consistent with the fact that every effort to relate ascorbic acid depletion to the increased production of adrenal steroids has, I think, proved false.

J. Weisz: My question really was only related to the rapidity, the enormous rapidity of that response.

P. F. Hall: Yes, one of the most extraordinary enigmas in the adrenal field is the rapidity of ascorbic acid depletion. What this means in relation to the whole stress response I cannot say.

J. Weisz: And the second question is an extension of Dr. Guela Gibori's question concerning the relevance of your findings *in vitro* to the situation *in vivo*. You have said that if the cultured cell is confined cultured to being round to begin with it fails to enhance steroidogenesis. Now the cell within the adrenal has constraints on the extent to which it can change its shape. Thus it resembles closely the cell in culture that was restricted to the rounded state and it does not have much latitude in changing its cytoskeletal structure.

P. F. Hall: I really can't answer that. We have no way at this time of relating a cell in culture to a cell within an organ. You are quite right in pointing out that the cells of the cortex are not flat but we don't have any idea whether the response to ACTH *in vivo* includes a change in shape or not. Such changes in shape may not be so necessary for cells *in vivo*. It is important to realize that the cell on the culture disk is stretched out in a very unnatural way. The cell must invest much of its actin into clinging for dear life onto the plastic surface. The change in shape may still be an important clue that may tell us something significant about ACTH. Evidently the cell has to be released from attachment to the dish and allowed to round up, but having rounded up it can then, to a large extent, flatten out again without any diminution in the steroidogenic response, but I boggle at the thought of trying to relate that to a cluster of adrenal cells in an organ.

J. D. Baxter: I have two questions. I think you presented data of course that suggest that at least a major amount of the stimulation of cholesterol to pregnenolone formation is the change in uptake of cholesterol; do you know, or did I miss this, that on top of that there is no stimulation of the side-chain cleavage itself.

P. F. Hall: I think it would be premature to make a hard and fast conclusion on that point. We have not been able to detect an additional effect on enzyme activity, in spite of a determined search. However, to examine the rate of a membrane-bound enzyme when you take it out of the cell, is extremely difficult and I don't think one can totally exclude an additional effect on activity. I should not imply that what I have described tonight are the only responses to ACTH. There are clearly other responses that occur but have not been studied as fully.

J. D. Baxter: I would also like to ask your opinion on another point. I am having trouble interdigitating the fact that you can get the effects on phorbol esters, that you demonstrate effects of calcium, that you demonstrate effects of cyclic AMP, and then there has been virtually no discussion here of all the extensive studies of Farese showing the role of phospholipids, some of which look like they are calcium dependent, some of which are calcium independent. Could you try to give me your best guess of an integrated conceptualization of which of these appear to be most dominant and which are primary, and which are secondary.

P. F. Hall: I think at this time it would be rash to give a summary sketch of the type medical students like you to give shortly before final exams. Without question the evidence points to cyclic AMP as a necessary mediator of the steroidogenic responses to ACTH; I have seen no data that indicate that one can by-pass that part of the response. Calcium appears to be necessary for one facet of that response and the calcium effect is calmodulin dependent and may simply be permissive, that is, it may be necessary to have the calcium-calmodulin to trigger whatever event occurs in the cytoskeleton to bring about the cholesterol transport. With protein kinase C it is far too early for me to say anything; all we know is that it does stimulate steroidogenesis, and this effect is accompanied by phosphorylation of proteins totally different from those of which are phosphorylated by cyclic AMP and we have no way of knowing whether that means that kinase C mediates the response to ACTH.

J. D. Baxter: Or any evidence that ACTH stimulates the same kinase that is stimulated by phorbol esters.

P. F. Hall: There is a report suggesting that ACTH stimulates protein kinase C; it is a very recent report. We have not examined the effect of ACTH on kinase C ourselves as yet. All I can tell you is that ACTH causes kinase C to move to the plasma membrane very rapidly. Such movement is characteristic of effects of various agents in other cells. As far as the phospholipid mechanism is concerned, we have not seen increased synthesis of poly-phosphoinositides in response to ACTH. Our data show increased breakdown of poly-phosphoinositides with ACTH and cyclic AMP.

S. Cohen: In conditions where LPL is increased, such as in the Brown Goldstein syndrome, is there any disturbance in the steroidogenesis?

P. F. Hall: Not as far as I'm aware.

S. Cohen: Because there's a tremendous increase in the LDL in the circulation.

P. F. Hall: Yes, there may be several explanations for the fact that the adrenal doesn't seem to show any abnormal response to high plasma LDL. Presumably the uptake is still limited by either the number or the avidity of the receptors. Presumably the supply of LDL in the plasma is not rate-limiting for steroid synthesis.

P. G. Quinn: What do you make of the report of Rainey and Hornsby that there are adrenal cell lines which can be kept in culture and respond very well to ACTH, but show no evidence of rounding up?

P. F. Hall: Beef adrenal cells do show evidence of rounding up. If you read that paper carefully you will find a statement to this effect. We have studied cultured bovine adrenal cells. They do not show the extreme rounding seen with Y-1 cells. They do, however, retract and leave behind elongated processes during retraction. Bovine adrenal cells are peculiar because they are the only adrenal cells that have been examined in which you cannot inhibit the steroidogenic responses to ACTH with cytochalasin B. Moreover, they contain very little cholesterol ester, but use free cholesterol for the most part; whether this is connected with the way in which the cholesterol is moved in the cell or not, I don't know. Certainly bovine cells show some cytoskeletal changes consistent with those which I showed for the Y-1 cells but they are much less obvious.

P. G. Quinn: Second, have you examined the effects of cycloheximide on skeletal transport, because most data seem to indicate that cycloheximide prevents movement of cholesterol from the outer to inner membrane, but does not prevent movement to the outer membrane?

P. F. Hall: That's entirely correct; at the present time it appears that the cycloheximide effect is beyond the transport to the mitochondria. Acceleration of cholesterol transport to mitochondria by ACTH is not inhibited by cycloheximide.

R. Moudgal: It is suggested that one of the principal ways by which tropic hormones like ACTH and LH could be increasing steroid hormone synthesis is by promoting cholesterol transport into the cell. If, however, you remove tropic support as for example LH from circulation by giving LH antibody, the first thing one observes is an increase in α-cholesterol, cholesterol ester in the case of the luteal cell. We see evidence for this ultrastructurally also.

P. F. Hall: Well isn't that what you would expect? LH and ACTH normally deplete stores of cholesterol by converting cholesterol ester stored in lipid droplets to free cholesterol which is used for steroid synthesis. When you remove these stimulating agents from the circulation, wouldn't you expect the lipid droplets with their contained cholesterol ester to accumulate?

R. Moudgal: Is it that very simplistic? If absence of LH is blocking esterase activity why is it not effecting cholesterol transport also the same way? Actually the results suggest that in the absence of LH, accumulation of cholesterol is occurring at a much faster rate compared to the reduction seen in progesterone output.

P. F. Hall: I think we must consider a balance of several steps. Cholesterol goes into the cell, is stored in vesicles, and is used by the transport process, which moves it to mitochondria. The relative effects of the trophic hormone on these different steps may be complex. Removal of the trophic hormone, could result in decrease, increase or no change in cholesterol levels. Presumably, to explain your observations we must postulate that the stimulation of uptake by the cell is not quite so active as the stimulation of transport to mitochondria.

G. Gibori: In the model you proposed for cholesterol transport, the microfilaments appear essential. Do you see any role for the cholesterol binding protein?

P. F. Hall: The protein binding is obviously essential. I don't think any steroid exists in any biological situation without being bound to protein, and so the question is simply translated from free cholesterol to cholesterol bound to protein; the mechanism of transport is not clear at this time. Either microfilaments shorten or they act as guidelines along which the cholesterol is moving. If you look at any living cell with video intensification (you can do this with the adrenal cell) one sees an extraordinary array of particle motion in the cell. It is difficult to sort out various forms of particle movement in the cell, but some of those particles are carrying cholesterol. This movement of cholesterol can be completely arrested almost instantly by adding cytochelasin B to the medium. Particle motion directed along the surface of the cytoskeletal elements provides one reasonable explanation for the role of the microfilaments in cholesterol transport. At this point I might add that it is very clear that most of the water in the cytoplasm of the cell is not free water in the sense that a chemist has free water in the beaker; at least 50% of the water is bound to cytoskeletal structures; otherwise it wouldn't be possible for cells to catalyze biosynthetic pathways at the rates seen *in vivo*. Cholesterol transport may take place in the water bound to the cytoskeleton and it is presumed to move with a binding protein.

M. H. J. Raj: I have a comment and question. Getting back to the movement of the cells and the cytoskeletal, we have observed in one of their cultures of human granulosa luteal cells, if you were to add LH, they pretty much undergo the same dramatic shape changes that they describe in the adrenal, and this is reversible after you remove the hormone 24 hours later, they get back to the normal structure, so perhaps it may have a similar biochemical basis that you alluded to in the adrenal cell. The question I wanted to ask is about the role of estrogen and also the role of testosterone that Dr. Gibori and her group have very elegantly demonstrated that is luteotrophic. In effect, they have been able, in the absence of LH, to promote steroidogenesis and progesterone production, so the question is could you give a biochemical explanation as to where in your scheme a molecule like testosterone or estrogen could be acting to increase the progesterone production.

P. F. Hall: I have to ask you in turn, is it known whereabouts in the steroidogenic pathway the testosterone or estrogen acts, i.e., could the steroid affect transport of cholesterol to mitochondria, for example?

M. H. J. Raj: No, because this is demonstrated in the hypophysectomized rats. I have been quite interested in looking at how a very different molecule-like steroid, like testosterone or estrogen, could pretty much bring about the same end result that LH would do in a normal physiologic setting in the progesterone production; I thought if anyone could put some biochemical sense in the system it might be yourself.

P. F. Hall: This is a rather difficult concept. All I can say is that the peptide hormones act through cyclic AMP; we don't think of the androgens as doing that, although it is always difficult to exclude subtle effects on adenylate cyclase. The only thing the adenylate cyclase can do is to phosphorylate proteins and either these steroids to which you refer phosphorylate the same proteins or they act by some totally different mechanism. If they act only in hypophysectomized animals (if I understand you correctly), then there is the whole question of whether that might not be serving a trophic function. The response might have something to do with the state of nutrition of the cell in its broadest sense, but it does not necessarily have anything to do with cholesterol transport.

G. Gibori: In luteal cells of pregnant rats estrogen appears to stimulate steroidogenesis by enhancing the content of cholesterol and its transport to the mitochondria. Estradiol increases the number of binding sites for high-density lipoprotein and stimulates the activity of HMG-CoA reductase, the enzyme responsible for *de novo* synthesis of cholesterol.

J. D. Veldhuis: There are additional circumstances, such as those which involve the *in vitro* culture of porcine granulosa cells, which can demonstrate direct effects of estrogen on ovarian cells in appropriately lipid-controlled environments in the complete absence of LH. Results from these serum-free conditions generally are in accord with what Dr. Gibori has said in the hypophysectomized *in vivo* model. The *in vitro* system has disclosed in work by Drs. James Hammond, Jerome Strauss, and myself (Veldhuis *et al., Endocrinology* **111,** 145, 1982; Toaff *et al., Endocrinology* **112,** 1156, 1983) that estrogen increases cholesterol side-chain cleavage activity, whether assessed by 25-hydroxycholesterol conversion to pregnenolone, cytochrome P-450 content in granulosa cells measured by difference spectroscopy, or (in work that is in abstract form) the incorporation of [^{35}S]methionine into immunoprecipitated cholesterol side-chain cleavage enzyme. Thus, it's curious that a steroid hormone has pivotal effects on sites similar to those influenced by peptide hormones. By the same token, *in vitro* it can be shown that estrogen, like ACTH, increases LDL binding sites by 2- to 3-fold. Whether estradiol also augments the internalization step per se remains a matter of some interest, but to my knowledge has not been demonstrated. Using an experimental inhibitor of the ACAT or cholesterol esterification reaction, we can show that estrogen appears to influence the relative partitioning of cholesterol into the lipid droplet pool. In relation to this, I'm sure you have ample further comments on the possible effect of ACTH on the relative movement of cholesterol in or out of the lipid storage pool.

W. Hansel: There are several tissues in which steroidogenesis can be turned on by raising intracellular calcium concentrations. For example, bovine placental cells do not respond at all to the cylic AMP system (Shepresh *et al., PNAS,* 1984) but increase progesterone synthesis in response to Ca^{2+}. Do you visualize this as a situation in which the cyclic AMP mechanism is turned off by the production of the Ca-mediated mechanism or are the two mechanisms completely independent? Perhaps the bovine placenta has not yet developed the cyclic AMP mechanism.

P. F. Hall: I'm not sure that I know enough about the placental system to comment on it. All I can say with the adrenal system is if you flood the cell with calcium, at any concentration that we have achieved, we do not see any change in steroidogenesis. We can only increase steroid synthesis if we put calmodulin and Ca^{2+} into the cell. Our explanation for this observation is that the calmodulim-calcium is necessary for cholesterol transport in these cells. There is no reason why calcium in other cells could not phosphorylate the same proteins as those which are phosphorylated by cyclic AMP. We do not have evidence for this in the adrenal, but Ca^{2+}-calmodulin may work in the placenta instead of cyclic AMP. One might propose that in the adrenal cyclic AMP requires the Ca^{2+}-calmodulin system to promote increased transport of cholesterol.

J. A. Holt: I would like to comment of the role of estrogens—the porcine granulosa cells do appear to show stimulation of cytochrome P-450 by the estrogens. Quite in contrast to that of the rabbit corpus luteum, we find very little effect of estrogens on the cytochrome P-450 system, but they are very potent in mobilizing lipid droplets—the cholesterol from the lipid droplets; now whether that's a carrier protein or skeletal or the enzymes involved, we haven't figured out yet.

P. Donahoe: Have you attempted to deliver the ACTH via the red cell ghosts in order to bypass the surface receptor cyclic AMP system?

P. F. Hall: Our attempts to do this have not been fruitful; it is very difficult to do such an experiment without some of the ACTH becoming accessible to the surface of the cell as well as to the interior. If you fuse Y-1 cells with red cell ghosts loaded with ACTH, you get a very good response to ACTH, as though you have added the hormone to the medium. But we cannot exclude the possibility that the response comes through the surface receptor mechanism. The liposomes undoubtedly have ACTH bound to the outside of the liposome.

G. Gibori: I would like to comment on Dr. Veldhuis' suggestion that estrogen may enhance steroidogenesis by stimulating the activity of the cholesterol side-chain cleavage enzyme. We were unable to demonstrate any such stimulation in luteal cells of pregnant rats which are highly responsive to estradiol. When the cholesterol side-chain cleavage activity was determined in luteal mitochondria of estrogen-treated rats in the absence of exogenous cholesterol, increased activity was found. However, when the activity of the enzyme was measured in the presence of 25-OH cholesterol no such increase was detected. These results, therefore, indicate that estradiol enhances the endogenous cholesterol available to the mitochondria but does not affect the activity of the enzyme per se. Dr. Jay Holt reported similar results in the rabbit.

Regulation of Hormone Receptors and Adenylyl Cyclases by Guanine Nucleotide Binding N Proteins

Lutz Birnbaumer,* Juan Codina,* Rafael Mattera,*
Richard A. Cerione,† John D. Hildebrandt,*,[1]
Teresa Sunyer,* Francisco J. Rojas,*,[2] Marc G. Caron,†
Robert J. Lefkowitz,† and Ravi Iyengar*

*Department of Cell Biology, Baylor College of Medicine, Houston, Texas, and
†Howard Hughes Medical Institute, Duke University Medical Center,
Durham, North Carolina

I. Introduction

Cellular functions are regulated by hormones. The capacity of a given cell to respond to a given hormone depends on the presence or absence in the cell of a receptive recognition system specific for the hormone, called receptor. It is now well recognized that there are several types of hormone receptors, each triggering a different type of response when occupied by its specific hormone. Receptor types can be subclassified, first on the basis of their location, and second on the basis of the signal transduction mechanism system they use. On the basis of their location receptors are either intracellular or of plasma membrane localization. The former encompass receptors for steroid hormones, vitamin D, and thyroid hormone, the latter encompass receptors for neurotransmitters, peptide and protein hormones, and a variety of regulatory and growth-promoting factors. On the basis of the signal transduction mechanism they use, membrane receptors can be classified into four different subtypes: (1) receptors that regulate cyclic AMP formation; (2) receptors that affect intracellular calcium levels via hydrolysis of phosphatidylinositol phosphates and formation of diacylglycerol and inositol phosphates; (3) receptors that possess tyrosine kinase activity and are assumed to act on cellular metabolism on the basis of this property; and (4) receptors that are ion channels and, on occupancy by their specific ligands, allow flux of specific ions

[1] Present address: Worcester Foundation for Experimental Biology, Shrewsbury, Massachusetts.

[2] Present address: Department of Obstetrics and Gynecology, University of Texas Health Science Center at San Antonio, San Antonio, Texas.

(cations or anions) through the plasma membrane and thereby trigger electrophysiological responses. Examples of the last class of receptors are nicotinic acetylcholine receptors, a cation channel, and receptors of GABA and glutamine which are chloride channels. Examples of tyrosine kinase receptors are insulin, platelet-derived growth factor, and epidermal growth factor receptors. Examples of receptors that affect phosphoinositide hydrolysis are receptors for vasopressin of the VP_1-type for TRH, and for catecholamines of the α_1-type. Finally, there are a multitude of examples of receptors that affect cyclic AMP formation. In fact, receptors that affect cyclic AMP are subclassified into two subtypes: R_s receptors, which increase cyclic AMP levels by stimulating the enzyme adenylyl cyclase, and R_i receptors, which decrease cyclic AMP levels by inhibiting the cyclic AMP-forming enzyme. Receptors for catecholamine of the β_1- and β_2-type, for ACTH, for glucagon, for secretin, for LH, FSH, and TSH, are of the R_s-type. Receptors for catecholamines of the α_2-type, for acetylcholine of muscarinic type (M), for opiod peptides, and somatostatin are of the R_i-type. A given cell can have any number of the above receptor types, indeed it can, and often does, have more than one of a given type, such as occurs, for example, with rat fat cells which have at least five different R_s-type receptors (ACTH, β-adrenergic, glucagon, secretin, and LH), two different R_i-type receptors (adenosine and PGE), and in addition have receptors for insulin (a tyrosine kinase). Although not yet specifically explored, it is likely that these same cells have receptors of the other classes as well. The receptor complement differs, of course, from cell type to cell type, and from tissue to tissue, and constitutes a complex address system that allows for coordinated but varied regulation of cellular responses and organ homeostasis.

The purpose of this chapter is to discuss in detail the transduction mechanism to which R_s- and R_i-type receptors couple to modulate adenylyl cyclase activity. At the center of this transduction mechanism are two oligomeric coupling proteins called N (or G) proteins. These proteins have the properties of binding as well as hydrolyzing GTP and of regulating hormone affinity for receptors as well as the catalytic activity of the cyclic AMP-forming enzyme. We will approach this complex receptor-coupling protein–adenylyl cyclase system by first reviewing structural and functional aspects that regulate cyclic AMP formation. As part of this, we will discuss the basic structure and regulation of adenylyl cyclase by nucleotides and magnesium, we will speculate on several aspects of the regulation of the activity of the signal transducing proteins. We will then review the actions of hormones on the nucleotide-regulated system. Finally, we will analyze what is known about the regulation of the hormone–receptor interaction by the coupling proteins. This last analysis, i.e., affinity regulation of receptors, leads to some unexpected conclusions that point toward the existence of at least two conformational states of receptors interacting with at least three conformational states or forms of the coupling proteins.

II. The Adenylyl Cyclase System: Structure and Regulation in the Absence of Hormonal Influence

A.   STRUCTURE: C, N_s AND N_i

The understanding of the mechanism by which occupied hormone receptors stimulate cyclic AMP formation by the enzyme adenylyl cyclase requires a prior understanding of both structural and functional properties of this response system. Both of these features have been studied extensively during recent years. At the center of the coupling process intervening between hormone receptor occupancy and enhanced catalytic activity are two coupling or signal transducing proteins, generically referred to as N (Rodbell, 1980) or G (Gilman, 1984) proteins. Each of these proteins binds Mg and guanine nucleotides. However, while one of these proteins, referred to as N_s (Rodbell, 1980; Codina et al., 1984a) or G_s (Gilman, 1984), is responsible for mediating in a guanine nucleotide- and Mg-dependent manner effects of stimulatory hormone receptors, the other, referred to as N_i (Rodbell, 1980; Hildebrandt et al., 1983) or G_i (Gilman, 1984) mediates in a guanine nucleotide and Mg-dependent manner the effects of inhibitory hormone receptors (Codina et al., 1984b; Jakobs et al., 1984). In fact, adenylyl cyclase systems to which receptors couple are best described as "three-components systems," formed of a catalytic unit C which forms cyclic AMP plus $MgPP_i$ from the substrate MgATP, and the above referred to N_s and N_i proteins.

Much less is known about C than about N's. C can be physically separated (resolved) from N_s and N_i without loss of activity (Strittmatter and Neer, 1980; Northup et al., 1983a). However, on resolution by biochemical (Strittmatter and Neer, 1980; Northup et al., 1983a) or genetic (Johnson et al., 1980) means, it changes its catalytic properties from being able to use with similar efficiency MgATP or MnATP as substrate, to being much less active (approximately 10%), and this only with MnATP as substrate with the k_{cat} for MgATP becoming vanishingly small, i.e., in the order of about 5% of the 10% activity seen with MnATP. The molecular weight of C appears to be ~150,000 (Schlegel et al., 1979). Although purified from Neurospora crassa (Reig et al., 1982), C has not yet been purified from somatic cells of a mammalian origin.

Both N proteins have been purified (Northup et al., 1980; Codina et al., 1983, 1984a,c; Bokoch et al., 1983, 1984) and, while distinct, are quite similar. They are both formed of α, β, and γ subunits (Hildebrandt *et al.*, 1984a), both bind GTP and its analogs (Northup *et al.*, 1982; Bokoch *et al.*, 1983), both are substrates for the ADP-ribosyltransferase activity of bacterial toxins (Northup *et al.*, 1980; Bokoch *et al.*, 1983; Codina *et al.*, 1983), and both interact with Mg (Iyengar, 1981; Hildebrandt and Birnbaumer, 1983), and are GTPases (Codina *et al.*, 1984b; Brandt *et al.*, 1983; Sunyer *et al.*, 1984; Cerione *et al.*, 1984a,b; Kanaho *et al.*, 1984; Asano *et al.*, 1984). Untreated (control) N proteins subjected to sucrose density gradient centrifugation migrate with an apparent S value of approximately 4.0 (3.8–4.1), and, as illustrated in Fig. 1 for N_i, the α, β, and γ subunit distribution across a sucrose density gradient coincides with the presence of the intrinsic GTPase activity of the protein. By combining sucrose density gradient centrifugation in both H_2O and D_2O with gel exclusion chromatography, the molecular weights of N proteins were calculated to be in the order of 80,000–100,000. Both proteins, on treatment with Mg and a nonhydrolyzable GTP analog, such as GNP-P(NH)P or $GTP_\gamma S$, undergo subunit dissociation to give α subunits of N_s (or N_i) with guanine nucleotide bound to them (α_s^G; α_i^G) (Howlett *et al.*, 1979; Sternweis *et al.*,

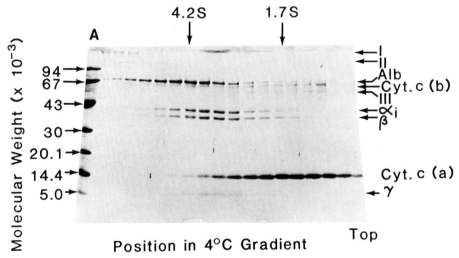

FIG. 1. Subunits of N_i protein (α_i, β, and γ) and GTPase activity comigrate on sucrose density gradients. N_i was applied to a 5–10% sucrose density gradient and centrifuged. The gradient was fractionated and analyzed for polypeptides content by SDS–PAGE (A and B) and GTPase activity (B). (A) Photograph of Coomassie blue-stained gel. Bands represent I, II, III, contaminants present in albumin; bovine serum albumin of 4.2 S; Cyt. C (a), cytochrome *c* of 1.75 S; Cyt. C (b), contaminant of cytochromes *c*; α_i, α subunit of N_i of 40 kDa; β; β subunit of N_i of 35 kDa; γ, γ subunit of N_i of ~5 kDa. N_i, 70 pmol; albumin, 10 μg; cytochrome *c*, 10 μg (41,000 rpm in SW 50.1 for 15 hours). (B) Staining intensities of α_i, β, and γ subunits of N_i shown in (A); GTPase activity in aliquots of the fractionated gradient.

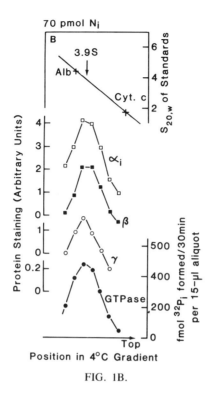

FIG. 1B.

1981; Hanski *et al.*, 1981; Hildebrandt *et al.*, 1984a) and what appears to be a complex of $\beta\gamma$ subunits (Hildebrandt *et al.*, 1984a). α_s and α_i differ in several respects: α_s is ADP-ribosylated by cholera toxin (Gill and Meren, 1978; Johnson *et al.*, 1978; Lai *et al.*, 1981; Schleifer *et al.*, 1982; Malbon and Greenberg, 1982); α_i is ADP-ribosylated by pertussis toxin (Katada and Ui, 1982a; Murayama and Ui, 1983; Bokoch *et al.*, 1983; Codina *et al.*, 1983); in most tissues, α_s shows size heterogeneity with a predominating form of $M_r = 42{,}000$ and lesser amounts with M_rs of 51,000–52,000 (Northup *et al.*, 1980; Gill and Meren, 1978; Johnson *et al.*, 1978; Lai *et al.*, 1981; Schleifer *et al.*, 1982; Malbon and Greenberg, 1982); similarly, in most tissues there appears to be only one type of α_i with $M_r = 40{,}000$–41,000 (Katada and Ui, 1982a; Murayama and Ui, 1983; Manning and Gilman, 1983; Hildebrandt *et al.*, 1984b; Bokoch *et al.*, 1983; Codina *et al.*, 1983). The β subunits of N_s and N_i are very similar if not identical (Manning and Gilman, 1983; Codina *et al.*, 1984a; Hildebrandt *et al.*, 1984b) and of $M_r = 35{,}000$ (Northup *et al.*, 1980; Codina *et al.*, 1983). Likewise, the γ subunits of N_s and N_i, approximately 5000–8000 in molecular weight (Hildebrandt *et al.*, 1984a), are very similar if not identical (Hildebrandt *et al.*, 1984c), making the $\beta\gamma$ complexes re-

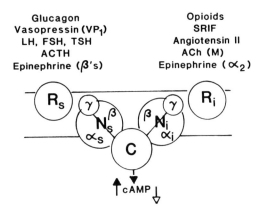

FIG. 2.   Basic constituents of a hormone-sensitive adenylyl cyclase system. R_s, Stimula-
tory receptors which interact with N_s. R_i, Inhibitory receptors which interact with N_i. N_s,
Stimulatory guanine nucleotide and Mg binding regulatory component (also referred to as
G/F or G_s), of M_r = 80,000–100,000, formed of the GTP-binding cholera toxin substrate α
subunit (M_r = 42,000–52,000), the β subunit (M_r = 35,000), and a ~5000-kDa γ subunit. N_i,
Inhibitory guanine nucleotide and Mg binding regulatory component (also referred to as G_i),
of M_r = 80,000–100,000, formed of the GTP-binding pertussis toxin substrate α_i subunit (M_r
= 40,000 or 41,000), the same M_r 35,000 β subunit as present in N_s and a ~5000-kDa γ
subunit. C, Catalytic unit of adenylyl cyclase affected in stimulatory way by N_s and inhibitory way by N_i. R_s receptors are a group of molecules which all interact with N_s but differ in
size, form, and specificity of their hormone binding site. Examples of different R_s receptors
are listed. R_i receptors also constitute a group of molecules, all of which interact with N_i but
differ, as R_s receptors, in size, form, and hormonal specificity. Examples of R_i receptors are
listed. Single cells may contain various R_s receptors *and* various R_i receptors.

leased on subunit dissociation interchangeable (Northup *et al.*, 1983b;
Katada *et al.*, 1984a). A complete N_sN_iC system and examples of hormones that affect either N_s or N_i via their respective R_s and R_i receptors is
shown in Fig. 2.

B.   THE ACTIVATION OF N_s BY GUANINE NUCLEOTIDES AND Mg

Stimulation of C by N_s, i.e., the increase in its k_{cat} for MnATP by
approximately 10-fold and that for MgATP by approximately 200-fold,
comes about by interaction of C with the activated guanine nucleotide-
liganded α_s^G subunit of N_s (Northup *et al.*, 1980, 1983a). Such activation
of N_s requires not only guanine nucleotides (Howlett *et al.*, 1979; Strittmatter and Neer, 1980), but also Mg (Iyengar and Birnbaumer, 1981;
Iyengar, 1981). The mechanism by which N_s is activated has been explored extensively, much having been learned from studying the time
courses of its activation. Recent such studies with pure N_s (Sternweis *et*

al., 1981; Northup *et al.*, 1982; Codina *et al.*, 1984c), as well as earlier studies both with crude cholate extracts containing N_s activity dissociated from C (Iyengar, 1981), and with N_s in association with C as found in intact membranes (Schramm and Rodbell, 1975; Birnbaumer *et al.*, 1980a; Iyengar *et al.*, 1980a) showed that the rate of activation of the coupling protein by a guanine nucleotide is a slow reaction that is critically dependent on the concentration of Mg ion (Iyengar and Birnbaumer, 1981; Iyengar, 1981). The effect of increasing the concentration of Mg on the rate of activation of pure human erythrocyte N_s by the nonhydrolyzable analog GMP-P(NH)P is shown in Fig. 3. It is clear that activation by this analog is very slow and very little at a "physiologic" concentration of Mg of approximately 0.5 mM, and that it is both accelerated and increased in extent when Mg concentrations are increased to supraphysiologic values. The same phenomenon, whereby Mg regulates both the extent and the rate of activation of adenylyl cyclase activity by GMP-P(NH)P, can be appreciated also in intact membranes, as illustrated for liver membranes in Fig. 4, and is seen likewise when GTP is used instead of one of its analogs.

The activation by GMP-P(NH)P differs from that by GTP in that, at any given concentration of Mg, the rates of activation by saturating GMP-P(NH)P are slower than those obtained with saturating GTP (Schramm and Rodbell, 1975). The fact that these rates of activation vary with the nature of the guanine nucleotide used—distinct rates were observed also for GTPγS and GMP-P(NH)P, GMP-P(CH$_2$)P (Birnbaumer *et al.*, 1980a)—indicated that slow activation by nucleotides cannot be due to existence of a common rate-limiting step, such as it would be if GDP dissociation were rate-limiting, but rather that the rate-limiting step in the process that leads from a resting (basal) state of N_s to a nucleotide-stimulated state must lie after the binding of the nucleotide and, hence, resides in the actual "activation" of N_s (Birnbaumer *et al.*, 1980b; Iyengar *et al.*, 1980a). Even though the rate of activation of N_s by GMP-P(NH)P is slower than that by GTP, the analog elicits a higher degree of stimulation than that obtained with GTP. This was proposed to be due to the nonhydrolyzable nature of the imidodiphosphate bond of the analog (Londos *et al.*, 1974) and substantiated in studies with both intact membranes (Cassel and Selinger, 1976) and purified N_s (Brandt *et al.*, 1983; Cerione *et al.*, 1984a,b), showing that GTP is hydrolyzed by N_s. Thus, in the presence of GTP, N_s traverses continuously a unidirectional kinetic cycle, whereby N_s binds GTP, becomes "activated" in a Mg-dependent manner, hydrolyzes its activating ligand, becomes "deactivated" with GDP remaining bound to it, and finally, exchanges rather readily GTP for GDP to reinitiate the cycle. Under physiologic conditions of 0.5 mM Mg and even at

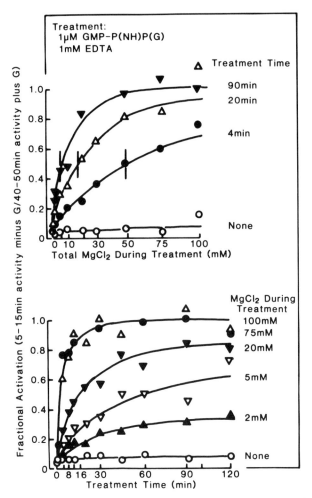

FIG. 3. Effects of time of incubation and Mg concentration on degree and rate of activation of pure N_s in the absence of C. Note that at low Mg the activation reaction is slow while at high Mg the activation reaction is fast. Also note that half maximal activation is obtained at lower concentrations of Mg on prolonged incubations as compared to that obtained on shorter incubations. Assay at 0.1 mM ATP, 15 mM MgCl$_2$, 1 mM EDTA. For conditions and details see Codina *et al.* (1984a).

higher concentrations (5–10 mM) of Mg, the relative rates of activation, GTP hydrolysis and deactivation are such that steady-state levels of N_s are but 5–10% of maximum. In contrast, substitution of GMP-P(NH)P or GTP$_\gamma$S for GTP leads to interruption of the kinetic regulatory cycle with establishment of an equilibrium between inactive and active forms of N_s

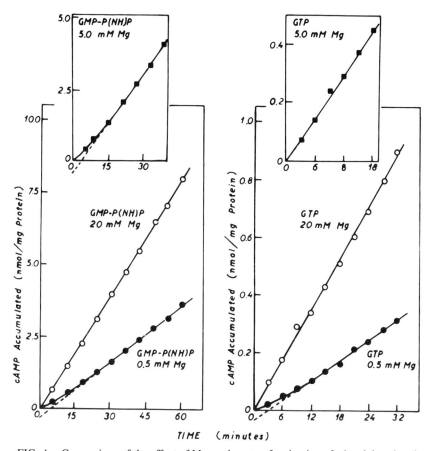

FIG. 4. Comparison of the effect of Mg on the rate of activation of adenylyl cyclase by GMP-P(NH)P to that by GTP. Note that the result is essentially the same as that shown in Fig. 3 which was obtained with pure N_s in solution. Note also that, except for the fact that the rate of stimulation by GTP is affected at lower concentrations of Mg than that by GMP-P(NH)P, the basic regulatory phenomenon by which Mg accelerates the action of the nucleotide applies to both the natural ligand GTP and its analog. From Iyengar and Birnbaumer (1981).

that is dependent only on the ratio of rate of activation of the nucleotide-occupied N_s and the rates of dissociation of the activating nucleotide from the active state and the consequential relaxation to a deactivated state of N_s. Clearly, acceleration of the rate of activation as occurs when concentrations of Mg ions are increased will, and does, lead to an increase in the proportion of total N_s in the active state.

Recent studies on the activation of pure N_s in the presence of nonhydrolyzable analogs showed this to be a multistep event in which the nucleotide first interacts reversibly with N_s, then the N_s–nucleotide complex isomerizes in a Mg-dependent manner to give a complex from which the nucleotide does not dissociate on dilution, and finally the N_s–nucleotide complex undergoes a temperature-dependent subunit dissociation reaction to give a α_s^G complex and a $\beta\gamma$ complex (Codina *et al.*, 1984c). Experimentally, this reaction sequence was traced not only by following the appearance of a tightly binding form of the N protein but also by studying changes in hydrodynamic behavior of the N protein, such as illustrated in Fig. 5. The experiments shown in Fig. 5 illustrate the hydrodynamic behavior of various forms of N_s. Figure 5A(i) shows the behavior

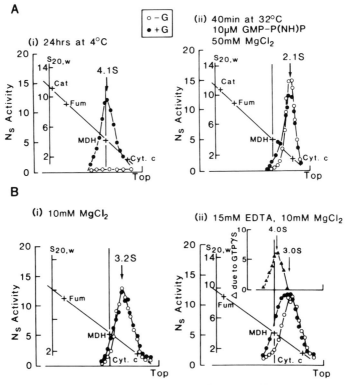

FIG. 5.   4 S, 3 S, and 2 S forms of N_s (1 μg; SW 50.1, 4°C) N_s, not pretreated (Ai), pretreated with GMP-(NH)P and Mg (Aii), or pretreated with GMP-P(NH)P and Mg and then diluted and incubated for 24 hours at 4°C without (Bi) or with (Bii) simultaneous chelation of Mg, was analyzed for its hydrodynamic behavior by centrifugation as in Fig. 1. After fractionation of the gradients, the fractions were assayed for their *cyc*⁻ reconstituting activity in the absence (−G, open symbols) and presence (+G, closed symbols) of 10 μM GMP-P(NH)P. Note that both the 2 S (2.1 S on figure) and 3 S (3.2 S on figure) form of N_s are preactivated.

of control inactive 4 S N_s, A(ii) shows the behavior of fully dissociated active 2 S N_s formed on incubation with GMP-P(NH)P and Mg at 32°C, B(i) shows the behavior of reassociated, yet still active, 3 S N_s formed on cooling from 2 S N_s (nucleotide and Mg present), and B(ii) shows the hydrodynamic behavior of reassociated deactivated (4 S) N_s formed from 3 S N_s on removal of Mg by chelation. Incubation in the cold of N_s with either nucleotide and Mg (not shown) or NaF and Mg (Fig. 6) resulted in formation of 3 S N_s without previous formation of 2 S N_s. Both the 3 S and 2 S forms of N_s are preactivated forms of the protein. This follows from the finding that no nucleotide has to be added to the cyc^- reconstitution

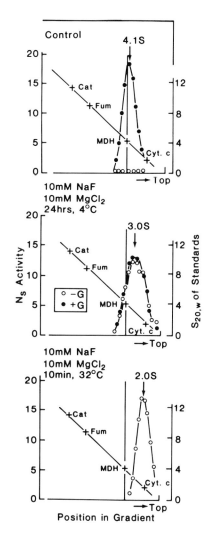

FIG. 6. Formation of 3 S N_s in the cold and 2 S N_s at 32°C on incubation with NaF and Mg. Note that the 3 S and 2 S forms of N_s, but not the 4 S form of the protein, are active in reconstituting cyc^- adenylyl cyclase activity in the absence of added stimulant. This indicates that both the 3 S and 2 S forms obtained with NaF are preactivated forms of the protein.

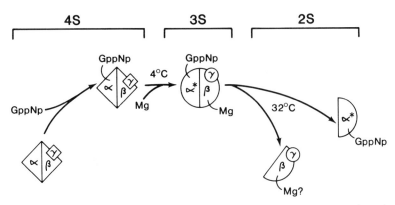

FIG. 7. Sequence of reactions leading from unactivated N protein to activated and dissociated N protein as they have been shown to occur with pure N_s and pure N_i in detergent solution in the presence of nonhydrolyzable GTP analogs. GppNp, 5'-guanylyl imidodiphosphate. Square shapes represent unactivated conformations; round shapes represent activated conformations. The assignment of the Mg binding site to the $\beta\gamma$ subunit complex is speculative and based on the experimental finding that while guanine nucleotides cause "left shifts" in the dose–response curves for hormones, hormones do not cause the thermodynamically expected reciprocal left shift in the dose–response curves for guanine nucleotides; rather they cause left shifts in the dose–response curves for Mg ion (Iyengar and Birnbaumer, 1982). The "3 S" comformation is assumed to be active because it has nucleotide tightly bound to it and, in the case of N_s, its activity can be assayed for without having to add free nucleotide. From Codina *et al.* (1984c).

assays of these forms (compare ratio of activity obtained minus guanine nucleotide to activity obtained plus guanine nucleotide). We conclude that tight binding of nucleotide precedes subunit dissociation. The sequence of reactions leading from a 4 S N_s to fully active and dissociated 2 S N_s as obtained with nonhydrolyzable GTP analogs or NaF is illustrated for the N-GMP-P(NH)P interaction in Fig. 7. As shown above in Fig. 5, all these reactions are reversible: subunits reassociate on cooling and nucleotide dissociates on removal of Mg.

The apparent K_m of N_s for GTP (or its analogs) is in the order of 1 μM. At the prevailing intracellular concentrations of GTP, which are approximately 10^{-4} M, N_s is therefore always saturated with guanine nucleotides. Two factors contribute to the fact that, under physiological conditions, and in the absence of hormonal stimulation, N_s does not stimulate the adenylyl cyclase system fully in a permanent way: (1) N_s is a GTPase (Brandt *et al.*, 1983; Cerione *et al.*, 1984a; Cassel and Selinger, 1976, 1977, 1978); it is, therefore, a regulatory protein that metabolizes its stimulatory ligand; and (2) the apparent K_m for Mg, without which activation of N_s does not occur, is 5–10 mM (Iyengar, 1981), or even more (Hanski

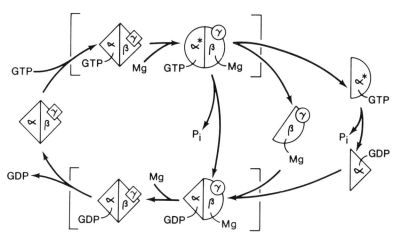

FIG. 8.   Regulatory cycle of N_s and N_i (indistinctly represented as N), as it may occur under the influence of GTP and Mg. In this representation the cycle has been subdivided into four steps: association of GTP, activation of N, hydrolysis of GTP and concomitant deactivation of N, and dissociation of GDP. It is not known at this time which form of the N protein hydrolyzes the GTP and both types of complexes, the undissociated $\alpha^{*GTP} \beta\gamma^{Mg}$ and the dissociated α^{*GTP} are represented as active GTPases.

et al., 1981; Hanski and Gilman, 1982; Codina *et al.*, 1984c), which is many times higher than the prevailing intracellular concentration which is in the neighborhood of 0.5 mM. Even though in avian erythrocytes the dissociation of GDP from N_s is extremely slow and thereby constitutes in these systems an additional barrier to persistent stimulation by GTP (Cassel and Selinger, 1978; Abramowitz *et al.*, 1980), this does not appear to apply to mammalian adenylyl cyclase systems (Iyengar and Birnbaumer, 1981), i.e., to mammalian N_s's, including that of the glucagon-sensitive liver membranes from which GDP dissociates readily (Iyengar and Birnbaumer, 1981) (see also below).

The kinetic regulatory cycle of N_s, as it can be thought to occur in the presence of GTP, is illustrated in Fig. 8.

Although it has been shown that the purified N_s protein in detergent solution undergoes subunit dissociation when treated with nonhydrolyzable GTP analogs (Northup *et al.*, 1983a,b; Codina *et al.*, 1984c), and that the dissociated and resolved α_s^G complex does stimulate C (Northup *et al.*, 1983a,b), it is not yet clear whether the subunit dissociation reaction (1) occurs with GTP, (2) is obligatory for stimulation of C, and (3) happens at all within the normal phospholipid environment of the plasma membrane, where regulation of C by N_s normally occurs. Initial experiments with pure N_s have revealed the following:

1. As isolated and in the presence of detergents, N_s exhibits little if any GTPase activity (turnover number less than 0.001 mol GTP hydrolyzed per mol N_s per minute at 32°C).

2. Under conditions where nonhydrolyzable GTP analogs lead to subunit dissociation and activation of N_s, GTP does neither.

It is our hypothesis that these findings, rather than being artifacts of the incubation conditions, especially interference by detergents, point to the fact that a component is missing without which activation of the N protein in the presence of GTP does not occur. Since on reconstitution with receptors both, the GTP hydrolysis by N_s and the activation of N_s are readily obtained (Brandt *et al.*, 1983; Cerione *et al.*, 1984a,b) (see below), we postulate the missing component to be the hormone receptor and that it is the specific role of the hormone receptor to catalize GTP-dependent activation and subunit dissociation of the N protein.

C. REGULATION OF N_i

N_i resembles N_s not only structurally but also functionally. The effect of N_i activation by guanine nucleotides on the catalytic unit of adenylyl cyclase is well-observed in membranes of the N_s-deficient cyc^- mutant of S49 lymphoma cells (Hildebrandt and Birnbaumer, 1982; Hildebrandt *et al.*, 1982, 1983). Studies with cyc^- membranes have, in fact, allowed the observation of N_i in the absence of a functional N_s. These studies have shown that the activity of N_i, like that of N_s, is not only guanine nucleotide (Hildebrandt *et al.*, 1982; Jakobs *et al.*, 1983a) but also Mg-dependent (Hildebrandt and Birnbaumer, 1983), and that GTP is less active than its nonhydrolyzable analogs (Hildebrandt *et al.*, 1982). This is because N_i, like N_s, is a GTPase (Fig. 1 and Codina *et al.*, 1984b; Sunyer *et al.*, 1984). Like N_s, N_i is also subject to a kinetic regulatory cycle. This cycle, although similar to that of N_s, differs in that while the apparent affinity of N_s for Mg is low, that of N_i is high. Low, micromolar, concentrations of Mg ion are sufficient to fulfill fully the Mg requirement at N_i for its activation by guanine nucleotides (Hildebrandt and Birnbaumer, 1983). Thus, under physiologic conditions, N_i is saturated not only by guanine nucleotides, but also by Mg. The rate-limiting step of the kinetic regulatory cycle of N_i is currently thought to be the dissociation of GDP from its deactivated state. However, this needs to be substantiated with the purified protein. It is possible that in the absence of receptor influence, activation rather than GDP dissociation is the rate limiting step. In fact, the latter is suggested by studies on N_i of cyc^- membranes after pertussis toxin treatment (see below).

N_i, like N_s, also undergoes subunit dissociation upon treatment with analogs (Bokoch *et al.*, 1983; Hildebrandt *et al.*, 1984a; Codina *et al.*, 1984c), leading to formation of α_i^G plus $\beta\gamma$. Also like with N_s, nonhydrolyzable GTP analogs lead to subunit dissociation via intermediary formation (in a Mg-dependent manner) of a 3 S form of N_i that binds the analog tightly. Figures 9 and 10 illustrate these points. Figure 9 shows the distinct conformations seen on sucrose density gradient centrifugation analyzed by densitometric scanning of Coomassie-stained gels such as shown in Fig. 1, and Fig. 10 shows Mg-regulated binding, dissociation and reassociation of a nonhydrolyzable GTP analog as seen with [^{35}S]GTPγS.

Thus the schemes shown on Figs. 7 and 8 apply to both N_s and N_i.

In spite of this knowledge it is not clear as yet how N_i attenuates the activity of C. On the one hand, it has been proposed (Katada *et al.*, 1984a,b), that inhibition of C, which is actually inhibition of the N_sC complex, comes about by an inhibition of the stimulatory action of N_s via reversal of the N_s activation reaction mediated by a local increase of $\beta\gamma$ complex stemming from stimulation of N_i by GTP plus Mg and the concomitantly occurring subunit dissociation reaction. A typical example of data that led to this concept represented in Fig. 11 where it is shown that addition of $\beta\gamma$ complex to a N_s activation reaction results in an inhibition of this reaction. Indeed, at low Mg, $\beta\gamma$ addition to a 2 S form of N_i obtained by NaF treatment results in rapid reversal to the 4 S deactivated form (Northup *et al.*, 1982; Cassel and Selinger, 1976). This mechanism of action of N_i, whereby it acts by facilitating the re-formation of 4 S N_s, requires, of course, that the subunit dissociation reaction seen with GTP analogs in detergent solution both occurs physiologically and is obligatory for N_s action on C. On the other hand, N_i is active not only in reducing the activity of N_sC systems, but also in an N_s-deficient system such as that present in the *cyc⁻* variant of the S49 cell (Hildebrandt *et al.*, 1982, 1984d; Jakobs *et al.*, 1983a; Katada *et al.*, 1984c) which lacks a functionally detectable N_s (Johnson *et al.*, 1980) (Fig. 12). This suggests the existence of a direct, N_s-independent, presumably α_i^G-mediated effect of N_i on C (Hildebrandt *et al.*, 1983, 1984d). Very likely both of these mechanisms are operative under physiologic conditions.

Kinetic studies on the reconstitution of *cyc⁻* S49 cell system, with varying concentrations of preactivated N_s under conditions of nonactivated and preactivated endogenous N_i (Hildebrandt *et al.*, 1984d), reveal that the interactions of activated N_s and activated N_i with C are of a noncompetitive type (Fig. 13). Furthermore, analysis of the state of activated N_s after inhibition of its action on the N_i C complex by activation of its N_i is not associated with deactivation of the stimulating N_s (Fig. 14). Thus, the aspect of N_i inhibition of cAMP formation that is due to direct

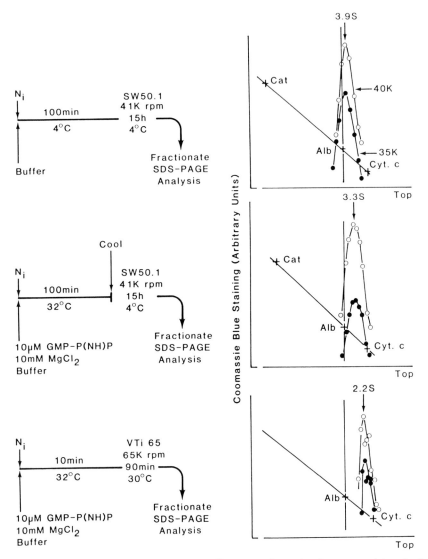

FIG. 9. N_i protein, as N_s, exists in three discrete conformational states, as determined by sucrose density gradient centrifugation. The basic treatment protocols are shown on the figure. In the top panel, treatment was without nucleotide or Mg ion and centrifugation was at 4°C. An apparent S value of 3.9 was obtained: "4 S form of N_i." In the middle panel the protein was treated at 32°C with guanine nucleotide and Mg and then cooled and analyzed as in the top panel. An apparent S value of 3.3 was obtained: "3 S form of N_i." The same result is obtained if N_i protein is treated for 10–12 hours at 4°C with nucleotide and Mg and then analyzed by centrifugation in the cold. In the bottom panel, treatment was the same as in the middle panel, but centrifugation was at 22°C: "2 S form of N_i." In other experiments, it was shown that 3 S N_i incubated for 10 hours at 4°C with EDTA (chelation of Mg) requires its 4 S conformation. From Codina *et al.* (1984c).

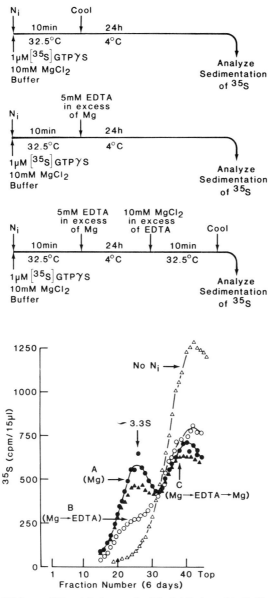

FIG. 10. The 3 S form of N protein has nucleotide tightly bound to it. The protocols used are shown in the top portion of the figure. From Codina *et al.* (1984c).

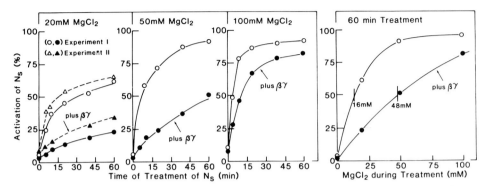

FIG. 11. Inhibition by $\beta\gamma$ complex of the activation of N_s by GMP-P(NH)P and Mg and abolishment of this inhibition by high concentrations of Mg ion. Treatment conditions: 10 μM GMP-P(NH)P, 1 mM EDTA, ΔMgCl$_2$, Δt, with or without $\beta\gamma$ subunit complex. After treatment of N_s, the mixture was diluted 400-fold in medium without Mg chloride or GMP-P(NH)P and then assayed for cyc^- reconstituting activity. For further details, see Codina *et al.* (1984a,c).

interaction with C is not due to a competitive displacement of the α_s^G complex from a common site on C.

D. EFFECTS OF TOXINS ON THE KINETIC REGULATORY CYCLES OF N_s AND N_i

ADP-Ribosylation of α_s by cholera toxin results in inhibition of the GTPase activity of N_s (Cassel and Selinger, 1977) and converts GTP into a

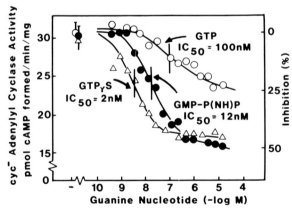

FIG. 12. Inhibitory effect of guanine nucleotides on cyc^- S49 cell adenylyl cyclase activity. Note that nonhydrolyzable GTP analogs cause more inhibition than the hydrolyzable GTP. ATP, 0.1 mM; Mg, 5.0 mM; forskolin, 100 μM.

FIG. 13. Noncompetitive nature of N_i-mediated inhibition of cyc^- adenylyl cyclase activity reconstituted with varying concentrations of $GTP_\gamma S$-preactivated N_s. A Lineweaver–Burke plot is shown of the steady-state reconstituted activity obtained on mixing preactivated N_s with cyc^- membranes containing either untreated ($GDP_\gamma S$-blocked) N_i or $GTP_\beta S$-pretreated N_i. The strategy followed for obtaining preactivated N_s and treated cyc^- membranes is outlined on the top of the figure. For details see Hildebrandt *et al.* (1984d).

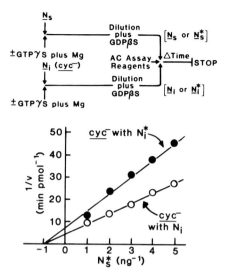

superactive nucleotide like its nonhydrolyzable analogs (Lin *et al.*, 1978; Birnbaumer *et al.*, 1980a) (Fig. 15). In contrast, ADP-ribosylation of α_i by pertussis toxin, while leading, like cholera toxin, to a decrease in the hormonal stimulation of N_i-dependent hydrolysis of GTP (Burns *et al.*, 1983) results in a blockade of the effect of GTP to activate N_i without affecting the activity of its nonhydrolyzable analogs (Hildebrandt *et al.*, 1983). We currently believe that pertussis toxin, rather than blocking the kinetic regulatory cycle at the level of GTP to GDP conversion, blocks it after the formation of N_i–GDP complex, very likely inhibiting its dissociation to give free N_s plus GDP.

E. DUAL REGULATION: SUMMARY

It is now clear that the adenylyl cyclase system is a multicomponent complex in which the catalytic unit serves as a monitor of the activity states of N_s and N_i. Under physiologic (basal) conditions, the system "idles" with N_s and N_i continuously cycling through the kinetic regulatory cycle of Fig. 8. This gives rise to *basal* steady-state levels of active N_s and N_i, as well as basal rates of GTP hydrolysis. The latter are therefore the sum of the rate at which GTP is hydrolyzed by N_s plus that by N_i. Since either activation (N_s) or GDP dissociation (N_i) is the rate-limiting step under "idling" conditions, hydrolysis of GTP becomes a measure of the rate at which N proteins traverse through their kinetic regulatory cycles (Cassel *et al.*, 1979). It follows that any increase in cycling rate due to increased rate of activation or GDP release (N_s and N_i, respectively)

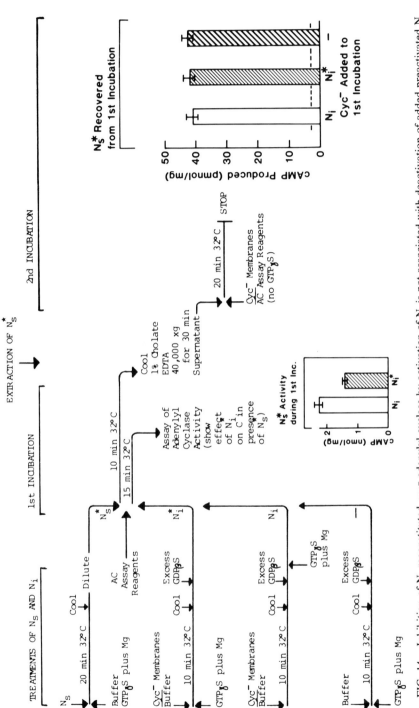

FIG. 14. Inhibition of N_s-reconstituted cyc^- adenylyl cyclase by activation of N_i is not associated with deactivation of added preactivated N_s (N_s^*). The design of the experiment, as well as activities obtained (means ± SD of triplicates) is shown. Note that N_s^* activity recovered from incubations where it had reconstituted cyc^- membrane is the same regardless of whether these membranes had a preactivated N_i or not. For further details see Hildebrandt et al. (1984c).

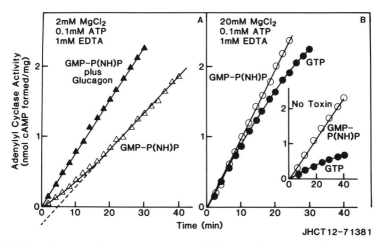

FIG. 15. Cholera toxin treatment converts GTP into a "superactive" guanine nucleotide, while not affecting to any significant degree hormonal stimulation of the system (A) or GMP-P(NH)P stimulated activity (B). Treatment: 10 minutes, 32.5°C; 100 μg/ml cholera toxin; 10 mM NAD⁺; 5 mM MgCl₂.

will automatically result in an increase in GTP hydrolysis by the affected N.

It is important to note that whenever GTP- (or GTP analog-)affected adenylyl cyclase is measured, the resulting activity is the balance of the effects of activated N_s (stimulatory to C) and activated N_i (inhibitory to N_s and C).

III. Hormonal Regulation of Adenylyl Cyclase Activity

A. PARAMETERS AFFECTED

Addition of a stimulatory hormone to a complete N_sN_iC system, as found in membranes, results in three major consequences. First, it results in what is commonly referred to as GTP-dependent stimulation of the adenylyl cyclase system which is in fact a stimulation of the GTP-mediated activation of the system (Rodbell *et al.*, 1974; Ross *et al.*, 1977; Iyengar *et al.*, 1980a). Second, it results in a stimulation of the low K_m GTPase activity of N_s (Cassel and Selinger, 1976, 1977). And third, it results in a stimulation of a guanine nucleotide release and/or exchange reaction (Cassel and Selinger, 1978).

Although the stimulation of adenylyl cyclase activity is readily observed in essentially all isolated membranes studied, including membranes from ovarian and testicular systems, stimulation of GTPase and nucleotide release are observed much less readily because of "noise" contributed by one or more of the many enzymatic and regulatory mechanisms that cohabitate the membrane in which the adenylyl cyclase system is located. Yet, it is now quite clear that hormonal stimulation results in all three of the above changes.

Addition of an inhibitory hormone to a complete N_sN_iC system affects the same three parameters: C activity, GTP hydrolysis, and nucleotide exchange. However, while an inhibitory hormone enhances, as does a stimulatory hormone, both GTP hydrolysis and nucleotide exchange by activating N_i, the same N_i-activating effect leads to an inhibition of C activity, which, as mentioned above, appears to be the combined result of direct inhibition of C by N_i (Hildebrandt *et al.*, 1984c; Katada *et al.*, 1984c) and deactivation of activated N_s (Katada *et al.*, 1984a,b).

B. STIMULATORY HORMONAL REGULATION

1. Increase in Affinity of N_s for Mg

The analysis of the mode of action of many stimulatory hormones, including glucagon and β-adrenergic ligands, in various systems, including S49 cells (Howlett *et al.*, 1979), brain (Strittmatter and Neer, 1980), erythrocytes (Neufeld *et al.*, 1980; Citri and Schramm, 1982; Codina *et al.*, 1984a), and liver (Northup *et al.*, 1982; Iyengar and Birnbaumer, 1982) has now clearly established that stimulation of C is due to an increase in the levels of active N_s, and that the increase in active N_s is due to a facilitation of the basic mechanism by which N_s is activated by guanine nucleotides (Birnbaumer *et al.*, 1980a; Iyengar *et al.*, 1980a; Iyengar, 1981; Iyengar and Birnbaumer, 1982). It has been established further that, both in membranes in which C has been inactivated (Iyengar and Birnbaumer, 1982) and in reconstituted systems (Citri and Schramm, 1980, 1982; Neufeld *et al.*, 1980; Pedersen and Ross, 1982; Cerione *et al.*, 1984a,b) stimulation of N_s by HR complex occurs in the absence of C, this being the primary reason for which C can be considered a monitor of N activity.

The mechanism by which N_s stimulation by guanine nucleotide is enhanced by a stimulatory HR complex was explored in detail studying the glucagon-sensitive liver membrane adenylyl cyclase system without (Iyengar *et al.*, 1980a) as well as after (Iyengar and Birnbaumer, 1982) inactivation of the C unit. These studies revealed that HR complex increases the steady-state levels of active N_s by accelerating the "activation reaction" by which N_{GTP} becomes N_{GTP}^*, and that it does so primarily by increasing the affinity of N_s for Mg (Iyengar and Birnbaumer, 1982) such that it becomes fully saturated by the divalent cation at physiologic ambient concentrations of Mg. As mentioned earlier, saturation of N_s by Mg leads, indeed, to fast activation, and, as a consequence, to an increase in the steady-state levels of active N_s (Iyengar, 1981; Iyengar and Birnbaumer, 1981). The effect of glucagon addition on the Mg requirement for activation of N_s in a C-free liver membrane is illustrated in Fig. 16. Studies such as these confirmed and provided a mechanistic explanation for much earlier findings with intact membrane adenylyl cyclases (Birnbaumer *et al.*, 1969, 1976) showing that, upon hormonal stimulation, the overall requirement of the system for Mg is decreased. R_s's have, therefore, been called Mg switches (Iyengar and Birnbaumer, 1981; Bockaert and Sebben-Perez, 1983).

It should be noted that even though addition of nucleotides results in a "left shift" in the dose–response curves for hormonal stimulation, the reverse is not true, i.e., hormone addition does not result in a comparable shift in the dose–response curves of nucleotide-dependent activation of N_s (Fig. 17).

Studies with rabbit corpus luteum membranes, similar to those with liver membranes, but substituting glucagon for LH, revealed a similar, but, by far, not as marked, effect on the requirement of the luteal N_s for Mg upon LH stimulation (Kirchick and Birnbaumer, unpublished). This drew attention to a second effect of hormonal stimulation, seen in both the glucagon and the LH-sensitive systems. This is the fact that hormonal stimulation, in addition to causing faster activation of N_s at lower Mg

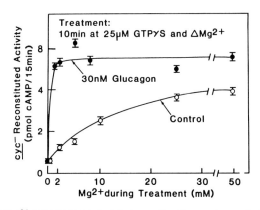

FIG. 16.   Effect of hormone (receptor) to lower the Mg requirement of N_s for its activation by guanine nucleotide. Note that in addition to the lowering in apparent K_m for Mg (~1000-fold), there is also an effect of hormone to increase the extent to which the guanine nucleotide activates N_s. From Iyengar and Birnbaumer (1982).

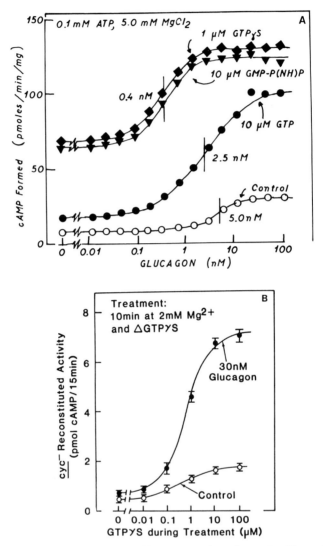

FIG. 17.   Lack of reciprocal effects of hormones and guanine nucleotides on the position of their respective dose–response curves. (A) Effect of guanine nucleotide on the dose–response curves with which glucagon stimulates adenylyl cyclase activity in intact liver membranes. From Iyengar *et al.* (1980a). (B) Lack of effect of glucagon to affect the dose–response curve with which GTP$_\gamma$S activates N_s in liver membranes. From Iyengar and Birnbaumer (1982).

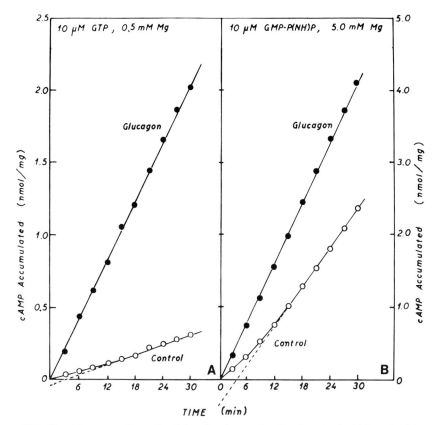

FIG. 18. Glucagon affects adenylyl cyclase by accelerating the rate at which nucleotides activate it (B) as well as by augmenting the extent to which they activate the system (A,B). ATP, 0.1 mM; EDTA, 1.0 mM. From Iyengar *et al.* (1980a).

concentrations, also causes an increase in the absolute level of active N_s over that obtainable with saturating Mg alone (see Figs. 16 and 18, and Iyengar and Birnbaumer, 1982). This indicates that hormone receptors, by coupling to N_s, not only modify the affinity of N_s for Mg, but cause changes in other properties as well. One of these is the dissociation of GDP from N_s and thereby facilitates its exchange for GTP.

2. Stimulation of Nucleotide Exchange

Studies with turkey erythrocyte membranes were the first to show that addition to membranes of [³H]GDP leads to accumulation of bound [³H]GDP, and that the [³H]GDP, so bound, is released upon addition of stimulatory hormone (isoproterenol, in this case) (Cassel and Selinger,

1978). Similarly, studies with platelet membranes showed that hormonal stimulation of N_s results in increased rates of release of preloaded [^{3}H]GMP-P(NH)P (Michel and Lefkowitz, 1982). This type of studies has not yet been carried out with pure N_s, although, as illustrated below, the techniques for doing so are being developed. All-in-all, the above data strongly suggest that, although in the regulatory kinetic cycle of mammalian N_s nucleotide exchange, i.e., N_{GDP} conversion to N_{GTP}, is not rate-limiting under basal conditions, it may very well be so after saturation of N_s with Mg ion, and that the nucleotide exchange reaction is a secondary rate-limiting step which is also abolished by the stimulatory HR complex. In fact, as shown in studies with turkey erythrocyte membranes, the secondary rate-limiting step of mammalian N_s appears to be the primary one of avian erythrocyte N_s (Cassel and Selinger, 1978; Sharma et al., 1975). Further, due to the clearly established size heterogeneity of α_s subunits (Gill and Meren, 1978; Johnson et al., 1978; Lai et al., 1981; Schleifer et al., 1982; Malbon and Greenberg, 1982), it may well be that, even though activation and nucleotide exchange are, respectively, the primary and secondary rate-limiting steps when N_s is idling in its basal unaffected state, the absolute values as well as the difference between the rates at which activation and nucleotide exchange proceed may vary widely from N_s to N_s, depending on both species and tissue origin. In fact, the difference between the two rates may be such that both of these effects of HR complexes, i.e., increase in Mg affinity and enhancement of nucleotide exchange, become essential for optimal increase in steady-state level of active N_s and, hence, for full stimulation of adenylyl cyclase activity.

C. INHIBITORY REGULATION

Just as N_i appears to be a universal component of adenylyl cyclase systems, R_i-type receptors seem to be so as well. Examples of R_i-type receptors, i.e., receptors that stimulate N_i to inhibit C, are opioid (Sharma et al., 1975; Blume et al., 1979), muscarinic acetylcholine (Murad et al., 1962), somatostatin (Jakobs et al., 1983b), α_2-adrenergic (Jakobs et al., 1976; Yamazaki et al., 1982), dopamine (Cote et al., 1982), and angiotensin II (Jard et al., 1981) receptors. In contrast to R_s receptors, R_i receptors are not likely to affect N_i activity by altering affinity for Mg because, even under basal conditions, N_i already has an apparent affinity for the divalent cation in the micromolar range (Hildebrandt and Birnbaumer, 1983). R_i receptors do, however, like R_s receptors, enhance the nucleotide exchange reaction at N_i. This has been well established for several R_i-type receptors, including α_2-adrenergic receptors in human platelets (Michel and Lefkowitz, 1982) and adenosine and prostaglandin receptors in guinea pig fat (Murayama and Ui, 1984). Thus, dual regulation of adenylyl cyclase is a general feature of hormone-responsive adenylyl cyclase systems.

D. STIMULATION OF GTP HYDROLYSIS BY STIMULATORY AND INHIBITORY HORMONES

Stimulation of both N_s by stimulatory H_sR_s complex and N_i by inhibitory H_iR_i complex leads to increased turnover of the kinetic regulatory cycle of the respective N protein by the mechanisms described above. This is, by necessity, associated with an increased rate of GTP hydrolysis. Although, as mentioned above, hormone- (or agonist-)mediated increase in GTP hydrolysis is not always readily observed because of background "noise," N-related GTP hydrolysis has been assessed by testing for presence of low K_m GTPases in several systems and has been related to N proteins because (1) the hydrolytic rate is stimulated by a hormone, and (2) this stimulation of GTP hydrolysis is inhibited by cholera toxin when N_s-related or pertussis toxin when N_i-related. Since both toxins block the turnover cycle, both abolish GTP hydrolysis, even though only cholera toxin blocks the cycle by actually inhibiting the hydrolytic reaction. Hormone-stimulated GTP hydrolysis was first discovered in turkey erythrocyte membranes in studies on β-adrenergic stimulation of what is now recognized as N_s (Hildebrandt et al., 1984b; Northup et al., 1983b). The adrenergic ligand-stimulated GTP hydrolysis was inhibited by β-adrenergic blockers, confirming the receptor dependency of the phenomenon, and was blocked by cholera toxin, establishing its relation to adenylyl cyclase, i.e., N_s. Since then, enhancement of GTP hydrolysis has been observed on receptor stimulation of N_s, such as obtained with PGE in platelet (Michel and Lefkowitz, 1982; Aktories et al., 1982a,b) and monocyte membranes (Bitonti et al., 1980) and of N_i, such as obtained with α_2-adrenergic ligands in human platelet and adipocyte membranes and with PGE in adipocyte membranes (Aktories et al., 1982a,b), with somatostatin in cyc^- S49 cell membranes (Jakobs et al., 1983b) and with opioids in neuroblastoma $\times$ glioma cell membranes (Koski and Klee, 1981; Burns et al., 1983b). As expected from the fact that N_s and N_i are independent molecules and under independent regulatory control of GTP and hormone receptors, enhancement of GTP hydrolysis due to hormonal stimulation of N_s turnover was found to be additive to enhancement of GTP hydrolysis due to hormonal stimulation of N_i turnover (Bitonti et al., 1980; Aktories and Jakobs, 1981; Jakobs et al., 1982; M. Ui, personal communication).

Although it is commonly spoken of as "hormone-stimulated GTPase," there is, as yet, no evidence to support that hormone–receptor complex in any way alters the intrinsic k_{cat} of GTP hydrolysis of either N_s or N_i. Thus far, GTP hydrolysis seems to come about simply as a result of increased cycling. Indeed, a direct stimulation of GTPase activity of an N protein would be counterproductive, for it would lead to an accelerated deactivation, as opposed to an increase in the steady-state levels of active N, as is found experimentally.

E. STIMULATION OF GTP HYDROLYSIS BY PURE N_s BY PURE R_s

Although pure N_i in detergent solution is able to hydrolyze GTP in a Mg-dependent manner (apparent K_m for GTP is approximately 10 nM; apparent K_m for Mg $< 1 \mu M$) and does so at very low rates (Hildebrandt et al., 1983a; Sunyer et al., 1984), N_s, under similar circumstances, hydrolyzes GTP at most at a 10% the rate of N_i (Sunyer et al., 1984). This raised the question whether or not N_s is indeed a GTPase or whether it merely supplies the substrate for an additional component which would be the GTPase proper. Further, the additional question arises as to whether, indeed, as assumed up to this point, the interaction of R and N is all that is needed to obtain signal transduction. Although successful reconstitution experiments have been published to indicate that R and N are necessary to obtain hormone-stimulated activation of N_s, these studies were all performed with preparations containing R free of N and N free of R, but not with preparations containing both pure R and pure N (Neufeld et al., 1980; Citri and Schramm, 1980, 1982; Iyengar and Birnbaumer, 1982; Pedersen and Ross, 1982). Recently, by reconstituting pure N_s from human erythrocytes with pure β-adrenergic receptors from guinea pig lung into synthetic phospholipid vesicles it has been possible to determine for the first time that indeed N_s is a GTPase under the control of R_s and that the interaction between R_s and N_s is sufficient to account for H-dependent stimulation of GTP hydrolysis by N_s (Cerione et al., 1984a). In these experiments, phospholipid vesicles were formed in the presence of the pure detergent-solubilized N_s and R_s proteins, by removing the detergent by chromatography over a detergent-binding resin. When such vesicles are incubated for GTPase activity, such an activity is indeed measurable. This was not seen if N_s or R_s were omitted from the reconstitution protocol. Interestingly, high levels of both R_s and N_s result in marked stimulation of GTPase at N_s, even in the absence of stimulatory hormonal ligand (not shown) (Cerione et al., 1984a). This indicates clearly that the relative concentrations of N_s and R_s are of critical importance for proper regulation of these proteins within the membrane.

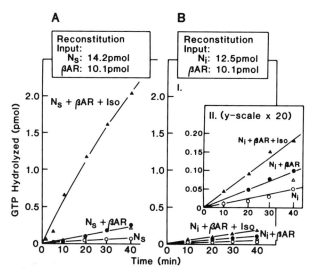

FIG. 19. N_s/N_s-specific reconstitution of agonist stimulable GTP hydrolysis as obtained in phosphatidylcholine vesicles. Phospholipid vesicles containing either N_s, N_s plus β-adrenergic receptor (βAR), N_i, or N_i plus βAR were prepared by mixing the purified proteins in the presence of sodium choride, phosphatidylcholine, and octyl glucoside and affecting vesicle formation by removal of detergent via passage of a deterging-adsorbing column (Extractigel). The vesicles thus formed were diluted with sodium chloride solution, precipitated with polyethylene glycol, and resuspended in 0.8 ml of 100 mM sodium chloride, 10 mM Tris–HCl, ph 7.4. Equal aliquots of the resuspended vesicles were then assayed for GTP hydrolyzing activity. N_s, Vesicles containing N_s only; N_i, vesicles containing N_i only; N_s + βAR, vesicles containing N_s and βAR assayed without agonists; N_s + βAR + Iso, vesicles containing N_s and βAR were assayed in the presence of isoproterenol; N_i + βAR, vesicles containing N_i and βAR assayed without agonists; N_i + βAR + Iso, vesicles containing N_i and βAR were assayed in the presence of isoproterenol; Δ, vesicles containing βAR and either N_s (A), or N_i (B), were assayed with isoproterenol and excess alprenolol. Note that isoproterenol stimulation of GTP hydrolysis by N_s is approximately 10-fold that of N_i. However, some stimulation of N_i by βAR was observed as well (B, inset).

As illustrated in Fig. 19A, coreconstitution of R_s with N_s results in a system that, on addition of agonist (isoproterenol), increases its rate of hydrolysis of GTP. That this is a receptor-dependent reaction is indicated by the fact that the effect was blocked by alprenolol, a specific β-adrenergic blocker. Coreconstitution of N_i with an R_s, on the other hand, results in little stimulation of N_i-mediated GTP hydrolysis (Fig. 19B), indicating that there is specificity in the interaction of R_s with N_s and very likely also between N_i- and R_i-type receptors. An apparent lack of such specificity of interaction reported recently (Asano *et al.*, 1984) may relate to different procedures used in the purification of N_i or to the fact that while pure N_i was used, those experiments employed only a partially (approximately 10%) pure β-adrenergic receptor preparation.

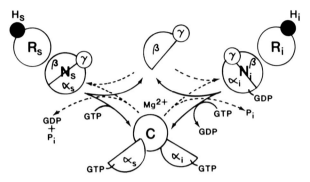

FIG. 20. Some aspects of dual regulation of adenylyl cyclase by N_s and N_i, which in turn are under regulation of ^HR_s and ^HR_i complexes, respectively. A steady-state situation is depicted whereby both N_s and N_i are undergoing cyclical GTP-dependent activation and GTPase-dependent deactivation. GTP-dependent activation is represented with concomitant subunit dissociation to give α^{GTP}'s, which each interact with C to enhance or, respectively, decrease catalytic activity, and a $\beta\gamma$ complex, which does not itself appear to dissociate. GTPase-dependent deactivation is assumed to be completed upon reassociation of α subunits with $\beta\gamma$ complexes. Current evidence suggests that $\beta\gamma$ of N_i is the same as $\beta\gamma$ of N_s. Due to this, a single pool of $\beta\gamma$ is represented. Activation of N_i may therefore affect cyclic AMP formation by two ways: direct inhibition of C activity and facilitation of deactivation of N_s by supplying $\beta\gamma$ subunits. Although not specifically depicted, ^HR_s is assumed to act by facilitating the rate of activation of N_s, a phenomenon that comes about, at least in part, by reduction of the apparent K_m for Mg. The mechanism by which ^HR_i complexes act is also assumed to be by accelerating that rate of activation of N_i, but this reaction is depicted to include the exchange of GDP for GTP.

In summary, the only two proteins required to account fully for the transduction of the signal generated by hormone receptor occupancy by stimulatory hormone into an effect are R_s and N_s.

Figure 20 presents in a scheme many of the above discussed structural and functional aspects of the dual regulation of adenylyl cyclase activity by nucleotides and hormones.

IV. Nucleotide and Mg Regulation of Hormone Binding

A. RECEPTORS AS TWO-STATE SYSTEMS

It is now clear that mere occupancy of a receptor by a specific ligand is not sufficient to trigger N_s activation. To activate N_s (or N_i), receptors need to be occupied by an agonistic ligand, i.e., an active hormone or neurotransmitter. This finding establishes that receptors need to exist in at least two states: inactive and active. Hormones and agonists, under proper conditions, act to stabilize, i.e., to favor the formation of the latter, while antagonists or blockers favor formation of the former. Chemical modification of natural agonists, i.e., hormones and neurotransmitters and *de novo* synthesis of analogs has led to the development of compounds that are neither blockers nor full agonists. They are characterized by eliciting responses that are partial and are therefore termed partial agonists. Although the situation may be more complex, one way of explaining why partial agonists, or hormones that elicit varying degrees of stimulation, are such, is by causing only part of the receptors to become activated. In isolated membranes, the capacity of hormones to elicit receptor activation leading to an activation of adenylyl cyclase is intimately related to the presence of Mg and guanine nucleotides. The original clue to this did not come from studies in which stimulation of adenylyl cyclase was evaluated, but rather from studies in which the interaction of a labeled hormone (iodoglucagon) with its receptor sites in liver plasma membranes was investigated (Rodbell *et al.*, 1971a). These studies showed that guanine nucleotides (present as contaminants in ATP used as substrate for adenylyl cyclase reactions) cause a reduction in the affinity of receptors for glucagon. Indeed, it was the search for a functional correlate at the level of adenylyl cyclase that eventually led to discovery of nucleotide regulation of adenylyl cyclases (Rodbell *et al.*, 1971b; Birnbaumer *et al.*, 1974; Birnbaumer and Yang, 1974; Neufeld *et al.*, 1980) and to the characterization of N proteins (Ross and Gilman, 1977a; Pfeuffer, 1977). The reduction in receptor affinity for agonists on addition of guanine nucleotides is observed in essentially all membrane-bound receptor systems that are coupled to the adenylyl cyclase system provided they bind the hormone in a reversible fashion (Abramowitz and Birnbaumer, 1982; Labarbera *et al.*, 1980). It is important to note that the affinity-reducing effect of guanine nucleotides applies only to agonistic receptor ligands and is not seen with antagonists (Rubalcava and Rodbell, 1973; Lefkowitz *et al.*, 1976; Maguire *et al.*, 1976a). This indicates a functional relationship between agonism (i.e., capacity to activate a receptor) and nucleotide regulation of the receptor.

From an experimental point of view, nucleotide regulation is visualized in one of two ways, depending on whether an agonist or an antagonist is used as a receptor probe. For example, with peptide hormone receptors such as glucagon receptors, the labeled receptor probe is the hormone itself (Rodbell *et al.*, 1971a; Rojas *et al.*, 1983). Addition of guanine nucleotides, therefore, causes a reduction in receptor occupancy at subsaturating, but not at saturating concentrations of the probe. This phenomenon was referred to as "nucleotide-induced inhibition of receptor binding." With neurotransmitter receptors, such as the much studied β-adrenergic receptor system, the receptor probes used are generally antagonists and insensitive to the regulatory effect of guanine nucleotides and affinities of the receptor for agonists are estimated from displacement curves (Caron and Lefkowitz, 1976; Aurbach *et al.*, 1974; Maguire *et al.*, 1976b; Baroosky and Brooker, 1981; Ezrailson *et al.*, 1981; Engel *et al.*, 1981). Since, as mentioned above, addition of guanine nucleotides causes reduction in affinity of the receptors for the agonistic ligands, the guanine nucleotide effect translates itself into a requirement for higher concentrations of agonists to cause 50% displacement of antagonist binding (Lefkowitz *et al.*, 1976; Maguire *et al.*, (1976a). This effect is commonly referred to as a nucleotide-induced affinity shift in the agonist displacement curve.

Although discovered after that of glucagon receptors, nucleotide regulation of β-adrenergic receptors has been explored in much more detail. Two features of β-adrenergic agonist displacement curves are of note. (1) In most, but not all, β-adrenergic systems, agonist displacement curves are unaffected by guanine nucleotides when tested in the absence of Mg. Thus, under these conditions the displacement curve is in a position corresponding to low affinity for agonist even though guanine nucleotides have not yet been added; (2) Mg addition causes an increase in agonist binding (Williams *et al.*, 1978) and a "left-shift" in the agonist displacement curves (Bird and Maguire, 1978), and it is this left shift that is abolished by guanine nucleotide addition. Thus, with β-adrenergic receptors, the phenomenology is best described by stating that, in the absence of Mg, receptors exhibit low affinity for agonist, that they acquire high affinity for agonist on addition of Mg, and that guanine nucleotides block or reverse the Mg-dependent formation of the high agonist affinity state of the receptor. This is illustrated for the S49 β-adrenergic receptor in Fig. 21A.

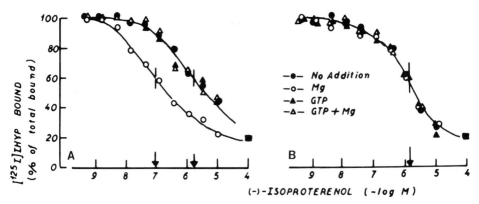

FIG. 21. Regulation of agonist binding to receptors by Mg and guanine nucleotides in wild-type S49 cell membranes (A) and the absence of this regulation in N_s-deficient *cyc⁻* S49 cell membranes (B). For details see Iyengar *et al.* (1980b).

Receptors exist, therefore, in two states in terms of both activity: active and inactive, and agonist affinity: high and low. In its simplest form, the Mg and guanine nucleotide regulation of receptor affinity states can therefore be described by Reaction (1), where H is the agonistic hormone and l and h denote the low- and the high-affinity states of receptors for the agonist H.

$$^{H}R_l \xrightleftharpoons[\text{GTP} (\pm \text{ Mg})]{\text{Mg}} {}^{H}R_h \qquad (1)$$

B. THE HIGH-AFFINITY FORM OF RECEPTOR AS A MEASURE OF ITS EFFICACY

A clear indication as to which of the two forms of R, R_h or R_l, is associated with activity came from studies that correlated affinity shifts with partial agonism of β receptor ligands (Kent *et al.*, 1980; DeLean *et al.*, 1980). As illustrated in Fig. 22A, it was found (Kent *et al.*, 1980) that the ratio affinity without guanine nucleotide (Mg present)/affinity in the presence of guanine nucleotide (Mg present), i.e., the magnitude of the Mg and nucleotide-induced affinity shifts, is positively and linearly correlated with the agonism of the ligand studied. Thus, antagonists, which by definition have an agonism activity index of 0, were unaffected by Mg and

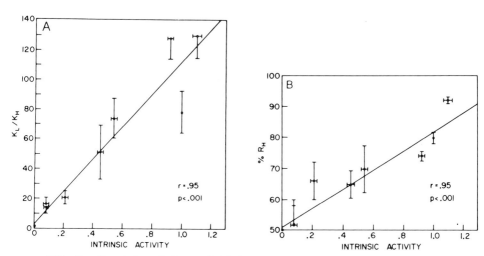

FIG. 22. Correlation of changes in N_s-dependent agonist affinity of frog β-adrenergic receptors with intrinsic activity of β ligands as obtained in assays such as illustrated in Fig. 21A. (A) Correlation of ratio K_H/K_L to intrinsic activity of the ligands. (B) Correlation of the proportion of total R in the high affinity R_H form with intrinsic activity. From Kent *et al.* (1980) and DeLean *et al.* (1980).

nucleotides, full agonists, capable of activating maximally the receptors as seen in adenylyl cyclase studies, showed affinity shifts that, for the frog erythrocyte β-adrenergic receptor system, were in the order of 100-fold, and partial agonists, capable of stimulating adenylyl cyclase 50% as much as the full agonists isoproterenol or hydroxybenzyl-isoproterenol (HBI), showed affinity shifts of about 50-fold. It is of interest, too, that the degree of agonism was found to be positively correlated not only with the magnitude of the affinity shift, but also with the calculated fraction of total receptors that, in the absence of guanine nucleotides (Mg present), could be found to be in a high affinity form (Fig. 22B) (Kent *et al.*, 1980).

Taken together, it is clear from these studies that the active form of a receptor correlates with, and we believe is synonymous to, its high-affinity form, the degree of agonism being dependent on the proportion of the receptors in their high-affinity form. Although it is not yet clear how the nucleotide effect on agonist affinity for receptor comes about, the effect of Mg leading together with the agonistic hormone H to both an affinity shift and a change in the relative distribution of receptors into high- and low-affinity forms can be readily analyzed in mathematical terms using a simple two-state model.

C. R_s/N_s INTERACTION AS THE MOLECULAR BASIS FOR ACTIVITY AND AFFINITY REGULATION OF RECEPTOR

In analyzing Mg and nucleotide regulation of hormone binding, it is necessary to address the question as to whether Mg exerts its effect by interacting directly with R or whether it does so by interacting with another protein which, in turn, interacts with (binds to) R. Experiments with both the N_s-deficient *cyc*⁻ membrane system and the above described R_s–N_s reconstituted system indicate that the effect of Mg is dependent on N_s. Figure 22B illustrates that the effect of Mg to induce the higher affinity form of the β-adrenergic receptor is absent in the *cyc*⁻ membrane system. Figure 23 illustrates that R_s-reconstituted with N_s in phospholipid vesicles distributes itself into forms of high and low affinity in the presence of Mg, and that nucleotide addition causes all of the receptors to reacquire their low-affinity form. Insertion of β-adrenergic receptor into phospholipid vesicles in the absence of N_s (Shorr *et al.*, 1981) or, as seen in experiments with less pure preparations of receptor (Kalleher *et al.*, 1983) in the presence of inactivated N_s, results without exception in all of the receptors being in their low-affinity form. Since N_s is a protein that depends on Mg for its activity, the most likely mode of action of Mg is to bind to N_s, causing it to adopt a new conformation that interacts with R to stabilize it

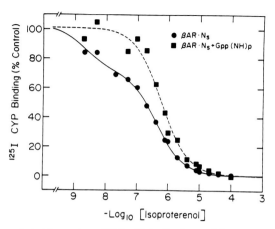

FIG. 23. N_s-mediated formation of high affinity R_H form of the pure β-adrenergic receptor from guinea pig lung as obtained after coreconstitution into phospholipid vesicles. From Cerione *et al.* (1984a).

in the R_h form. Thus, the most likely composition of a hormone-occupied receptor in its high-affinity form is $^HR_hN_s^{Mg}$.[3]

D. N PROTEINS AS THREE-STATE SYSTEMS

The final questions to be raised in this section of this article relate to which of the several forms that N_s adopts throughout its kinetic regulatory cycle interacts with R_s to stabilize its high-affinity form, and how R_s regulation by N_s compares to R_i regulation by N_i. Although the final answers to these questions are not yet available, a comparative analysis of different hormone binding reactions provides for interesting clues, and suggests that, while the receptor systems can be interpreted well by considering them as two-state systems, N systems appear to behave as three-state systems.

1. Regulation of Binding of the Rat Liver Glucagon Receptor: Lack of Effect of Mg

Contrary to findings with the β-adrenergic receptor system, glucagon receptors require no Mg to show high affinity for glucagon (Rojas *et al.*,

---

[3] Recent experiments by Schramm and collaborators on agonist "locking" suggests that under special circumstances a magnesium-dependent high-affinity form of HR complex can be obtained after inactivation of N_s by alkali treatment (Neufeld *et al.*, 1983; Nedivi and Schramm, 1984). This suggests that an additional magnesium-binding site may exist and hence participate in receptor regulation. This site may be located on the receptor, provided alkali treatment inactivates *all* functions of N_s and not only its capacity to bind guanine nucleotide and hence to activate the catalytic unit C of the system.

1983). Thus, in the rat liver, free N_s occupied by neither Mg nor guanine nucleotides is able to interact with the rat liver glucagon R, and the interaction between these proteins, presumably in a glucagon-facilitated manner, is sufficient to lead for the formation of a high affinity $^HR_hN_s$ complex between R_s, N_s, and the hormone. Defining N_s^{r+} as the form of N_s that interacts with R_s to stabilize its high h form, the complex formed between glucagon, rat liver glucagon receptor and rat liver N_s in the absence of Mg can be described as $^HR_hN_s^{r+}$. This complex "survives" solubilization, being detected in gel filtration experiments as a macromolecule with labeled glucagon bound to it that releases glucagon upon incubation with guanine nucleotide (Lad *et al.*, 1977; Welton *et al.*, 1977).

2. GDP as the Regulator of N_s/R_s Interaction

It is a general finding, not only with the Mg-insensitive glucagon receptor system (Rodbell *et al.*, 1971a; Rojas *et al.*, 1983; Lebarbara *et al.*, 1980), but also with other Mg-sensitive receptor systems (Iyengar *et al.*, 1980b) that the reduction in apparent affinity by guanine nucleotide can be brought about by addition of either GTP or GTP analogs or GDP and GDP analogs including $GDP_\beta S$. Concentration-effect curves obtained for the glucagon receptor system have recently shown that the order of potencies for guanine nucleotides, surprisingly, is GDP = $GDP_\beta S$ > GTP > GMP-P(NH)P, with GTP being 10-fold less potent than GDP and GMP-P(NH)P being 100-fold less potent than GDP. This is illustrated in part in Fig. 24A. That the effect of GDP might have been due to transphosphorylation is unlikely (1) because of direct measurement of transphosphorylation,

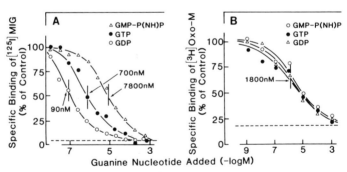

FIG. 24. Comparison of dose–response curves of nucleotide regulation of an R_sN_s complex (glucagon binding to liver glucagon receptor) to that of an R_iN_i complex (oxotremorine M binding to heart M_2 cholinergic receptors). Note that while GDP is significantly more potent than GTP, and even more so than the analog of GTP in the R_sN_s system (Rojas *et al.*, 1983), the three nucleotides are equipotent in the R_iN_i system. (A) Liver membranes, 32.5°C; 0.3 nM [^{125}I]monoiodoglucagon. (B) Heart membranes, 22°C; 3.6 nM [^{3}H]oxotremorine M.

which was found to be minimal under the conditions used; (2) because of the paradox by which small quantities of GTP formed from GDP would have to be more effective than directly added GTP; and (3) because of the fact that the nonphosphorylatable analog $GDP_\beta S$ is equipotent with GDP. On the other hand, it cannot be ruled out that a significant proportion of added GTP is degraded to GDP, very likely by N_s itself, and that, likewise, GMP-P(NH)P may be contaminated up to 1% by a GDP-like breakdown product. These findings strongly suggest, therefore, that the form of N_s that leads to formation of R_l states is a N_s–GDP complex rather than a N_s–GTP complex. Thus, in the rat liver membrane system, N_s, N_s^{Mg}, N_s–GTP, and N_s^*–GTP are of the N_s^{r+}-type and N_s–GDP is of the N_s^{r-}-type.

3. The Three States of N_s: r^+c^-, r^-c^-, and r^+c^+

Since it is clear that N_s and N_s^{Mg}, as well as the initial N_s–GTP complex, are inactive in terms of C regulation, it is clear also that receptor and C regulation are separate properties of N_s which segregate in such manner that N_s can be defined to adopt any one of three conformations: N_s^{r+c-}, N_s^{r+c+}, and N_s^{r-c-}, where r^+ denotes the "trait" by which N_s is capable of inducing or maintaining R stabilized in its h form and c^+ is the "trait" by which N_s is capable of stimulating the k_{cat} of C. The sequential changes that N_s undergoes when traversing a regulatory cycle in terms of its r^+/r^- and c^+/c^- properties are depicted in Fig. 25.

Solubilization of receptor systems with nonionic detergents has shown that the solubilized complexes are smaller if solubilization is performed under conditions where R is in its low-affinity form (DeLean et al., 1980; Limbird and Lefkowitz, 1978; Limbird et al., 1980) and that the larger complexes solubilized under conditions where R is in its high-affinity form, but not the smaller ones, are associated, in terms of size, with N_s assayed for by ADP-ribosylation with cholera toxin (Limbird et al., 1980). These findings, together with the fact that biologically active pure R_s is isolated in its low-affinity form (DeLean et al., 1980; Cerione et al., 1984a) requiring interaction with N_s to show high affinity for agonists (Cerione et al., 1984a), suggest that the low-affinity R_l form of receptor is representative of "free" receptor and that, therefore, receptors "accompany" N_s throughout only a part of its kinetic regulatory cycle, dissociating from it during the phase when N_s is under the influence of GDP and reassociating after GDP release, requiring Mg to do so in the case of β-adrenergic receptors but not in the case of liver membrane glucagon receptors.

Based on the combined information that indeed agonists promote R_sN_s complex formation and that very likely only the N_s–GDP state leads to formation of free R, the scheme of Fig. 26 can be postulated. This scheme, more elaborate than that of Fig. 25, incorporates knowledge

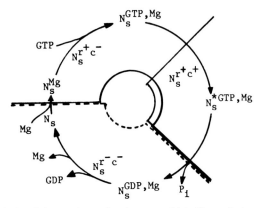

FIG. 25. Analysis of the conformational states which N_s needs to acquire to regulate both the activity of C and the affinity of R. The c^+ conformation denotes capacity of N to affect C and is synonymous with active N. The c^- conformation denotes lack of capacity to affect C; and is synonymous with inactive N. The r^+ conformation denotes capacity of N to positively interact with ^HR complex to stabilize it in the high affinity R_h form. The r^- conformation denotes lack of capacity of N to induce the R_h state, i.e., the conformation in which N is when the low-affinity form of R is seen. Based on the experimental results available, the kinetic regulatory cycle of N_s has been independently subdivided into two section delineating the c^+/c^- distribution and into two sections delineating the r^+/r^- distribution. This gives rise to three forms or states of N_s: N_s^{r+c-}, N_s^{r+c+}, and N_s^{r-c-}. For further details see text.

about conformations that N_s adopts (4 S, 3 S, and 2 S), and the subunit composition and its dissociation into α_s plus $\beta\gamma$. Further, it presents points in the cycle where G nucleotides may bind and dissociate from N_s, where R_s associates and dissociates from N_s and *when* GTP is hydrolyzed to initiate deactivation of N_s. With respect to this last point, it is specifically postulated that the $^HR_h\alpha_s^{GTP}$ complex is not only the actual activator of C but also the active form of the GTPase intrinsic to N_s. Mg is assumed to bind to the $\beta\gamma$ complex, however, there is no experimental proof for this location other than kinetic reasonings. For further discussion of this figure, see legend.

It is interesting to note that nature has gone to great pains to assure that adenylyl cyclases do not become persistently activated: (1) it has built into N_s the capacity to turn itself off by conferring to it GTP-hydrolyzing activity, and (2) it has made sure that upon formation of N_s–GDP, hormone receptors uncouple, and that this uncoupling phenomenon is followed by cessation of hormonal stimulation by forcing the uncoupled receptor to release the hormone due to a change in affinity. This primary uncoupling phenomenon is, of course, reversible, such that if a receptor interacts with N_s in its r^+c^- state, it reacquires high affinity for the hor-

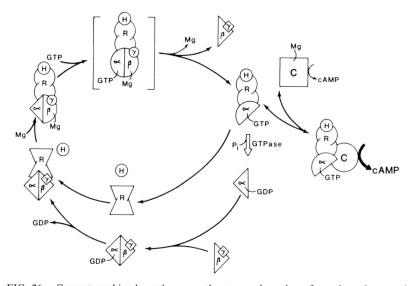

FIG. 26. Current working hypotheses on the type and number of reactions that may be involved in the reciprocal regulation of a stimulatory receptor and a stimulatory N protein. The receptor is assumed to have two domains responsible for interacting with the receptor and the N protein, respectively, and to have two affinity states, a low-affinity state, depicted by the angular shapes and a high-affinity form depicted by rounded shapes. N_s is assumed to have three conformations in the undissociated state and to dissociate in the presence of HR complexes into $^HR\alpha^G + \beta\gamma^{Mg}$, the latter losing its affinity for Mg yielding free $\beta\gamma$ complex. However, as mentioned in the text, the site for Mg could also be on the α subunit. A cycle is represented where R_sN_s forms from R_s and N_s-GDP with concomitant dissociation of GDP. High-affinity binding is represented as being promoted by the subsequent interaction of R_sN_s with Mg. While this would be the adequate description for a β-adrenergic receptor–N_s interaction sequence, it is not for the glucagon receptor–N_s interaction in rat liver membranes. In this latter case, the high-affinity binding conformation of the receptor, and presumably the corresponding conformation of N_s, are stabilized in the absence of Mg. The next step depicted is GTP-dependent, leading to formation of the active (c^+) 3 S-type conformation of N_s with receptor retaining its high affinity. It is conceivable that this complex could interact with the catalytic unit of the adenylyl cyclase system and activate it for as long as GTP is not hydrolyzed. Hydrolysis of GTP would then lead to a dissociation or relaxation of the system yielding N_s-GTP, R_s in its low-affinity state and C in an inactive state. In the figure, however, it is assumed that the dissociation of N_s into its α and $\beta\gamma$ subunits is an obligatory step prior to GTP hydrolysis, and that the role of ^HR_s complex is to facilitate this reaction by stabilizing the α_s^{GTP} complex as $^HR_s\alpha^{GTP}$, the latter complex being the actual activator of the catalyst C of the system. Only the $^HR_s\alpha_s^{GTP}$ complex is depicted as an active GTPase. Recent reconstitution experiments (Cerione et al., 1984b) have shown that catalyst C does not reduce significantly the isoproterenol-stimulated GTPase activity of a β-adrenergic receptor–N_s complex reconstituted in phospholipid vesicles. This implies either that GTP can be hydrolyzed by both the $^HR_s\alpha^{GTP}$ and the $^HR_s\alpha^{GTP}C$ complexes, or that the two complexes are in rapid equilibrium such that hydrolysis of GTP at $^HR_s\alpha^{GTP}$ to give H plus R_s plus α^{GDP} results immediately in reequilibration of $^HR_s\alpha^{GTP}C$ to $^HR_s\alpha^{GTP}$ plus C. To complete the cycle, α^{GDP} is depicted to recombine with $\beta\gamma$ to give $\alpha^{GDP}\beta\gamma$ (N_s–GDP) which then loses its GDP on interaction with an R_s.

mone, leading to eventual restimulation of N_s, i.e., to the transient formation of N_s^{r+c+}. There is an additional set of reactions—not the subject of this discussion—which are referred to generically as *desensitizations* and which also lead to the turn-off of the system. These assure further that, even if the relative concentrations of hormone receptors and N_s are such as to lead effectively to permanent elevation of cyclic AMP, the system is modified in a more lasting way by which receptors become uncoupled and N_s properties are changed so as to make it less susceptible to stimulation by R_s.

4. N_i Regulation of Agonist Binding to R_i

An analysis of agonist binding to R_i, such as epinephrine, by associating with α_2-adrenergic receptors (Tsai and Lefkowitz, 1979), dopamine interacting with D_2-dopaminergic receptors (Sibley and Creese, 1983) and carbachol binding to muscarinic receptors (Wei and Sulakhe, 1980; Berrie *et al.*, 1979) shows that R_i receptors are also under a dual control of Mg and guanine nucleotides which is essentially indistinguishable from that observed for R_s receptors. Thus, addition of Mg induces high-affinity forms of R_i, and addition of guanine nucleotides reverts R_i to its low-affinity form. As with R_s, solubilization of R_i receptors under conditions where they are in their high affinity form (Mg and agonist present) leads to a macromolecule that is larger than that obtained upon solubilization of the low-affinity form of R_i (Mg or H absent) (Smith and Limbird, 1981; Michel *et al.*, 1981; Kilpatrick and Caron, 1983). Although not yet proven experimentally, it is likely that, by analogy to the solubilization of $^HR_hN_s^{r+Mg}$ complex (H and Mg present), that the larger macromolecular form of R_i solubilized in the presence of Mg and agonist, represents a $^HR_hN_i^{r+Mg}$ complex, and that existence of an R_h form of R_i is therefore an indication of R_i/N_i interaction.

5. The Three States of N_i: r^+c^-, r^-c^-, and r^-c^+

There are two fundamental difference between N_s regulation of R_s and N_i regulation of R_i: (1) GTP and its analogs are equipotent with GDP and its analogs in promoting the high-low affinity transition of R_i (Fig. 24B); and (2) while pertussis toxin, which via ADP-ribosylation of α_i blocks the action of GTP but not that of nonhydrolyzable GTP analogs to stimulate N_i to inhibit C^4, impedes the formation of the R_h form of R_i, cholera toxin—which via ADP-ribosylation of N_s blocks GTP to GDP without affecting the capacity of N_s to stimulate C—does not impede the R_h formation of R_s and, in fact, decreases the potency of added GTP to uncouple R_h from N_s^{r+c+} by as much as 80-fold (Rojas *et al.*, 1983). Taken together, these findings indicate that the c^+ form of N_i is r^-.

Figure 27 illustrates the changes that N_i undergoes when cycling through the regulatory cycle expressed in terms of its r^+c^-, r^-c^+, and r^-c^- states. Figure 28 incorporates for N_i, as does Fig. 26 for N_s, knowledge recently gained on the conformations that N_i is able to adopt, on the subunit composition of this molecule, and on the possibility that it dissociates on activation into α_i and $\beta\gamma$.

Note that based on the data shown in Fig. 24 the main difference between the R_i/N_i and R_s/N_s systems is the rather "explosive" separation of components that occurs when the $^HR_hN^{Mg}$ complex of the R_i/N_i system is "activated" by GTP to give $^HR_l + \alpha_i^{GTP} + \beta\gamma^{Mg}$. It is not clear on thermodynamic grounds why, if the role of a receptor is to "catalyze" activation and subunit dissociation, it should in fact have no preference for any of the intermediary reaction products. It is clear, therefore, that even though much new information has been gained in recent years, especially in terms of definition of how many molecules make up a hormone-sensitive adenylyl cyclase system and what type of reactions occur on activation of this system (high- and low-affinity forms of receptors, conformational changes at N_s and N_i, subunit dissociation, and GTP hydrolysis) the pictures we are currently able to draw to describe a signal transduction reaction are still incomplete. The king-pin may be the catalytic unit, which after all may play a much more important role in the reciprocal regulation of R and N proteins than the mere monitoring of the activity states of the N proteins. C, of course, has not yet been purified, although work on this is in progress.

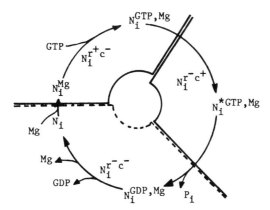

FIG. 27. Analysis of the conformational states which N_i needs to acquire to regulate C activity and R affinity. For details see legend to Fig. 25. The c^+ conformation denotes the capacity of N_i to affect C, i.e., to inhibit the catalytic activity; c^+ is synonymous with active N_i. The c^- conformation denotes the lack of capacity of N_i to affect the activity of C and is synonymous with inactive N_i. For the rest of the details, see legend to Fig. 25 and text.

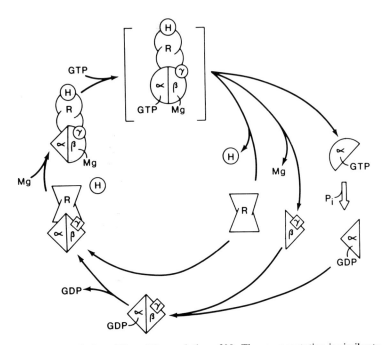

FIG. 28. N_i regulation of R_i and R_i regulation of N_i. The representation is similar to that shown in Fig. 26 for R_s–N_s interactions. The scheme differs mainly in that upon formation of the active N_i–GTP 3 S-type conformation of N_i under the influence of receptor, the receptor does not induce or facilitate subunit dissociation of N_i by stabilizing the free α_i^{GTP} subunit in the form of a $^H R_i \alpha_i^{GTP}$ complex. Rather, for reasons that are unknown, the $^H R_i N_i^*$–GTP appears to be unstable and to "decompose" into α_iGTP, $\beta\gamma$ (identical to the $\beta\gamma$ of N_s) and R_i in its low-affinity form.

V. Effects of Other Regulators of Activity

A. FLUORIDE ION

Addition of NaF to assays measuring cyclic AMP formation by complete $N_s N_i C$ systems, as found in membranes, leads in all mammalian adenylyl cyclase systems studied (except that from sperm cells), to an increased rate of cyclic AMP formation. This stimulatory effect of NaF is absent in the N_s-deficient *cyc⁻* S49 membrane system and is restored upon readdition of pure N_s (Ross and Gilman, 1977b; Ross *et al.*, 1978). Thus, N_s mediates not only stimulatory effects of guanine nucleotides, but also that of fluoride ion. Because of this, and before the discovery of N_i, N_s has also been abbreviated as G/F (Ross and Gilman, 1977b; Ross *et al.*, 1978). It was recently shown that fluoride, to act, requires aluminum ion as a co-ion (Sternweis and Gilman, 1982). The actions of NaF resemble those of the nonhydrolyzable GTP analogs in that they lead to a persistent activation of N_s and, as analyzed in detergent solutions with crude (Howlett and Gilman, 1980) and pure (Northup *et al.*, 1983b) N_s, it promotes the subunit dissociation of this protein. An analysis of the fate of the three subunits of N_s revealed that the $\alpha_s \beta\gamma$ complex dissociates under the influence of NaF to give α_s^* plus undissociated $\beta\gamma$ (Codina, Hildebrandt, and Birnbaumer, unpublished). It is not known with which of these subunits fluoride interacts to activate and dissociate the N_s molecule. Like guanine nucleotide activation, fluoride activation of N_s, and in intact membranes of the intact adenylyl cyclase system (Iyengar and Birnbaumer, 1981), is dependent on and regulated in its rate by Mg. It is not clear whether activation by fluoride requires a guanine nucleotide to be present. Pure N_s can be activated merely by addition of aluminum fluoride and Mg (Hildebrandt, Codina, and Birnbaumer, unpublished). However, in turkey erythrocytes, a nucleotide requirement was reported (Downs *et al.*, 1980).

It has often been assumed that since fluoride is a very effective stimulator of adenylyl cyclase activity, fluoride-stimulated activities are a measure of total activity present in membranes. Several lines of evidence should discourage this notion strongly. Thus, it was shown, as early as in 1969, that hormonal stimulation of the rat fat cell adenylyl cyclase exceeded stimulation by NaF (Birnbaumer *et al.*, 1969). Similarly, in 1971, the liver membrane adenylyl cyclase was shown to be stimulated up to 60% more by glucagon than NaF (Birnbaumer *et al.*, 1971). Further, studies with NaF and epinephrine showed that, under given assay conditions, the halogen ion not only stimulates less than the hormones, but that indeed it can inhibit hormonal stimulation (Harwood and Rodbell, 1973). This pointed to a possible dual effect of fluoride, one to stimulate and another to inhibit adenylyl cyclase activity. The existence of this dual action of fluoride ion was underscored by experiments in which NaF-preactivated adenylyl cyclase, from which fluoride had been removed to ineffective levels by dilution, was shown to be inhibited (up to 50%) by "stimulatory concentrations" of fluoride (Manganiello and Vaughan, 1976). This finding pointed out clearly that a "NaF-stimulated activity," however high it may be, is but the balance of two actions, one to stimulate, which is persistent, and another to inhibit, albeit partially, which reverses upon dilution of the ion.

It is now known that the inhibitory effect of NaF is due to its effect to activate N_i. This was shown by the finding that, like guanine nucleotides, NaF inhibits the N_s-deficient N_iC system of cyc^- membranes (Fig. 29) (Hildebrandt *et al.*, 1982) and that treatment of pure N_i results in subunit

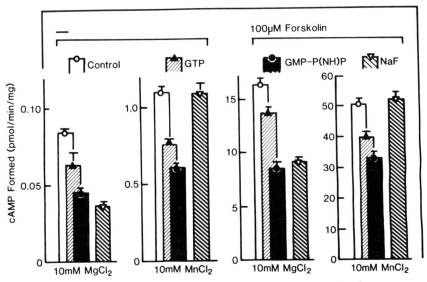

FIG. 29.   Inhibitory regulation of activity of the cyc^- S49 cell adenylyl cyclase system as seen in the absence and presence of forskolin. Note that the inhibitory modulation, although seen "better" on addition of forskolin (activities are approximately 100-fold greater), is by no means dependent on the presence of this stimulator of activity. ATP, 0.1 mM; EDTA, 1.0 mM. From Hildebrandt and Birnbaumer (1983).

dissociation (Bokoch *et al.*, 1983) to give α_i plus undissociated $\beta\gamma$ (Codina, Hildebrandt, and Birnbaumer, unpublished). It is interesting to note that NaF inhibits the intrinsic GTPase activity of N_i (Figure 30) (Hildebrandt *et al.*, 1983; Sunyer *et al.*, 1984) and that in the presence of GTP this might be a mechanism by the action of NaF is potentiated. The fact that no nucleotide is required for the action of fluoride to cause subunit dissociaton indicates that activation of N_i comes about by a mechanism other than prevention of GTP hydrolysis by the N protein. It is, of course, not yet known which mechanism this is.

B.   FORSKOLIN

This compound is a diterpine that activates all adenylyl cyclase systems studied (for review see Seamon *et al.*, 1981), except that of sperm cells (Stengel *et al.*, 1982; Forte *et al.*, 1983). Its action, while stimulated by presence of N_s (Hildebrandt and Birnbaumer, 1983; Clark *et al.*, 1982), is not dependent on N_s for it is readily seen in the N_s-deficient cyc^- system (Fig. 30). Forskolin stimulates C after solubilization and therefore does

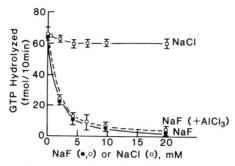

FIG. 30.   Endogenous GTP hydrolytic activity of N_i is selectively inhibited by NaF. Pure human erthrocyte N_i was incubated for 10 minutes in the presence of the indicated additions and [γ-^{32}P]GTP hydrolyzed to ^{32}P$_i$ was monitored. Aluminum chloride, when present, was 10-6M. N_i, 500 fmol; GTP, 100 nM; Mg^{2+}, 2 mM. From Sunyer *et al.* (1984).

not require an intact membrane milieu to act (Pfeuffer and Metzger, 1982; Northup *et al.*, 1983a). By prolonged incubation of solubilized C under adenylyl cyclase assay conditions, it is possible to obtain a preparation of C which has lost its capacity to be stimulated by forskolin, yet retains its capacity to respond to N_s addition (Sunyer and Birnbaumer, unpublished). Thus, susceptibility to forskolin stimulation is not a property that is obligatorily associated with C. Indeed forskolin responsiveness appears to be dependent on a rapidly turning over protein of unknown identity (Brooker *et al.*, 1983). To date, its mode of action is obscure. While it may be that forskolin acts by interacting with C, as proposed (Seamon and Daly, 1981; Pfeuffer and Metzger, 1982), it seems that the expression of its effect is dependent on, and/or affected by, additional factors and/or compounds, N_s being one of them (Clark *et al.*, 1982).

The action of forskolin has stimulated interest for three reasons: (1) it is a new regulator, and the study of its action may provide new and unexpected clues as to adenylyl cyclase regulation; (2) it stimulates a complete N_sN_iC system many times more than any other stimulator, such as NaF or GMP-P(NH)P, and the mechanism of this action is of basic interest; and (3) often (Insel *et al.*, 1982; Hudson and Fain, 1983), but not always (Mattera and Birnbaumer, unpublished), inhibitory regulation by guanine nucleotides and hormones acting through activation of N_i are better seen in a forskolin-stimulated system than in the unaffected system. This was recently well-exploited to demonstrate inhibitory regulation in the rabbit corpus luteum adenylyl cyclase system (Abramowitz and Campbell, 1983, 1984). Thus, at present, forskolin is a tool, the mode of action of which is unknown.

ACKNOWLEDGMENTS

This work was supported in part by NIH Research Grants AM-19318 and HD-09581 to LB, CA-29808 and AM-26905 to RI, HL-16037 to RJL, by the Robert A. Welch Foundation, by the Cystic Fibrosis Foundation, and by NIH Center Grants AM-27685 and HD-07495. Part of this work will be presented in partial fulfillment of the Ph.D degree of TS. RM was a 1982–1984 recipient of fellowship TW-03159 form the Fogarty International Center and JC was a 1982–1984 trainee of NIH Diabetes and Endocrinology Training Grant AM-07348.

REFERENCES

Abramowitz, J., and Birnbaumer, L. (1982). Temporal characteristics of gonadotropin interaction with its receptors and activation of ovarian adenylyl cyclase in the corpus luteum. Comparison to the mode of action of catecholamines. *Endocrinology* **111**, 970.

Abramowitz, J., and Campbell, A. R. (1983). Enkephalin-mediated inhibition of Forskolin-stimulated rabbit adenylyl cyclase activity. *Biochem. Biophys. Res. Commun.* **116**, 574.

Abramowitz, J., and Campbell, A. R. (1984). Effects of guanine nucleotides and divalent cations on forskolin activation of rabbit luteal adenylyl cyclase: Evidence for the existence of an inhibitory guanine nucleotide-binding regulatory component. *Endocrinology* **114**, 1955.

Abramowitz, J., Iyengar, R., and Birnbaumer, L. (1980). On the mode of action of catecholamines on the turkey erythrocyte adenylyl cyclase: Evaluation of basic activity states after removal of endogenous GDP and interpretation of nucleotide regulation and hormone activation in terms of a two state model. *J. Biol. Chem.* **255**, 8259.

Aktories, K., and Jakobs, K. H. (1981). Epinephrine inhibits adenylate cyclase and stimulates a GTPase in human platelet membranes via α-adrenoceptors. *FEBS Lett.* **130**, 235.

Aktories, K., Schultz, G., and Jakobs, K. H. (1982a). Cholera toxin inhibits prostaglandin E_1 but not adrenaline induced stimulation of GTP hydrolysis in human platelet membranes. *FEBS Lett.* **146**, 65.

Aktories, K., Schultz, G., and Jakobs, K. H. (1982b). Stimulation of a Low K_m GRPase by inhibitors of adipocyte adenylate cyclase. *Mol. Pharmacol.* **21**, 336.

Asano, T., Katada, T., Gilman, A. G., and Ross, E. M. (1984). Activation of the inhibitory GTP-binding protein of adenylate cyclase, G_i, by β-adrenergic receptors in reconstituted phospholipid vesicles. *J. Biol. Chem.* **259**, 9351.

Aurbach, G. D., Fedak, S. A., Woodward, C. J., Palmer, J. S., Hauser, D., and Troxler, F. (1974). β-Adrenergic receptor: Stereospecific interaction of iodinated β-blocking agent with high affinity sites. *Science* **186**, 1223.

Baroosky, K., and Brooker, G. (1980). [^{125}I]-Iodopindolol, a new highly selective radioiodinated β-adrenergic receptor antagonist: Measurement of β-receptors on intact rat astrocytoma cells. *J. Cyclic Nucleotide Res.* **6**, 297.

Berrie, C. P., Birdsall, N. J. M., Burgen, A. S. V., and Hulme, E. C. (1979). Guanine nucleotides modulate muscarinic receptor binding in the heart. *Biochem. Biophys. Res. Commun.* **87**, 1000.

Bird, S. J., and Maguire, M. E. (1978). The agonist-specific effect of magnesium ion on binding by β-adrenergic receptors in S49 lymphoma cells. Interaction of GTP and magnesium in adenylate cyclase activation. *J. Biol. Chem.* **253**, 8826.

Birnbaumer, L., and Yang, P. Ch. (1974). Studies on receptor-mediated activation of adenylyl cyclases. III. Regulation by purine nucleotides of the activation of adenylyl cyclases from target organs for prostaglandins, luteinizing hormones, neurohypophyseal hormones and catecholamines. Tissue and hormone-dependent variations. *J. Biol. Chem.* **249**, 7867.

Birnbaumer, L., Pohl, S. L., and Rodbell, M. (1969). Adenyl cyclase in fat cells. I. Properties and the effects of adrenocorticotropin and fluoride. *J. Biol. Chem.* **244**, 3468.

Birnbaumer, L., Pohl, S. L., and Rodbell, M. (1971). The glucagon-sensitive adenyl cyclase system in plasma membranes of rat liver. II. Comparison between glucagon- and fluoride-stimulated activities. *J. Biol. Chem.* **246**, 1857.

Birnbaumer, L., Nakahara, T., and Yang, P.-Ch. (1974). Studies on receptor-mediated activation of adenylyl cyclases. II. Nucleotide and nucleoside regulation of the activities of the renal medullary adenylyl cyclase and their stimulation by neurohypophyseal hormones. *J. Biol. Chem.* **249**, 7857.

Birnbaumer, L., Yang, P.-Ch., Hunzicker-Dunn, M., Bockaert, J., and Duran, J. M. (1976). Adenylyl cyclase activities in ovarian tissues. I. Homogenization and conditions of assay in Graafian follicles and corporal lutea of rabbits, rats, and pigs; regulation by ATP and some comparative properties. *Endocrinology* **99**, 163.

Birnbaumer, L., Swartz, T. L., Abramowitz, J., Mintz, P. W., and Iyengar, R. (1980a). Transient and steady state kinetics of the interaction of nucleotides with the adenylyl cyclase system from rat liver plasma membranes: Interpretation in terms of a simple two-state model. *J. Biol. Chem.* **255**, 3542.

Birnbaumer, L., Bearer, C. F., and Iyengar, R. (1980b). A two-state model of an enzyme with an allosteric regulatory site capable of metabolizing the regulatory ligand: simplified mathematical treatments of transient and steady state kinetics of an activator and its competitive inhibition as applied to adenylyl cyclases. *J. Biol. Chem.* **255**, 3552.

Bitonti, A. J., Moss, J., Tandon, N. N., and Vaughan, M. (1980). Prostaglandins increase GTP hydrolysis by membranes from human mononuclear cells. *J. Biol. Chem.* **255**, 2026.

Blume, A. J., Lichtshtein, D., and Boone, G. (1979). Coupling of opiate receptors to adenylate cyclase: Requirement for Na^+ and GTP. *Proc. Natl. Acad. Sci. U.S.A.* **76**, 5626.

Bockaert, J., and Sebben-Perez, M. (1983). Adenylate cyclase inhibition by hormones. The Mg^{2+} hypothesis. *FEBS Lett.* **161**, 113.

Bokoch, G. M., Katada, T., Northup, J. K., Hewlett, E. L., and Gilman, A. G. (1983). Identification of the predominant substrate for ADP-ribosylation by islet activating protein. *J. Biol. Chem.* **258**, 2072.

Bokoch, G. M., Katada, T., Northup, J. K., Ui, M., and Gilman, A. G. (1984). Purification and properties of the inhibitory guanine nucleotide-binding regulatory component of adenylate cyclase. *J. Biol. Chem.* **259**, 3560.

Brandt, D. R., Asano, T., Pedersen, S. E., and Ross, E. T. (1983). Reconstitution of catecholamine-stimulated guanosine triphosphatase activity. *Biochemistry* **22**, 4357.

Brooker, G., Pedone, C., and Baroosky, K. (1983). Selective reduction in forskolin-stimulated cyclic AMP accumulation by inhibitors of protein synthesis. *Science* **220**, 1169.

Burns, D. L., Hewlett, E. L., Moss, J., and Vaughan, M. (1983a). Pertussis toxin inhibits enkephalin stimulation of GTPase of NG 108-15 cells. *J. Biol. Chem.* **258**, 1435.

Caron, M. G., and Lefkowitz, R. J. (1976). Solubilization and characterization of the β-adrenergic receptor binding sites of frog erythrocytes. *J. Biol. Chem.* **251**, 2374.

Cassel, D., and Selinger, Z. (1976). Catecholamine-stimulated GTPase activity in turkey erythrocyte membranes. *Biochim. Biophys. Acta* **452**, 538.

Cassel, D., and Selinger, Z. (1977). Mechanism of adenylate cyclase activation by cholera toxin: Inhibition of GTP hydrolysis at the regulatory site. *Proc. Natl. Acad. Sci. U.S.A.* **74**, 3307.

Cassel, D., and Selinger, Z. (1978). Mechanism of adenylate cyclase activation through the β-adrenergic receptor: Catecholamine-induced displacement of bound GDP by GTP. *Proc. Natl. Acad. Sci. U.S.A.* **75**, 4155.

Cassel, D., Eckstein, F., Lowe, M., and Selinger, Z. (1979). Determination of the turn-off reaction for the hormone-activated adenylate cyclase. *J. Biol. Chem.* **254**, 9835.

Cerione, R. A., Codina, J., Benovic, J. L., Lefkowitz, R. J., Birnbaumer, L., and Caron, M. G. (1984a). The mammalian β₂-adrenergic receptor: Reconstitution of the pure receptor with the pure stimulatory nucleotide binding protein (N$_s$) of the adenylate cyclase system. *Biochemisty* **23**, 4579.

Cerione, R. A., Sibley, D. R., Codina, J., Benovic, J. L., Winslow, J., Neer, E. J., Birnbaumer, L., Caron, M. G., and Lefkowitz, R. J. (1984b). Reconstitution of a hormone-sensitive adenylate cyclase system: The pure β-adrenergic receptor and guanine nucleotide regulatory protein confer hormone responsiveness to the resolved catalytic unit. *J. Biol. Chem.* **259**, 9979.

Citri, Y., and Schramm, M. (1982). Probing of the coupling site of the *beta*-adrenergic receptor. Competition between different forms of the guanyl nucleotide binding protein for interaction with receptor, *J. Biol. Chem.* **257**, 13257–13262.

Citri, Y., and Schramm, M. (1980). Resolution, reconstitution and kinetics of the primary action of a hormone receptor. *Nature (London)* **287**, 297–300.

Clark, R. B., Goka, T. J., Green, D. A., Barber, R., and Butcher, R. W. (1982). Differences in the forskolin activation of adenylate cyclase in wild-type and variant lymphoma cells. *Mol. Pharmacol.* **22**, 609.

Codina, J., Hildebrandt, J. D., Iyengar, R., Birnbaumer, L., Sekura, R. D., and Manclark, C. R. (1983). Pertussis toxin substrate, the putative N$_i$ of adenylyl cyclases, is an α/β heterodimer regulated by guanine nucleotide and magnesium. *Proc. Natl. Acad. Sci. U.S.A.* **80**, 4276.

Codina, J., Hildebrandt, J. D., Sekura, R. D., Birnbaumer, M., Bryan, J., Manclark, R., Iyengar, R., and Birnbaumer, L. (1984a). N$_s$ and N$_i$, the stimulatory and inhibitory regulatory components of adenylyl cyclase. Purification of the human ertythrocyte proteins without the use of activating regulatory ligands. *J. Biol. Chem.* **259**, 5871.

Codina, J., Hildebrandt, J. D., Sunyer, T., Sekura, R. D., Manclark, C. R., Iyengar, R., and Birnbaumer, L. (1984b). Mechanisms in the vectorial receptor-adenylyl cyclase signal transduction. *Adv. Cyclic Nucleotide Protein Phosphorylat. Res.* **17**, 111–125.

Codina, J., Hildebrandt, J. D., Birnbaumer, L., and Sekura, R. D. (1984c). Effects of guanine nucleotides and Mg on human erythrocyte N$_i$ and N$_s$, the regulatory components of adenylyl cyclase. *J. Biol. Chem.* **259**, 11408.

Cote, T. E., Grewe, C. W., Tsuruta, K., Stoof, J. C., Eskay, R. L., and Kebabian, J. W. (1982). D-2 dopamine receptor-mediated inhibition of adenylate cyclase activity in the intermediate lobe of the rat pituitary gland requires guanosine 5′-triphosphate. *Endocrinology* **110**, 812.

DeLean, A., Stadel, J. M., and Lefkowitz, R. J. (1980). A ternary complex model explains the agonist-specific binding properties of the adenylate cyclase-coupled β-adrenergic receptor. *J. Biol. Chem.* **255**, 7108.

Downs, R. W., Spiegel, A. M., Singer, M., Reen, S., and Aurbach, G. D. (1980). Fluoride stimulation of adenylate cyclase is dependent on the guanine nucleotide regulatory protein. *J. Biol. Chem.* **255**, 949.

Engel, G., Hoyer, D., Berthold, R., and Wagner, H. (1981). [^{125}I]Cyanopindolol, a new ligand for β-adrenoceptors: Identification and quantitation of subclasses of β-adrenoceptors in guinea pig. *Naunyn-Schmiedeberg's Arch. Pharmacol.* **317**, 227.

Ezrailson, E. G., Garber, A. J., Munson, P. J., Swartz, T. L., Birnbaumer, L., and Entman, M. L. (1981). [^{125}I]Iodopindolol: A new β-adrenergic receptor probe. *J. Cyclic Nucleotide Res.* **7**, 13.

Forte, L. R., Bylund, D. B., and Zahler, W. L. (1983). Forskolin does not activate sperm adenylate cyclase. *Mol. Pharmacol.* **24**, 42.

Gill, D. M., and Meren, R. (1978). ADP-ribosylation of membrane proteins catalyzed by cholera toxin: Basis for the activation of adenylate cyclase. *Proc. Natl. Acad. Sci. U.S.A.* **75**, 3050.

Gilman, A. G. (1984). G Proteins and dual control of adenylate cyclase. *Cell* **36**, 577.

Hanski, E., and Gilman, A. G. (1982). The guanine nucleotide-binding regulatory component of adenylate cyclase in human erythrocytes. *J. Cyclic Nucleotide Res.* **8**, 323.

Hanski, E., Sternweis, P. C., Northup, J. K., Dromerick, A. W., and Gilman, A. G. (1981). The regulatory component of adenylate cyclase. Purification and properties of the turkey erythrocyte protein. *J. Biol. Chem.* **256**, 12911.

Harwood, J. P., and Rodbell, M. (1973). Inhibition by fluoride ion of hormonal activation of fat cell adenylate cyclase. *J. Biol. Chem.* **248**, 4901.

Hildebrandt, J. D., and Birnbaumer, L. (1982). Guanine nucleotides inhibit the adenylyl cyclase activity of the *cyc⁻* variant of S49 mouse lymphoma cells in the presence of forskolin. *Program Annu. Meet. Endocrine Soc., 64th,* A711.

Hildebrandt, J. D., and Birnbaumer, L. (1983). Inhibitory regulation of adenylyl cyclase in the absence of stimulatory regulation. Requirements and kinetics of guanine nucleotide induced inhibition of the *cyc⁻* S49 adenylyl cyclase. *J. Biol. Chem.* **258**, 13141.

Hildebrandt, J. D., Hanoune, J., and Birnbaumer, L. (1982). Guanine nucleotide inhibition of *cyc⁻* S49 mouse lymphoma cell membrane adenylyl cyclase. *J. Biol. Chem.* **257**, 14723.

Hildebrandt, J. D., Sekura, R. D., Codina, J., Iyengar, R., Manclark, C. R., and Birnbaumer, L. (1983). Stimulation and inhibition of adenylyl cyclases mediated by distinct proteins. *Nature (London)* **302**, 706.

Hildebrandt, J. D., Codina, J., Risinger, R., and Birnbaumer, L. (1984a). Identification of a γ subunit associated with the adenylyl cyclase regulatory proteins N_s and N_i. *J. Biol. Chem.* **259**, 2039.

Hildebrandt, J. D., Codina, J., Rosenthal, W., Sunyer, T., and Birnbaumer, L. (1984b). Properties of human erythrocyte N_s and N_i, the regulatory components of anenylyl cyclase, as purified without regulatory ligands. *In* "Bimodal Regulation of Adenylate Cyclases" (D. M. F. Cooper and K. Seamon, eds.). Raven, New York, in press.

Hildebrandt, J. D., Codina, J., Rosenthal, W., and Birnbaumer, L. (1984c). Characterization by two dimensional peptide mapping of the subunit of the regulatory N proteins of adenylyl cyclase and transducin, the guanine nucleotide regulatory component of rod outer segments of the eye. Submitted.

Hildebrandt, J. D., Codina, J., and Birnbaumer, L. (1984d). Interaction of the stimulatory and inhibitory regulatory proteins of the adenylyl cyclase system with the catalytic component of *cyc⁻* S49 cell membranes. *J. Biol. Chem.* **259**, 13178.

Howlett, A. C., and Gilman, A. G. (1980). Hydrodynamic properties of the regulatory component of adenylate cyclase. *J. Biol. Chem.* **255**, 2861.

Howlett, A. C., Sternweis, P. C., Macik, B. A., VanArsdale, P. M., and Gilman, A. G. (1979). Reconstitution of catecholamine-sensitive adenylate cyclase. Association of a regulatory component of the enzyme with membranes containing the catalytic protein and β-adrenergic receptors. *J. Biol. Chem.* **254**, 2287.

Hudson, T. H., and Fain, J. N. (1983). Forskolin-activated adenylate cyclase. Inhibition by guanyl-5'-yl imidodiphosphate. *J. Biol. Chem.* **258**, 9755.

Iyengar, R. (1981). Hysteretic activation of adenylyl cyclases. II. Mg ion regulation of the activation of the regulatory component as analyzed by reconstitution. *J. Biol. Chem.* **256**, 11042.

Iyengar, R., and Birnbaumer, L. (1981). Hysteretic activation of adenylyl cyclases. I. Effect of mg ion on the rate of activation by guanine nucleotides and fluoride. *J. Biol. Chem.* **256**, 11036.

Iyengar, R., and Birnbaumer, L. (1982). Hormone receptor modulates the regulatory component of adenylyl cyclase by reducing its requirement for MG^{2+} and enhancing its extent of activation by guanine nucleotides. *Proc. Natl. Acad. Sci. U.S.A.* **79**, 5179.

Iyengar, R., Abramowitz, J., Riser, M., and Birnbaumer, L. (1980a). Hormone receptor-mediated stimulation of the rat liver plasma membrane adenylyl cyclase system: Nucleotide effects and analysis in terms of a two-state model for the basic receptor-affected enzyme. *J. Biol. Chem.* **255**, 3558.

Iyengar, R., Abramowitz, J., Bordelon-Riser, M. E., Blume, A. J., and Birnbaumer, L. (1980b). Regulation of hormone-receptor coupling to adenylyl cyclase. Effects of GTP and GDP. *J. Biol. Chem.* **255**, 10312.

Insel, P. A., Stengel, D., Ferry, N., and Hanoune, J. (1982). Regulation of adenylate cyclase of human platelet membranes by forskolin. *J. Biol. Chem.* **257**, 7485.

Jakobs, K. H., Saur, W., and Schultz, G. (1976). Reduction of adenylate cyclase activity of human platelets by the α-adrenergic component of epinephrine. *J. Cyclic Nucleotide Res.* **2**, 381.

Jakobs, K. H., Lasch, P., Minuth, M., Aktories, K., and Schultz, G. (1982). Uncoupling of α-adrenergic-mediated inhibition of human platelet adenylate cyclase by N-ethyl-maleimide. *J. Biol. Chem.* **257**, 2829.

Jakobs, K. H., Gehring, U., Gaugler, B., Pfeuffer, T., and Schultz, G. (1983a). Occurrence of an inhibitory guanine nucleotide-binding regulatory component of the adenylate cyclase system in cyc^- variants of S49 lymphoma cells. *Eur. J. Biochem.* **130**, 605.

Jakobs, K. H., Aktories, K., and Schultz, G. (1983b). A nucleotide regulatory site for somatostatin inhibition of adenylate cyclase in S49 lymphoma cells. *Nature (London)* **303**, 177.

Jakobs, K. H., Aktories, K., and Schultz, G. (1984). Mechanisms and components involved in adenylate cyclase inhibition by hormones. *Adv. Cyclic Nucleotide Protein Phosphorylat. Res.* **17**, 135–143.

Jard, S., Cantau, B., and Jakobs, K. H. (1981). Angiotensin II and α_2-adrenergic agonists inhibit rat liver adenylate cyclase. *J. Biol. Chem.* **256**, 2603.

Johnson, G. L., Kaslow, H. R., Farfel, L., and Bourne, H. R. (1980). Genetic analysis of hormone-sensitive adenylate cyclase. *Adv. Cycl. Nucl. Res.* **13**, 1–37.

Johnson, G. L., Kaslow, H. R., and Bourne, H. R. (1978). Genetic evidence that cholera toxin substrates are regulatory components of adenylyl cyclase. *J. Biol. Chem.* **253**, 7120–7123.

Kalleher, D. J., Rashidbaig, A., Ruoho, A. E., and Johnson, G. L. (1983). Rapid vesicle reconstitution of alprenolol-sepharose-purified β_1-adrenergic receptors. Interaction of the purified receptor with N_s. *J. Biol. Chem.* **258**, 12881.

Kanaho, Y., Tsai, S.-C., Adamik, R., Hewlett, E. L., Moss, J., and Vaughan, M. (1984). Rhodopsin-enhanced GTPase activity of the inhibitory GTP-binding protein of adenylate cyclase. *J. Biol. Chem.* **259**, 7378.

Katada, T., and Ui, M. (1982a). Direct modification of the membrane adenylate cyclase system by islet-activating protein due to ADP-ribosylation of a membrane protein. *Proc. Natl. Acad. Sci. U.S.A.* **79**, 3129.

Katada, T., and Ui, M. (1982b). ADP ribosylation of the specific membrane protein of C6 cells by islet-activating protein associated with modification of adenylate cyclase activity. *J. Biol. Chem.* **257**, 7210.

Katada, T., Bokoch, G. M., Northup, J. K., Ui, M., and Gilman, A. G. (1984a). The inhibitory guanine nucleotide-binding regulatory component of adenylate cyclase. Properties and function of the purified protein. *J. Biol. Chem.* **259**, 3568.

Katada, T., Northup, J. K., Bokoch, G. M., Ui, M., and Gilman, A. G. (1984b). The inhibitory guanine nucleotide-binding regulatory component of adenylate cyclase. Subunit dissociation and guanine nucleotide-dependent hormonal inhibition, *J. Biol. Chem.* **259**, 3578.

Katada, T., Bokoch, G. M., Smigel, M. D., Ui, M., and Gilman, A. G. (1984c). The inhibitory guanine nucleotide-binding regulatory component of adenylate cyclase. Subunit dissociation and the inhibition of adenylate cyclase in S49 lymphoma cyc$^-$ and wild type membranes. *J. Biol. Chem.* **259**, 3586.

Kent, R. S., DeLean, A., and Lefkowitz, R. J. (1980). A quantitative analysis of β-adrenergic receptor interactions: Resolution of high and low affinity states of the receptor by computer modeling of ligand binding data. *Mol. Pharmacol.* **17**, 14.

Kilpatrick, B. F., and Caron, M. G. (1983). Agonist binding promotes a guanine nucleotide reversible increase in the apparent size of the bovine anterior pituitary dopamine receptors, *J. Biol. Chem.* **258**, 13528.

Koski, G., and Klee, W. A. (1981). Opiates inhibit adenylate cyclase by stimulating GTP hydrolysis, *Proc. Natl. Acad. Sci. U.S.A.* **78**, 4185.

Labarbera, A. R., Richert, N. D., and Ryan, R. J. (1980). Nucleotides do not modulate rat luteocyte human chorionic gonadotropin responsiveness by inhibiting human chorionic gonadotropin binding. *Arch. Biochem. Biophys.* **200**, 177.

Lad, P. M., Welton, A. F., and Rodbell, M. (1977). Evidence for distinct nucleotide sites in the regulation of the glucagon receptor and of adenylate cyclase activity. *J. Biol. Chem.* **252**, 5942.

Lai, E., Rosen, O. M., and Rubin, C. S. (1981). Differentiation-dependent expression of catecholamine-stimulated adenylate cyclase. Roles of the β-receptor and G/F protein in differentiating 3T3-L1 adipocytes. *J. Biol. Chem.* **256**, 12866.

Lefkowitz, R. J., Mullikin, D., and Caron, M. G. (1976). Regulation of .-adrenergic receptors by guanyl-5'-yl imidodiphosphate and other purine nucleotides. *J. Biol. Chem.* **251**, 4686.

Limbird, L. E., and Lefkowitz, R. J. (1978). Agonist-induced increase in apparent β-adrenergic receptor size. *Proc. Natl. Acad. Sci. U.S.A.* **75**, 228.

Limbird, L. E., Gill, D. M., and Lefkowitz, R. J. (1980). Agonist-promoted coupling of the β-adrenergic receptor with the guanine nucleotide regulatory protein of the adenylate cyclase system. *Proc. Natl. Acad. Sci. U.S.A.* **77**, 775.

Lin, M. C., Welton, A. F., and Behrman, M. F. (1978). Essential role of GTP in the expression of adenylate cyclase activity after cholera toxin treatment. *J. Cyclic Nucleotide Res.* **4**, 159.

Londos, C., Salomon, Y., Lin, M. C., Harwood, J. P., Schramm, M., Wolff, J., and Rodbell, M. (1974). 5'guanylylimidodiphosphate, a potent activator of adenylate cyclase systems in eukaryotic cells. *Proc. Natl. Acad. Sci. U.S.A.* **71**, 3087.

Maquire, M. E., Van Arsdale, P. M., and Gilman, A. G. (1976a). An agonist-specific effect of guanine nucleotides on binding to the β adrenergic receptor. *Mol. Pharmacol.* **12**, 335.

Maguire, M. E., Wiklund, R. A., Anderson, H. J., and Gilman, A. G. (1976b). Binding of [^{125}I]iodohydroxybenzylpindolol to putative β-adrenergic receptors of rat glioma cells and other cell clones. *J. Biol. Chem.* **251,** 1221.

Malbon, C. G., and Greenberg, M. L. (1982). 3,3',5-Triiodothyronine administration *in vivo* modulates the hormone-sensitive adenylate cyclase of rat hepatocytes. *J. Clin. Invest.* **69,** 414.

Manganiello, V. C., and Vaughan, M. (1976). Activation and inhibition of fat cell adenylate cyclase by fluoride. *J. Biol. Chem.* **251,** 6205.

Manning, D. R., and Gilman, A. G. (1983). The regulatory components of adenylate cyclase and transducin. A family of structurally homologous guanine nucleotide-binding proteins. *J. Biol. Chem.* **258,** 7059.

Michel, T., and Lefkowitz, R. J. (1982). Hormonal inhibition of adenylate cyclase. α-adrenergic receptors promote release of [^{3}H]guanylylimidodiphosphate from platelet membranes. *J. Biol. Chem.* **257,** 13557.

Michel, T., Hoffman, B. B., Lefkowitz, R. J., and Caron, M. G. (1981). Different sedimentation properties of agonist- and antagonist-labeled platelet α_2-adrenergic receptor. *Biochem. Biophys. Res. Commun.* **100,** 1131.

Murad, F., Chi, Y.-M., Rall, T. W., and Sutherland, E. W. (1962). Adenyl cyclase. III. The effect of catecholamines and choline esters on the formation of adenosine 3',5'-Phosphate by preparations from cardiac muscle and liver. *J. Biol. Chem.* **237,** 1233,

Murayama, T., and Ui, M. (1983). Loss of the inhibitory function of the guanine nucleotide regulatory component of adenylate cyclase due to its ADP ribosylation by islet-activating protein, pertussis toxin, in adipocyte membranes. *J. Biol. Chem.* **258,** 3319.

Murayama, T., and Ui, M. (1984). [^{3}H]GDP release from rat and hamster adipocyte membranes independently linked to receptors involved in activation or inhibition of adenylate cyclase. Differential susceptibility to two bacterial toxins. *J. Biol. Chem.* **259,** 761.

Nedivi, E., and Schramm, M. (1984). The β-adrenergic receptor survives solubilization in deoxycholate while forming a stable association with the agonist. *J. Biol. Chem.* **259,** 5803.

Neufeld, G., Schramm, M., and Weinberg, N. (1980). Hybridization of adenylate cyclase components by membrane fusion and the effect of selective digestion by trypsin. *J. Biol. Chem.* **255,** 9268.

Neufeld, G., Steiner, S., Korner, M., and Schramm, M. (1983). Trapping of the β-adrenergic receptor in the hormone-induced state. *Proc. Natl. Acad. Sci. U.S.A.* **80,** 6441.

Northup, J. K., Sternweis, P. C., Smigel, M. D., Schleifer, L. S., Ross, E. M., and Gilman, A. G. (1980). Purification of the regulatory component of adenylate cyclase. *Proc. Natl. Acad. Sci. U.S.A.* **77,** 6516.

Northup, J. K., Smigel, M. D., and Gilman, A. G. (1982). The guanine nucleotide activating site of the regulatory component of adenylate cyclase. *J. Biol. Chem.* **257,** 11416.

Northup, J. K., Smigel, M. D., Sternweis, P. C., and Gilman, A. G. (1983a). The subunits of the stimulatory regulatory component of adenylate cyclase. Resolution of the activated 45,000-dalton (α) subunit. *J. Biol. Chem.* **258,** 11369.

Northup, J. K., Sternweis, P. C. and Gilman, A. G. (1983b). The subunits of the stimulatory regulatory component of adenylate cyclase. Resolution, activity, and properties of the 35,000-dalton (β) subunit. *J. Biol. Chem.* **258,** 11361.

Pedersen, S. E., and Ross, E. M. (1982). Functional reconstitution of β-adrenergic receptors and the stimulatory GTP-binding protein of adenylate cyclase. *Proc. Natl. Acad. Sci. U.S.A.* **79,** 7228.

Pfeuffer, T. (1977). GTP-binding proteins in membranes and the control of adenylate cyclase activity. *J. Biol. Chem.* **252,** 7224.

Pfeuffer, T., and Metzger, H. (1982). 7-O-Hemisuccinyl-deacetyl forskolin-sepharose: A novel affinity support for purification of adenylate cyclase. *FEBS Lett.* **146**, 369.

Reig, J. A., Körnblihtt, A. R., Flawia, M. M., and Torres, H. N. (1982). Soluble adenylate cyclase acitivity in neurospora crassa. *Biochem. J.* **207**, 43.

Rodbell, M. (1980). The role of hormone receptors and GTP-regulatory proteins in membrane transduction. *Nature (London)* **284**, 17.

Rodbell, M., Krans, H. M. J., Pohl, S. L., and Birnbaumer, L. (1971a). The glucagon-sensitive adenyl cyclase system in plasma membranes of rat liver. IV. Effects of guanyl nucleotides on binding of ^{125}I-glucagon. *J. Biol. Chem.* **246**, 1872.

Rodbell, M., Birnbaumer, L., Pohl, S. L., and Krans, H. M. J. (1971b). The glucagon-sensitive adenyl cyclase system in plasma membranes of rat liver. V. An obligatory role of guanylnucleotides in glucagon action. *J. Biol. Chem.* **246**, 1877.

Rodbell, M., Lin, M. C., and Salomon, Y. (1974). Evidence for interdependent action of glucagon and nucleotides on the hepatic adenylate cyclase system. *J. Biol. Chem.* **249**, 59.

Rojas, F. J., Garber, A. J., and Birnbaumer, L. (1983). Synthesis, purification by HPLC of [^{125}I-Tyr^{10}]monoiodoglucagon ([^{125}I]MIG) and its use as a receptor probe. *Diabetes* **32** (Suppl. 1, *Annu. Meet. Am. Diabetes Assoc., 43rd, San Antonio, June 12–14* Abstr. 175).

Ross, E. M., and Gilman, A. G. (1977a). Reconstitution of catecholamine-sensitive adenylate cyclase activity: Interaction of solubilized components with receptor-replete membranes. *Proc. Natl. Acad. Sci. U.S.A.* **74**, 3715.

Ross, E. M., and Gilman, A. G. (1977b). Resolution of some components of adenylate cyclase necessary for catalytic activity. *J. Biol. Chem.* **252**, 6966.

Ross, E. M., Maguire, M. E., Sturgill, T. W., Biltonen, R. L., and Gilman, A. G. (1977). Relationship between the β-adrenergic receptor and adenylate cyclase. Studies of ligand binding and enzyme activity in purified membranes of S49 lymphoma cells. *J. Biol. Chem.* **252**, 5761.

Ross, E. M., Howlett, A. C., Ferguson, K. M., and Gilman, A. G. (1978). Reconstitution of hormone-sensitive adenylate cyclase activity with resolved components of the enzyme. *J. Biol. Chem.* **253**, 6401.

Rubalcava, B., and Rodbell, M. (1973). The role of acidic phospholipids in glucagon action on rat liver adenylate cyclase. *J. Biol. Chem.* **248**, 3831.

Schlegel, W., Kempner, E. S., and Rodbell, M. (1979). Activation of adenylate cyclase in hepatic membranes involves interactions of the catalytic unit with multimeric complexes of regulatory proteins. *J. Biol. Chem.* **254**, 5168.

Schleifer, L. S., Kahn, R. A., Hanski, E., Northup, J. K., Sternweis, P. C., and Gilman, A. G. (1982). Requirements for cholera toxin-dependent ADP-ribosylation of the purified regulatory component of adenylate cyclase. *J. Biol. Chem.* **257**, 20.

Schramm, M., and Rodbell, M. (1975). A persistent active state of the adenylate cyclase system produced by the combined actions of isoproterenol and guanyl imidodiphosphate in frog erythrocyte membranes. *J. Biol. Chem.* **250**, 2232.

Seamon, K. B., and Daly, J. W. (1981). Activation of adenylate cyclase by the diterpene forskolin does not require the guanine nucleotide regulatory protein. *J. Biol. Chem.* **256**, 9799.

Seamon, K. B., Padgett, W., and Daly, J. W. (1981). Forskolin: Unique diterpene activator of adenylate cyclase in membranes and in intact cells. *Proc. Natl. Acad. Sci. U.S.A.* **78**, 3363.

Sharma, S. K., Nirenberg, M., and Klee, W. A. (1975). Morphine receptors as regulators of adenylate cyclase activity. *Proc. Natl. Acad. Sci. U.S.A.* **72**, 590.

Shorr, R. G. L., Lefkowitz, R. J., and Caron, M. G. (1981). Purification of the β-adrenergic receptor. Identification of the hormone binding subunit. *J. Biol. Chem.* **256,** 5820–5826.

Sibley, D. R., and Creese, I. (1983). Regulation of ligand binding to pituitary D-2 dopaminergic receptors. Effects of divalent cations and functional group modification. *J. Biol. Chem.* **258,** 4957.

Smith, S. K., and Limbird, L. E. (1981). Solubilization of human platelet α-adrenergic receptors: Evidence that agonist occupancy of the receptor stabilizes receptor-effector interactions. *Proc. Natl. Acad. Sci. U.S.A.* **78,** 4026.

Stengel, D., Guenet, L., Desmier, M., Insel, P. A., and Hanoune, J. (1982). Forskolin requires more than the catalytic unit to activate adenylate cyclase. *Mol. Cell. Endocrinol.* **28,** 681.

Sternweis, P. C., and Gilman, A. G. (1982). Aluminum: A requirement for activation of the regulatory component of adenylate cyclase by fluoride. *Proc. Natl. Acad. Sci. U.S.A.* **79,** 4888.

Sternweis, P. C., Northup, J. K., Smigel, M. D., and Gilman, A. G. (1981). The regulatory component of adenylate cyclase. Purification and properties. *J. Biol. Chem.* **256,** 11517.

Strittmatter, S., and Neer, E. J. (1980). Properties of the separated catalytic and regulatory units of brain adenylate cyclase. *Proc. Natl. Acad. Sci. U.S.A.* **77,** 6344.

Sunyer, T., Codina, J., and Birnbaumer, L. (1984). GTPase properties of N_i, the inhibitory regulatory component of adenylyl cyclase. *J. Biol. Chem.* **259,** 15447.

Tsai, B. S., and Lefkowitz, R. J. (1979). Agonist-specific effects of guanine nucleotides on *alpha*-adrenergic receptors in human platelets. *Mol. Pharmacol.* **16,** 61.

Wei, J. W., and Sulakhe, P. V. (1980). Requirement for sulfhydryl groups in the differential effects of magnesium ion and GTP on agonist bindings of muscarinic cholinergic receptor sites in rat atrial membrane fraction. *Naunyn-Schmeideberg's Arch. Pharmacol.* **314,** 51.

Welton, A. F., Lad, P. M., Newby, A. C., Yamamura, H., Nicosia, S., and Rodbell, M. (1977). Solubilization and separation of glucagon receptor and adenylate cyclase in guanine nucleotide-sensitive states. *J. Biol. Chem.* **252,** 5947.

Williams, L. T., Mullikin, D., and Lefkowitz, R. J. (1978). Magnesium dependence of agonist binding to adenylate cyclase-coupled hormone receptors. *J. Biol. Chem.* **253,** 2984.

Yamazaki, S., Katada, T., and Ui, M. (1982). α_2-Adrenergic inhibition of insulin secretion via interference with cyclic AMP generation in rat pancreatic islets. *Mol. Pharmacol.* **21,** 648.

DISCUSSION

G. D. Aurbach: I would like to address the question of mechanism of action of N_i itself. As you indicated in your scheme there are 2 or more possible mechanisms, one by dissociation of the β subunit of N_i which then competes for free α_s subunits. Another would be a direct combination of N_i α with the catalytic unit; the latter possibility you illustrated on your slide. Is there any direct evidence as there is for N_s, of association of N_i α with a catalytic subunit?

L. Birnbaumer: No, up to now there is no direct evidence for α_i interacting directly with a catalytic subunit. In fact, the frustrating point is that there are innumerable negative experiments in which partially resolved C subunit, mixed or reconstituted with α_i subunits, shows no modulation. Yet, if, for example, one takes platelet membranes that have been trained with pertussis toxin to inactive endogenous N_i, then stimulates these platelet membranes with a stimulatory agent such as prostaglandin E_i and adds excess $\beta\gamma$ complex, one does get inhibition. There is, therefore, no question that if one adds high enough concentration of $\beta\gamma$ to a N_s-modulated system, either in solution, as I showed during my talk, or to membranes, one gets inhibition of N_s activity. But since data with the cyc^- membrane system, which has no functional N_s, indicate that there is a direct action of N_i on the catalytic subunit independently of the activity state of N_s, one currently has to consider both mechanisms of action of N_i as possible.

M. R. Walters: I have two very general questions. The first is whether you think that there is any relationship between the killing of S49 lymphoma cells by cortisol and that by cyclic AMP?

L. Birnbaumer: Gordon Tomkin's group did that experiment and they found that the cells which are resistant to cyclic AMP are still killed by glucocorticoids and vice versa, that cells that have lost response to glucocorticoids are still killed by cyclic AMP. The problem with this result is that there is no informational content in it. We already know that there are two ways of inhibiting the killing response; what we do not know is how many common steps are involved.

M. R. Walters: Do you think that the interaction of somatostatin with the inhibitory receptor is the sole pathway by which somatostatin inhibits cellular responses or is that too naive a summary?

L. Birnbaumer: There is more to the action of somatostatin than its action on the adenylyl cyclase. Experiments by Terry Reisine at the NIH showed that somatostatin can block 8-bromocyclic AMP-induced ACTH release from pituitary tumor cells and that this is not blocked by pertussis toxin treatment, even though the toxin treatment used was sufficient to block the action of somatostatin to reduce cyclic AMP formation. This would suggest that somatostatin inhibits secretory processes by mechanisms that are more complex than mere attenuation of adenylyl cyclase activity.

T. Chen: It appears that in hCG desensitization in the luteal cell it is the N_i that is being activated, is that right?

L. Birnbaumer: I don't know. The desensitization of the luteal cell by hCG is a complex set of reactions of which we have studied two: one involves the loss of LH receptors and, of course, this leads to loss of adenylyl cyclase stimulation by hCG. The second involves a smaller but significant loss in isotoproterenol stimulation which correlates with a similarly small but significant decrease in N_s activity. Whether there is also a change in N_i is not yet known.

T. Chen: How about the $PGF_{2\alpha}$-induced luteolysis? It has been hypothesized that this prostaglandin causes uncoupling of the LH receptor from the adenylyl cyclase. Do you have any evidence that N_i plays a role in this action of prostaglandin $F_{2\alpha}$?

L. Birnbaumer: We are currently testing this hypothesis.

J. Abramowitz: You speculated that the hormone receptors interact with the α subunits of N_s or N_i. Do you have any direct experimental evidence that would support that?

L. Birnbaumer: No, other than negative reasonings. There are two alternatives to the possibility that I have raised: (1) that there is no dissociation of the subunits and that the receptor is always interacting with the whole molecule, and (2) that the receptors interact with the $\beta\gamma$ complex of the system. Before we knew about the existence of N_i, we actually suggested in print that receptors would remain with the $\beta\gamma$ subunit after N_s activation and subunit dissociation. But since the $\beta\gamma$ complex of N_i appears to be the same as that of N_s and definitely is interchangeable between N_s and N_i, that hypothesis is no longer tenable, especially in view of the fact that R_s and R_i receptors discriminate between N_s and N_i. The possibility that remains, therefore, is that receptors need to "look" at the α subunits and, in molecular terms, this would involve an interaction of the R's with α's. Whether R's interact only with the α aspect of N proteins or whether they need simultaneously to interact with the

$\beta\gamma$ aspect of the coupling proteins is not known. It could be tested by probing with cross-linking reagents for protein–protein interactions in the reconstituted systems.

R. L. Stouffer: Would you comment on the fact that investigators have observed in adenylate cyclase systems with N_i components at best a 50% inhibition of activity. Can you relate this characteristic to any physiologic event, such as gonadotropin-sensitive adenylate activity in the corpus luteum during prostaglandin-induced luteolysis?

L. Birnbaumer: I have tried to hint at this problem during my talk. There is indeed only attenuation of adenylate cyclase on activation of N_i. Yet, if one looks at the abundance of N proteins in membranes—and I haven't really pointed this out throughout my talk—one finds that there is about 4 to 10 times more N_i in any given membrane than N_s. Thus, N_i exists in excess of N_s. If it happens to be true that the attenuation of adenylyl cyclase activity comes about by the release of the $\beta\gamma$ complex, acting to competitively interfere with the activation of N_s, then we need to contend with the associated fact that free activated α_i is also formed and that this subunit must play a function. One elegant speculation is that we have not yet discovered the primary function that is regulated by α_i. There may be very important functions other than adenylyl cyclase modulation that are affected by α_i and which are truly responsible for most of the physiologic actions that we see.

G. D. Aurbach: Going back to the interaction of purified receptor with N_s or N_i components, you now have the opportunity of looking at GTPase activity in reconstituted liposomal vesicles. What would be your speculation in terms of the mechanism of the GTPase reaction; is there an intermediate formation of phosphoprotein involved? Does the receptor get phosphorylated by the γ phosphate of GTP, and does this have anything to do with phosphorylation of the receptor as shown by Lefkowitz and collaborators in association with desensitization?

L. Birnbaumer: Those experiments are planned but they have not yet been done. What we have done in our laboratory is that we have taken the N proteins and incubated them with γ-labeled GTP and asked the question whether there is a GTP-dependent autophosphorylation, such as occurs with one of the *ras* gene product. The result of that experiment was negative. To my knowledge, this experiment has not yet been done in the presence of receptor after reconstitution into phospholipid vesicles. On the other hand, one can phosphorylate a receptor after reconstitution with N_s in phospholipid vesicles. With lung β-adrenergic receptors we have shown, in collaboration with Lefkowitz, Caron, and collaborators, that this results in a small but significant loss of the capacity of the receptor to stimulate the GTPase activity of N_s.

J. Abramowitz: Most of what we know with regard to regulation of catalytic activity tends to indicate that magnesium and guanine nucleotide regulation from cell type to cell type appears to be quite similar while the way hormone receptors are regulated from system to system appears to demonstrate great diversity. Studies that I did while I was in your laboratory as well as studies I've done since on the LH receptor and data that you presented on glucagon would tend to indicate that depending upon the receptor system that you are looking at, you can either get an increase in affinity with magnesium as we would see with the LH or β receptor, or no increase in affinity due to magnesium as we would see with the glucagon receptor. You can get a guanine nucleotide effect of decreasing affinity with both glucagon or β receptors or no decrease in affinity due to guanine nucleotide with the LH receptor. The question I have is how much of this do you feel is due to the N_s protein versus what's happening at the level of the receptor. Where do you think these regulations are taking place?

L. Birnbaumer: What you are asking is very important and can be addressed by reconstitution experiments where the effect of heterologous proteins on the degree of coupling can be evaluated. It is clear that there must be common complementary domains between receptors and N proteins and we know, in fact, that these domains are largely conserved throughout the animal kingdom. But there are differences as well. To exemplify. If one extracts N_s protein from a turkey erythrocyte and reconstitutes it with cyc^- membrane adenylyl cyclase, what one obtains is an adenylyl cyclase system that is guanine nucleotide-regulated in a manner that resembles that of the turkey erythrocyte adenylyl cyclase. For example, one does not get fast activation by GMP-P(NH)P in this reconstituted system, unless one added also isoproterenol. On the other hand, if one takes an N protein from a liver membrane and puts it into the same cyc^- membrane system, the resulting reconstituted system is now stimulated rapidly by GMP-P(NH)P without the need of adding a hormone. Howard Kirchick and I did some experiments where we looked at the activity of corpus luteum N_s before and after treatment of animals with a desensitizing dose of hCG. When we assayed the luteal N_s for its activity in cyc^- membranes we found that this N_s has a specific activity or intrinsic activity that is very low in comparison to what we could obtain with liver N_s. This was not a difference in concentration of N_s added for the difference in effectiveness in reconstituting cyc^- membrane adenylyl cyclase persisted even on addition of saturating concentrations of the luteal N_s. Such studies have not been done with different receptors, but I think that it will come out to be that both receptors and the N proteins together will define the fine turning of the system that one is looking at.

J. Abramowitz: Do you think that this would possibly have any role in the regulation of hormone specificity of the target tissue, where more than one hormone interacts with the same cell to potentially activate adenylyl cyclase.

L. Birnbaumer: No, I don't think that specificity is going to be the point, since it is an all or none phenomenon defined by the presence or absence of a receptor. But the quality of the response will depend on the quality of the N_s protein present in that tissue.

R. Moudgal: You don't need a battery of antibodies—you need only one antibody and if this reacts with different species of receptors, you would then know that there is at least some amount of conservation. Such techniques have been successfully used in other cases to establish conservation.

L. Birnbaumer: Craig Venter, Claire Fraser, and their collaborators have made mono-clonal antibodies to partially purified muscarinic receptors and obtained one set of them which cross-reacts with β-adrenergic receptors. I do not know whether this is because this monoclonal antibody is looking at a very small common epitope which has no real functional meaning or whether their observation is proof for the presence in both types of molecules of a major common domain. The type of experiments and recognition studies that you are talking about have not been done, to my knowledge, and would be very informative.

V. Ramirez: Dr. Birnbaumer, you started your excellent conference by showing that prostaglandin E_2 activates adenylate cyclase and norepinepherine inhibits that activation. We are interested in the action of prostaglandin E_2 that has many effects in different tissues. I wondered if you would like to speculate what the mechanism is by which prostaglandins act on adenylate cyclase.

L. Birnbaumer: I will subdivide prostaglandins to give a meaningful answer. There are prostaglandins of the F type (e.g., $PGF_{2\alpha}$). $PGF_{2\alpha}$ given to intact animals or intact cells will cause an inhibitory effect of adenylyl cyclase. The mechanism by which this occurs is unknown. It may be the result of a direct or an indirect action on the system. In this last case, changes in adenylyl cyclase activity would be but secondary expressions of a primary effect, the mechanism of which is unknown. The other class of prostaglandins are of the E and D kind and include prostacyclins. They interact with classic receptors, detectable by direct binding assays, and affect adenylyl cyclase through their receptors exactly by the guanine nucleotide-dependent mechanism that led to the discovery of N_s and N_i. In adipose tissue, prostaglandin E receptors are of the R_i-type, couple to N_i, and trigger an antilipolytic effect. In platelets, prostaglandin E receptors are of the R_s-type and trigger the antiaggregating effect of prostaglandins

P. Wise: I have two questions related to the action of agonists versus antagonists on the conversion of receptors from a high-affinity conformation. Can you tell us whether or not the reason that antagonists allow the conversion but agonists do not is that they bind to different sites on the receptor, and therefore have different actions on the N protein? The second question is, as I understand it, if one incubates β-adrenergic receptors in the presence of agonist for prolonged periods of time, one can also convert the receptor to low-affinity form; can that be explained, based upon a long-term action on the N protein?

L. Birnbaumer: I want to change the emphasis of your question from say the conversion of receptors from a high-affinity to a low-affinity form and turn it around and ask the question which ligand can induce their high-affinity form? I shall exemplify with the β-adrenergic receptor system. The purified β-adrenergic receptor, as it is obtained free of N proteins, is in its low-affinity form. Addition of either an agonist or an antagonist does not change its affinity. The situation here is not that agonist has acquired the capacity to induce the low-affinity form, but rather that it is unable to induce the high-affinity form. On reconstitution with N_s protein, agonists, but not antagonists, will now induce the high-affinity form of the receptor. Thus, when an agonist binds to an R_sN_s complex, it stabilizes a high-affinity form of the receptor, which an antagonist cannot do. In terms of the desensitization experiment, what happens is that, as the system is desensitizing the ability of the receptor to be able to go into the high-affinity form is being lost, which is an agonist specific effect. This loss may be because N_s alone, R_s alone, or both are changing.

M. O. Thorner: Maybe you answered this question, but I didn't catch it. You discussed the γ subunit and I didn't pick up from what you said whether you have a role for that, and whether in your reconstitution experiments you can produce all the activity that you find with the βγ combined subunit, with β subunit alone or γ subunit alone.

L. Birnbaumer: No, I didn't postulate any function for the γ subunit of the N proteins. There have been no experiments done to date where β and γ subunits have been separated without denaturation and all published work that reads "β subunit" or "35K" should be read as "βγ complex." Your question, however, is very important. It points to the fact that we do not know of what the function of either the β or the γ subunit is. Some information as to the function of the γ subunit may come from analyzing, in a comparative way, the phenomenology that surrounds the transduction of light impulses, i.e., transduction of rhodopsin bleaching in retinal rod outer segments into activation of cyclic GMP specific phosphodiesterase. Transducin is the guanine nucleotide binding protein that couples the processes and, structurally, is almost identical to the N proteins of the adenylyl cyclase system. That is, like the N proteins, transducin is an α-β-γ heterotrimer, the β subunits of transducin are identical, or least indistinguishable from the β subunits of the N proteins, the α subunit of transducin is a substrate for the ADP-ribosylating activity of cholera and pertussis toxin and is a GTPase, and there is a γ subunit which is always associated with the β subunit. Yet there are fundamental differences between the behavior of transducin and of the N proteins when they are activated. Thus, treatment of rod outer segment discs with GTP results in a dissociation of transducin from the discs, yet treatment of adenylyl cyclase containing membranes with GTP does not result in a release of the N proteins. Since structurally transducin has the same β subunit as the N protein but their γ subunits differ from that of transducin, a function for the γ subunit may be the anchoring of the N proteins into the membrane. However, since the α subunits of transducin and N proteins also differ, and activation by a nucleotide such as GMP-P(NH)P results in subunit dissociation of both transducin and the N proteins, one would expect both α_s and α_T to dissociate when subjected to such a treatment. Yet, this does not happen with both types of α subunits: only α_T dissociates from the membrane, α_s and α_i subunits do not. If one would not want to save the "γ is the anchor" argument, one would have to postulate that either the N proteins do not, but transducin does, dissociate into its subunits on activation or, alternatively, that γ is not the sole peptide responsible for anchoring. Clearly, further research is necessary to unravel the functions of each and every one of these subunits.

RECENT PROGRESS IN HORMONE RESEARCH, VOL. 41

Regulation of Luteal Function in Domestic Ruminants: New Concepts[1]

G. D. NISWENDER, R. H. SCHWALL, T. A. FITZ,[2] C. E. FARIN, AND H. R. SAWYER

Department of Physiology and Biophysics, Colorado State University, Fort Collins, Colorado

I. Introduction

The critical role of the corpus luteum for successful pregnancy has long been recognized. In 1901 Fraenkel and Cohn reported "The ovary has a function beside maturation and ovulation of eggs, that was unknown until now; it is necessary to prepare the uterus for the implantation of the egg, and for that reason it is an indispensible factor for the implantation of the egg and the normal induction of pregnancy." They localized this effect of the ovary to the corpus luteum by developing a "fine galvanocaustic needle" and cauterizing the individual corpora lutea in rabbits, which resulted in abortion or resorption of the embryos. These early observations were remarkably correct and Corner and Allen (1929; reviewed by Corner, 1947) identified progesterone as the primary endocrine secretory product of the corpus luteum. Further studies have demonstrated that normal function of the corpus luteum and secretion of progesterone are requirements for the maintenance of gestation in mammals. On the other hand, abnormal luteal function has been implicated in failure of implantation and embryonic wastage. Regulation of the function of the corpus luteum has been used for synchronization of estrus, contraception, and/or abortion. Thus, this gland occupies a central position in the reproductive processes of all mammals.

This review will be concerned primarily with the control of luteal function in domestic ruminant animals. It will focus on data regarding the

---

[1] This paper is dedicated to Dr. A. V. Nalbandov who has provided over four decades of leadership for studies of the reproductive physiology of domestic animals. He has provided training and encouragement to a large number of reproductive biologists and made major contributions to our understanding of luteal function.

[2] Present address: Department of Obstetrics and Gynecology, Uniformed Services University of the Health Sciences, Bethesda, Maryland.

101

regulation of receptors for luteinizing hormone (LH) and the characterization of two distinct types of steroidogenic luteal cells.

II. Endocrine Regulation of Luteal Function

The function of the corpus luteum in ruminants is regulated by a complex interaction of the secretions from at least two other endocrine organs. The adenohypophysis secretes LH, which generally is accepted to
be the primary luteotropic hormone in these species (Hansel et al., 1973;
Nalbandov, 1973; Niswender et al., 1980). The uterus, on the other hand,
produces prostaglandin (PG) $F_{2\alpha}$, which causes luteolysis at the end of the
estrous cycle (McCracken et al., 1971; Poyser, 1973). The presence of an
embryo within the uterus results in maintenance of the corpus luteum,
perhaps due to the enhanced secretion of PGE_2 (Ellinwood et al., 1979;
Silvia et al., 1984a).

A. ROLE OF LH IN REGULATING LUTEAL FUNCTION

The results of Denamur and Mauleon (1963) suggested that formation
and maintenance of corpora lutea in ewes were not influenced by hypophysectomy. However, studies in Nalbandov's laboratory indicated that
hypophysectomy of ewes on day 1 after ovulation resulted in failure of the
corpus luteum to form, while hypophysectomy on day 5 resulted in regression of the partially formed corpus luteum (Kaltenbach et al., 1968).
Thus, the anterior pituitary gland is necessary for normal luteal formation
and function in sheep.

To determine which of the adenohypophyseal hormones was responsible for maintenance of luteal function, injections of LH and/or prolactin
have been administered to hypophysectomized ewes. Thibault (1966)
found that injections of prolactin maintained corpora lutea in hypophysectomized, hysterectomized ewes, but that injections of LH, prolactin, or
combinations of the two hormones had no effect in hypophysectomized
ewes with an intact uterus. These results were at odds with those of
Kaltenbach et al. (1968) who showed that constant infusions of crude
pituitary preparations containing LH and follicle-stimulating hormone
(FSH) maintained luteal function in both pregnant and nonpregnant ewes.
Further studies suggested that LH was the luteotropic material in this
crude preparation and that constant infusions of prolactin had no luteotropic effect. Subsequent studies by Karsch et al. (1971a) demonstrated that
constant infusions of LH also prolonged the lifespan and function of the
corpus luteum in intact, cycling ewes. Fuller and Hansel (1970) demonstrated that daily injections of antiserum to LH caused luteal regression in

cycling ewes, and Domanski *et al.* (1967) reported that infusion of LH enhanced secretion of progesterone. Thus, it is now widely accepted that LH is critical for formation and maintenance of the corpus luteum in sheep. Furthermore, LH stimulates progesterone secretion from ovine luteal tissue *in vitro* (Kaltenbach *et al.*, 1967; Simmons *et al.*, 1976).

Simmons and Hansel (1964) suggested that LH was luteotropic in the cow. Injections of LH lengthened the estrous cycle (Donaldson and Hansel, 1965), prevented the luteolytic effects of oxytocin injected early in the cycle (Simmons and Hansel, 1964; Donaldson *et al.*, 1965), and increased concentrations of progesterone in corpora lutea from hysterectomized cows (Brunner *et al.*, 1969). Daily injections of antiserum to LH reduced luteal weight and content of progesterone in intact and hysterectomized heifers (Snook *et al.*, 1969). Finally, the fact that LH stimulates synthesis and secretion of progesterone by bovine luteal tissue *in vitro* is consistent with the conclusion that this hormone is the primary luteotropin in cattle (Hansel, 1971).

B. ROLE OF PROLACTIN IN REGULATING LUTEAL FUNCTION

The early observation that prolactin was a primary component of the luteotropic complex in rats (Astwood, 1941) led to a number of studies in domestic animals. That injections of prolactin into hypophysectomized–hysterectomized ewes resulted in maintenance of luteal function suggested a similar role for this hormone in ewes (Thibault, 1966). Schroff *et al.* (1971) and Hixon and Clegg (1969) also suggested that prolactin supported luteal function in hypophysectomized ewes. These data do not support the concept that LH is the primary luteotropin in sheep; however, highly purified hormones were not available for replacement therapy when these studies were conducted. Thus, the results obtained following injection or infusion of relatively crude preparations of anterior pituitary hormones were difficult to interpret. Therefore, alternative approaches have been utilized to resolve this issue.

Injections of 2-Br-α-ergocryptine (CB-154) reduced serum concentrations of prolactin by more than 95% for an entire estrous cycle; however, there was no effect on concentrations of progesterone in serum or length of the cycle (Niswender, 1974). When excess quantities of specific antiserum to prolactin were administered in conjunction with CB-154 (to neutralize the remaining prolactin) there still was no effect on serum concentrations of progesterone (Niswender *et al.*, 1976; Reimers and Niswender, 1975). Constant infusion of prolactin into intact ewes had no effect on luteal function (Karsch *et al.*, 1971b), nor did infusions of large quantities of prolactin into the ovarian artery result in increased secretion of progesterone (McCracken *et al.*, 1971). Administration of exogenous prolactin to cows does not alter the length of the estrous cycle (Smith *et al.* 1957), prevent oxytocin-induced luteolysis (Donaldson *et al.*, 1965), or stimulate secretion of progesterone from luteal slices (Hansel, 1967). In addition, injections of CB-154 in cows did not reduce serum concentrations of progesterone or influence the length of the estrous cycle (Hoffman *et al.*, 1974). Thus, there is general consensus that prolactin is not luteotropic in ruminants.

C. EFFECTS OF PROSTAGLANDINS ON LUTEAL FUNCTION

There is good evidence that $PGF_{2\alpha}$ of uterine origin is the agent responsible for normal regression of the corpus luteum in ewes (for reviews see Goding, 1974; Horton and Poyser, 1976). A number of actions of $PGF_{2\alpha}$ have been proposed to explain its luteolytic action including reduced ovarian blood flow (Niswender *et al.*, 1976; Nett *et al.*, 1976a), uncoupling of the LH receptor from adenylate cyclase (Evrard *et al.*, 1978; Fletcher and Niswender, 1982), and a direct cytotoxic effect (Silvia *et al.*, 1984b). All of these actions may be important for normal regression of the corpus luteum in ewes.

Maintenance of early pregnancy in the ewe requires extension of the lifespan and function of the corpus luteum, but the mechanism whereby pregnancy prevents the luteolytic process is poorly understood. The embryo must be present in the uterus by the thirteenth day postestrus to prevent luteolysis (Moor and Rowson, 1966), although attachment of the trophoblast to the endometrium does not occur until day 18 postestrus (Amoroso, 1951) and interdigitation of embryonic and maternal tissues does not occur until the fourth week of gestation (Boshier, 1969). Thus, the embryo somehow prevents luteolysis 4 to 5 days prior to attachment to the uterus.

The hypothesis that the embryo reduces synthesis and/or secretion of $PGF_{2\alpha}$ from endometrial tissue has received considerable attention, but results have been contradictory. Thorburn *et al.* (1973) and Barcikowski *et al.* (1974) reported that concentrations of PGF in uteroovarian venous plasma were lower during early pregnancy than during luteolysis in a small number of ewes. In contrast, concentrations of $PGF_{2\alpha}$ in uteroovarian venous plasma of pregnant ewes were reported to be greater (Wilson *et al.*, 1972; Ellinwood *et al.*, 1979) or not different (Pexton *et al.*, 1975a,b; Cerini *et al.*, 1976; Nett *et al.*, 1976b; Lewis *et al.*, 1977) than those in cycling ewes on days 13–17 postestrus. Contrary to its effects *in vivo* $PGF_{2\alpha}$ has a slight stimulatory effect on secretion of progesterone by bovine (Hixon and Hansel, 1974) and ovine (Kaltenbach *et al.*, 1969) luteal tissue *in vitro*.

Inskeep *et al.* (1975) suggested that luteolysis was prevented at the ovarian level by a factor produced during early pregnancy. In a series of elegant studies involving vascular anastomoses, Mapletoft *et al.* (1975, 1976) confirmed that a factor from the gravid uterine horn prevents luteolysis at the ovarian level and that this effect is exerted through a local venoarterial pathway. Prostaglandin E_2 is a likely candidate as the luteotropic factor secreted from the pregnant uterus since (1) PGE_2 is a potent vasodilator and could overcome the vasoconstrictive effects of $PGF_{2\alpha}$ (Bergstrom *et al.*, 1968; Dunham *et al.*, 1974); (2) PGE_2 stimulates production of progesterone by luteal tissue *in vitro* (Marsh, 1971; Speroff and Ramwell, 1970); (3) simultaneous infusion of PGE_2 will prevent the decreased secretion of progesterone after treatment with $PGF_{2\alpha}$ (Henderson *et al.*, 1977); (4) intrauterine administration of PGE_2 will prolong the estrous cycle in ewes (Pratt *et al.*, 1977) and prevent natural and estradiol-induced luteolysis (Magness *et al.*, 1978; Colcord *et al.*, 1978); and (5) PGE_2 secretion is greater from the pregnant than the nonpregnant uterus on days 15 to 17 postestrus (Ellinwood *et al.*, 1979; Silvia *et al.*, 1984a). Since $PGF_{2\alpha}$ appears to be transferred from the uteroovarian vein to the ovarian artery in ewes (McCracken *et al.*, 1971; Land *et al.*, 1976) and cows (Hixon and Hansel, 1974), it seems likely that PGE_2 could reach the ovary via the same mechanism.

III. Regulation of Receptors for LH

It has been generally accepted that the actions of protein hormones, including LH, are mediated via a specific receptor residing in the plasma membrane. The effects of LH on the kinetics of receptor turnover, production of cAMP, and secretion of progesterone will be discussed in detail in the following sections. However, there is at least one action of LH on the ovary which is not well understood. Injections of LH during the luteal phase of the estrous cycle in rats (Wurtman, 1964) or ewes (Niswender *et al.*, 1976) results in a rapid increase in blood flow to the ovary. The result was so consistent in the prepubertal rat that ovarian hyperemia has been used as a bioassay for LH (Ellis, 1961). Szego and Gitin (1961) postulated that a primary action of LH on the ovary was to increase release of histamine and increase blood flow to the ovary. This was supported by the data of Piacsek and Huth (1971). Although the effects of LH on blood flow to the ovary are important and it seems likely that these effects are mediated via specific receptors, the mechanisms involved remain to be elucidated.

A.   NUMBERS OF LH RECEPTORS DURING DIFFERENT
REPRODUCTIVE STATES

Most studies in which the number of receptors for LH has been measured have utilized the binding of radioactive LH or hCG. One problem
with these methods is that they fail to detect receptors occupied by endogenous hormone. However, it is the number of receptors occupied by
endogenous hormone which should be responsible for the biological response at the time the sample was collected. Therefore, methods for
quantification of both occupied and unoccupied receptors for LH were
developed (Diekman *et al.*, 1978a) and these methods were utilized to
quantify the number of receptors for LH throughout the estrous cycle and
early pregnancy in ewes (Fig. 1). The number of occupied receptors increased from days 2 to 10 of the estrous cycle, remained high through day
14 and then declined dramatically by day 16. There were parallel changes
in the number of unoccupied receptors (Fig. 1). On day 10 of the estrous
cycle when secretion of progesterone had reached maximal levels, only
0.6% of the luteal receptors was occupied by LH. This observation agrees
with data which indicate that only 1% of the 6000 receptor sites per
Leydig cell needs to be occupied to elicit maximal secretion of testosterone *in vitro* (Mendelson *et al.*, 1975). The number of occupied and unoccupied receptors for LH were both highly correlated with the weight of
the corpus luteum, serum levels of progesterone (Fig. 1), and luteal concentrations of progesterone ($p < 0.01$) throughout the estrous cycle.
Thus, the total number of receptors for LH and the number of occupied
receptors are more highly correlated with secretion of progesterone than
are circulating levels of LH (Fig. 1). There was no change in the association constant of the LH receptor for hCG at any of the times studied
(Diekman *et al.*, 1978a). The binding of ^{125}I-labeled hCG to rat ovarian
tissue is also correlated with ovarian content of progesterone (Hacik and
Kolena, 1975; Lee *et al.*, 1975; Solano *et al.*, 1980). Maximum binding of
hCG to bovine (Rao *et al.*, 1976; Spicer *et al.*, 1981) and equine (Roser
and Evans, 1983) luteal tissue also occurred during the mid-luteal phase of
the cycle. In addition, capacity to bind hCG and the functional state of the
human corpus luteum are correlated (Lee *et al.*, 1973; Rao *et al.*, 1977).
Thus, for a number of species it is clear that the secretion of progesterone
is maximal when the number of luteal receptors for LH is highest, but
when the circulating concentrations of LH are lowest during the cycle.

As reviewed above, there is considerable controversy regarding the
mechanisms responsible for maintenance of the corpus luteum during
early pregnancy. Diekman *et al.* (1978a) examined changes in the numbers of receptors for LH in the corpus luteum of pregnancy. As illustrated

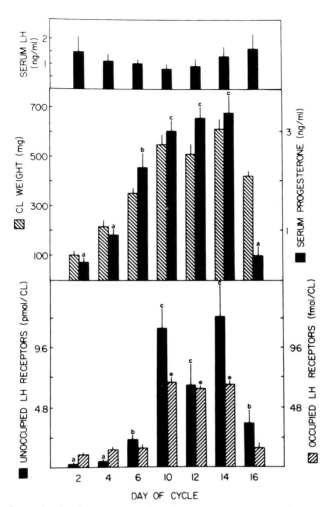

FIG. 1. Serum levels of LH (top panel) and progesterone, weight of the corpora lutea (middle panel), and number of occupied and unoccupied receptors for LH in corpora lutea (bottom panel) collected throughout the estrous cycle from ewes ($n=6$). Taken from Diekman *et al.* (1978a).

in Table I, the numbers of either occupied or unoccupied receptors for LH on days 12, 16, and 20 of pregnancy were not different from each other and, in fact, were the same as the numbers observed on day 12 of the estrous cycle (Fig. 1). Thus, an increase in the number of receptors, or the number occupied by endogenous LH was not associated with maintenance of the corpus luteum of pregnancy. On the other hand, the decrease in the number of receptors noted on day 16 in cycling ewes did not occur

TABLE I

Weight and Progesterone Content of Corpora Lutea, Concentration of Progesterone in Serum, and the Numbers of Occupied and Unoccupied Luteal Receptors for Luteinizing Hormone in Ewes during Early Pregnancy[a]

	Day of pregnancy		
	12	16	20
CL weight (mg)	622 ± 38^b	490 ± 24	561 ± 48
Serum progesterone (ng/ml)	3.07 ± 0.51	2.0 ± 0.5	3.8 ± 0.5
Luteal progesterone (μg/CL)	20.32 ± 1.25^c	14.6 ± 1.7^d	18.7 ± 1.5^c
Unoccupied LH receptors (M $\times 10^{-11}$/CL)	1.07 ± 0.37	1.3 ± 0.2	1.3 ± 0.1
Occupied LH receptors (M $\times 10^{-13}$/CL)	0.64 ± 0.04	0.66 ± 0.05	0.67 ± 0.03

[a] From Diekman *et al.* (1978a).
[b] Mean $\pm$ SE ($n=6$).
[c,d] Means followed by different letters are different ($p < 0.05$).

in pregnant ewes. This observation raised a second question. Does the mechanism of $PGF_{2\alpha}$-induced luteolysis in sheep involve a reduction in the number of receptors for LH or decreased occupancy of receptors as has been shown in rats (Behrman *et al.*, 1979)? To address this question, ewes on day 9 of the estrous cycle were administered $PGF_{2\alpha}$ to induce luteolysis and concentrations of progesterone in serum, and occupied and unoccupied luteal receptors for LH were quantified (Diekman *et al.*, 1978b). Although serum levels of progesterone had decreased by 63% at 7.5 hours (Table II), there was no change in the number of luteal receptors for LH or the number occupied by endogenous hormone by this time. However, the number of both occupied and unoccupied receptors had declined significantly by 22.5 hours. It was concluded that a decrease in the number of receptors for LH was not involved in the initial luteolytic actions of $PGF_{2\alpha}$.

B. HOMOLOGOUS REGULATION OF LH RECEPTORS

Part of the biological response to protein hormones appears to be modulation of the number of receptors for that hormone. The number of receptors for LH in the luteinized rat ovary (Conti *et al.*, 1976, 1977a) and testis (Sharpe, 1976; Haour and Saez, 1977; Hseuh *et al.*, 1977; Tsuruhara *et al.*, 1977) decreases dramatically after exposure to hCG. Since hCG,

TABLE II

Weight and Progesterone Content of Corpora Lutea (CL), Concentrations of Progesterone in Serum, and Numbers of Occupied and Unoccupied Luteal Receptors for Luteinizing Hormone after Treatment with $PGF_{2\alpha}$ on Day 9 of the Estrous Cycle[a]

	Hours after $PGF_{2\alpha}$			
	0	2.5	7.5	22.5
CL weight (mg)	$546 \pm 41^{b,c}$	460 ± 30^c	453 ± 35^c	288 ± 22^d
Serum progesterone (% pretreatment)	100 ± 5^c	90 ± 8^c	37 ± 8^d	13 ± 3^d
Luteal progesterone (μg/CL)	13.63 ± 1.56^c	11.15 ± 1.48^c	8.87 ± 0.46^c	0.69 ± 0.09^d
Unoccupied LH receptors ($M \times 10^{-11}$/CL)	1.12 ± 0.15^c	0.99 ± 0.12^c	0.63 ± 0.14^c	0.10 ± 0.02^d
Occupied LH receptors ($M \times 10^{-13}$/CL)	0.68 ± 0.05^c	0.68 ± 0.04^c	0.46 ± 0.04^c	0.09 ± 0.01^d

[a] From Diekman *et al.* (1978b).
[b] Mean $\pm$ SE ($n=6$).
[c,d] Means followed by different letters are different ($p < 0.05$).

which has a prolonged half-life in blood (Catt and Pierce, 1978), was used in these studies it was not possible to precisely determine the time course for changes in number of receptors after exposure to hCG. Therefore, an experiment was conducted to examine fluctuations in the number of both occupied and unoccupied receptors for LH, concentrations of LH and progesterone in serum, and content of progesterone in the corpus luteum for up to 72 hours following injection of 1 mg of oLH (Suter *et al.*, 1980). Luteinizing hormone was used for these experiments since it is cleared from the blood of sheep with a $t_{\frac{1}{2}}$ of 25 to 30 minutes compared to a $t_{\frac{1}{2}}$ of approximately 48 hours for hCG.

The results of this study are depicted in Fig. 2. Serum concentrations of LH were increased approximately 1000-fold within 10 minutes following the injection of LH, but had decreased 90% within 2 hours and returned to preinjection levels by 24 hours. Serum concentrations of progesterone were significantly elevated within 10 minutes and remained elevated at 2 hours but were not different from values observed in uninjected control ewes by 6 hours. The total number (occupied plus unoccupied) of receptors for LH increased 260% ($p < 0.05$) within 10 minutes, but had returned to control levels by 2 hours and was significantly decreased by 24 hours. The increase in total receptors at 10 minutes was due to a 1300% increase

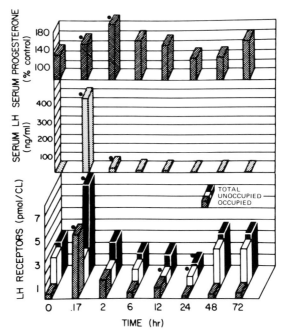

FIG. 2.   Serum levels of progesterone (top panel) and LH (middle panel) and the number of total, occupied and unoccupied receptors for LH in corpora lutea collected from ewes (*n*=7) at different times after injection of 1 mg ovine LH. Taken from Suter *et al.* (1980).

in the number of occupied receptors, which had returned to preinjection levels by 6 hours. The number of unoccupied receptors was significantly less than preinjection levels at 12 and 24 hours. At 24 hours the total number of receptors for LH was decreased 63% when compared to preinjection levels, or 85% if compared to the elevated number observed 10 minutes after the injection of LH.

There were three interesting results from this study. First, although the number of receptors for LH was decreased 63 to 85% at 24 hours after the injection of LH, at no time did serum concentrations of progesterone fall below levels noted prior to the injection. Similarly, serum levels of testosterone were not decreased in male rats following a loss of testicular receptors for LH (Hseuh *et al.*, 1976; Sharpe, 1976, 1977). This observation may not be surprising in view of the fact that the number of luteal receptors occupied by LH did not decrease below the number occupied prior to the injection of LH. There was a high degree of correlation between the number of occupied receptors and the secretion of progesterone in this study although the increase in serum levels of progesterone was of considerably less magnitude. The failure of an injection of 1 mg oLH to induce a greater loss of LH receptors may have been due to its relatively rapid clearance from blood as compared to hCG. The fact that serum concentrations of LH decreased by 90% between 10 minutes and 2 hours after its injection indicated that the ovary was exposed to a high concentration of LH for a relatively short period of time.

The second interesting observation was the excellent agreement between the number of receptors occupied by hormone 10 minutes after the injection of LH (5.43×10^{-12} mol/corpus luteum) and the number of receptors lost between 12 and 24 hours (6.75×10^{-12} mol/corpus luteum). This suggests that the loss of receptors for LH was related to occupancy of the receptor. These findings are in contrast to those of Conti *et al.* (1977b) who reported that <10% occupancy of receptors for LH resulted in a loss of 50% of rat luteal receptors for this hormone. This discrepancy may be due to differences in times at which data were obtained. For example, in the present study over 50% of the total receptors lost after the injection of LH were already lost within the first 6 hours, a time when Conti *et al.* (1977b) first estimated occupied receptors.

Finally, the increase in total number of receptors for LH at 10 minutes (up-regulation) raises the question of how lost receptors are replaced. In a subsequent study using similar methods, Niswender *et al.* (1982) demonstrated that the number of receptors was increased in a linear fashion up to 30 minutes after injection of 1 mg oLH but returned to preinjection levels by 100 minutes. Hseuh *et al.* (1977) suggested that a similar increase in numbers of receptors for LH observed in rat testis was a gonadotropin-induced conformational change in the plasma membrane leading to the "unmasking" of surface receptors. Alternatively, there have been a number of mechanisms suggested for recycling of hormone receptors and insertion into the plasma membrane which may explain "up-regulation" (Willingham *et al.*, 1984).

C. PATHWAY FOR LOSS OF LH–RECEPTOR COMPLEXES

Internalization by cells of specifically bound ligands via receptor-mediated endocytosis occurs for a number of protein hormones (Carpenter and Cohen, 1976; Chen *et al.*, 1977; Schlessinger *et al.*, 1978; Goldstein *et al.*, 1979). That the receptor is internalized along with the bound ligand is suggested by the decreased receptor-binding capacity for specific ligands (Gavin *et al.*, 1974; Conti *et al.*, 1976; Sharpe, 1976) coupled with direct electron microscopic (McKanna *et al.*, 1979) and biochemical evidence (Conn *et al.*, 1978; Niswender *et al.*, 1980). In the case of the ovary, internalization of hCG has been demonstrated using autoradiographic techniques (Chen *et al.*, 1977; Conn *et al.*, 1978; Han *et al.*, 1974). Ascoli and Puett (1978) and Amsterdam *et al.* (1979) determined that following internalization, receptor-bound ^{125}I-labeled hCG was degraded to such an extent that iodotyrosine was the major radioactive product. However, there were few kinetic data regarding the rates of internalization and catabolism of receptor-bound hormone. Therefore, experiments were conducted to obtain precise kinetic data for these processes (Ahmed *et al.*, 1981).

Ovine luteal cells in suspension or monolayer culture were pulse labeled (5 to 7 minutes) with ^{125}I-labeled hCG. The quantities of hormone that were bound to plasma membrane were determined by elution of the hormone from the receptor at pH 3.9. The hormone present in the cell pellet was defined as nonreleasable while the quantity which had been

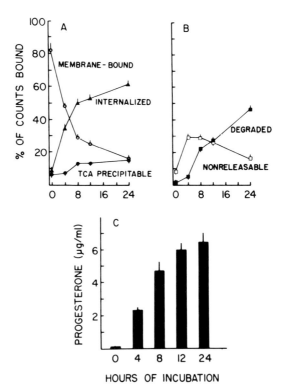

FIG. 3.   Suspended luteal cells were incubated with 0.5 μg ^{125}I-labeled hCG for 6 minutes at 21°C, washed five times in ice cold medium, resuspended, and incubated at 37°C for the times indicated. Results are the means ± SEM from three separate experiments each performed in triplicate. (●) TCA-precipitable cpm; (○) membrane bound cpm; (▲) internalized cpm; (□) nonreleasable cpm; and (■) degraded cpm. Taken from Ahmed *et al.* (1981).

degraded and that which had dissociated from the cells was determined by TCA precipitation (Ahmed *et al.*, 1981). The quantity of hormone which had been internalized was calculated by adding the nonreleasable and the degraded hormone. More than 60% of the radioactive hCG initially bound to the cells had been internalized and/or degraded by 24 hours while only 16% of the hormone was still present on the cell surface (Fig. 3A). Approximately 15% of the radioactivity initially bound appeared to have dissociated from the cells. The nonreleasable, internalized radioactivity reached a plateau and was constant between 4 and 12 hours but decreased by 24 hours. This decrease was probably due to the reduced radioactivity on the membrane available for internalization. Radioactivity in the medium attributable to degraded hormone increased throughout the 24-hour period. These data clearly indicate that internalization and degradation are the major mechanisms by which the ovine luteal cell rids itself of hCG bound to receptor. There is excellent agreement in the time required for luteal cells to lose ^{125}I-labeled hCG *in vitro* and *in vivo* (Niswender *et al.*, 1980). As discussed previously, there is extensive evidence that the receptor is internalized along with the hCG. Thus, this mechanism likely represents the major biological basis for "down-regulation." That receptors for LH, once internalized and separated from their hormone, are recycled is suggested by the data of Suter and Niswender (1983).

IV. Differential Effects of LH and hCG on the Luteal Cell

A. EFFECTS ON STEROIDOGENESIS

Human chorionic gonadotropin frequently is used to study gonadotropin-stimulated steroidogenesis and receptor-mediated endocytosis (Diekman *et al.*, 1978a; Ahmed *et al.*, 1981). The primary reasons for using hCG, instead of LH, are that both hormones bind to the same receptor, hCG can be radioiodinated to a higher specific activity and still retain its ability to bind to receptor, ^{125}I-labeled hCG is more stable than ^{125}I-labeled LH upon storage, and less nonspecific binding occurs with hCG (Diekman *et al.*, 1978a). However, the assumption that similar steroidogenic responses are elicited in target cells by LH and hCG appears to be incorrect.

Segaloff *et al.* (1981) investigated the steroidogenic response of perfused Leydig tumor cells to both hCG and oLH. A 10-minute pulse of hCG (maximum stimulating dose) produced a response similar to that obtained during continuous perfusion of this hormone. However, a pulse of oLH (maximum stimulating dose) elicited a response of much shorter duration. Thus, the steroidogenic response of Leydig tumor cells to hCG is different from that to oLH. A similar effect was observed with normal Leydig cells. Similar information was not available for the corpus luteum. Therefore, we investigated secretion of progesterone by ovine luteal cells in response to different doses of oLH and hCG administered as a 15-minute pulse or continuously (Bourdage et al., 1984).

Corpora lutea were obtained from ewes on day 10 of the estrous cycle and small luteal cells were isolated as described by Fitz et al. (1982). Experiments were performed on isolated preparations of small luteal cells (12–22 μm in diameter) since these cells respond to oLH or hCG with enhanced steroid secretion. After 24 hours in culture the cells were exposed to increasing amounts of oLH or hCG administered either as a 15-minute pulse or continuously throughout the 6-hour incubation period.

In the absence of hormone the cells secreted progesterone at a constant level (7.3 ± 3.1% of the experimental maximum) for the duration of each experiment (Figs. 4 and 5). Maximum secretion of progesterone occurred

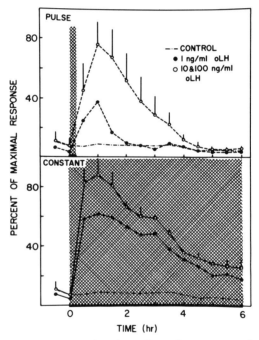

FIG. 4. Progesterone concentrations in medium after exposure of plated small luteal cells to oLH. Progesterone levels are presented as percentage of maximal progesterone secretion (mean ± SEM) over time for two separate experiments each performed in triplicate. The hatched area on each figure depicts the duration of exposure of the cells to hormone. Taken from Bourdage et al. (1984).

1 hour following addition of 10 or 100 ng/ml oLH whether administered as a 15-minute pulse or continuously (Fig. 4). The amount of progesterone in the medium declined to basal levels by 4 hours after pulse treatment, but remained elevated at 6 hours (25.1 ± 5.6% of experimental maximum) following continuous treatment. A 1 ng/ml pulse of oLH resulted in an increase ($p < 0.001$) in progesterone which had returned to basal levels by 2 hours. However, continuous stimulation with 1 ng/ml oLH produced a response that was similar to the 10 and 100 ng/ml treatments ($p > 0.01$) which had not returned to basal levels by 6 hours.

A small, but significant ($p < 0.001$) increase in secretion of progesterone was obtained with a 15-minute pulse of 0.2 ng/ml hCG. Maximum secretion of progesterone was obtained with 2 and 20 ng/ml hCG when administered as a 15-minute pulse ($p < 0.001$). Continuous administration of hCG at any of the three doses elicited an increase in progesterone

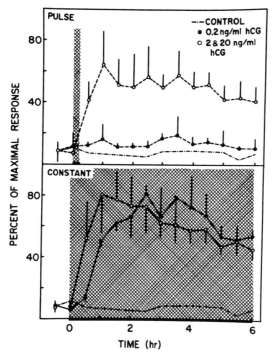

FIG. 5. Progesterone concentrations in medium after exposure of plated small luteal cells to hCG. Progesterone levels are presented as percentage of maximal progesterone (mean ± SEM) over time for two separate experiments each performed in triplicate. The hatched area on each figure depicts the duration of exposure of the cells to hormone. Taken from Bourdage *et al.* (1984).

secretion. The higher doses of hCG maintained secretion of progesterone at 40 to 55% of the experimental maximum for at least 6 hours. In addition, there was no difference ($p > 0.1$) in the responses of luteal cells to either 2 or 20 ng/ml hCG when administered either as a pulse or continuously.

Luteal cells exposed to a maximally stimulating dose of either oLH or hCG exhibited a similar initial response, which peaked by 1 hour. However, after reaching maximal levels, oLH-stimulated secretion of progesterone declined steadily while hCG-stimulated secretion of progesterone remained elevated. Thus, the response pattern was different ($p < 0.001$) for the two hormones. Results from this study with ovine luteal cells were similar to those obtained with rat Leydig cells (Segaloff et al., 1981), i.e., a short pulse of hCG resulted in prolonged secretion of steroid comparable with that obtained with a constant treatment while a short pulse with oLH stimulated steroid secretion only briefly.

B. INTERNALIZATION OF LH AND hCG

The next series of experiments was conducted to determine if differences in the rate of internalization of oLH versus hCG could explain the differences in duration of the steroidogenic response following short-term treatment with these two hormones. Several ligands are internalized and degraded by a receptor-mediated process (Goldstein et al., 1979). The time required for internalization of hCG by ovine luteal cells (Ahmed et al., 1981) was considerably longer than that observed for other hormones such as epidermal growth factor (Carpenter and Cohen, 1976) and insulin (Schlessinger et al., 1978). It could not be ascertained whether the prolonged time required for internalization of hCG was due to some unique property of this hormone or to a difference in the mechanism involved in internalization and degradation that was characteristic of luteal cells. Therefore, a study was designed to determine the rates of internalization and degradation of hCG compared to oLH, human LH (hLH), and epidermal growth factor by ovine luteal tissue (Mock and Niswender, 1983).

Corpora lutea were collected surgically from superovulated ewes and dissociated into single cell suspensions. The suspended cells were then pulse-labeled for 15 minutes with radioiodinated hCG, ovine LH, mouse epidermal growth factor, or hLH. The methods described by Ahmed et al. (1981) were used to determine the quantity of hormone bound to plasma membrane, that which had been internalized, and that which had dissociated from the cells. There were major differences in the rates of internalization of the various molecules (Table III). Human chorionic gonadotropin was internalized at least 60 times slower than was oLH. Human LH

TABLE III
Time Required for Loss of Radioiodinated Hormone
from the Membranes of Ovine Luteal Cells
in Culture[a]

Hormone	$t_\frac{1}{2}$ (hours)[b]
Human chorionic gonadotropin	22.8 ± 2.3[c]
Human luteinizing hormone	15.1 ± 1.4[d]
Ovine luteinizing hormone	0.4 ± 0.2[e]
Mouse epidermal growth factor	0.3 + 0.1[e]

[a] Data summarized from Mock and Niswender (1983).

[b] Mean ± SEM for five separate experiments each performed in triplicate.

[c-e] Values with different letter are different ($p <$ 0.01).

was internalized at a rate more comparable to that of hCG. The rates of loss of ovine LH and mouse epidermal growth factor were comparable (Table III) and quite similar to those observed for epidermal growth factor and insulin in different target cells (Carpenter and Cohen, 1976; Haigler et al., 1980). Thus, it appears that the slow rate of internalization of hCG by ovine luteal cells is due to some unique property of the hCG–LH receptor complex and not to an inability of the luteal cell to rapidly internalize receptor-bound ligand.

The particular characteristic of hCG that resulted in its being internalized much slower than oLH by ovine luteal cells was not apparent. However, there are several possible explanations based on differences in molecular weight and carbohydrate content of the molecules. First, hCG binds to the receptor for LH with an apparent K_a approximately 50 times greater than that for oLH (Mock and Niswender, 1983). Since both hormones bind to the same receptor (Diekman et al., 1978a) a second possibility is that the 30 additional amino acids in the β-subunit of hCG (Birken and Canfield, 1978), that are not present in oLH, somehow interact with components of the plasma membrane to prevent, or at least slow down, migration of the hormone–receptor complex. If this were true, the rate of internalization of hCG ($t_\frac{1}{2}$ = 22.8 hours) should, and does, approach the rate of loss of general membrane proteins ($t_\frac{1}{2}$ = 26 hours; Ahmed et al., 1981). Interestingly, the rate of internalization was influenced by an annual cycle (Mock and Niswender, 1983).

The results of this study combined with those which demonstrated that hCG stimulation of ovine luteal cells results in a prolonged steroidogenic response clearly indicate that internalization of the hormone–LH receptor complex is associated with attenuation of the steroidogenic response. Thus, it appears that internalization is a mechanism used by the cell to terminate the response to stimulation by the tropic hormone.

The next series of experiments was performed to determine which portion of the hCG molecule was responsible for the reduced rate of internalization of this hormone. The individual subunits of hCG and oLH were radioiodinated and all possible recombinations of these subunits were made (Mock et al., 1983). There was no difference in the rate of internalization of hCG which had been radioiodinated in the α-subunit when compared to hCG which contained the radioiodine in the β-subunit (Table IV). Likewise, there was no significant difference in the rate of internalization of oLH which had been radioiodinated in either the α- or the β-subunit. When the α-subunit of hCG was recombined with radioiodinated β-subunit of oLH, the rate of loss from the membrane was similar to that observed for intact oLH. On the other hand, when the α-subunit of oLH was recombined with the radioiodinated β-subunit of hCG, the rate of internalization was much closer to that observed for radioiodinated hCG than to that for oLH. Thus, it appears that the component responsible for the reduced rate of internalization of hCG resides in the β-subunit, however, the precise mechanisms involved are not apparent.

TABLE IV

Comparison of the Time Required for Loss of Hormones from the Membranes of Ovine Luteal Cells in Culture[a]

Hormone/recombinant[b]	$t_{\frac{1}{2}}$ (hours)[c]
αhCG[b]	16.8 ± 2.5[d]
αhCG/βhCG[b]	22.8 ± 3.8[d]
αoLH/βhCG[b]	8.9 ± 4.5[e]
αoLH[a]	0.5 ± 0.1[f]
αoLH/βoLH[b]	0.7 ± 0.2[f]
αhCG/βoLH[b]	0.5 ± 0.1[f]

[a] Data summarized from Mock et al. (1983).

[b] Indicates the subunit which contained the [125]I.

[c] Values are mean $\pm$ SEM for four separate experiments each performed in triplicate.

[d-f] Means followed by different letters are different ($p < 0.01$).

C. MOBILITY OF THE LH RECEPTOR WHEN OCCUPIED BY oLH VS hCG

Since hCG–LH receptor complexes migrate in the membrane prior to internalization (Amsterdam *et al.*, 1979), the next series of experiments was conducted to determine if there were differences in the lateral mobility of the LH receptor in the membrane of the luteal cell when occupied by oLH versus hCG.

Preparations of hCG, deglyco-hCG, oLH, hLH, and succinylated concanavalin A were labeled with tetramethylrhodamine-B isothiocyanate (Niswender *et al.*, 1985). Biological activity of the rhodamine-labeled oLH and hCG preparations was verified in two ways. First, it was demonstrated that the addition of the rhodamine label did not influence the ability of these hormones to prevent binding of radioactive hCG to the LH receptor in a radioreceptor assay system. Second, it was demonstrated that both oLH and the hCG rhodamine preparations were capable of stimulating secretion of progesterone from isolated, small, ovine luteal cells. The biological activity of the rhodamine-labeled hLH and deglyco-hCG was not tested since insufficient quantities of these two preparations were available.

When suspensions of ovine luteal cells were incubated with rhodamine-labeled preparations for 2 hours, labeling was seen exclusively in the small steriodogenic luteal cells. Additional evidence of specificity of that binding was the fact that labeling of the steriodogenic luteal cells could be prevented with simultaneous exposure to 100- to 1000-fold excesses of non-rhodamine-labeled oLH or hCG.

Fluorescence photobleaching recovery methods (Peacock and Barisas, 1981) were then used to determine the lateral mobility of the oLH-LH receptor and hCG-LH receptor complexes present in the ovine luteal cell. The diffusion constant for the LH receptor when occupied by oLH was 1.9×10^{-10} cm^2/second (Table V). This is in marked contrast to the diffusion constant for the same receptor when occupied by hCG. In this case, the mobility of the receptor in the membrane could not be measured but was $<1 \times 10^{-11}$ cm^2/second. Even when the duration of the study was extended dramatically we were unable to detect any movement of hCG–LH receptor complexes into the photobleached area, indicating that the hormone–receptor complex had been essentially immobilized in the membrane. That this unique property of hCG is dependent upon the carbohydrate portion of the molecule is suggested by the data obtained with the deglyco-hCG preparation. When the LH receptor was labeled with this preparation it had a diffusion constant equivalent to that observed when the receptor was occupied by oLH (Table V). Similarly, when the oLH

TABLE V

Lateral Diffusion of Receptors for LH when Occupied by Different Hormones[a]

Ligand[b]	Diffusion constant (cm²/second)	n
oLH	$1.9 \pm 0.6 \times 10^{-10}$	37
hCG	$<1 \times 10^{-11}$	31
Deglyco-hCG	$1.1 \pm 0.1 \times 10^{-10}$	9
hLH	$1.4 \pm 0.1 \times 10^{-10}$	12
S Con A[c]	$2.1 \pm 0.4 \times 10^{-10}$	7

[a] Data summarized from Niswender *et al.* (1985).
[b] All ligands were labeled with tetramethylrhodamine-B isothiocyanate.
[c] Succinylated concanavalin A.

receptor was occupied by hLH, the diffusion constant in the membrane tended to be similar to that observed with oLH. This observation was surprising since hLH is internalized at a much slower rate than oLH (Table III). Finally, when succinylated concanavalin A was used to monitor diffusion of glycoproteins in the membrane, the diffusion constant was 2.1×10^{-10} cm²/second, similar to that observed for oLH. This suggests that the receptor for LH in the ovine luteal cell has a lateral mobility within the membrane similar to that observed for other glycoproteins. This finding suggests that the binding of hCG to the receptor immobilizes the receptor in the plasma membrane. Further experiments will be required to determine the mechanisms involved in this immobilization of the LH receptor in the plasma membrane by hCG.

V. Types of Steroidogenic Luteal Cells

A. MORPHOLOGICAL DIFFERENCES

In several species the parenchyma of the corpus luteum consists of two distinct cell types (Corner, 1919; Warbritton, 1934; Mossman and Duke, 1973), both of which have been shown to secrete progesterone (Lemon and Loir, 1977; Ursely and Leymarie, 1979; Koos and Hansel, 1981; Fitz *et al.*, 1982; Rodgers and O'Shea, 1982). The most conspicious, but less numerous, of these is the large luteal cell (Donaldson and Hansel, 1965; Deane *et al.*, 1966; Priedkalns *et al.*, 1968; Lemon and Loir, 1977; O'Shea *et al.*, 1979; Ursely and Leymarie, 1979; Koos and Hansel, 1981; Fitz *et*

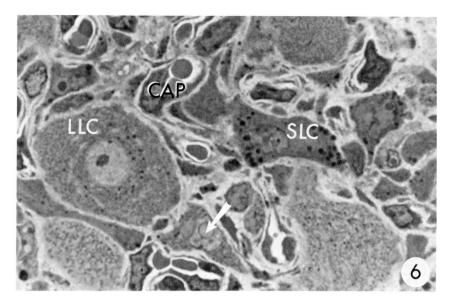

FIG. 6. In one micrometer thick sections stained with toluidine blue small luteal cells (SLC) can be easily distinguished from large luteal cells (LLC). Small luteal cells are usually spindle shaped, whereas LLC are typically spherical or polyhedral. In addition, the dark staining cytoplasm of SLC contains large lipid droplets. The nuclei of such cells sometimes possess cytoplasmic inclusions (arrow). Both cell types are in close apposition to capillaries (CAP). ×1000.

al., 1982) also referred to as granulosa-lutein (Sinha *et al.*, 1971; Mossman and Duke, 1973), Type II (Foley and Greenstein, 1958) or D (Wilkinson *et al.*, 1976) cell. In sheep, the diameter of cells classified as large luteal cells range from 22 to 35 μm, although cells with diameters greater than 35 μm are sometimes seen (Fitz *et al.*, 1982). In comparison, the diameter of cells classified as small luteal cells ranges from 12 to 22 μm (Fitz *et al.*, 1982; Rodgers and O'Shea, 1982). These cells are more numerous than large luteal cells (Niswender *et al.*, 1976; Fitz *et al.*, 1982; O'Shea *et al.*, 1979) and can be identified at the light microscopic level by their small size, characteristic spindle or elongated shape, darkly stained cytoplasm, large lipid droplets, and irregularly shaped nuclei that frequently contain what appear to be cytoplasmic inclusions (O'Shea *et al.*, 1979; Fig. 6). Although we have chosen to use the term small luteal cell, alternative terms include theca-lutein (Sinha *et al.*, 1971; Mossman and Duke, 1973), Type I (Foley and Greenstein, 1958) and/or I (Wilkinson *et al.*, 1976) cells. The relative contribution of each cell type to the corpus luteum has been examined using morphometric techniques. Although large luteal cells are fewer in number than small luteal cells, because of their large size they account for approximately 30% of the corpus luteum on a volume basis (Niswender *et al.*, 1976) compared to 16% for small luteal cells.

The ultrastructural characteristics of both large luteal cells (Deane *et al.*, 1966; Enders, 1973; Gulyas, 1984) and small luteal cells (O'Shea *et al.*, 1979) have been described and are consistent with those reported for other steroid-secreting cells (Christensen and Gillim, 1969). Although both types of luteal cells possess fine structural features typical of steroid-secreting cells (Figs. 7–9), the large luteal cell also has characteristics normally found in cells specialized for the secretion of polypeptides and/or proteins (Fawcett *et al.*, 1969). Thus, large luteal cells not only have numerous mitochondria and an abundance of smooth endoplasmic reticulum, consistent with a steroid-secreting function, but they also have an elaborate and extensive endomembrane system (i.e., numerous Golgi complexes, rough endoplasmic reticulum, secretory granules) consistent with a protein-secreting function as well.

The presence of electron dense, membrane-bound secretory granules that measure approximately 0.2 to 0.4 μm in diameter is one obvious distinguishing characteristic between large luteal cells and small luteal cells (Figs. 7–9). Such granules are abundant throughout the cytoplasm of large luteal cells, but are virtually absent in small luteal cells (Fig. 7). Although secretory granules overlap in size and appearance with lysosomes and peroxisomes, they represent a distinct class of cytoplasmic granule (Paavola and Christensen, 1981). They are released at the cell surface by exocytosis (Corteel, 1973; Gemmell *et al.*, 1974; Gemmell and Stacy, 1979; Sawyer *et al.*, 1979) and do not possess acid phosphatase or catalase activity (Gemmell *et al.*, 1974; McClellan *et al.*, 1977; Paavola and Christensen, 1981). The exocytotic release of these secretory granules is correlated with the secretion of progesterone, both *in vivo* (Gemmell *et al.*, 1974) and *in vitro* (Sawyer *et al.*, 1979). Several investigators (Corteel, 1973; Gemmell *et al.*, 1974; Sawyer *et al.*, 1979; Quirk *et al.*, 1979; Parry *et al.*, 1980) have suggested that these granules contain progesterone (and a progesterone binding protein) and represent a mechanism by which progesterone is actively secreted. However, others argue that once progesterone is synthesized it leaves the cell by diffusion (Enders, 1973; Carlson *et al.*, 1983). Rodgers *et al.* (1983a) and Wathes *et al.* (1983) have suggested that secretory granules present in the cytoplasm of large ovine cells contain oxytocin, while they appear to contain relaxin in rats (Anderson and Long, 1978; Anderson and Sherwood, 1984), pigs (Belt *et al.*, 1971; Kendall *et al.*, 1978; Fields, 1984), and cows (Fields *et*

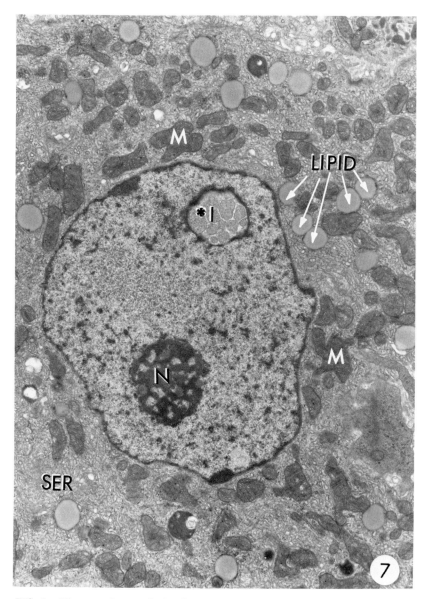

FIG. 7.   Electron micrograph showing a portion of a small luteal cell. The cytoplasm is characterized by an abundance of smooth endoplasmic reticulum (SER), numerous mitochondria (M), and lipid droplets. Besides the nucleolus (N), the nucleus contains what appears to be a cytoplasmic inclusion (I). ×9000.

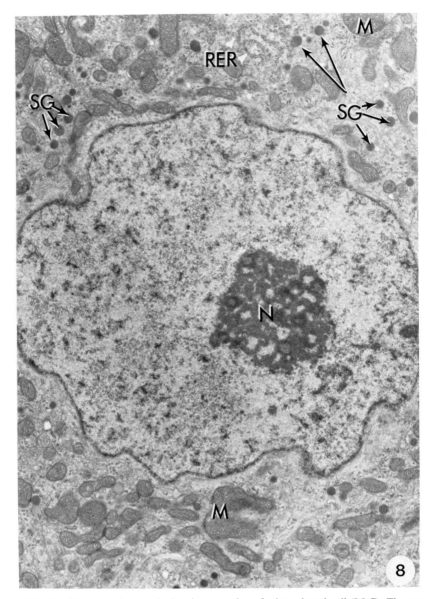

FIG. 8. Electron micrograph showing a portion of a large luteal cell (LLC). The presence of numerous electron-dense, membrane-bound secretory granules (SG) in the cytoplasm of LLC distinguishes these cells from small luteal cells (SLC; compare to Fig. 7). Note the absence of lipid droplets comparable to those found in SLC. Mitochondria (M), nucleolus (N), rough endoplasmic reticulum (RER). ×9000.

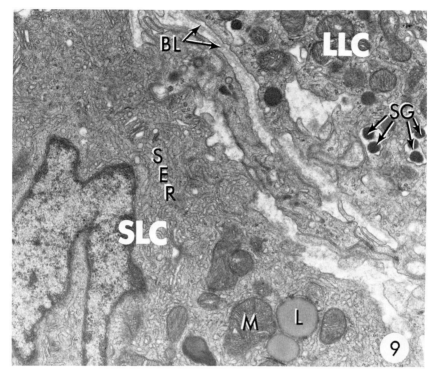

FIG. 9.   Both small (SLC) and large luteal cells (LLC) possess fine structural characteristics consistent with a steroid-secreting function. However, as illustrated in this figure, LLC also have characteristics typical of a protein secreting function and secretory granules (SG) are released at the cell surface via exocytosis. Moreover, LLC usually possess a more conspicuous basal lamina (BL) then do SLC. ×17,600.

al., 1980). It seems likely that there may be more than one protein present in granules in large luteal cells. Thus, while it is clear that large luteal cells contain secretory granules that are released at the cell surface via exocytosis, the precise chemical nature of the contents of such granules remains to be determined.

In addition to the presence of secretory granules, large luteal cells also differ from small luteal cells in that (1) the basal lamina surrounding large luteal cells is more prominent than that associated with small luteal cells (O'Shea *et al.,* 1979; Fig. 9), and (2) the surface of large luteal cells is characterized by the presence of numerous microvillous folds (Enders, 1973). Thus, although the two respective parenchymal cell types share many structural features they also display marked differences.

B.   BIOCHEMICAL DIFFERENCES

1.   Distribution of Receptors

In addition to morphological differences, small and large cells differ in several biochemical parameters (Fitz et al., 1982). One striking difference is the distribution of receptors between the cells (Table VI). There are numerous receptors for LH on small luteal cells, but very few on large cells. Conversely, large cells contain receptors for prostaglandins (PG) E_2 and $F_{2\alpha}$, whereas small cells do not. Receptors for estradiol are 5-fold more abundant in large luteal cells (Glass et al., 1985).

2.   Control of Steroidogenesis

Both large and small cells secrete progesterone, but the regulation of steroidogenesis in the two cell types appears to be quite different. In the unstimulated state, large cells secrete approximately 20 times as much progesterone as do small cells (Table VII). Particularly important is the observation that LH stimulates secretion of progesterone in small cells but has no effect on large cells. Similar observations have been made by others for luteal cells from sows (Ursely and Leymarie, 1979), cows (Lemon and Loir, 1977; Koos and Hansel, 1981) and ewes (Rodgers et al., 1983b). This is consistent with the finding that LH receptors are present almost exclusively on small cells. Since large cells produce much more progesterone than small cells, these data probably explain the relatively minor, short-term increase in serum concentrations of progesterone observed after a 1000-fold increase in serum levels of LH (Fig. 2).

In small cells, steroidogenesis can be stimulated by dibutyryl cAMP (Table VII) or by agents that activate adenylate cyclase, such as cholera

TABLE VI

Receptor Content of Ovine Luteal Cells during the Mid-Luteal Phase of the Estrous Cycle[a]

	Receptor sites/cell	
Hormone	Small cells	Large cells
LH	33260 ± 13928^b	3074 ± 5324
PGE_2	904 ± 1144^b	10955 ± 2428
$PGF_{2\alpha}$	2115 ± 975^b	68143 ± 14713
Estradiol	971 ± 298^b	8053 ± 1963

[a] Data summarized from Fitz et al. (1982) and Glass et al. (1985).

[b] When data from small cells were compared to data from large cells all values were different ($p < 0.01$).

TABLE VII
Progesterone Secretion by Ovine Luteal Cells[a]

	Progesterone (fg/cell/minute)	
	Small cells	Large cells
Basal	2.2 ± 1.0^b	42.3 ± 29.7
+ LH (10 ng/ml)	27.3 ± 8.8	50.8 ± 35.7
+ dibutyryl cAMP (10 mM)	19.7 ± 4.3	28.3 ± 21.7

[a] Data summarized from Fitz *et al.* (1982).
[b] Mean $\pm$ SEM for 7 experiments each performed in triplicate.

toxin and forskolin (Hoyer *et al.*, 1984). Thus, steroidogenesis in small cells is regulated in a cAMP-dependent manner. However, the mechanisms involved in regulating steroid secretion by large cells are not clear. Dibutyryl cAMP does not stimulate the secretion of progesterone from large cells (Table VII) nor does cholera toxin or forskolin (Table VIII), although these latter agents dramatically increase intracellular levels of cAMP and the secretion of cAMP into the incubation medium. Treatment

TABLE VIII
The Effects of oLH Cholera Toxin, and Forskolin on cAMP Accumulation in Cells and Media and Progesterone Secretion from Small and Large Luteal Cells[a]

	Percentage of control values[b]		
Agent	Intracellular cAMP	cAMP in medium	Progesterone in medium
Small cells			
oLH (100 ng/ml)	307^c	7681^c	471^c
Cholera toxin (100 ng/ml)	214^c	3185^c	330^c
Forskolin (50 μM)	324^c	17110^c	243^c
Large cells			
oLH (100 ng/ml)	135	74	131
Cholera toxin (100 ng/ml)	170^c	502^c	138
Forskolin (50 μM)	201^c	1920^c	113

[a] Data summarized from Hoyer *et al.* (1984).
[b] Mean increase for two separate experiments each performed in triplicate.
[c] Signifies a significant ($p < 0.05$) difference from control values.

of large luteal cells with cholera toxin or forskolin also enhances the occupancy of cAMP-dependent protein kinase by cAMP (Niswender and Hoyer, 1985), yet there is no concomitant increase in the secretion of progesterone. The simplest explanation for this observation is that the steroidogenic machinery in large cells is already functioning at maximum capacity and cannot be further stimulated. If, as discussed later, small steroidogenic luteal cells differentiate into large luteal cells, it is possible that during this differentiation the steroidogenic machinery of the cell becomes permanently turned on. However, progesterone secretion from large luteal cells can be stimulated by PGE_2 (Silvia et al., 1984b; Fitz et al., 1984) although this response does not appear to be mediated by activation of adenylate cyclase (Fitz et al., 1984). Previous studies have demonstrated an important role for calcium in the secretion of progesterone from ovine luteal tissue (Higuchi et al., 1976) and it is very likely that the calcium, calmodulin, lipid-dependent protein kinase C system is the primary steroidogenic regulatory system in large cells.

3. Secretion of Peptides and Proteins

The corpus luteum secretes a variety of protein and peptide hormones. Since only large cells have the intracellular organelles specialized for secretion of proteins and peptides, it seems likely that these cells are the source of these hormones. Oxytocin and vasopressin have been identified in luteal tissue from sheep (Wathes and Swann, 1982), women (Wathes et al., 1982) and cows (Wathes et al., 1983). Rodgers et al. (1983a) have shown that large ovine cells, but not small cells, contain oxytocin. Relaxin has been found in corpora lutea of rats (Steinetz et al., 1959; Anderson and Long, 1978; Anderson and Sherwood, 1984), pigs (Kendall et al., 1978; Fields, 1984), cows (Castro-Hernandez, 1975; Fields et al., 1980), humans (O'Byrne et al., 1978; Mathieu et al., 1981), and other species (for reviews see Schwabe et al., 1978; Bryant-Greenwood, 1982).

Small luteal cells, on the other hand, appear to have receptors for oxytocin since this peptide inhibits LH-stimulated progesterone secretion from these small cells (Mayan and Niswender, unpublished observation). These observations suggest that oxytocin may play a role in the cell-to-cell communication between the two cell types.

C. ONTOGENY OF LUTEAL CELLS

Because of the marked differences in the biochemical properties of large and small luteal cells, changes in the relative proportion of the two cell types during the estrous cycle may be an important means of regulating the function of the corpus luteum. Therefore, an experiment was conducted to determine the number of different cell types throughout the estrous cycle.

Corpora lutea were collected from normally cycling ewes on days 4, 6, 8, 12, and 16 of the estrous cycle and dissociated into single cells (Ahmed *et al.*, 1981). The cells were then suspended in a known volume of buffer and their concentration determined cytometrically. The total number of cells in each corpus luteum was calculated and the results are illustrated in Fig. 10. There was a 400% increase in the total number of cells between days 4 and 8, no change between days 8 and 12, and a 70% decrease by day 16.

To examine changes in the steroidogenic cell populations during the cycle, an aliquot of fixed cells was dried onto a microscope slide and stained for 3β-hydroxysteroid dehydrogenase (3HSD) activity by the method of Shaw *et al.* (1979). The presence of this enzyme, which converts pregnenolone to progesterone, is a good marker for the steroidogenic capacity of cells. Four randomly selected fields from each slide were photographed and the proportion of cells that were 3HSD positive was quantified. To calculate the number of 3HSD positive cells this proportion was multiplied by the total number of cells per corpus luteum. The number of steroidogenic cells increased several fold between days 4 and 8 of the estrous cycle and then decreased substantially by day 16 (Fig. 10). The percentages of cells that were 3HSD positive remained relatively

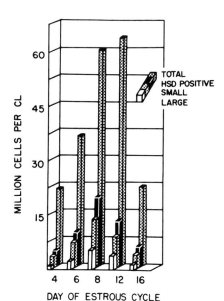

FIG. 10. The number of total, 3β-hydroxysteroid dehydrogenase (3HSD) positive, small and large steroidogenic luteal cells in ovine corpora lutea collected on different days of the estrous cycle. See text for details of the methods.

constant and was 20.9 ± 1.7 ($\overline{X}$ ± SEM), 26.0 ± 2.7, 31.4 ± 3.2, 20.2 ± 2.7 and 21.9 ± 4.4 on days 4, 6, 8, 12, and 16, respectively.

The diameter of all 3HSD positive cells in each photograph was measured using a Zeiss-Videoplan Image Analyzer to quantitate the number of large and small steroidogenic luteal cells. After correction for shrinkage due to fixation, those 3HSD positive cells with diameters greater than 22 μm were classifed as large luteal cells, and those less than 22 μm as small luteal cells. The number of both large and small steroidogenic luteal cells increased 4-fold through day 8 and then decreased through day 16 (Fig. 10), a pattern similar to that observed for the total cells per corpus luteum.

The size of nonsteroidogenic (3HSD negative) cells was also measured with the Zeiss-Videoplan Image Analyzer. On day 4, the mode of the size distribution of these cells was 8–10 μm, but by day 12 the mode was 6–8 μm (data not shown). Thus, it appeared that there was a shift toward smaller sizes as the cycle progressed. However, these data were calculated on a percentage basis, making it impossible to know whether the shift was due to a decrease in the number of cells larger than 8 μm or an increase in the number smaller than 8 μm. Therefore, the luteal content of cells larger and smaller than 8 μm was calculated from the total number of cells per corpus luteum, the proportion that were 3HSD negative, and the proportion of 3HSD negative in each size range. The results are shown in Fig. 11. The number of cells larger than 8 μm increased 2-fold between days 4 and 8, and progressively declined through day 16. In contrast, the

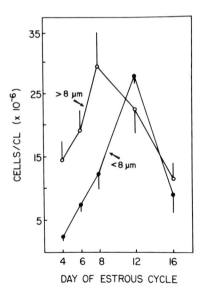

FIG. 11. The number of nonsteroidogenic luteal cells < 8 μ or > 8 μm in diameter in ovine corpora lutea collected on different days of the estrous cycle.

number of cells smaller than 8 μm did not reach a peak until day 12. It is interesting to speculate that the small nonsteroidogenic cells contain a population of stem cells that give rise to steroidogenic luteal cells. This concept is discussed in more detail below.

D. FOLLICULAR ORIGIN OF LUTEAL CELLS

The extent to which cells of the theca interna and granulosa layers in the follicle contribute to the corpus luteum has been a subject of debate for many years. In the late 1800s and early 1900s two schools of thought existed. One was that the granulosa cells degenerated shortly after ovulation and that cells of the theca interna developed into the corpus luteum. The other held just the opposite view—that the theca cells degenerated and the corpus luteum was derived solely from granulosa cells. In 1906, Loeb performed a detailed examination of luteinization in the guinea pig and concluded that both theca interna and granulosa cells become incorporated into the corpus luteum. Corner (1919) reached a similar conclusion for the sow, and subsequent studies have yielded the same result for the cow (McNutt, 1924; Donaldson and Hansel, 1965; Lobel and Levy, 1968; Priedkalns et al., 1968), ewe (O'Shea et al., 1980), rat (Pederson, 1951), and woman (Guraya, 1971).

Although it now is accepted that both theca and granulosa cells are incorporated into the corpus luteum of many species, the extent of their individual contributions remains unclear. Loeb (1906) concluded that cells from both the theca interna and the granulosa layer of the guinea pig follicle differentiated into large luteal cells. Pederson (1951) reached the same conclusion for the rat. In contrast, Dawson (1941) proposed that theca cells of the cat migrate into the granulosa layer, where they form the interstitial and connective tissue elements of the corpus luteum.

A popular, but unproven, hypothesis is that large luteal cells are derived from granulosa cells and small luteal cells are derived from theca interna cells. This has been proposed for the cow (Donaldson and Hansel, 1965; Priedkalns et al., 1968), ewe (McClellan et al., 1975; O'Shea et al., 1980), sow (Corner, 1919), and woman (Guraya, 1971). Donaldson and Hansel (1965) extended this hypothesis by proposing that theca cells develop into small luteal cells and that LH stimulates small luteal cells to develop into large luteal cells. This hypothesis is supported by the observation that under certain conditions theca cells will luteinize and acquire characteristics typical of large luteal cells (Cran, 1983).

One problem in obtaining quantitative data regarding the origin and fate of cell types in the corpus luteum is the difficulty in accurately identifying the follicular source of origin of the different cell types. After ovulation, the follicular wall becomes highly convoluted and the basement membrane, which clearly delineates cells of the theca interna from granulosa cells, disappears. One approach to distinguish theca interna from granulosa cells has been the use of alkaline phosphatase as a histochemical marker. In the pig (Corner, 1948) and the ewe (O'Shea *et al.*, 1980), cells of the theca interna stain positively for alkaline phosphatase, but granulosa cells do not. Thus, one can trace the fate of theca cells by following the distribution of the activity of this enzyme. Data obtained using this procedure led O'Shea *et al.* (1980) to conclude that theca cells develop into small luteal cells in the ewe. Unfortunately, the alkaline phosphatase method works for only a few species, such as the ewe and sow, in which the enzyme is limited to the theca layer. In addition, cell specificity is maintained for only the first 48 hours after ovulation in the ewe; at later times alkaline phosphatase activity is scattered throughout the corpus luteum. It is unclear whether this is due to the migration of theca-lutein cells or the acquisition of alkaline phosphatase by granulosa-lutein cells. In the pig, the reaction remains cell specific until the sixth week of pregnancy (Corner, 1948).

A novel approach to distinguishing theca-lutein from granulosa-lutein cells was the use of a monoclonal antibody that recognized a granulosa-specific antigen and another that recognized a theca-specific antigen (Alila, 1983). These antibodies were used in an indirect immunofluorescence procedure to follow the fate of granulosa and theca cells after ovulation. Early in the estrous cycle, most of the large luteal cells bound the granulosa antibody and very few bound the theca antibody. In contrast, most of the small cells bound the theca antibody and few bound the granulosa antibody. Late in the cycle, the proportion of large cells that bound the granulosa antibody was decreased and the proportion that bound the theca antibody was increased. The proportion of small luteal cells that bound the granulosa antibody remained low and the proportion that bound theca antibody remained as high as it was early in the cycle. These data support the model that theca cells become small luteal cells and that small luteal cells may develop into large luteal cells.

Interestingly, by days 16–18 only 76% of the large cells and 58% of the small cells bound either antibody. Thus, the cellular source of origin of 30–40% of the luteal cells is uncertain, although it is also possible that during luteinization or luteolysis, some theca-lutein and granulosa-lutein cells had lost the antigens being detected by the antibody.

A mechanism which could explain most of these observations is that the corpus luteum contains a population of stem cells which give rise to small steroidogenic luteal cells which in turn develop into large luteal cells. The large luteal cells may function for several days and then degenerate, as was proposed by Donaldson and Hansel (1965). Luteal regression would occur if the stem cell population became depleted or the differentiation of stem cells into small luteal cells was blocked hormonally.

Although this model is highly speculative, it is supported by several observations presented in this manuscript. The number of steroidogenic (Fig. 10) and nonsteroidogenic cells larger than 8 μm (Fig. 11) exhibits a similar pattern throughout the estrous cycle, reaching a maximum on day 8 and declining through day 16, whereas, the number of nonsteroidogenic cells smaller than 8 μm peaked on day 12. In terms of the model, these data could be interpreted to mean that nonsteroidogenic cells smaller than 8 μm grow to be larger than 8 μm and then acquire steroidogenic capacity, and that between days 8 and 12, the growth of small, nonsteroidogenic cells is blocked. Such a block would lead to an accumulation of precursor cells (< 8 μm) and a depletion of product cells (> 8 μm), which we have observed.

The model is also supported by several lines of indirect evidence. First, mitoses frequently are observed in stromal cells of the corpus luteum, but rarely in parenchymal cells (McClellan *et al.,* 1975) as is typical of a stem cell-differentiated system, such as the spermatogonia–spermatocyte system (Roosen-Runge, 1962). Second, cells intermediate in structure between small and large luteal cells have been observed in the sow (Corner, 1919) and cow (Foley and Greenstein, 1958). Our own data indicate that luteal cells of the ewe cover an entire spectrum of sizes, rather than occurring in two discrete modes. It should be noted that other investigators have found no cells of intermediate size in the ewe (O'Shea *et al.,* 1980) or woman (Guraya, 1971); however, O'Shea *et al.* (1980) did observe cells that were intermediate in size between fibroblasts and small luteal cells. This is suggestive evidence for a putative population of stem cells.

E. EFFECTS OF hCG ON THE SIZE DISTRIBUTION OF LUTEAL CELLS

Since it has been suggested that LH might stimulate the differentiation of small steroidogenic cells into large steroidogenic cells, an experiment was designed to determine the effects of injections of hCG on the size distribution of luteal cells during the mid-luteal phase of the estrous cycle.

Injections of hCG (300 IU) were given on day 8 of the cycle, the ewes were laparotomized on day 10 and corpora lutea from each ewe were

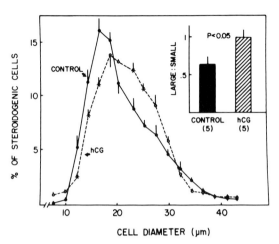

CELL DIAMETER (μm)

FIG. 12. The size distribution of steroidogenic luteal cells following dissociation of corpora lutea collected on day 10 of the estrous cycle from control and hCG-injected ewes. The inset depicts the large to small luteal cell ratio.

collected and individually dissociated into single cells (Fitz *et al.*, 1982). The total number of cells, the number of 3HSD positive cells and the number of large and small steroidogenic cells was determined.

A shift in the size distribution of steroidogenic cells occurred with hCG treatment (Fig. 12). There was a significant decrease in the proportion of cells in the 11 to 17 μm range when compared to corpora lutea obtained from control ewes, while there was a significant increase in the proportion of cells in the 21 to 27 μm cell size range (Fig. 12). The large cell to small cell ratio in the two groups was different ($p < 0.05$).

The results of this study are compatible with the hypothesis that LH or hCG can induce the differentiation of small steroidogenic luteal cells into large luteal cells. However, it was not possible from this study to conclude that the apparent shift in the diameter of luteal cells was associated with a shift in function of these cells since morphological, biochemical, and/or functional studies were not performed. The large luteal cell populations collected from the two groups of ewes need to be carefully compared biochemically and morphologically before these data can be meaningfully interpreted.

F.   CELLULAR SOURCE OF PROGESTERONE DURING THE MID-LUTEAL PHASE OF THE ESTROUS CYCLE

Finally, since the number of large and small luteal cells during the mid-luteal phase of the estrous cycle (Fig. 10) and the relative ability of these

FIG. 13. Serum levels of LH and the percentage of progesterone secreted by small luteal cells over a 4-hour period typical of the mid-luteal phase of the estrous cycle. See text for method of calculation.

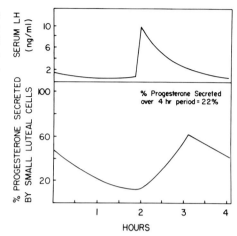

cells to produce progesterone (Fig. 4; Table VII) with and without LH were known, it was possible to calculate the percent of the progesterone present in blood which was secreted by small cells (Fig. 13). For the calculations we assumed a single episodic release of LH once every 4 hours resulting in peak levels of 10 ng/ml in serum (Goodman and Karsch, 1980). We also assumed a constant basal secretion of progesterone from large cells, without consideration of enhanced secretion of progesterone by these cells due to the stimulatory actions of PGE_2 or other factors. The contribution of small cells to the total amount of progesterone being secreted ranged from 12 to 63%, with a total contribution over the 4-hour period of 22%. This estimation of 22% of the progesterone being secreted by small cells is likely to be an overestimate. Clearly most of the progesterone secreted by the ovine corpus luteum is from large cells which are not under the direct control of LH.

VI. Summary

Data have been presented which suggest that the number of luteal receptors for LH, but not circulating concentrations of LH, is highly correlated with serum levels of progesterone throughout the estrous cycle of ewes. "Down-regulation" of receptors for LH depends upon occupancy of the receptor, based on the high correlation between the number of receptors occupied and the number lost after administration of 1 mg of LH *in vivo*. The major pathway for loss of hCG or LH bound to the luteal receptor for LH is via internalization and degradation of the hormone. Over 80% of ^{125}I-labeled hCG bound to luteal cells in culture is internalized and degraded. Somewhat less ^{125}I-labeled oLH is internalized and degraded apparently because more of this hormone dissociates from the receptor. A major portion of the internalized population of receptors is recycled to the plasma membrane.

The receptor for LH in ovine luteal cells responds quite differently when occupied by oLH versus hCG. The steroidogenic response to a 15-minute pulse of hCG is prolonged and similar to that observed with constant exposure to hCG. The response to a 15-minute pulse of oLH, on the other hand, is much shorter. The apparent reason for the prolonged response to hCG appears to be the reduced rate of internalization of this hormone ($t_{\frac{1}{2}} = 22.8$ hours) compared to oLH ($t_{\frac{1}{2}} = 0.4$ hours). These data also suggest that internalization of the hormone–receptor complex is one of the mechanisms used by the cell to terminate hormonally stimulated steroidogenesis and is not a component of the mechanism of action for these hormones. The slow rate of internalization of the hCG–LH receptor complex appears to be due to immobilization of the LH receptor in the plasma membrane as a result of occupancy by hCG.

Finally, two distinct populations of steroidogenic luteal cells were characterized. The cells have both shared and different morphological characteristics. They differ in size and the large (>22 μm in diameter) luteal cells have the intracellular organelles necessary to synthesize, package, and secrete proteins. The biochemical characteristics of the two cell types also differ. Small cells contain receptors for LH and probably oxytocin, and progesterone synthesis appears to be regulated by a cAMP-dependent mechanism. Large luteal cells have few, if any, receptors for LH, but contain receptors for PGE_2, $PGF_{2\alpha}$, and most of the luteal receptors for estradiol. Large luteal cells secrete proteins which include relaxin and oxytocin, depending upon the species and reproductive state. Initially, follicular granulosa cells appear to develop into large luteal cells while cells of the theca interna develop into small luteal cells. However, data are presented which suggest that small luteal cells can differentiate into large luteal cells and that LH may be one of the factors which controls this process. Further elucidation of the cell-to-cell and hormonal interactions responsible for regulation of luteal function in domestic ruminants should provide new insights into mechanisms which can be regulated for the synchronization of estrus and prevention of embryonic mortality. There is considerable evidence which suggests that many of the concepts discussed regarding the regulation of luteal function in ruminants may be applicable to primates. If this proves to be true it may form the basis for development of improved methods of contraception and/or treatments to prevent embryonic loss due to inadequate luteal function.

ACKNOWLEDGMENTS

We want to thank our many colleagues including Carol Ahmed, Rupert Amann, George Barisas, Robert Bourdage, Mark Diekman, Paul Fletcher, Patricia Hoyer, Hans Mayan, Edward Mock, Terry Nett, Harold Papkoff, Leo Reichert, Debra Roess, Robert Ryan, and Diane Suter for their contributions to this research. This research has been supported by grants from NIH (HD11590, HD07031, HD06254) and the Colorado Experiment Station.

REFERENCES

Ahmed, C. E., Sawyer, H. R., and Niswender, G. D. (1981). *Endocrinology* **109**, 1380.
Alila, H. W. (1983). *Biol. Reprod.* **28** (Suppl. 1), Abstr. No. 55.
Amoroso, E. C. (1951). *J. Anat.* **85**, 428.
Amsterdam, A., Kohen, F., Nimrod, A., and Lindner, H. R. (1979). *Adv. Exp. Med. Biol.* **112**, 69.
Anderson, M. L., and Long, J. A. (1978). *Biol. Reprod.* **18**, 110.
Anderson, M. L., and Sherwood, O. D. (1984). *Endocrinology* **114**, 1124.
Ascoli, M., and Puett, D. (1978). *J. Biol Chem.* **253**, 4892.
Astwood, E. B. (1941). *Endocrinology* **28**, 309.
Baird, D. T. (1978). *Biol. Reprod.* **18**, 359.
Barcikowski, B., Carlson, J. C., Wilson, L., and McCracken, J. A. (1974). *Endocrinology* **95**, 1340.
Behrman, H. R., Luborsky-Moore, J. L., Pang, C. Y., Wright, K., and Dorflinger, L. J. (1979). *Adv. Exp. Med. Biol.* **112**, 557.
Belt, W. D., Anderson, L. L., Cavazos, L. F., and Melampy, R. M. (1971). *Endocrinology* **89**, 1.
Bergstrom, S., Carlson, L. A., and Weeks, J. R. (1968). *Pharmacol. Rev.* **20**, 1.
Birken, S., and Canfield, R. E. (1978). *In* "Structure and Function of the Gonadotropins" (K. W. McKerns, ed.), p. 47. Plenum, New York.
Boshier, D. P. (1969). *J. Reprod. Fertil.* **19**, 51.
Bourdage, R. J., Fitz, T. A., and Niswender, G. D. (1984). *Proc. Soc. Exp. Biol. Med.* **175**, 483.
Brunner, M. A., Donaldson, L. E., and Hansel, W. (1969). *J. Dairy Sci.* **52**, 1849.
Bryant-Greenwood, G. D. (1982). *Endocrinol. Rev.* **3**, 62.
Carlson, J. C., Gruber, M. Y., and Thompson, J. E. (1983). *Endocrinology* **113**, 190.
Carpenter, G., and Cohen, S. (1976). *J. Cell Biol.* **71**, 159.
Castro-Hernandez, A. (1975). Thesis, University of Florida, Gainesville.
Catt, K. J., and Pierce, J. G. (1978). *In* "Reproductive Endocrinology—Physiology, Pathophysiology, and Clinical Management" (S. S. C. Yen and R. B. Jaffe, eds.), p. 34. Saunders, Philadelphia.
Cerini, M., Findlay, J. K., and Lawson, R. A. S. (1976). *J. Reprod. Fertil.* **46**, 65.
Chen, T. T., Abel, J. H., Jr., McClellan, M. C., Sawyer, H. R., Diekman, M. A., and Niswender, G. D. (1977). *Cytobiologie* **14**, 412.
Christensen, A. K., and Gillim, S. W. (1969). *In* "The Gonads" (K. W. McKerns, ed.), p. 415. Appleton, New York.
Colcord, M. L., Hoyer, G. L., and Weems, C. W. (1978). *Annu. Meet. Am. Soc. Anim. Sci.,* *70th* p. 352.
Conn, P. M., Conti, M., Harwood, J. P., Dufau, M. L., and Catt, K. J. (1978). *Nature* (*London*) **274**, 598.

Conti, M., Harwood, J. P., Hsueh, A. J. W., Dufau, M. L., and Catt, K. J. (1976). *J. Biol. Chem.* **251**, 7729.

Conti, M., Harwood, J. P., Dufau, M. L., and Catt, K. J. (1977a). *Mol. Pharmacol.* **13**, 1024.

Conti, M., Harwood, J. P., Dufau, M. L., and Catt, K. J. (1977b). *J. Biol. Chem.* **252**, 8869.

Corner, G. W. (1919). *Am. J. Anat.* **26**, 117.

Corner, G. W. (1947). "The Hormones in Human Reproduction." Princeton Univ. Press, Princeton, New Jersey.

Corner, G. W. (1948). *Carnegie Inst., Washington* (Contributions to Embryology) **32**, 1.

Corner, G. W., and Allen, W. M. (1929). *Am. J. Physiol.* **88**, 326.

Corteel, M. (1973). *Ann. Biol. Anim. Biochim. Biophys. Suppl.* **13**, 249.

Cran, D. G. (1983). *J. Reprod. Fertil.* **67**, 415.

Dawson, A. B. (1941). *Anat. Rec.* **79**, 155.

Deane, H. W., Hay, M. F., Moor, R. M., Rowson, L. E. A., and Short, R. V. (1966). *Acta Endocrinol.* **51**, 245.

Denamur, R., and Mauleon, P. (1963). *C.R. Acad. Sci. (Paris)* **257**, 527.

Diekman, M. A., O'Callaghan, P. L., Nett, T. M., and Niswender, G. D. (1978a). *Biol. Reprod.* **19**, 999.

Diekman, M. A., O'Callaghan, P. L., Nett, T. M., and Niswender, G. D. (1978b). *Biol. Reprod.* **19**, 1010.

Domanski, E., Skrzeczkowski, L., Stupnicka, E., Fitko, R., and Dobrowolski, W. (1967). *J. Reprod. Fertil.* **14**, 365.

Donaldson, L., and Hansel, W. (1965). *J. Dairy Sci.* **48**, 905.

Donaldson, L. E., Hansel, W., and Van Vleck, L. D. (1965). *J. Dairy Sci.* **48**, 331.

Dunham, E. W., Haddox, M. K., and Goldberg, N. D. (1974). *Proc. Natl. Acad. Sci. U.S.A.* **71**, 815.

Ellinwood, W. E., Nett, T. M., and Niswender, G. D. (1979). *Biol. Reprod.* **21**, 845.

Ellis, S. (1961). *Endocrinology* **68**, 334.

Enders, A. C. (1973). *Biol. Reprod.* **8**, 158.

Evrard, M., Leboulleux, P., and Hermier, C. (1978). *Prostaglandins* **16**, 491.

Fawcett, D. W., Long, J. A., and Jones, A. L. (1969). *Recent Prog. Horm. Res.* **25**, 315.

Fields, P. A. (1984). *Biol. Reprod.* **30** (Suppl. 1), Abstr. No. 172.

Fields, M. J., Fields, P. A., Castro-Hernandez, A., and Larkin, L. H. (1980). *Endocrinology* **107**, 869.

Fitz, T. A., Mayan, M. H., Sawyer, H. R., and Niswender, G. D. (1982). *Biol. Reprod.* **27**, 703.

Fitz, T. A., Hoyer, P. B., and Niswender, G. D. (1984). *Prostaglandins* **28**, 19.

Fletcher, P. W., and Niswender, G. D. (1982). *Prostaglandins* **23**, 803.

Foley, R. C., and Greenstein, J. S. (1958). *In* "Reproduction and Infertility" (F. X. Gassner, ed.), p. 88. Pregamon, Oxford.

Fraenkel, L., and Cohn, F. (1901). *Anat. Anzeiger* **20**, 294.

Fuller, G. B., and Hansel, W. (1970). *J. Anim. Sci.* **31**, 99.

Gavin, J. R., III, Roth, J., Neville, D. M., Jr., DeMeyts, P., and Buell, D. N. (1974). *Proc. Natl. Acad. Sci. U.S.A.* **71**, 84.

Gemmell, R. T., and Stacy, B. D. (1979). *Cell Tissue Res.* **197**, 413.

Gemmell, R. T., Stacy, B. D., and Thorburn, G. D. (1974). *Biol. Reprod.* **11**, 447.

Glass, J. D., Fitz, T. A., and Niswender, G. D. (1985). *Biol. Reprod.* **31**, 967.

Goding, J. R. (1974). *J. Reprod. Fertil.* **38**, 261.

Goldstein, J. L., Anderson, R. G. W., and Brown, M. S. (1979). *Nature (London)* **279**, 679.

Goodman, R. L., and Karsch, F. J. (1980). *Endocrinology* **107**, 1286.

Gulyas, B. J. (1984). *In* "Ultrastructure of Endocrine Cells and Tissues" (P. M. Motta, ed.), p. 238. Nijhoff, The Hague.

Guraya, S. S. (1971). *Physiol. Rev.* **51**, 785.

Hacik, T., and Kolena, J. (1975). *Endokrinologie* **66**, 15.

Haigler, H. T., Maxfield, F. R., Willingham, M. C., and Pastan, I. (1980). *J. Biol. Chem.* **255**, 1239.

Han, S. S., Rajaniemi, H. J., Cho, M. I., Hirschfield, A. N., and Midgley, A. R., Jr. (1974). *Endocrinology* **95**, 589.

Hansel, W. (1967). *In* "Reproduction in the Female Mammal" (G. E. Lamming and E. C. Amoroso, eds.), p. 346. Butterworths, London.

Hansel, W. (1971). *In* "Karolinska Symposia on Research Methods in Reproductive Endocrinology", 3rd Symposium: In Vitro Methods in Reproductive Cell Biology, (E. Diczfalusy, ed.), p. 295. Peratica, Copenhagen.

Hansel, W., Concannon, P. W., and Lukaszewska, J. H. (1973). *Biol. Reprod.* **8**, 222.

Haour, F., and Saez, J. M. (1977). *Mol. Cell. Endocrinol.* **7**, 17.

Henderson, K. M., Scaramuzzi, R. J., and Baird, D. T. (1977). *J. Endocrinol.* **72**, 379.

Higuchi, T., Kaneko, A., Abel, J. H., Jr., and Niswender, G. D. (1976). *Endocrinology* **99**, 1023.

Hixon, J. E., and Clegg, M. T. (1969). *Endocrinology* **84**, 828.

Hixon, J. E., and Hansel, W. (1974). *Biol. Reprod.* **11**, 543.

Hoffman, B., Schams, D., Bopp, R., Ender, M. L., Gimenez, T., and Karg, H. (1974). *J. Reprod. Fertil.* **40**, 77.

Horton, E. W., and Poyser, N. L. (1976). *Physiol. Rev.* **56**, 595.

Hoyer, P. B., Fitz, T. A., and Niswender, G. D. (1984). *Endocrinology* **114**, 604.

Hsueh, A. J. W., Dufau, M. L., and Catt, K. J. (1976). *Biochem. Biophys. Res. Commun.* **72**, 1145.

Hsueh, A. J. W., Dufau, M. L., and Catt, K. J. (1977). *Proc. Natl. Acad. Sci. U.S.A.* **74**, 592.

Inskeep, E. K., Smutny, W. J., Butcher, R. L., and Pexton, J. E. (1975). *J. Anim. Sci.* **41**, 1098.

Kaltenbach, C. C., Cook, B., Niswender, G. D., and Nalbandov, A. V. (1967). *Endocrinology* **81**, 1407.

Kaltenbach, C. C., Graber, J. W., Niswender, G. D., and Nalbandov, A. V. (1968). *Endocrinology* **82**, 818.

Kaltenbach, C. C., Barrett, S., Funder, J. W., Mole, B. J., Aldridge, R. A., and Goding, J. R. (1969). *Proc. Soc. Study Reprod.*

Karsch, F. J., Cook, B., Ellicott, A. R., Foster, D. L., Jackson, G. L., and Nalbandov, A. V. (1971a). *Endocrinology* **89**, 272.

Karsch, F. J., Roche, J. F., Noveroske, J. W., Foster, D. L., Norton, H. W., and Nalbandov, A. V. (1971b). *Biol. Reprod.* **4**, 129.

Kendall, J. Z., Plopper, L. G., and Bryant-Greenwood, G. D. (1978). *Biol. Reprod.* **18**, 94.

Koos, R. D., and Hansel, W. (1981). *In* "Dynamics of Ovarian Function" (N. B. Schwartz and M. Hunzicker-Dunn, eds.), p. 197. Raven, New York.

Land, R. B., Baird, D. T., and Scaramuzzi, R. J. (1976). *J. Reprod. Fertil.* **47**, 209.

Lee, C. Y., Coulam, C. B., Jiang, N. S., and Ryan, R. J. (1973). *J. Clin. Endocrinol. Metab.* **36**, 148.

Lee, C. Y., Kayako, T., Ryan, R. J., and Jiang, N. S. (1975). *Proc. Soc. Exp. Biol. Med.* **148**, 505.

Lemon, M., and Loir, M. (1977). *J. Endocrinol.* **72**, 351.

Lewis, G. S., Wilson, L., Jr., Wilks, J. W., Pexton, J. E., Fogwell, R. L., Ford, S. P., Butcher, R. L., Thayne, W. V., and Inskeep, E. K. (1977). *J. Anim. Sci.* **45**, 320.

Lobel, B. L., and Levy, E. (1968). *Acta Endocrinol. Suppl.* **132**, 7.

Loeb, L. (1906). *J. Am. Med. Assoc.* **46**, 416.

McClellan, M. C., Diekman, M. A., Abel, J. H., Jr., and Niswender, G. D. (1975). *Cell. Tissue Res.* **164**, 291.

McClellan, M. C., Abel, J. H., Jr., and Niswender, G. D. (1977). *Biol. Reprod.* **16**, 499.

McCracken, J. A. (1971). *Ann. N.Y. Acad. Sci.* **180**, 456.

McCracken, J. A., Baird, D. T., and Goding, J. R. (1971). *Recent Prog. Horm. Res.* **27**, 537.

McKanna, J. A., Haigler, H. T., and Cohen, S. (1979). *Proc. Natl. Acad. Sci. U.S.A.* **76**, 5689.

McNutt, G. W. (1924). *J. Am. Vet. Med. Assoc.* **65**, 556.

Magness, R. P., Huie, J. M., and Weems, C. W. (1978). *J. Anim. Sci.* **46** (Suppl. 1), 376 (Abstr. No. 401).

Mapletoft, R. J., DelCampo, M. R., and Ginther, O. J. (1975). *Proc. Soc. Exp. Biol. Med.* **150**, 129.

Mapeltoft, R. J., Lapin, D. K., and Ginther, O. J. (1976). *Biol. Reprod.* **15**, 414.

Marsh, J. M. (1971). *Ann. N.Y. Acad. Sci.* **180**, 416.

Mathieu, Ph., Rahier, J., and Thomas, K. (1981). *Cell Tissue Res.* **219**, 213.

Mendelson, C., Dufau, M., and Catt, K. (1975). *J. Biol. Chem.* **250**, 8818.

Mock, E. J., and Niswender, G. D. (1983). *Endocrinology* **113**, 259.

Mock, E. J., Papkoff, H., and Niswender, G. D. (1983). *Endocrinology* **113**, 265.

Moor, R. M., and Rowson, L. E. A. (1966). *J. Endocrinol.* **34**, 497.

Mossman, H. W., and Duke, K. L. (1973). *Handb. Physiol. Endocrinol.* **II**, 389.

Nalbandov, A. V. (1973). *Handb. Physiol. Endocrinol.* **II**, 153.

Nett, T. M., McClellan, M. C., and Niswender, G. D. (1976a). *Biol. Reprod.* **15**, 66.

Nett, T. M., Staigmiller, R. B., Akbar, A. M., Diekman, M. A., Ellinwood, W. E., and Niswender, G. D. (1976b). *J. Anim. Sci.* **42**, 876.

Niswender, G. D. (1974). *Endocrinology* **94**, 612.

Niswender, G. D., and Hoyer, P. B. (1985). *Can. J. Physiol. Pharmacol.,* in press.

Niswender, G. D., Reimers, T. J., Diekman, M. A., and Nett, T. M. (1976). *Biol. Reprod.* **14**, 64.

Niswender, G. D., Sawyer, H. R., Chen, T. T., and Endres, D. B. (1980). *In* "Advances in Sex Hormone Research" (J. A. Thomas and R. L. Singhal, eds.), p. 153. Urban & Schwarzenberg, Baltimore.

Niswender, G. D., Fletcher, P. W., Ahmed, C. E., Sawyer, H. R., and Reichert, L. E., Jr. (1982). *In* "Perspectives in Differentiation and Hypertrophy" (W. Anderson and W. Sadler, eds.), p. 235. Elsevier, Amsterdam.

Niswender, G. D., Roess, D. A., Sawyer, H. R., Silvia, W. J., and Barisas, B. G. (1985). *Endocrinology,* **116**, 164.

O'Byrne, E. M., Flitcraft, J. F., Sawyer, W. K., Hochman, J., Weiss, G., and Steinetz, B. G. (1978). *Endocrinology* **102**, 1641.

O'Shea, J. D., Cran, D. G., and Hay, M. F. (1979). *J. Anat.* **128**, 239.

O'Shea, J. D., Cran, D. G., and Hay, M. F. (1980). *Cell Tissue Res.* **210**, 305.

Paavola, L. G., and Christensen, A. K. (1981). *Biol. Reprod.* **25**, 203.

Parry, D. M., Wilcox, D. L., and Thorburn, G. D. (1980). *J. Reprod. Fertil.* **60**, 349.

Peacock, J. S., and Barisas, B. G. (1981). *J. Immunol.* **1297**, 900.

Pederson, E. S. (1951). *Am. J. Anat.* **88**, 397.

Pexton, J. E., Ford, S. P., Wilson, L., Jr., Butcher, R. L., and Inskeep, E. K. (1975a). *J. Anim. Sci.* **41**, 144.

Pexton, J. E., Weems, C. W., and Inskeep, E. K. (1975b). *Prostaglandins* **9**, 501.
Piacsek, B. E., and Huth, J. F. (1971). *Proc. Soc. Exp. Biol. Med.* **138**, 1022.
Poyser, N. L. (1973). *In* "Clinics in Endocrinology and Metabolism" (J. Loraine, ed.), Vol. 2, No. 3, p. 393. Saunders, Philadelphia.
Pratt, B. R., Butcher, R. L., and Inskeep, E. K. (1977). *J. Anim. Sci.* **45**, 784.
Priedkalns, J., and Weber, A. F. (1968). *Z. Zellforsch.* **91**, 554.
Priedkalns, J., Weber, A. F., and Zemjanis, R. (1968). *Z. Zellforsch.* **85**, 501.
Quirk, S. J., Wilcox, D. L., Parry, D. M., and Thorburn, G. D. (1979). *Biol. Reprod.* **20**, 1133.
Rao, Ch. V., Estergreen, V. L., Carman, F. R., Moss, G. E., and Frandle, K. A. (1976). *Int. Cong. Endocrinol., 5th* Abstr.
Rao, Ch. V., Griffin, L. P., and Carman, F. R. (1977). *Am. J. Obstet. Gynecol.* **128**, 146.
Reimers, T. J., and Niswender, G. D. (1975). *In* "Immunization with Hormones in Reproductive Research" (E. Nieschlag, ed.), p. 95. North-Holland Publ., Amsterdam.
Rodgers, R. J., and O'Shea, J. D. (1982). *Aust. J. Biol. Sci.* **35**, 441.
Rodgers, R. J., O'Shea, J. D., Findlay, J. K., Flint, A. P. F., and Sheldrick, E. L. (1983a). *Endocrinology* **113**, 2302.
Rodgers, R. J., O'Shea, J. D., and Findlay, J. K. (1983b). *J. Reprod. Fertil.* **69**, 113.
Roosen-Runge, E. C. (1962). *Biol. Rev.* **37**, 343.
Roser, J. F., and Evans, J. W. (1983). *Biol. Reprod.* **29**, 499.
Sawyer, H. R., Abel, J. H., Jr., McClellan, M. C., Schmitz, M., and Niswender, G. D. (1979). *Endocrinology* **104**, 476.
Schlessinger, J., Shechter, Y., Willingham, M. C., and Pastan, I. (1978). *Proc. Natl. Acad. Sci. U.S.A.* **75**, 2659.
Schroff, C., Klindt, J. M., Kaltenbach, C. C., Graber, J. W., and Niswender, G. D. (1971). *J. Anim. Sci.* **33**, 268.
Schwabe, C., Steinetz, B., Weiss, G., Segaloff, A., McDonald, J. K., O'Byrne, E., Hochman, J., Carriere, B., and Goldsmith, L. (1978). *Recent Prog. Horm. Res.* **34**, 123.
Segaloff, D. L., Puett, D., and Ascoli, M. (1981). *Endocrinology* **108**, 632.
Sharpe, R. M. (1976). *Nature (London)* **264**, 644.
Sharpe, R. M. (1977). *Biochem. Biophys. Res. Commun.* **75**, 711.
Shaw, M. J., Georgopoulos, L. E., and Payne, A. H. (1979). *Endocrinology* **104**, 912.
Silvia, W. J., Ottobre, J. S., and Inskeep, E. K. (1984a). *Biol. Reprod.* **30**, 936.
Silvia, W. J., Fitz, T. A., Mayan, M. H., and Niswender, G. D. (1984b). *Anim. Reprod. Sci.* **7**, 57.
Simmons, K. R., and Hansel, W. (1964). *J. Anim. Sci.* **23**, 136.
Simmons, K. R., Caffrey, J. L., Phillips, J. L., Abel, J. H., Jr., and Niswender, G. D. (1976). *Proc. Soc. Exp. Biol. Med.* **152**, 366.
Sinha, A. A., Seal, U. S., and Doe, R. P. (1971). *Am. J. Anat.* **132**, 189.
Smith, V. R., McShan, W. H., and Casida, L. E. (1957). *J. Dairy Sci.* **40**, 443.
Snook, R. B., Brunner, M. A., Saatman, R. R., and Hansel, W. (1969). *Biol. Reprod.* **1**, 49.
Solano, A. R., Vela, A. G., Catt, K. J., and Dufau, M. L. (1980). *FEBS Lett.* **122**, 184.
Speroff, L., and Ramwell, P. W. (1970). *J. Clin. Endocrinol. Metab.* **30**, 345.
Spicer, L. J., Ireland, J. J., and Roche, J. F. (1981). *Biol. Reprod.* **25**, 832.
Steinetz, B. G., Beach, V. L., and Kroc, R. L. (1959). *In* "Recent Progress in Endocrinology of Reproduction" (C. H. Lloyd, ed.), p. 389. Academic Press, New York.
Suter, D. E., and Niswender, G. D. (1983). *Endocrinology* **112**, 838.
Suter, D. E., Fletcher, P. W., Sluss, P. M., Reichert, L. E., Jr., and Niswender, G. D. (1980). *Biol. Reprod.* **22**, 205.
Szego, C. M., and Gitin, E. S. (1964). *Nature (London)* **201**, 682.

Thibault, C. (1966). *J. Reprod. Fertil. Suppl.* **1,** 63.

Thorburn, G. D., Cox, R. I., Currie, W. B., Restall, B. J., and Schneider, W. (1973). *J. Reprod. Fertil. Suppl.* **18,** 151.

Tsuruhara, T., Dufau, M. L., Cigorraga, S., and Catt, K. J. (1977). *J. Biol. Chem.* **252,** 9002.

Ursely, J., and Leymarie, P. (1979). *J. Endocrinol.* **83,** 303.

Warbritton, V. (1934). *J. Morphol.* **56,** 181.

Wathes, D. C., and Swann, R. W. (1982). *Nature (London)* **297,** 225.

Wathes, D. C., Pickering, B. T., Swan, R. W., Porter, D. G., Hull, M. G. R., and Drife, J. O. (1982). *Lancet* **2,** 410.

Wathes, D. C., Swann, R. W., Birkett, S. D., Porter, D. G., and Pickering, B. T. (1983). *Endocrinology* **113,** 693.

Wilkinson, R. F., Anderson, E., and Aalberg, J. (1976). *J. Ultrastruct. Res.* **57,** 168.

Willingham, M. C., Hanover, J. A., Dickson, R. B., and Pastan, I. (1984). *Proc. Natl. Acad. Sci. U.S.A.* **81,** 175.

Wilson, L., Jr., Butcher, R. L., and Inskeep, E. K. (1972). *Prostaglandins* **1,** 479.

Wurtman, R. J. (1964). *Endocrinology* **75,** 927.

DISCUSSION

W. Hansel: I'd like to show some figures on our work on the bovine corpus luteum. Let me say at the outset that most of the things that Dr. Niswender has talked about in the ewe are also true for the cow. But there are some differences. For example, we think that the luteotropin for the large luteal cell in the cow is prostacyclin (PGI_2) rather than PGE. PGE will cause an increase in progesterone secretion but our workers sing a song that goes "anything that E can do, I can do better." Probably, both PGE and PGI_2 bind to the same receptor, but the cow corpus produces large amounts of PGI_2 and the tissue contains more PGI_2 receptors than any other tissue studied to date (Fig. A).

A lot of our recent work, as you might guess from what has already said, is an attempt to rationalize some new concepts of control of steroidogenesis with the older ideas of cAMP controlled steroid secretion. A new, rapidly evolving concept is that increased intracellular calcium, mediated by inositol phosphate (IP_3), and C-kinase, activated by diacylglycerol combine to increase progesterone synthesis. We are testing the concept that this mechanism is responsible for mediating steroidogenesis in the large luteal cells, which, as has been indicated, do not respond to LH. Calcium-dependent steroidogenesis occurs in bovine placental cells (Shemesh *et al.*, *PNAS* **81,** 1984, in press) and probably in cells of the zona glomerulosa, which produce aldosterone in the bovine adrenal (Capponi, A. M. *et al.*, *J. Biol. Chem.* **259,** 8863, 1984). These are the only two tissues where it is known that steroidogenesis is strongly influenced by this second messenger system.

In the cow, as in the sheep, theca-derived small luteal cells appear to develop into large luteal cells (Alila and Hansel, *Biol. Reprod.* **30,** 1015, 1984). As was previously mentioned, we have made highly specific monoclonal antibodies to cell surface antigens of the large and the small bovine luteal cells, and labeled these with fluorescent compounds. Using these fluorescent antibodies, we were able to count the number of cells throughout the estrous cycle and pregnancy that originated from the theca and from the granulosa cells of the follicle. As may be seen in Fig. B, all of the small cells and the one large (green-staining) cell in the center are of thecal origin. The large orange-staining cells are of granulosa origin. These antibodies do not change as long as cells of that origin are produced. By the 100th day of pregnancy there are no longer any granulosa-derived cells left in the bovine corpus luteum. Thus, these cells have a limited life span and during most of pregnancy all of the cells are derived from theca cells.

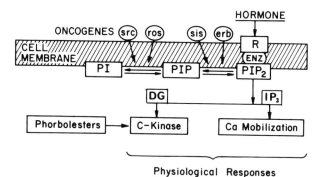

FIG. A. Proposed model for the role of polyphosphoinositides in receptor mediated hormone action. Inositol triphosphate (PIP₂) is split into diacyclglycerol (DG), which activates protein kinase C and inositol triphosphate (IP₃) which increases intracellular Ca²⁺. The phonbol esters also activate kinase C. (Adapted from Nishizuka, *Proc. Int. Cong. Endocrinol. 7th,* Exerpta Medica International Congress Series 652, p. 8, 1984.)

Table A shows some preliminary data on the effects of agents that increase intracellular calcium on progesterone production by the small cells. To date, we have not been able to get a really good large cell preparation and, in any event, large cell preparations separated on the basis of size or density will contain two kinds of cells—those derived from the theca and those derived from granulosa cells. Under light microscopy these cells appear identical.

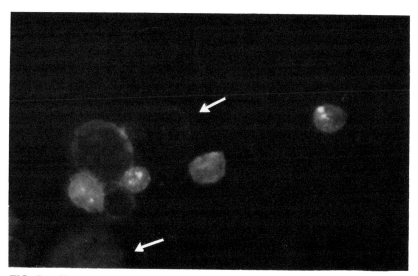

FIG. B. Simultaneous binding of granulosa and theca monoclonal antibodies to dispersed bovine luteal cells as determined by immunofluorescence. Binding of the granulosa antibody was detected with rhodamine-conjugated goat anti-rat IgG (arrows) and theca antibody with sheep anti-mouse antibody conjugated to flourescein isothiocyanate ×520. (From Alila and Hansel, *Biol. Reprod.,* **30,** 1015, 1984).

TABLE A

Progesterone Synthesis By Small Theca-Derived Bovine Luteal Cells

		Net progesterone synthesis	
	N	ng/10^6 cells/3 hours	Treated/basal
Basal	5	114 ± 39	—
LH (10 ng)	5	493 ± 164	5.05 ± 0.94
MIX (1 mM)	4	159 ± 51	2.09 ± 0.25
A23187 (0.3 μM)	5	55 ± 17	0.53 ± 0.13
LH + MIX	1	611	3.13
LH + A23187	1	119	0.55
MIX + A23187	4	77 ± 35	0.83 ± 0.45
8 Br-cAMP (3 mM)	4	267 ± 91	4.18 ± 1.37

Ultimately, we will have to separate these two subpopulations of large cells. I'm not going to say more about large cells today, but obviously it is suspected that the large amounts of progesterone produced by one of these large cell populations is controlled by the calcium-phosphoinositol system, shown in Fig. A. As shown in Table A, agents which increase intracellular calcium concentrations, such as the calcium ionophore A23187, inhibit progesterone synthesis in the small theca-derived cells. Methyl-isoxanthine (MIX), which mobilizes intracellular calcium and is also a phosphodiesterase inhibitor, results in a small stimulation of these cells. A23187 also inhibits LH-stimulated progesterone synthesis. A23187 inhibited cyclic AMP production (data not shown), indicating that there is an interaction between these two methods for controlling steroidogenesis. I have no idea as to the mechanisms involved but products of the cAMP system may block diglycerol acetate activation of the C kinase and, perhaps the reverse can also occur. During the coming years we hope to unravel the interrelationships between these two control mechanisms in the three types of luteal cells.

C. W. Bardin: In the first part of your talk you showed us some rodamine labeling of large cells, and you said "and there you can see a small cell labeling down" and you said that you couldn't see it very well in the light; and indeed, you couldn't—did we misunderstand that?

G. D. Niswender: What I think I said was that the two cells which were darkly labeled, were both about 18 to 20 μm in diameter, therefore, they are still small cells. The other cell that was labeled was about 12 μm so all labeled cells were small cells.

C. W. Bardin: Damaged cells may have receptors but they do not attach to tissue culture plates. Have you looked at plating efficiency of your small cells and your large cells? Specifically if you look at large cells that plate more efficiently are their properties different from the ones that don't attach to culture dishes.

G. D. Niswender: We have not looked at that the way you have just suggested. Large cells are much more fragile than small cells, and there are days when they don't plate well at all.

C. W. Bardin: When you are examining isolated cells that are steroidogenic, the ones that will plate efficiently have a much better response to hormones than those that don't.

G. D. Niswender: Most of those initial studies were done with suspensions of cells and the experiments were done within a matter of hours after the tissue had been collected.

L. Birnbaumer: What do you know about the role of estradiol in the maintenance of these large cells?

G. D. Niswender: The corpus luteum in sheep does not make estradiol. Estradiol has no biological effect in this tissue in terms of the secretion of progesterone. However, we are now interested in determining whether estradiol is regulating the numbers of receptors for prostaglandins, prostaglandin synthesis, and/or whether estradiol is regulating oxytocin synthesis and secretion. We should know a lot more about the biological importance of estradiol within the next year.

L. Birnbaumer: Did you add oxytocin to the small cells and look at what would happen?

G. D. Niswender: Yes, oxytocin has little effect when used by itself to treat small cells. However, if we stimulate the small cells to secrete progesterone maximally with LH, we now get a dose-dependent inhibition of progesterone secretion with oxytocin. This has been repeated in preliminary experiments. Clearly oxytocin can prevent LH-stimulated progesterone secretion from small cells.

L. Birnbaumer: Maybe I can ask you to put together the beginning and the end of your talk. At the beginning you correlated progesterone production in the animal with the levels of LH receptors in the corpus luteum. If I understood you well, at the end of your talk you stated that LH is regulating the progesterone secretion of but a small proportion of the total.

G. D. Niswender: LH in terms of its direct regulation of progesterone secretion from small cells, and LH receptors are becoming less interesting in terms of the overall regulation of luteal function. However, the thing that I have stressed, although it's still very speculative, is that LH action on small cells may also be the driving force that causes them to differentiate into large cells. What I'm saying is that LH may have another important action besides regulation of progesterone secretion. The other point that I would like to make is that almost half of the small cells do not appear to be steroidogenic. It is our opinion that these cells may well acquire steroidogenic potential with appropriate stimulation (i.e., exposure to LH, etc).

K. Sterling: If these ungulates are different from the cows, I wonder how far you can go in thinking about carnivores and primates. You mentioned a couple of times possible relationships to the human subject and I wonder how far you can push this, or whether you have primary data or not, on other species?

G. D. Niswender: I think Dr. Hansel would agree that the similarities between the cow and the sheep are far more numerous than are the differences. There is also excellent morphological data that there are two cell types in both the monkey and the woman, but I know of no one who has begun to purify the two cell types, and to study them independently.

K. Sterling: So that you think from existing evidence that probably it does apply?

G. D. Niswender: There is one other bit of evidence which I think is very important and that's the work by Hamburger in Sweden where they've shown that if you look at ovarian venous prostaglandins F during luteolysis in the woman, there are higher levels in the ovarian vein on the side of the corpus luteum than on the opposite side. This observation suggests that there may be an intraluteal source of prostaglandins. They also have data which indicate that as a result of prostaglandins treatment of human luteal tissue *in vitro* the LH receptor is uncoupled from adenylate cyclase. Therefore, 2 or 3 little bits of information we have are perfectly compatible with the hypothesis that prostaglandins of ovarian rather than of uterine origin may cause luteolysis in women.

K. Sterling: It seems to me you could also do it in monkeys, with great ease, with a few monkeys.

G. D. Niswender: We do not have ready access to monkeys.

W. F. Crowley: There is a pulsatile secretion of progesterone from the human corpus luteum which follows an LH pulse and that slide where you showed a single LH pulse causing the increase of progesterone from the small cells rising from 20 to 60% looks exactly like you see in the mid-luteal phase of the human, so I think it is very interesting. My questions are then twofold: we were puzzled by the fact that in the *early* corpus luteum of the human, progesterone secretion is tonic, i.e., there is no pulsatile secretion of progesterone. This fact fits with an apparent difference between the early and late corpus luteum by a number of probes such as antibodies to LH GnRH analog administration, estrogen administration, and now their pattern of pulsatile secretion. I wonder if you would speculate and try to relate your morphologic and function studies to these differences in the early and late corpus luteum that have existed in many species. Second, you told us about the corpus luteum of pregnancy, what it doesn't have in it, in terms of changes and small cells and large cells. What are the differences in the pregnancy corpus luteum?

G. D. Niswender: You asked me to speculate, so that is what I am doing. I am now of the opinion that the preovulatory surge of LH may interact with LH receptors on the granulosa cells, and that whatever mechanism turns on luteinization probably irreversibly sets in motion, in those cells, a process which results in biochemical changes. This may result in those cells being irreversibly turned on to produce progesterone, without regulation by LH and it is not until this initial group of granulosa cells wanes that we begin to see real LH regulation of the theca-derived cells.

B. F. Rice: Your talk was so full of provocative notions that it is hard to limit oneself to a few questions. I would like to ask just a couple. Is there anything that would correspond to what has been described as the "K" cell in the human corpus luteum that was described many years ago in the Carnegie collection?

G. D. Niswender: I do not know. Dr. Sawyer, do you have an answer to that question?

H. R. Sawyer: "Dark" and "light" staining cells have been observed in a variety of steroid-secreting tissues and are also present in ovine corpora lutea. The functional significance, if any, of the differential staining densities between large and small luteal cells is not known, but may be related to fixation as discussed by Christensen and Gillim [*In* "The Gonads" (K. W. McKerns, ed.). North Holland, Amsterdam, 1969].

B. F. Rice: The other question I had deals with receptor occupancy and whether or not there are species differences. I would agree that it is easier to get a human corpus luteum than monkey corpus luteum and probably ovine corpus luteum. My first job was to run out to the slaughter house to get ovine corpora lutea until I realized that it was a lot easier to walk across the street into the operating room and get human corpora lutea. In studies with hCG receptors in the human corpus luteum obtained at different times in the cycle, certain observations were made and were quite reproducible, namely that you could not demonstrate any receptor binding on day 28 of the cycle, when the corpus luteum was dead. You could not demonstrate any receptor binding at day 14 of the cycle when you have a brand new corpus luteum, at a time where large amounts of progesterone were being synthesized which was rather puzzling. We decided to attack this problem by a biologic approach which was to get a corpus luteum which was nice, big, and firm from midtrimester and that also did not demonstrate any binding; now the one common thread in the two corpora lutea that does not bind the brand new corpus luteum versus the pregnancy corpus luteum, the course of very high *in vivo* LH or chorionic gonadotropins and our conclusion was that these were just saturated receptors and not that the receptors were not there at any particular time.

G. D. Niswender: On day 2 of the estrous cycle, there was a higher ratio of occupied to nonoccupied receptors than on any other day. We suggested that this was due to the high degree of occupancy of LH receptors following the preovulatory surge of LH. This however was speculation.

N. Ben-Jonathan: Your group was among the first, about 6 years ago, to show the presence of β-adrenergic receptors in the corpus luteum, which are coupled to cyclic AMP and progesterone secretion. Since then, quite a few groups confirmed the presence of β receptors on granulosa cells, luteinized granulosa cells, and luteal cells from several species. Now that you can differentiate between the luteal cells and show different receptor distribution, have you had a chance to look at the β receptor distribution?

G. D. Niswender: β receptors appear to be primarily on small cells, based on data which indicate that isoproterenol stimulates progesterone secretion in small but not large cells.

N. Ben-Jonathan: Second, would you care to speculate on how the β receptor and norepinephrine maintain progesterone secretion, as compared to the LH, throughout the life of the corpus luteum?

G. D. Niswender: No. We have stopped those experiments because we have not been able to figure out the biological relevance of this phenomenon. Once someone makes the key observation which tells us how we should proceed we are likely to initiate new studies in this area.

R. Moudgal: I would like to make a general comment and raise a question. You indicated earlier that there are distinct differences in the way the ovine luteal cell handles hCG and oLH—particularly that hCG stays on the cell membrane for a longer time and that compared to oLH it is internalized to a lesser extent. Recently, Dr. Sheela Rani and myself working with rat granulosa and Leydig cells observed that there are distinct differences in the way these cells handle hCG compared to other LHs like PMSG, rLH, oLH, and eLH. Cells incubated with the above hormones for a period of 15–30 minutes were washed of excess medium LH and reincubated in medium containing either normal serum or appropriate antiserum. Binding of ^{125}I-labeled hormones and progesterone production following incubation with cold hormone were followed. While hCG's effect could not be terminated by antiserum treatment or washing and it stayed bound despite the above treatment, the other LHs produced a varied response, rLH and PMSG being on the other end of the spectrum. Their effect could even be terminated by the simple process of washing (*Endocrinology*, in press). hCG appears to be an atypical hormone and the way gonadal cells of different species react to their "homologous" hormone seems to be distinctly different. All the same, a number of generalizations on LH–receptor interaction have been made using primarily hCG as the ligand. In the light of these differences between hCG and other LHs, do you think it is correct to extrapolate from the data obtained with hCG on the physiological regulation of a luteal cell of a species to which hCG is not native?

G. D. Niswender: Radioactive hCG is fine for quantification of receptors and for a number of other techniques. However, I am the first to tell you that a sheep never sees a molecule of hCG and that data obtained regarding "down-regulation," "up-regulation," or other processes related to the kinetics of receptor movement, internalization, degradation, etc., may not be pertinent biologically. You must be careful how you use hCG for research purposes. Let me make one other point; ovine LH binds to LH receptor with a 30 times lower affinity than does hCG; however, if you wash these cells and perform the experiments carefully, we still find better than 75% of the oLH internalized and degraded and not dissociated from the cell. Thus, although it is not as clear for oLH as it is for hCG, we still feel that the major pathway for loss of the hormone from the cell is internalization and degradation not dissociation.

R. Moudgal: We do not see such an effect in the rat system.

H. A. Bern: It's graceless after such a splendidly, thorough presentation to suggest that maybe you should have done other things as well, but there is at least a curiosity as to whether prolactin has anything to do with either of these two cell populations and whether anyone has looked for receptors for prolactin in either population.

G. D. Niswender: Let me tell you that prolactin has been suggested by a number of people to play a role in luteal function in both the cow and the sheep. However, we cannot find prolactin receptors and we have looked exhaustively. In addition, we cannot find a biological action of prolactin in this gland, at least as related to the secretion of progesterone. It may be that we are not addressing the problem correctly, but we have expended a considerable amount of effort trying to identify the role of prolactin in the sheep corpus luteum and have not been able to find one.

H. A. Bern: Does your statement also include ovine placental prolactin?

G. D. Niswender: No, that is a different issue.

M. C. Chang: Whenever you people talk about corpus luteum I always think about the difference between the corpus luteum of the pseudopregnancy and the corpus luteum of the pregnancy. I always wondered whether these two corpora lutea are the same or different. My first question is: do your sheep have a pseudopregnancy as the rabbit or ferret?

G. D. Niswender: It does not.

M. C. Chang: Then, I would also like to ask Dr. Hansel whether your cow has pseudopregnancy or not?

W. Hansel: The cow has none.

M. C. Chang: You see, I am working on rabbits and ferrets; they always have pseudopregnancy. In the rabbit, the life of the corpus luteum lasts for about 20 days during pseudopregnancy, but lasts 31 days during pregnancy. In the ferret, the life of the corpus luteum lasts for 4 days in both pseudopregnancy and pregnancy. It seems that in the rabbit, the corpus luteum of pseudopregnancy and pregnancy is different while in the ferret, the corpus luteum of pseudopregnancy and pregnancy is very similar. Concerning the function of the corpus luteum, we should also consider how the corpus luteum changes from a cyclic corpus luteum into a pseudopregnant or pregnant corpus luteum. These are also important problems to be considered when we talk about corpus luteum.

R. L. Stouffer: I was intrigued by two things and I would like to relate them together. One is the apparent difference in action of LH and hCG. Since sheep never see both of these hormones but primates do, would you speculate on the possible importance of this difference in gonadotropin action in the primate. Second, would you relate this phenomenon to the conversion of small luteal cells to large luteal cells, which I find very intriguing. Do you think that cell conversion occurs similarly during the menstrual cycle and during pregnancy; obviously in a primate these intervals are very different in terms of the LH and hCG milieu.

G. D. Niswender: First, the relative role of hCG versus LH. I think that the differences in the two hormones are probably important in the primate. It is amazing to me that mother nature developed a molecule like hCG which sticks around in blood with a t_i of 48 hours; it binds to the receptor, and immobilizes it in the membrane for a long time and thereby prolongs the steroidogenic response. If ever there was a molecule designed to maximize the chances for maintenance of pregnancy, it seems to me that hCG is that molecule. How all of this developed evolutionarily would make interesting discussion for a few hours. It is very interesting that primates have devised a system that is so elegant, in order to maintain pregnancy.

R. L. Stouffer: In your system you used hCG-treated animals. Can you convert the small cells to large cells with LH?

G. D. Niswender: We probably can but we have not performed that experiment. We used hCG because we didn't want to inject oLH 6 or 8 times a day. We should repeat those experiments with LH. We have experiments on the drawing board where we intend to label theca and granulosa cells with radioactive thymidine since we know when each cell type undergoes maximal mitosis, and then using the monoclonal antibodies for thecal and granulosa cells we will get a handle on whether small cells are converted to large cells during the normal cycle.

J. Abramowitz: This has to do with the LH–hCG story. If I remember from one of your slides you have indicated that both hCG and human LH have a slow decay or remove from the surface of these luteal cells. Some data that we have comparing different types of LH and their ability to stimulate cyclase, would also tend to indicate that both hCG and human LH tend to act differently with regards to the extent to which they can stimulate cyclase when compared to other LHs, such as ovine LH, bovine LH, and porcine LH. This appears to be related to the way in which these hormones interact with their receptors. In the rabbit and rat corpus luteum both human LH and human chorionic gonadotropin are unable to form a high-affinity binding state with their receptors in the presence of magnesium whereas in the case of ovine LH and porcine LH and bovine LH you can. What we see then is that gonadotropins that do form this high-affinity state give a greater degree of stimulation of adenylyl cyclase than those that do not. So there is another difference between not necessarily LH versus hCG but the source of LH.

G. D. Niswender: Obviously we are anxious to repeat those steroidogenic studies using human tissue. We think that this is important since the differences may be a difference between bovine LH and human hCG on sheep luteal cells which may not occur when human luteal tissue is used for the experiments.

P. Kelly: My question deals with something that you covered at the beginning of the presentation, namely you showed that internalization is important for removal of the ligand, but what happens to the receptor molecule itself? What is the fate of the receptor molecule: is degradation of the receptor and recycling necessary in the corpus luteum?

G. D. Niswender: We can tell you that if we block protein synthesis, much like they've done for studies of the acetylcholine receptor, and then look at the ability of the cell to process hormones, we can get at least 8 times more hormone molecules internalized and degraded than we had receptor molecules to start with. This is the kind of evidence that has been used to demonstrate that the receptor is in fact recycled. We are not totally happy with this kind of evidence but at least we have the same kind of data that they have used in other systems.

S. Cohen: I was interested to see that your chorionic gonadotropin comes from the human, the LH comes from the pig, and the animal injected was the sheep. What happens if you use sheep products?

G. D. Niswender: There must have been some mistake in your interpretation of our data. We have never injected pig LH, it has always been sheep LH.

S. Cohen: I thought ovine stood for pig.

O. V. Dominguez: You mentioned that the large cells seem to have another mechanism of response to LH besides the one involving cyclic AMP. I was interested in this particular point, because for some time and on many occasions, it has been mentioned that cyclic AMP mimmicks ACTH actions on the adrenals as well as LH actions on the gonads.

However, in support of your suggestion, I wish to say that we found and reported some time ago that ACTH on the adrenals and LH on the gonads seem to have another alternative mechanism of action, not necessarily involving cyclic AMP, oriented to the utilization of precursors Δ^5-3β-ol-steroid sulfates, that do not enter into the steroid hormone biosynthesis, unless their 3β-ol-sulfate is removed by a specific sulfatase. This sulfatase is stimulated by ACTH in the adrenal and by LH in the gonads and it is of a particular interest that cyclic AMP does not enhance the sulfatase activity, which seems to require ADP as a cofactor.

Perhaps ACTH or LH, depending on the organ in which they act, could stimulate ATPase that converts ATP to ADP, facilitating the desulfation of pregnenolone sulfate, the release to free pregnenolone, the substrate required for steroid hormone biosynthesis, not involving cyclic AMP. You did not mention anything about steroid sulfates in your two types of cells and I was wondering if you have found something in relation to this alternative in your experiments.

G. D. Niswender: No, we have not looked at steroid sulfatase. However, I think the reason we haven't understood and still don't understand totally the control of steroidogenesis in these cells is because we are not playing the game with a full deck of cards. We don't even know who the rest of the participants in this game are going to be, let alone what the rules will be. Until we begin to look at the whole picture, we can't put it all together and we can't look at the whole picture until we know who all the participants are, so we have a ways to go.

N. Schwartz: Some years ago I heard you start a paper on the sheep by calling it a large, woolly rat. I can understand why the sheep and the cow are really attractive in terms of the kinds of studies you are doing because of the mass of corpus luteum. But the rat has the advantage that it naturally goes through or permits the investigator to go through three different stages. You have the corpus luteum of the cycle which does not do very much in terms of progesterone secretion; you can move on to the pseudopregnant corpus luteum and then the pregnant corpus luteum. Have you been able to do any similar kinds of studies with this rather small amount of material?

G. D. Niswender: We have not worked at all with the rat.

N. Schwartz: You said it was a large woolly rat.

G. D. Niswender: There are some morphological data that there are two cell types in the rat but we have not tried to separate them to characterize them. However, I believe that our chairwoman has initiated these studies.

G. Gibori: To answer your question, the rats have indeed two cell types which can be separated by differential sedimentation.

M. Raj: I enjoyed your very elegant presentation. You have made a very interesting suggestion that the protein secretory granules are limited to the large cells and if I understood correctly and correct me if I am wrong, we have observed that when we put human granulosa lutein cells in culture and stimulate them with gonadotropins FSH, LH combination they make tons and tons of proteins as in [$^{S}35$]methionine uptake and secretion of labeled protein into the medium. Not only that the LH further stimulates synthesis and secretion of new proteins which were not present before and were not being secreted before, so if as you suppose these are secreted by, let us say the large cell type which presumably do not have any LH receptors do you think that there is a transformation of small cells to large cells during culture going on and then these are secreting. Could you speculate on that?

G. D. Niswender: When you take granulosa cells and put them in culture, clearly they are not and they do not differentiate into normal luteal cells. The proof for that is simply if you take sheep granulosa cells and put them in culture they "luteinize" and they produce progesterone and they keep responding to tropic hormone. If you take luteal cells and put them in culture within 2 or 3 days they no longer respond to tropic hormone. It seems to me that the response of cells luteinized *in vitro* is different from that of cells which luteinize *in vivo*.

L. Birnbaumer: Your comment about injecting hCG and having a long lasting LH reminded me to ask you about what would happen with FSH or a "long lasting" FSH-like material, such as PMSG, in relation to the conversion of small to large cells.

G. D. Niswender: We have not done those experiments. We should because I would predict that it might work since there is evidence that PMS will bind to the same receptor that binds hCG.

M. Lipsett: (1) Does either cell type make steroids further down the biosynthetic pathway past progesterone? (2) You quoted several other studies where the cells have been separated, and I've always been interested in where estrogen is being synthesized in the corpus luteum of the pig and the human. Do you have any idea what cell type would be involved there?

G. D. Niswender: I should know but I can't tell you whether anybody has looked at estrogen biosynthesis by the two cell types. These cells will make 20α-hydroxyprogesterone.

B. F. Rice: I noticed you expressed a lot of your data in terms of the amount of progesterone in the medium; progesterone, at least in human corpora lutea in the tissue culture and things of that nature often stays in the cell, and does not get out into the medium; do you have any notion about total progesterone synthesis, or is it any different, or is the secretion in the medium a good, accurate indicator of what is really going on?

G. D. Niswender: In general it's a good, accurate indicator of what's going on. But there are some treatments such as microfilament inhibitors and so on, that clearly result in a build-up of progesterone inside the cell versus what is secreted. So you have to be very careful. We always make sure that what's in the media reflects what's in the cells and vice versa.

RECENT PROGRESS IN HORMONE RESEARCH, VOL. 41

Regulation of Microsomal Cytochrome *P*-450 Enzymes and Testosterone Production in Leydig Cells

ANITA H. PAYNE, PATRICK G. QUINN, AND C. S. SHEELA RANI

*Departments of Obstetrics and Gynecology and Biological Chemistry,
The University of Michigan, Ann Arbor, Michigan*

I. Introduction

Androgen biosynthesis by Leydig cells is stimulated by the anterior pituitary hormone, luteinizing hormone (LH). Binding of LH to specific high-affinity receptors on the surface of Leydig cells (Catt *et al.*, 1972) results in increased production of intracellular cAMP (Dufau *et al.*, 1973) and activation of cAMP-dependent protein kinase (Cooke *et al.*, 1976; Dufau *et al.*, 1977). Steroidogenesis can also be stimulated in Leydig cells by human chorionic gonadotropin (hCG), an analog of LH, which binds to the LH receptor (Dufau *et al.*, 1977) and by analogs of cAMP (Tsuruhara *et al.*, 1977; Cooke *et al.*, 1977). Although the exact mechanism is not known, acute cAMP stimulation is believed to result in an increased rate of association of the substrate, cholesterol, with the mitochondrial cholesterol side-chain cleavage enzyme, P-450$_{scc}$ (Hall, 1970; van der Vusse *et al.*, 1975). Cholesterol is cleaved by P-450$_{scc}$ to yield the C_{21} steroid, pregnenolone, which is further metabolized to testosterone by enzymes associated with the smooth endoplasmic reticulum. Δ^5-3β-Hydroxysteroid dehydrogenase-isomerase, a non-P-450 enzyme, catalyzes the conversion of pregnenolone to progesterone. The conversion of the C_{21} steroid, progesterone, to the C_{19} steroid, androstenedione, is catalyzed by the cytochrome P-450 enzymes, 17α-hydroxylase and C_{17-20} lyase. The conversion of pregnenolone to testosterone is not acutely stimulated by LH or cAMP (Hall *et al.*, 1979). A schematic diagram of LH- or cAMP-stimulated testosterone production in Leydig cells is shown in Fig. 1.

In addition to acute effects, LH has trophic effects on Leydig cell androgen biosynthesis. Chronic treatment with LH or hCG of intact or hypophysectomized rats results in an increased capacity for LH-stimulated testosterone production (Payne *et al.*, 1980; O'Shaughnessy and Payne, 1982; Zipf *et al.*, 1978) and induces enzymes of the steroidogenic pathway (O'Shaughnessy and Payne, 1982; Purvis *et al.*, 1973a,b). In

153

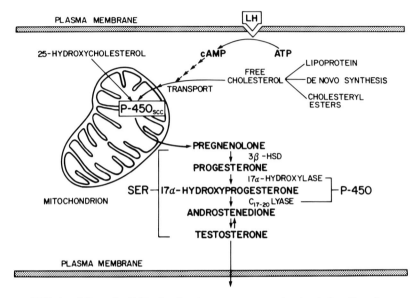

FIG. 1.　LH- and cAMP-stimulated testosterone production in Leydig cells.

contrast, treatment of animals with a single high dose of LH or hCG results in steroidogenic desensitization of Leydig cells, which is characterized by a diminished capacity to produce testosterone in response to subsequent acute stimulation with LH or cAMP (Zipf *et al.*, 1978; Sharpe, 1977; Hsueh *et al.*, 1977; Saez *et al.*, 1978; Cigorraga *et al.*, 1978; Chasalow *et al.*, 1979), and decreases in *P*-450 enzyme activities (O'Shaughnessy and Payne, 1982; Cigorraga *et al.*, 1978; Chasalow *et al.*, 1979). The present article describes studies that examine the mechanisms by which LH or cAMP bring about desensitization of the steroidogenic response on one hand, but cause an increase in steroidogenic capacity in the same cell type under other conditions. The main focus of these studies will be on the effects of LH or cAMP on the degradation and synthesis of the microsomal *P*-450 enzymes, 17α-hydroxylase and C_{17-20} lyase, and the relationship of changes in these activities to changes in steroidogenic capacity.

II.　Desensitization of Leydig Cells

Gonadotropin-induced down-regulation of testicular LH receptors was first reported by Hsueh *et al.* (1976) and Sharpe (1976), and the same authors also described the accompanying desensitization of testicular cAMP and testosterone responses to hCG (Sharpe, 1977; Hsueh *et al.*, 1977). It was evident from these studies that there was a marked dissociation of the extent of LH receptor loss from the capacities to produce cAMP or testosterone (Sharpe, 1977), as has also been demonstrated in studies of the effects of LH on receptor number and steroidogenic capacity in hypophysectomized (Zipf *et al.*, 1978; Hauger *et al.*, 1977) and gonadotropin-desensitized animals (Zipf *et al.*, 1978). It was subsequently demonstrated that desensitization of the cAMP response was not responsible for the defect in testosterone production, since steroidogenic desensitization could not be overcome by addition of cAMP analogs *in vitro* (Tsuruhara *et al.*, 1977; O'Shaughnessy and Payne, 1982; Chasalow *et al.*, 1979) and protein kinase binding activity toward cAMP was not diminished in desensitized Leydig cells (Dufau *et al.*, 1977).

The decrease in testosterone biosynthesis of desensitized Leydig cells was later hypothesized to result from two defects in the testosterone biosynthetic pathway (Cigorraga *et al.*, 1978). The first of these defects was found to be prior to the production of pregnenolone. This defect was characterized by decreased pregnenolone accumulation (when its further metabolism was inhibited) in response to subsequent stimulation with gonadotropin or cAMP. The second defect was shown to be a decrease in the activities of the *P*-450 enzymes, 17α-hydroxylase and C$_{17-20}$ lyase, which catalyze the conversion of progesterone to androstendione (and testosterone), since the substrates of these enzymes, progesterone and 17α-hydroxyprogesterone, accumulate in desensitized Leydig cells. This latter defect was also demonstrated directly by measuring decreases in these enzyme activities in desensitized Leydig cells (Chasalow *et al.*, 1979). Because of the large reductions in *P*-450 activities and accumulation of intermediates of the steroidogenic pathway, it has been inferred that this defect in *P*-450 activities is a primary cause of the diminished steroidogenic capacity of desensitized Leydig cells. Data from our laboratory (O'Shaughnessy and Payne, 1982; Quinn and Payne, 1984, 1985), however, demonstrate that decreases in 17α-hydroxylase and C$_{17-20}$ lyase activities, following desensitization with LH or cAMP, are not necessarily associated with a decrease in testosterone biosynthetic capacity.

A. EFFECTS OF *IN VIVO* GONADOTROPIN-INDUCED DESENSITIZATION ON MAXIMAL TESTOSTERONE PRODUCTION AND MICROSOMAL CYTOCHROME *P*-450 ENZYMES

The effect of a single high dose of gonadotropin (a desensitizing dose) on microsomal *P*-450 enzyme activities and maximal testosterone production *in vitro* was examined in two populations of rat Leydig cells (O'Shaughnessy and Payne, 1982). Mature rats were injected subcutaneously with 150 μg LH or 50 IU hCG. Animals were killed 72 hours later and Leydig cells were separated into two populations by Metrizamide gradient centrifugation (O'Shaughnessy *et al.*, 1981; O'Shaughnessy and Payne, 1982). The effects of a desensitizing dose of LH or hCG on population II Leydig cells are shown in Fig. 2. The administration of a single high dose of LH or hCG resulted in the expected decrease in the activities of 17α-hydroxylase and C_{17-20} lyase, associated with a diminished capacity for testosterone production of population II Leydig cells. In contrast, as illustrated in Fig. 3, the same dose of LH did not cause a decrease in maximal testosterone production by population I Leydig cells, in spite of the marked reduction in 17α-hydroxylase and C_{17-20} lyase. These data suggest that the LH- or hCG-induced decreases in the microsomal P-450s

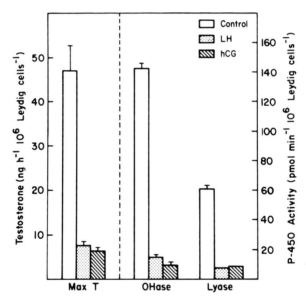

FIG. 2.   Effect of gonadotropin-induced desensitization on maximal testosterone production and microsomal P-450 activities in population II Leydig cells. Mature rats were injected subcutaneously with saline (control), 150 μg LH or 50 IU hCG and killed 72 hours later. Leydig cell population II was obtained by Metrizamide gradient centrifugation of dispersed testicular cells. For determination of maximal testosterone production (Max T), cells were incubated for 3 hours at 34°C with 30 pmol hCG. Testosterone was measured in cells plus medium by RIA. 17α-Hydroxylase (OHase) and C_{17-20} lyase (Lyase) activities were determined by incubating aliquots of homogenates of population II Leydig cells for 5 minutes with a saturating concentration of the appropriate substrate and cofactor (adapted from O'Shaughnessy and Payne, 1982).

are probably not a major contributing factor to the diminished capacity to produce testosterone in response to subsequent, acute stimulation with gonadotropin or cAMP.

B. DEPLETION OF INTRACELLULAR CHOLESTEROL IN DESENSITIZED LEYDIG CELLS

The above data suggested that the decrease in capacity for testosterone production of desensitized Leydig cells was due to a metabolic defect preceding the microsomal *P*-450 enzymes in the steroidogenic pathway. An obvious candidate for this defect was a limitation in the availability of the steroid precursor, cholesterol, in desensitized Leydig cells.

Serum lipoproteins provide a source of exogenous cholesterol for several extrahepatic tissues (Brown and Goldstein, 1976). The rat differs from the human in that the major cholesterol carrying lipoprotein is HDL instead of LDL (Schonfeld *et al.*, 1974). In addition, specific binding sites for rat HDL had been demonstrated in isolated interstitial tissue from rat testes (Chen *et al.*, 1980). We, therefore, investigated the possibility that lipoproteins can provide exogenous cholesterol for testosterone production by Leydig cells from hCG-desensitized rats.

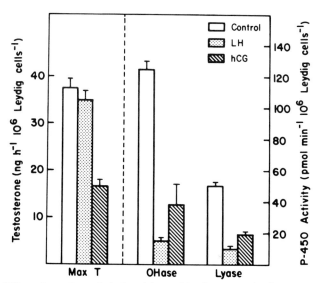

FIG. 3.   Effect of gonadotropin-induced desensitization on maximal testosterone production and microsomal *P*-450 activities in population I Leydig cells. Methods were identical to those described in Fig. 2, except that population I Leydig cells were used (adapted from O'Shaughnessy and Payne, 1982).

Mature male rats were injected subcutaneously with 50 IU hCG or with saline. Rats were killed 72 hours later and a Leydig cell-enriched dispersion was prepared (Quinn *et al.*, 1981). When Leydig cells from hCG-treated (desensitized) animals were incubated *in vitro* with hCG, a marked decrease in maximal testosterone production was observed compared to saline treated control animals (Fig. 4, control, N− vs N+ compared to hCG-treated, N− vs N+). The addition of exogenous cholesterol in the form of HDL or LDL to Leydig cells from saline-treated control rats had essentially no effect on *in vitro* basal or hCG-stimulated testosterone production (Fig. 4). In contrast, both basal and hCG-stimulated testosterone production by Leydig cells from desensitized rats, which had synthesized large quantities of testosterone, were significantly increased by the addition of equivalent amounts of HDL or LDL cholesterol (140 μg/ml) to the incubation medium (*p*0.05). The addition of HDL had a greater effect than LDL and, furthermore, HDL restored the hCG-stimulated testosterone production to the maximal amount produced by hCG-stimulated

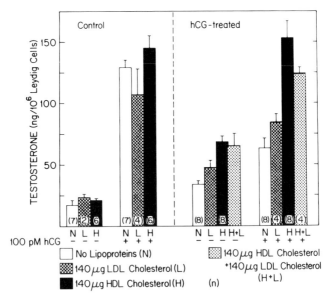

FIG. 4.   Effects of high density (HDL) and low-density (LDL) lipoprotein particles on gonadotropin-induced desensitization. Mature rats were injected subcutaneously with either saline (control) or 50 IU hCG (hCG-treated) and killed 72 hours later. A Leydig cell enriched dispersion was prepared by collagenase treatment of decapsulated testes. Cells were incubated for 6 hours in the presence or absence of 100 p*M* hCG and in the presence or absence of HDL and/or LDL. Testosterone production was measured in cells plus medium by RIA. (*n*) represents the number of determinations (from Quinn *et al.*, 1981).

Leydig cells from control animals. These results have subsequently been confirmed by other investigators in rat (Charreau *et al.*, 1981), murine tumor (Freeman and Ascoli, 1982), and pig (Benahmed *et al.*, 1981) Leydig cells. These data suggest that the major effect of a desensitizing dose of hCG is depletion of the endogenous cholesterol available for steroid biosynthesis, since the addition of cholesterol in the form of HDL or LDL largely restored the capacity for testosterone production of these Leydig cells.

C. OXYGEN-MEDIATED DAMAGE OF MICROSOMAL CYTOCHROME *P*-450 ENZYMES IN CULTURED LEYDIG CELLS: RELATIONSHIP TO STEROIDOGENIC DESENSITIZATION

The results of the studies described above, on gonadotropin-induced desensitization *in vivo,* were paradoxical. Cholesterol depletion appeared to be largely responsible for the diminished steroidogenic capacity of desensitized Leydig cells, yet these cells exhibited large decreases in the activities of the microsomal *P*-450 enzymes. We, therefore, developed a primary culture system of purified mouse Leydig cells to examine the relationship of decreases in the *P*-450 activities to the decrease in steroidogenic capacity occurring in steroidogenic desensitization (Quinn and Payne, 1984). This model system was also used to study the mechanism responsible for the decrease in hydroxylase and lyase activities. Various hypotheses have been proposed for the decrease in the microsomal *P*-450 activities.

We have proposed that the mechanism by which microsomal *P*-450 activities are decreased in desensitized Leydig cells involves oxygen free radical-initiated damage (Quinn and Payne, 1984, 1985). This hypothesis is based on studies by Hornsby and colleagues (Hornsby, 1980; Crivello *et al.*, 1982, 1983) demonstrating oxygen-tension-sensitive, antioxidant-preventable damage to *P*-450 enzymes of cultured adrenocortical cells. Hornsby (1980) demonstrated that the loss of 11β-hydroxylase activity of cultured adrenal cells could be prevented by reduction of the oxygen tension or by addition of antioxidants to the culture medium. In addition, the study by Hornsby (1980) demonstrated that incubation of cultures with substrates for, or the 11β-hydroxylated products of, the enzyme resulted in accelerated loss of 11β-hydroxylase activity. It was proposed that the product (pseudosubstrate) interacted with the *P*-450 enzyme to form a pseudosubstrate–*P*-450–O_2 complex, from which damaging oxygen free radicals are released, due to the inability of the substrate to be hydroxylated. These findings have been confirmed for the 11β-hydroxylase and extended to the 21-hydroxylase of adrenal cells in subsequent studies (Crivello *et al.*, 1982). These data suggested that the microsomal *P*-450 enzymes of Leydig cells might be sensitive to this type of damage. It also seemed probable that the extent of *P*-450 damage would be increased in desensitized Leydig cells, due to the accumulation of steroid products which could act as pseudosubstrates.

An alternative hypothesis suggests that a desensitizing dose of hCG causes increased production of estradiol, which decreases microsomal *P*-450 activities via a steroid receptor-mediated process (Nozu *et al.*, 1981a,b; Cigorraga *et al.*, 1978). Dufau and colleagues presented evidence that the effects of hCG on these *P*-450 enzymes and on testosterone synthesis could be prevented by simultaneous administration of the estrogen receptor antagonist, Tamoxifen (Dufau *et al.*, 1979). They presented additional evidence that nuclear estradiol receptors are increased, and that estradiol could reduce testosterone synthesis of cultured testicular cells (Nozu *et al.*, 1981b). Relatively high concentrations of estradiol were required to produce this effect, however, and, as in previous reports, the increase in intermediates of the biosynthetic pathway was too small to account for the observed decrease in testosterone synthesis (Cigorraga *et al.*, 1978; Nozu *et al.*, 1981a,b; Dufau *et al.*, 1979; Cigorraga *et al.*, 1980). Other investigators have also examined the effects of estradiol and/or Tamoxifen on testicular steroidogenesis and have been able to demonstrate depletion of cytosolic estradiol receptors following gonadotropin-induced desensitization, but have failed to demonstrate a causal relationship between this decline and the desensitization process (Moger, 1980; Melner and Abney, 1980; Brinkman *et al.*, 1981, 1982).

Based on the above observations, we designed experiments to determine whether the decrease in microsomal *P*-450 activities, 17α-hydroxylase and C_{17-20} lyase, of desensitized Leydig cells resulted from oxygen-mediated damage, and the extent to which the decline in these *P*-450 activities contributes to the decreased steroidogenic capacity of desensitized Leydig cells. In subsequent studies, we also evaluated the possibility that the decrease in *P*-450 activities was due to a steroid hormone receptor-mediated mechanism.

1. Effects of Oxygen Tension and Dimethyl Sulfoxide on Microsomal Cytochrome P-450 Activities

The model system used for these studies consisted of primary cultures of purified mouse Leydig cells maintained in serum-free medium under a standard or low-oxygen atmosphere (Quinn and Payne, 1984). For standard culture conditions (19% O_2), the atmosphere was 95% air:5% CO_2, which vastly exceeds physiological oxygen tension (Hornsby and Crivello, 1983a). For low oxygen tension, the gas was a certified mixture of 1% O_2, 5% CO_2, 94% N_2, which is somewhat below physiological oxygen tension. When required, dimethyl sulfoxide (Me_2SO) was added to a final concentration of 100 mM.

In order to determine whether the *P*-450 activities of Leydig cells were sensitive to oxygen-mediated damage, the effects of reduction of oxygen tension (from 19 to 1% O_2) or addition of the hydroxyl radical scavenger, Me_2SO, on 17α-hydroxylase and C_{17-20} lyase activities in cultures of control Leydig cells were investigated. Enzyme activities were determined at the indicated times during a 1-hour period of incubation using ^3H-labeled substrates (Quinn and Payne, 1984). Prior to enzyme assay, Leydig cell cultures were subjected to a 1-hour wash period to deplete cells of endogenous substrate (Quinn and Payne, 1984). As illustrated in Fig. 5, the enzyme activities of control cultures are stable during the initial 24 hours of culture in all cases. In cells maintained under standard culture conditions (19% O_2), these activities decline markedly by day 2 and continue to do so as a function of time. Both addition of Me_2SO and reduction of oxygen tension were effective in maintaining these enzyme activities at higher levels for longer periods of time ($p < 0.05$). The reduction in oxygen tension was more effective than the addition of Me_2SO ($p < 0.05$), and the combination of these treatments was more effective than either alone ($p < 0.05$) in preserving the microsomal cytochrome *P*-450-dependent activities of cultured Leydig cells. The combined treatments appear to act synergistically, at least at later time points.

These data indicate that microsomal *P*-450 activities, 17α-hydroxylase and C_{17-20} lyase, of cultured Leydig cells are very sensitive to oxygen-mediated damage. The lag period of 24 hours in the decline of these *P*-450s is probably due to the utilization of endogenous antioxidants, and once these are depleted the *P*-450 activities decline rapidly. The observation that Me_2SO, a potent scavenger of hydroxyl radicals, was partially effective in preventing this decline, as was the reduction of oxygen tension, together with the observation that Me_2SO and low O_2 act synergistically to prevent the decline in *P*-450 activities, suggests that more than one form of active oxygen is responsible for the decline in *P*-450 activities. Reactive oxygen species (superoxide and H_2O_2) are generated during catalysis by *P*-450 and by autoxidation of *P*-450 (Coon *et al.,* 1982; Chance *et al.,* 1979; Ernster *et al.,* 1982; Hornsby and Crivello, 1983a; Kuthan and Ullrich, 1982). The production of O_2^- and H_2O_2 is often increased by pseudosubstrates (Hornsby and Crivello, 1983a; Nordblom and Coon, 1977; Kuthan *et al.,* 1978; Gunsalus and Sligar, 1977). In the presence of ferrous iron and ADP, H_2O_2 is converted to hydroxyl radicals

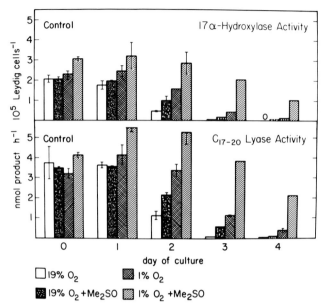

FIG. 5.   Effects of oxygen tension and Me₂SO on microsomal *P*-450 activities of control
Leydig cells in primary culture. Enzyme activities were determined during a 1-hour period
of incubation after a 3-hour attachment period on day 0 and then at 24-hour intervals. Cells
were maintained at the indicated culture conditions. 17α-Hydroxylase activity was determined by measuring the conversion of (^{3}H)progesterone to 17α-[^{3}H]hydroxyprogesterone,
[^{3}H]androstenedione, and [^{3}H]testosterone. C_{17-20} lyase activity was determined by measuring the conversion of 17α-[^{3}H]hydroxyprogesterone to [^{3}H]androstenedione and [^{3}H]testos-
terone. Determinations were done in duplicate. Values are the means; bars indicate the
range of two experiments (from Quinn and Payne, 1984).

via the Fenton reaction (Hornsby and Crivello, 1983a). H_2O_2 and other
organic peroxides can react with the heme of *P*-450 and inactivate the
enzyme (Coon *et al.*, 1982; Gunsalus and Sligar, 1977; Guengerich, 1978).
In addition, both hydroxyl radicals and superoxide anions can initiate
lipid peroxidation (Hornsby and Crivello, 1983a). Thus, the cytochrome
P-450 enzyme and/or its associated reductase can generate active oxygen
species which destroy the heme group directly or indirectly, by initiating
peroxidation of the membrane lipids in which it is embedded. Possible
mechanisms for the inactivation of *P*-450 enzymes based on our studies
and those mentioned above are illustrated in Fig. 6.

   The effects of oxygen tension and Me₂SO on 17α-hydroxylase and
C_{17-20} lyase activities in desensitized, as compared to control, Leydig cells
were also examined. Leydig cells were desensitized by treatment with 1
m*M* 8-Br-cAMP during the first 24 hours of culture only. This treatment

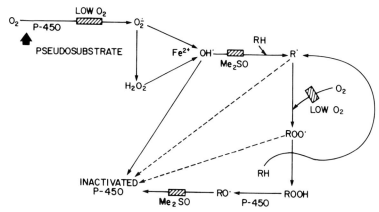

FIG. 6. Possible mechanisms for the inactivation of *P*-450 enzymes (adapted from Hornsby and Crivello, 1983). This scheme is based on investigations of purifed and microsomal preparations of *P*-450 enzymes from liver and on studies of *P*-450 activities in cultured adrenocortical and Leydig cells. PH, Polyunsaturated lipid; Me_2SO, dimethyl sulfoxide.

caused a 15-fold increase in testosterone production over basal levels during the first 24 hours of culture. 8-Br-cAMP was used, rather than LH or hCG, to induce steroidogenic desensitization, independently of LH receptor down-regulation. Studies from this and other laboratories have demonstrated that desensitization of steroidogenesis is independent of receptor down-regulation (Zipf *et al.*, 1978; Ascoli, 1981; Rani *et al.*, 1983). Preliminary experiments showed that LH and 8-Br-cAMP produced identical changes in enzyme activity and testosterone production. The effects of desensitization on 17α-hydroxylase and C_{17-20} lyase are illustrated in Figs. 7 and 8, respectively. In cells maintained under standard culture conditions (19% O_2), the enzyme activities of desensitized Leydig cells were significantly decreased relative to controls ($p < 0.05$): by one-half at 24 hours and by two-thirds at 48 hours. The addition of Me_2SO to the medium of cells cultured at 19% O_2 had no significant effect ($p > 0.05$) on the pattern observed, but the absolute level of enzyme activities was higher ($p < 0.05$). In contrast, when Leydig cells were cultured in an atmosphere of 1% O_2, the *P*-450 activities of desensitized cells were maintained at higher levels than in either 19% O_2 or 19% O_2 + Me_2SO ($p < 0.05$), and were not significantly different than control values ($p > 0.05$). Although these enzyme activities declined on days 3 and 4 of culture, the ratio of activities in control and desensitized Leydig cells remained near unity (Quinn and Payne, unpublished data). In cultures maintained at 1% O_2 in the presence of Me_2SO, the enzyme activities of desensitized Leydig cells were not significantly different from controls

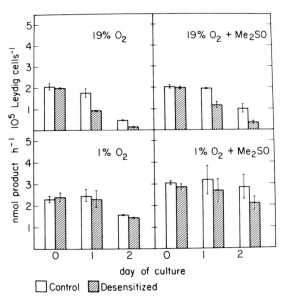

FIG. 7.   Effects of oxygen tension and Me₂SO on 17α-hydroxylase activity of control and desensitized Leydig cells in primary culture. 17α-Hydroxylase activity was determined as described in Fig. 5. To induce desensitization, cultures were treated with 1mM 8-Br-cAMP during the initial 24 hours of culture (from Quinn and Payne, 1984).

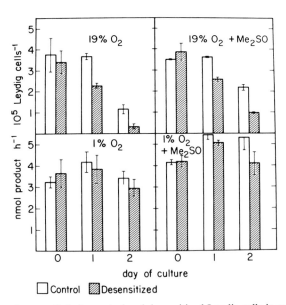

FIG. 8. C_{17-20} lyase activity in control and desensitized Leydig cells in primary culture. C_{17-20} lyase activity was determined as described under Figs. 5 and 7 (from Quinn and Payne, 1984).

during the initial 48 hours of culture ($p > 0.05$). Thus, the increased rate of loss of *P*-450 activities in desensitized Leydig cells could be prevented by lowering the oxygen tension, but not by the addition of the antioxidant.

The activity of 3β-hydroxysteroid dehydrogenase-isomerase, a microsomal enzyme which is not a *P*-450 enzyme, was determined after 3 hours and again on day 2 of culture in control and desensitized Leydig cells maintained under various conditions. It is clear from the data in Fig. 9 that desensitization did not decrease this enzyme activity under any culture conditions tested and that the level of this activity remained similar to control values during the initial 48 hours of culture. This is in marked contrast to the effects of desensitization and culture conditions on microsomal *P*-450 activities. These data indicate that the effects of desensitization, oxygen tension, and Me$_2$SO are specific for *P*-450 enzyme activities of Leydig cells and are not due to a general effect on the membrane in which these enzymes are embedded.

These data demonstrate that the increased rate of loss of *P*-450 activities in desensitized Leydig cells was not diminished by Me$_2$SO, but was entirely prevented by reduction of the oxygen tension. The large and rapid reduction of 17α-hydroxylase and C$_{17-20}$ lyase activities of desensi-

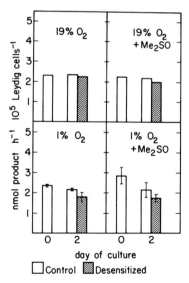

FIG. 9. Δ^5-3β-Hydroxysteroid dehydrogenase-isomerase activity of cultured Leydig cells. Δ^5-3β-Hydroxysteroid dehydrogenase-isomerase was determined by measuring the conversion of [^{3}H]pregnenolone to [^{3}H]progesterone, 17α-[^{3}H]hydroxyprogesterone, [^{3}H]androstenedione, and [^{3}H]testosterone during a 1-hour period of incubation after 3 or 48 hours in culture (from Quinn and Payne, 1984).

tized Leydig cells at 19% O_2 is consistent with the model described by
Hornsby and colleagues (Hornsby, 1980; Crivello *et al.*, 1982, 1983) for
the 11β-hydroxylase and 21-hydroxylase activities of cultured adrenocortical cells (reviewed in Hornsby and Crivello, 1983a,b). As mentioned
earlier, Hornsby (1980) proposed that destruction of P-450 activity results
from the interaction of products (pseudosubstrates) with the P-450 to
form a pseudosubstrate–P-450–O_2 complex, from which damaging oxygen-derived free radicals are released, due to the inability of the steroid to
be hydroxylated (Fig. 6). In the process of desensitization, Leydig cells
are exposed to high concentrations (>2 μM) of the product, testosterone.
Testosterone or other products of the P-450 catalyzed reaction could act
as pseudosubstrates and combine with the P-450 and thus increase generation of oxygen-free radicals.

2. *Effects of Oxygen Tension and Me$_2$SO on Maximal*
    Testosterone Production

The maximal steroidogenic capacity of control and desensitized Leydig
cells was assessed by incubating cultures with a maximally stimulatory
dose of 8-Br-cAMP (1 mM) for 3 hours and determining the amount of
testosterone produced. Preliminary data indicated that 8-Br-cAMP-stimu-
lated testosterone production was linear over the time period employed.
The maximal rate of testosterone production of Leydig cells during the
first 3 hours in culture and after 24 and 48 hours of culture in both control
and desensitized Leydig cells is shown in Fig. 10. The data are expressed
as the rate of testosterone production (nmol/hour/10^5 Leydig cells) to
facilitate comparison with the enzyme activities. Regardless of the culture
conditions, desensitized Leydig cells exhibited a 50% reduction in maximal capacity at 24 hours and a 75–80% reduction in maximal capacity by
48 hours. This finding is in marked contrast to the protective effect of
reduced oxygen tension on the hydroxylase and lyase activities of desensitized Leydig cells. Control cultures do not exhibit any reduction in maximal capacity to produce testosterone over 48 hours at either oxygen tension. Comparison of C_{17-20} lyase activity to maximal testosterone
production of control and desensitized Leydig cells on day 0 and day 2 of
culture is illustrated in Fig. 11. It can be seen, when comparing enzyme
activity to maximal testosterone production in control Leydig cells maintained in culture at 19% O_2, that Leydig cells can sustain a 75% loss in
lyase activity without any loss in the maximal rate of testosterone production. Conversely, when the lyase activity of desensitized Leydig cells is
maintained at control values by incubating the cells under reduced oxygen
tension (1% O_2) in the presence of Me$_2$SO, the maximal rate of testosterone production is still decreased by at least 50%. Similar results are seen
when comparing 17α-hydroxylase activity to maximal testosterone pro-

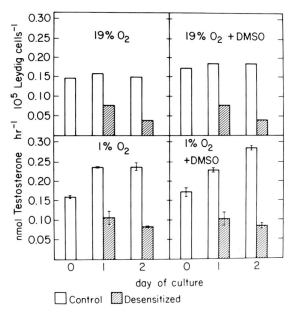

FIG. 10.   Maximal testosterone production in response to 8-Br-cAMP of cultured Leydig cells. Cultured Leydig cells were incubated in fresh medium containing 1 mM 8-Br-cAMP for a 3-hour period at 0, 24, and 48 hours. Control cells had not been previously exposed to 8-Br-cAMP, whereas desensitized cells had been treated with 1 mM 8-Br-cAMP during the initial 24 hours of culture (from Quinn and Payne, 1984).

duction (compare Fig. 7 to Fig. 10). It should be noted that the rate of testosterone production is only 10% of the rate of conversion of a saturating concentration of substrate to products by the microsomal enzymes of the testosterone biosynthetic pathway. Thus, even with the marked re-

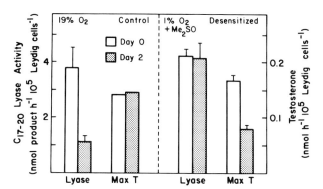

FIG. 11.   Relationship of microsomal *P*-450 activity to maximal testosterone production. Data from Fig. 5 and Fig. 10 for day 0 and day 2 of culture in control and desensitized Leydig cells are illustrated for comparison of lyase activity to maximal testosterone production.

duction in microsomal P-450 activities, observed at 48 hours in nondesensitized cells, these activities are still greater than the rate of testosterone production and therefore are not limiting. Further reductions of these P-450 activities to less than 10% of the original values as observed on day 4 of culture at 19% O_2 (Fig. 5), would make these activities become rate limiting in testosterone biosynthesis and could result in decreased steroidogenic capacity. The data demonstrate that the loss of the P-450 enzyme activities, 17α-hydroxylase and C_{17-20} lyase, in desensitized Leydig cells cannot account for the reduction in testosterone synthesis in response to cAMP observed in these cells.

3. Regulation of P-450 Activities by Steroid-Pseudosubstrates and Oxygen

The studies described above demonstrated that the microsomal P-450 enzymes of Leydig cells are susceptible to oxygen-mediated damage and that this is increased during desensitization, but did not evaluate the pseudosubstrate hypothesis directly or the possibility that steroid hormone receptor-mediated processes are involved in P-450 loss.

Other investigators have proposed that steroid hormone receptor-mediated mechanisms are involved in the regulation of Leydig cell testosterone biosynthesis and/or regulation of the level of microsomal P-450 activities in Leydig cells. Adashi and Hsueh (1981) reported that, in long-term cultures of Leydig cells derived from hypophysectomized rats, testosterone synthesis was regulated by a short-loop feedback mechanism, which is mediated by an androgen receptor. As discussed earlier, it has also been proposed that increased production of estradiol, resulting from a desensitizing dose of hCG, causes a decrease in Leydig cell microsomal P-450 activities via a steroid–receptor-mediated process (Nozu et al., 1981a,b). We, therefore, designed experiments to determine (1) whether increased concentrations of steroid products and/or product-related steroids could decrease microsomal P-450 enzyme activities by acting as pseudosubstrates, (2) whether androgen receptor agonists could induce or androgen receptor antagonists could prevent microsomal P-450 loss, (3) whether estradiol could induce microsomal P-450 loss, and (4) whether steroid-induced P-450 loss, in the absence of substrate depletion, could diminish the steroidogenic capacity of Leydig cells.

To determine whether the effects of cAMP-induced decreases in microsomal P-450 activities were due to increased steroid hormone production or a direct effect of cAMP on the P-450 enzymes, Leydig cell cultures were incubated for 48 hours at 19% O_2 in the absence or presence of aminoglutethimide alone, or in combination with cAMP. As shown in Table I, treatment with aminoglutethimide prevented cAMP from increas-

TABLE I

Effects of Inhibition of Steroid Hormone Synthesis on
17α-Hydroxylase Activity[a]

Treatment	Testosterone (ng 48 h^{-1} 10^{-5} Leydig cells)	17α-Hydroxylase activity (% of control)
Control	65 ± 1	100
Aminoglutethimide	4 ± 1	105 ± 11
cAMP	1659 ± 228	35 ± 7
cAMP+ aminoglutethimide	39 ± 1	93 ± 4

[a] Leydig cell cultures were incubated for 48 hours at 19% O_2 in the absence or presence of aminoglutethimide (0.25 mM) alone, or in combination with cAMP (1 mM). Culture medium from each 24-hour period was analyzed for testosterone by RIA and the amount of testosterone produced during the entire 48 hours in each treatment group is presented as accumulated testosterone. 17α-Hydroxylase activity was determined as described in Fig. 5.

ing testosterone production above basal values. Treatment with aminoglutethimide had no effect, by itself, on 17α-hydroxylase activity, but treatment with cAMP reduced 17α-hydroxylase activity to one-third of control values. However, when cultures were treated with cAMP in the presence of aminoglutethimide, the decrease in 17α-hydroxylase activity was prevented, indicating that the cAMP-induced decrease was dependent on increased steroid hormone production.

In order to determine whether the presence of increased concentrations of steroid products was sufficient to cause a decrease in 17α-hydroxylase activity, or whether additional factors, resulting from the stimulation of steroidogenesis, were required, Leydig cell cultures were maximally stimulated with LH or cAMP, or treated with steroid products of the enzyme pathway (Fig. 12), androstenedione or testosterone. The results of this experiment are illustrated in Fig. 13.

The steroid products were added to give a concentration of 2 μM steroid in the culture medium, which is equivalent to the concentration of testosterone present in the medium of cultures following stimulation with LH or cAMP for 24 hours. At 19% O_2, treatment with LH or cAMP, which increases endogenous steroid hormone production, resulted in a significant decrease in 17α-hydroxylase activity ($p < 0.05$). Reduction of the oxygen tension, in which Leydig cell cultures were maintained, to 1% O_2 prevented this decline. Treatment of Leydig cells with exogenous steroid products, androstenedione or testosterone, also caused a significant

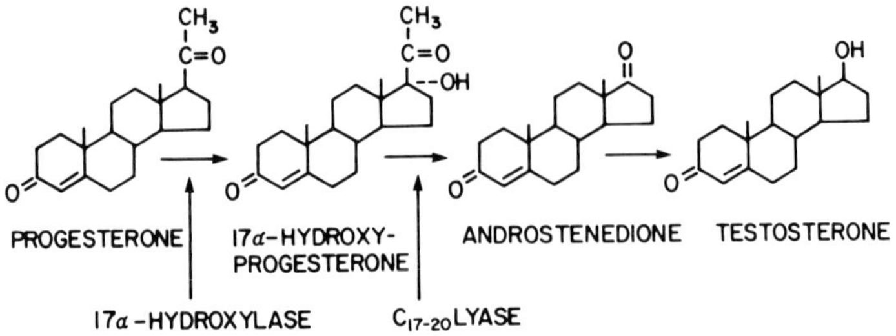

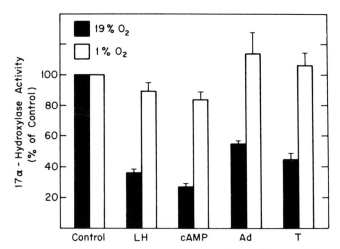

FIG. 12.　Micromal cytochrome P-450-catalyzed reactions of testosterone synthesis.

decrease in 17α-hydroxylase activity in cultures maintained at 19% O_2 ($p < 0.05$), which was similarly prevented by reduction of the oxygen tension, indicating that the presence of increased concentrations of steroid products, equivalent to those resulting from maximal stimulation of Leydig cell steroidogenesis, was sufficient to induce oxygen tension-sensitive decreases in 17α-hydroxylase activity.

The effects of steroid analogs of the products of the hydroxylase reaction, 17α-hydroxyprogesterone, and the steroidogenic pathway, testoster-

FIG. 13.　Effects of steroid products on 17α-hydroxylase activity. Leydig cell cultures were maintained at 19 and 1% O_2 and treated for 48 hours with no additions (control), 100 ng/ ml of luteinizing hormone (LH), 1 mM 8-Br-cAMP (cAMP), 2 μM androstenedione (Ad), or 2 μM testosterone (T). Cultures were then washed to remove treatment agents and 17α-hydroxylase activity was determined as described in Fig. 5. Results are expressed as a percentage of the respective control activities of cultures maintained at either 19 or 1% O_2 (from Quinn and Payne, 1985).

one, on 17α-hydroxylase activity of Leydig cells cultured at both 19 and 1% O_2 were also determined, and the results are presented in Fig. 14. Treatment of Leydig cell cultures with the 17α-hydroxy epimer of testosterone, epitestosterone, or with 17α-methyltestosterone, significantly reduced 17α-hydroxylase activity in cultures maintained at either 19 or 1% O_2 ($p < 0.05$). However, there was a significant reversal of the decrease in hydroxylase activity by reduction of the oxygen tension to 1% O_2 ($p < 0.05$). Treatment of cultures with 17α-hydroxyprogesterone acetate decreased 17α-hydroxylase activity slightly, but not significantly ($p > 0.05$), at either oxygen tension. In contrast, treatment with testosterone acetate maintained 17α-hydroxylase activity at values markedly and significantly higher than those observed in control cultures of Leydig cells ($p < 0.05$). Since 17α-hydroxylase activity of Leydig cell cultures decreases by 40–60% during the initial 48 hours of culture, the effect of testosterone acetate does not represent an increase in hydroxylase activity but, rather, represents nearly total protection of the hydroxylase activity present at the initiation of culture. Treatment of cultures with cortisol, which is not closely related to products of the enzyme pathway, had no effect on 17α-hydroxylase activity and was not affected by oxygen tension ($p > 0.05$). These data suggest that steroids with structures highly

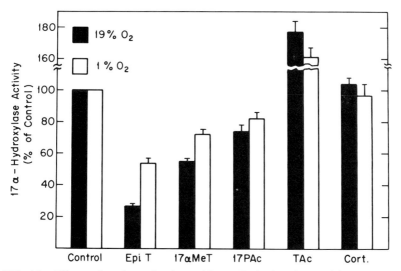

FIG. 14.   Effects of product-related steroids on 17α-hydroxylase activity. Leydig cell cultures were maintained and treated as described in Fig. 13. Steroids were added at a concentration of 2 μM. EpiT, Epitestosterone; 17αMeT, 17α-methyltestosterone; 17PAc, 17α-hydroxyprogesterone acetate; TAc, testosterone acetate; Cort, cortisol. 17α-Hydroxylase activity was determined as described in Fig. 5 (from Quinn and Payne, 1985).

analogous to those of products of the enzyme or pathway are required to affect 17α-hydroxylase activity.

In order to determine whether low concentrations of steroids would be effective at decreasing hydroxylase activity, as would be expected for a steroid hormone receptor-mediated action, or if higher concentrations were required, as would be expected of a steroid-pseudosubstrate-mediated action, the effects on hydroxylase activity of increasing concentrations of testosterone and epitestosterone, the most effective steroid analog, were determined (Fig. 15). The concentrations chosen were 50 nM, which is equivalent to the testosterone concentration in unstimulated Leydig cell cultures; 2 μM, which is equivalent to the concentration of testosterone in cAMP-stimulated cultures; and 10 μM, which is equivalent to the concentration of substrate required for saturation of the hydroxylase activity when assayed in these cultures. In cultures maintained at 19% O_2, neither steroid decreased hydroxylase activity at the lowest concentration (50 nM), whereas both steroids decreased hydroxylase activity at higher concentrations. Reduction of the oxygen tension to 1% O_2 prevented the testosterone-induced decrease in hydroxylase activity and reduced the extent of epitesterone-induced loss of hydroxylase activity, which is consistent with the hypothesis that these steroids act as pseudosubstrates.

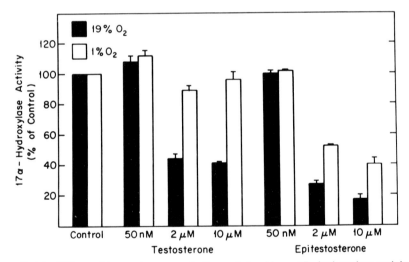

FIG. 15.   Effects of increasing concentrations of steroids on 17α-hydroxylase activity. Leydig cell cultures were maintained and treated as described in Fig. 13, except that cultures were treated for 48 hours with the indicated concentrations of either testosterone or epitestosterone. 17α-Hydroxylase activity was determined as described in Fig. 5 (from Quinn and Payne, 1985).

4. Effects of Steroid Hormone Receptor Agonists and an Androgen Receptor Antagonist on P-450 Activities

The effects of steroid receptor agonists on 17α-hydroxylase activity were determined and compared to the effects of cAMP, in order to evaluate further the possibility that testosterone or its metabolites act via a steroid hormone receptor-mediated mechanism (Fig. 16). The effect of testosterone was similar to that of cAMP; both caused significant decreases in hydroxylase activity which were reversible by reduction of oxygen tension ($p < 0.05$). Estradiol, which is produced only in small quantities (nM) by aromatization of testosterone in Leydig cells (Valladares and Payne, 1979), had no significant effect on hydroxylase activity ($p > 0.05$), even at a concentration of $2\mu M$. Treatment of Leydig cell cultures with the potent androgen receptor agonist, methyltrienolone (R 1881), had no significant effect on 17α-hydroxylase activity either ($p > 0.05$), indicating that androgen or estrogen receptor-mediated mechanisms are not likely to be involved in the cAMP- or testosterone-induced decrease in hydroxylase activity.

To evaluate the possibility that cAMP or testosterone acted via an androgen receptor-mediated mechanism which was inhibited by the reduction in oxygen tension, Leydig cell cultures were treated with cAMP or testosterone in the presence and absence of the androgen receptor

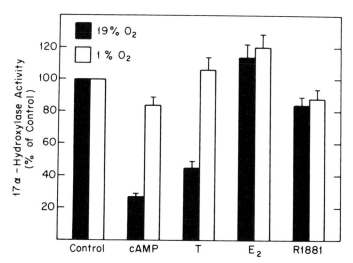

FIG. 16. Effects of steroid hormone receptor agonists on 17α-hydroxylase activity. Culture conditions were the same as described in Fig. 13. Steroids or agonist were added at a concentration of 2 μM: T, Testosterone; E$_2$, 17β-estradiol; R1881, methyltrienolone. 17α-Hydroxylase activity was determined as described in Fig. 5 (from Quinn and Payne, 1985).

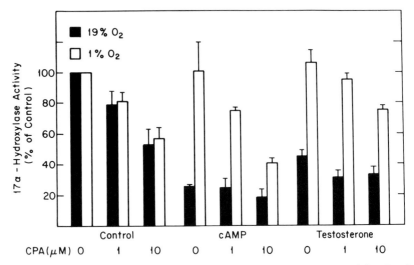

FIG. 17. Effects of androgen receptor antagonist on 17α-hydroxylase activity. Leydig cells were plated in culture medium containing the indicated concentration of cyproterone acetate (CPA) and incubated for 1 hour to allow occupation of receptor sites. At this time, treatment was initiated by addition of medium containing no additions (control), 1 mM 8-Br-cAMP (cAMP) or 2 μM testosterone and cultures were incubated for 48 hours at either 19 or 1% O_2 and analyzed as described in Fig. 13 (from Quinn and Payne, 1985).

antagonist, cyproterone acetate (Fig. 17). Treatment of Leydig cell cultures with 1 or 10 μM cyproterone acetate not only failed to reverse the effects of cAMP or testosterone on hydroxylase activity, but actually exacerbated the cAMP- or testosterone-induced loss of hydroxylase activity, especially at 1% O_2. Treatment of Leydig cell cultures with cyproterone acetate alone resulted in a decrease in hydroxylase activity, which was greater with the higher concentration of antagonist.

The effects of cAMP and steroids on C_{17-20} lyase activity were similar in pattern, except that the loss of hydroxylase activity was somewhat greater than that of lyase activity (Quinn and Payne, 1985).

These data support the hypothesis that the decline in microsomal P-450 activities of desensitized Leydig cells results from an increased concentration of steroid products, which act as pseudosubstrates for the P-450 enzymes to increase generation of oxygen-derived, free radical species, resulting in inactivation of the P-450 enzymes. The results do not support any role for estrogen or androgen receptor-mediated actions in the reduction of microsomal P-450 activities.

Several features of our data support the hypothesis that the decline in microsomal cytochrome P-450 activities in desensitized Leydig cells is a result of increased steroid products acting as pseudosubstrates for these P-450 enzymes. First, increased concentrations of steroid products, equivalent to those resulting from maximal stimulation of steroidogenesis, are required to reduce hydroxylase activity, as is demonstrated by the ability to block the cAMP-induced decrease in hydroxylase activity by blocking steroid hormone synthesis with aminoglutethimide, and by the lack of effect of low concentrations of steroids which reduce hydroxylase activity at higher concentrations. Second, the mere presence of increased concentrations of appropriate steroids is sufficient to induce hydroxylase loss, whether generated *in situ* by stimulation of Leydig cell steroidogenesis or by addition of exogenous steroids. Third, some degree of structural homology to the product of the enzyme and/or pathway is required for steroids to reduce hydroxylase activity. Δ^4-3-Ketosteroids bearing a substituent at position 17, such as androstenedione, testosterone, epitestosterone, and 17α-methyltestosterone, were effective in reducing hydroxylase activity at 19% O_2, whereas cortisol, which is also hydroxylated in the 11β and 21 positions, and estradiol, which contains an aromatic A ring, were not effective in reducing hydroxylase activity. In this regard, it should be noted that cyproterone acetate, which has been characterized and used as an androgen receptor antagonist (Neumann *et al.*, 1970), has substituents in the C and D ring identical to those of 17α-hydroxyprogesterone acetate and appears to act as a pseudosubstrate toward 17α-hydroxylase. Fourth, the cAMP- and steroid-induced decreases in P-450 activities, induced by cAMP and product-related steroids, were partially or wholly reversible by reduction of the oxygen tension from 19 to 1% O_2.

Our data are in general agreement with the reports of pseudosubstrate-induced, oxgen tension-sensitive damage of the 11β-hydroxylase (Hornsby, 1980; Crivello *et al.*, 1983) and the 21-hydroxylase (Crivello *et al.*, 1982; Crivello and Gill, 1983) activities of adrenocortical cell cultures. However, the 17α-hydroxylase activity of cultured adrenocortical cells appeared to be less sensitive to this process (Crivello *et al.*, 1982; Crivello and Gill, 1983). It is suggested that, rather than the 17α-hydroxylase of Leydig and adrenal cells differing in basic properties, the apparent difference in regulation of degradation of 17α-hydroxylase activity between adrenal and Leydig cells is a result of the relative position of this enzyme in the steroidogenic pathways of these tissues. The 17α-hydroxylase activity of adrenal cells occurs rather early in the pathway and 17α-hydroxylated products are rapidly metabolized to products hydroxylated in the 11β and 21 positions, such as 11β-hydroxyandrostenedione and cortisol, which may not be recognized by the 17α-hydroxylase enzyme. However, in Leydig cells the 17α-hydroxylase activity occurs later in the pathway and the products which build up have not been hydroxylated in other positions and differ from the enzyme's substrate only in the substituent at C_{17}, and therefore, could be candidates for binding to the enzyme.

An unexpected finding was that testosterone acetate appeared to protect rather than destroy hydroxylase activity. This is not simply a function of the acetate moiety, since 17α-hydroxyprogesterone acetate slightly reduced hydroxylase activity and epitestosterone acetate caused a decrease in hydroxylase activity similar to that caused by epitestosterone (Quinn and Payne, unpublished data). Since hydroxylase activity declined by 40–60% during the initial 48 hours of culture, the apparent increase in activity actually represents nearly entire preservation of hydroxylase activity present at the initiation of the culture. Preliminary results from spectral binding studies indicate that testosterone acetate binds tightly to a testicular microsomal preparation of cytochrome P-450 and induces a spectral change which is distinct in character from that induced by substrates (Quinn and Payne, unpublished data). Thus, testosterone acetate may bind to the P-450 enzyme without stimulating electron transport and oxygen-radical generation and serve a protective function.

The data in this study are not consistent with the involvement of an androgen receptor in mediating the cAMP- or steroid-induced decrease in hydroxylase activity. While this study was in progress, Ruiz de Galaretta *et al.* (1983) provided evidence that Δ^5-3β-hydroxysteroid dehydrogenase-isomerase levels are controlled by an androgen receptor-mediated mechanism. Our data are also not consistent with the cAMP-induced decreases in microsomal P-450 activities being mediated by estradiol as had been suggested (Nozu *et al.*, 1981a,b; Cigorraga *et al.*, 1978).

5. Relationship of P-450 Loss to Steroidogenic Capacity

In order to determine the relative contribution of decreases in P-450 activities and depletion of the substrate, cholesterol, to the diminished steroidogenic capacity of desensitized Leydig cells, cultures were treated for 48 hours with cAMP or steroids and the capacity of these Leydig cells to produce testosterone from endogenous cholesterol in response to acute stimulation with cAMP or from exogenous 22R-hydroxycholesterol, was determined in the same experiments in which hydroxylase and lyase activities had been determined (Fig. 18). Treatment with cAMP, which both depletes cholesterol stores and decreases P-450 activities, as a result of prolonged stimulation of steroidogenesis, drastically reduced the ability of cAMP-desensitized Leydig cells to synthesize testosterone in response to acute stimulation with cAMP (10–20% of control). It should be noted that, in spite of the fact that cAMP-induced P-450 loss was essentially prevented at 1% O_2, this had no effect on the marked decline in steroido-

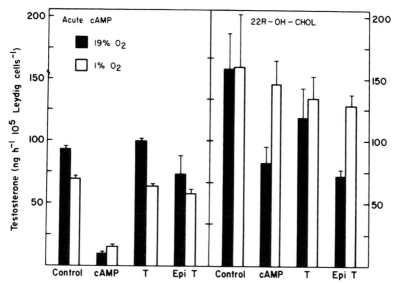

FIG. 18.   Effect of chronic cAMP and steroid treatment on acute, cAMP-stimulated and 22*R*-hydroxycholesterol-supported testosterone production. Leydig cell cultures were maintained at 19 or 1% O_2 and were treated for 48 hours with 8-Br-cAMP (1 m*M*) or the indicated steroid (2 μM). Cultures were incubated with either 8-Br-cAMP (1 m*M*) or 22*R*-hydroxycholesterol (22*R*-OH-CHOL : 20 μM) for 3 hours at 19% O_2. Testosterone was determined by RIA (from Quinn and Payne, 1985).

genic capacity of desensitized Leydig cells. In contrast, treatment of Leydig cell cultures with testosterone or epitestosterone, which decreases the *P*-450 activities of Leydig cell cultures without depleting cholesterol stores, had little or no effect on the capacity of Leydig cells to synthesize testosterone in response to acute stimulation with cAMP (80–100% of Control). Testosterone production resulting from metabolism of 22*R*-hydroxycholesterol, which bypasses the rate-limiting transport of substrate to *P*-450$_{scc}$ and therefore is limited only by the enzyme activities of the steroidogenic pathway, was 2-fold higher than cAMP-stimulated testosterone production in control Leydig cell cultures. Chronic treatment with cAMP had less effect, relative to control, on 22*R*-hydroxycholesterol-supported testosterone production than it had on acute cAMP-stimulated testosterone synthesis. In contrast, treatment with testosterone or epitestosterone, which had little or no effect on acute cAMP-stimulated testosterone production, reduced 22*R*-hydroxycholesterol-supported testosterone production by 25–55% at 19% O_2. Reduction of the oxygen tension decreased the extent to which 22*R*-hydroxycholesterol-supported testosterone production declined in cAMP- or steroid-treated Leydig cells. Although metabolism of 22R-hydroxycholesterol more closely reflects the extent of P-450 enzyme loss, testosterone production was not decreased to as great an extent as were the P-450 activities. In addition, 22R-hydroxycholesterol-supported testosterone production remained at or near values for cAMP-stimulated testosterone production in spite of the large decreases in P-450 activities caused by cAMP or steroid treatment. The data demonstrate that depletion of endogenous cholesterol stores contributes more than does the decrease in P-450 activities to the reduced steroidogenic capacity of desensitized Leydig cells.

III. Hormone and cAMP Induction of Microsomal Cytochrome P-450 Enzymes

The above studies describe the mechanisms by which degradation of microsomal P-450s occurs in Leydig cells. Little is known about the regulation of synthesis of these enzymes. *In vivo* studies in hypophysectomized rats suggest that LH/hCG is essential for the maintenance of testicular microsomal P-450 activities. Purvis *et al.* (1973b) reported that daily administration of hCG to hypophysectomized rats resulted in large increases in testicular microsomal P-450 which correlated quite closely to increases observed in the activities of 17α-hydroxylase and C$_{17-20}$ lyase. However, daily treatment of intact rats with hCG for 9 days resulted in relatively small increases (~30%) in both of these enzyme activities in microsomes of whole testes. These data suggest that LH regulates the activities of microsomal P-450 enzymes. However, the increase could be a reflection of a gonadotropin-stimulated increase in the number of Leydig cells, as reported by Christensen and Peacock (1980). In order to differentiate between these two possible effects of LH/hCG, our laboratory designed experiments to determine whether chronic treatment with gonadotropin could increase microsomal P-450 content per Leydig cell and whether a correlation exists between increases in the microsomal P-450 activities and maximal testosterone production.

A. EFFECTS OF CHRONIC GONADOTROPIN TREATMENT *IN VIVO*

To examine the effect of daily treatment with hCG *in vivo* on microsomal P-450 enzymes and on testosterone production, we used the two populations of rat Leydig cells as a model system. We had previously reported that differences in maximal testosterone production between the

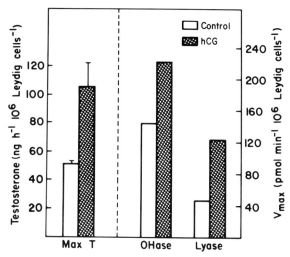

FIG. 19. Effect of chronic hCG treatment on maximal testosterone production and microsomal *P*-450 activities in population I Leydig cells. Mature rats were injected subcutaneously with saline (control) or 5 IU hCG for 6 days. Rats were killed on day 7, 24 hours after the last injection. Leydig cell population I was obtained as described in Fig. 2. Maximal testosterone production and 17α-hydroxylase (OHase) and C_{17-20} lyase (Lyase) activities were determined as described in Fig. 2 (adapted from O'Shaughnessy and Payne, 1982).

two populations of Leydig cells from untreated animals may be related, in part, to differences in the activity of C_{17-20} lyase (O'Shaughnessy *et al.*, 1981). In another study, we demonstrated that daily treatment with gonadotropin caused a marked increase in maximal testosterone production in population I, but only a relatively small increase in maximal testosterone production in population II (Payne *et al.*, 1980).

In the studies decribed here, we examined changes in enzyme activities and maximal testosterone production in the same pool of Leydig cells, obtained from rats after daily treatment with 5 IU hCG for 6 days. Rats were killed on the seventh day and Leydig cells were separated into two populations by Metrizamide gradient centrifugation (O'Shaughnessy *et al.*, 1981; O'Shaughnessy and Payne, 1982). Changes in maximal testosterone production and microsomal *P*-450 activities in population I and population II Leydig cells following daily administration of hCG are shown in Figs. 19 and 20, respectively. Prior to treatment, population I Leydig cells have a lower capacity for testosterone production than population II Leydig cells. After daily treatment with hCG, Leydig cell population I exhibited a 2-fold increase in maximal testosterone production which was associated with increases in both 17α-hydroxylase and C_{17-20} lyase activity (Fig. 19). Daily hCG treatment resulted in a smaller increase

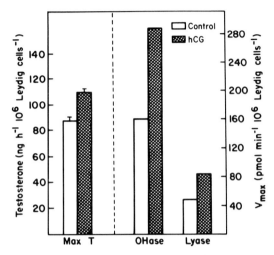

FIG. 20. Effect of chronic hCG treatment on maximal testosterone production and microsomal *P*-450 activities in population II Leydig cells. Methods were identical to those described for Fig. 19, except that population II Leydig cells were used (adapted from O'Shaughnessy and Payne, 1982).

in maximal testosterone production and a smaller increase in C_{17-20} lyase activity in population II Leydig cells, compared to the increases observed in population I (Fig. 20). The increase in 17α-hydroxylase activity was of similar magnitude in both of the populations. The effect of hCG on microsomal *P*-450 enzymes was not a general effect of gonadotropin on microsomal steroidogenic enzymes, since this treatment did not cause increases in two other microsomal enzymes related to steroid biosynthesis. No change was observed in 17-ketosteroid reductase activity in population I, but a marked decrease was observed in this activity in population II Leydig cells, while no change was detected in 5α-reductase activity in either population (O'Shaughnessy and Payne, 1982).

Our data, together with the earlier studies by Purvis *et al.* (1973b), suggest that under normal *in vivo* conditions, LH is essential for the maintenance of the microsomal *P*-450 enzymes, 17α-hydroxylase and C_{17-20} lyase.

B. LH AND cAMP-STIMULATED INDUCTION OF MICROSOMAL CYTOCHROME *P*-450 ENZYMES IN CULTURED MOUSE LEYDIG CELLS

In order to establish whether the increase observed in Leydig cell microsomal *P*-450s after *in vivo* treatment of animals is a direct effect of LH on the Leydig cell and to examine the intracellular mechanism by which LH increases these enzymes, the culture system of purified mouse Leydig cells was adapted, using conditions appropriate for induction of the *P*-450 enzymes. There have been no previous reports of hormone- or cAMP-stimulated induction of steroid biosynthetic enzymes in Leydig cells *in vitro*. Functionally active Leydig cells from mature animals have been difficult to maintain in primary culture (Mather, 1980; Hunter *et al.*, 1982; Murphy and Moger, 1982).

Many investigators have shown that the induction process can be demonstrated only after cells have been maintained in culture for a week. Leydig cells were maintained in culture for 6 to 7 days at standard oxygen tension in media containing the hydroxyl radical scavenger, Me_2SO, prior to the initiation of hormonal treatment. The decrease in 17α-hydroxylase and C_{17-20} lyase activity (to 5–10% of initial activity) observed during the initial period of culture is analogous to the demonstrated decrease in these enzymes that occurs following hypophysectomy (Purvis *et al.*, 1973b).

1. Effects of Oxygen

Since we had found that lowering the oxygen tension, from 19 to 1% O_2, reduced degradation of the microsomal *P*-450 enzymes (Figs. 5–8), we first tested the effect of reduction of oxygen tension on LH induction of 17α-hydroxylase. As can be seen in Fig. 21, cells incubated in the presence of LH exhibited a greater increase in 17α-hydroxylase activity when incubated in an atmosphere of 1% O_2 than when incubated under standard culture conditions (19% O_2). In the absence of LH, 17α-hydroxylase activity remained constant at both oxygen tensions. Therefore, all subsequent treatments of Leydig cell cultures were done in an atmosphere of 1% O_2, unless otherwise indicated.

2. cAMP as a Mediator of LH Action

We compared the induction of 17α-hydroxylase activity by LH to that by cAMP. The optimal dose for induction had been established to be 3 ng/ml of LH (Malaska and Payne, 1984) and 0.3–0.5 mM 8-Br-cAMP (Malaska, Rani and Payne, unpublished data). Treatment of cultures with cAMP for 6 days resulted in a markedly greater induction of 17α-hydroxylase, compared to cultures treated with LH (Fig. 22). Previous studies, *in vivo* and *in vitro*, have demonstrated a LH- or hCG-induced down-regulation of free LH receptors (Payne *et al.*, 1980) and desensitization of adenylate cyclase in Leydig cells (Mather *et al.*, 1982). These findings probably account for the lower level of induction seen in the presence of LH, as compared to the cAMP response, which is independent of receptor regulation and adenylate cyclase activity.

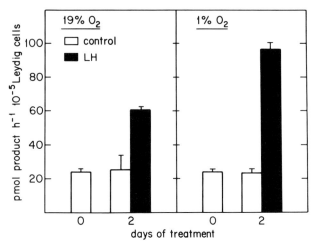

FIG. 21.   Effect of oxygen tension on the induction of 17α-hydroxylase activity by LH in cultured mouse Leydig cells. Prior to treatment with LH, Leydig cells were maintained in serum-free culture medium under standard incubation conditions (19% O_2) for 7 days. On day 7 (day 0 of treatment), cultures were either continued at 19% O_2 or transferred to 1% O_2 and treated with or without LH (1.0 ng/ml) for 2 days. 17α-Hydroxylase activity was determined as described in Fig. 5 (from Malaska and Payne, 1984).

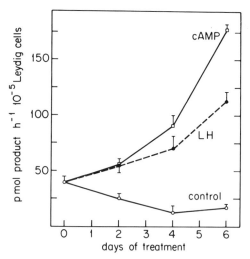

FIG. 22.   Effect of treatment with LH or cAMP on induction of 17α-hydroxylase activity. Prior to treatment, Leydig cells were maintained under standard oxygen tension (19% O_2) for 6 days. On day 6 (day 0 of treatment), cultures were transferred to 1% O_2. Treatment, with LH (3 ng/ml), 8-Br-cAMP (0.5 mM), or no additions (control), was initiated and continued for 6 days. Media containing appropriate treatment agents was replaced daily. 17α-Hydroxylase activity was determined as described in Fig. 5 at the indicated times.

To examine whether induction of C_{17-20} lyase activity occurred in a similar manner as that of 17α-hydroxylase activity, cultures were treated for 11 days with cAMP. As shown in Fig. 23, treatment with cAMP caused a markedly greater extent of induction of C_{17-20} lyase than 17α-hydroxylase. However, the final ratio of activity of C_{17-20} lyase to 17α-hydroxylase of 2 : 1 is comparable to the ratio of these activities of freshly isolated Leydig cells, indicating that the induction process in the *in vitro* model system accurately reflects the processes occurring *in vivo*.

To determine whether the effect of cAMP was specific for the *P*-450 enzymes, the activity of 3β-hydroxysteroid dehydrogenase-isomerase was measured in cultures incubated in the presence and absence of cAMP, under standard culture conditions (19% O_2) or under a reduced oxygen tension (1% O_2). The data in Table II show that treatment of cultures with cAMP at either oxygen tension did not cause an increase in 3β-hydroxysteroid dehydrogenase-isomerase activity. These data demonstrate that cAMP induction of 17α-hydroxylase and C_{17-20} lyase is not a general effect on all of the microsomal enzymes. This observation is consistent with the report by Purvis *et al.* (1973b), who found that chronic treatment of hypophysectomized rats with hCG resulted in large increases in testicular 17α-hydroxylase and C_{17-20} lyase activities, but not in another testicular microsomal *P*-450 enzyme, 7α-hydroxylase, or in the activity of 17β-hydroxysteroid dehydrogenase (17-ketosteroid reductase). It should

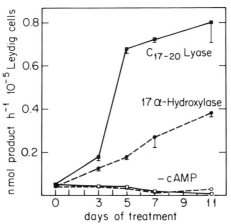

FIG. 23.   Effect of cAMP treatment on the induction of 17α-hydroxylase and C_{17-20} lyase activities. Leydig cells were maintained in culture as described in Fig. 22. Cultures were transferred to 1% O_2 and treatment with or without 0.5 mM 8-Br-cAMP was initiated. On days indicated, the activities of 17α-hydroxylase (○, −cAMP; ●, +cAMP) and C_{17-20} lyase (□, −cAMP; ■, +cAMP) were determined as described in Fig. 5.

TABLE II

3β-Hydroxysteroid Dehydrogenase-Isomerase Activity in Cultured Leydig Cells[a]

Day of treatment	19% O_2		1% O_2	
	Control	cAMP	Control	cAMP
0	1.56 ± 0.14[b]	—	—	—
1	1.54 ± 0.04	1.43 ± 0.06	1.54 ± 0.03	1.43 ± 0.06
3	1.17 ± 0.01	1.21 ± 0.04	1.24 ± 0.02	1.26 ± 0.06
5	0.99 ± 0.11	1.07 ± 0.01	1.21 ± 0.11	1.09 ± 0.02
7	0.71 ± 0.04	0.81 ± 0.05	0.99 ± 0.02	0.82 ± 0.04

[a] Leydig cells were maintained in culture at 19% O_2 for 6 days. On day 7 (day 0 of treatment) cultures were either continued at 19% O_2 or transferred to 1% O_2 and treated for 7 days without or with 0.5 mM 8-Br-cAMP. The activity of 3β-hydroxysteroid dehydrogenase-isomerase was determined on the day indicated as described in Fig. 9.

[b] nmol h^{-1} 10^{-5} Leydig cells.

be noted that the rate of decay of 17α-hydroxylase and C_{17-20} lyase activities during the initial 6 days in culture differs markedly from that of 3β-hydroxysteroid dehydrogenase-isomerase activity; after 6 days in culture, 17α-hydroxylase and C_{17-20} lyase activities are less than 5% of initial activity, while the 3β-hydroxysteroid dehydrogenase-isomerase is 67% of the initial activity of the enzyme.

To determine whether cAMP has to be present continuously for induction of C_{17-20} lyase activity or whether, once initiated, induction can proceed in the absence of cAMP, Leydig cell cultures were maintained in the presence of cAMP for 5 days or for only 2 days, followed by incubation for 3 more days in the absence of cAMP. Enzyme activity and testosterone production were measured daily (Fig. 24). The data shown in Fig. 24A indicate that induction of C_{17-20} lyase activity proceeded at a markedly reduced rate during the 24-hour period after removal of cAMP, and then decreased during the following 48 hours to a value equivalent to that found in control cultures. A similar pattern in production of testosterone was observed following the removal of cAMP (Fig. 24B). These data indicate that cAMP is the mediator of induction and that its continued presence is essential for the continuous induction of enzyme activity and increase in testosterone production.

In order to evaluate whether the cAMP-stimulated increase in *P*-450 activities reflects a true induction phenomenon involving protein synthesis, the effect of a 24-hour exposure of cultures to cycloheximide was investigated. Leydig cell cultures were incubated in the presence or ab-

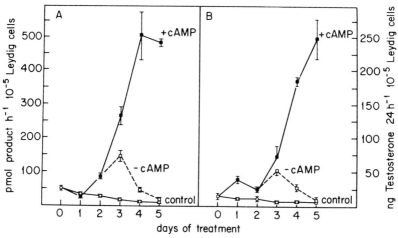

FIG. 24. Effect of removal of cAMP on the induction of C_{17-20} lyase activity (A) and on testosterone production (B). Leydig cells were maintained in culture as described in Fig. 22. Treatment was initiated after cells were transferred to 1% O_2. Cells were incubated in the absence (○) or presence of 0.3 m*M* 8-Br-cAMP for 5 days (■) or for 2 days with 0.3 m*M* 8-Br-cAMP followed by 3 days in the absence of cAMP (□). C_{17-20} lyase activity (A) and 24-hour testosterone accumulation (B) were determined daily as described earlier (from Malaska and Payne, 1984).

sence of cAMP for the first 24 hours of treatment. Each set of cultures was then divided into two groups and one set in each group was treated with cycloheximide (10 μg/ml) for the next 24 hours and the other set served as controls, with and without cAMP. Cultures were washed twice with medium to remove the cycloheximide and incubated for an additional 72 hours with or without cAMP. In control cultures, treated with cAMP but not cycloheximide, C_{17-20} lyase activity increased markedly after a 24-hour lag period and testosterone synthesis increased after a 48-hour lag period. In contrast, it was found that the addition of cycloheximide to cAMP-treated Leydig cell cultures completely inhibited the increase in C_{17-20} lyase activity as well as the increase in testosterone accumulation (Fig. 25). Induction of the enzyme resumed after a 24-hour lag period following the removal of cycloheximide (Fig. 24A), while there was a longer delay (48 hours) before testosterone production increased following removal of cycloheximide (Fig. 25B), as had been observed in the control groups. The resumption of induction in a parallel manner in both extent of induction and the lag period compared to non-cycloheximide-treated control cultures indicate that cycloheximide was not toxic to the cells. These data are consistent with cAMP-mediated induction of *de novo* protein synthesis and suggest that the increase in C_{17-20} lyase activ-

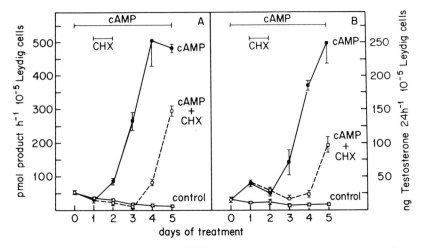

FIG. 25. Effect of cycloheximide (CHX) on cAMP induction of C_{17-20} lyase activity (A) and testosterone production (B). Leydig cells were maintained as described in Fig. 22 until treatment was initiated. Cells were treated for 5 days in the absence (○) or presence (■) of 0.3 mM 8-Br-cAMP. Replicate cultures, incubated in the presence of 0.3 mM 8-Br-cAMP, were treated with cycloheximide (10 μg/ml) for 24 hours only, between days 1 and 2 (□). C_{17-20} lyase activity (A) and 24-hour testosterone accumulation (B) were determined as described earlier.

ity represents an increase in the amount of enzyme synthesized and not just an activation of the preexisting enzyme.

3. Effects of Steroid Synthesis on Induction of P-450 Activities

Data presented in Section II demonstrate that steroid products can act as pseudosubstrates for the microsomal P-450 enzymes and thereby accelerate degradation of these enzymes. Inhibition of steroid hormone biosynthesis by the addition of aminoglutethimide to the cultures was shown to completely prevent the degradation of 17α-hydroxylase during a 48-hour period of incubation (Table I, Section II). It was therefore of interest to evaluate the effect of cAMP on the induction of these enzymes when increased steroid production was prevented by the addition of aminoglutethimide. Treatment with cAMP, in the presence of aminoglutethimide, resulted in higher activity of both 17α-hydroxylase and C_{17-20} lyase at all times, compared to treatment with cAMP alone (Figs. 26 and 27). Inhibition of steroid hormone biosynthesis allowed treatment with cAMP to completely restore 17α-hydroxylase and C_{17-20} lyase activities to levels observed in freshly isolated Leydig cells. With each of these enzyme activities, induction in the absence of steroid hormone biosynthesis was

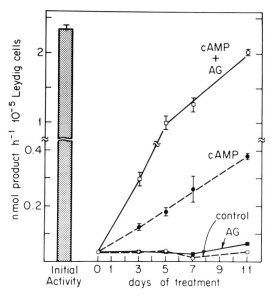

FIG. 26.   Effect of inhibition of steroid biosynthesis on cAMP induction of 17α-hydroxy-lase activity. Leydig cells were maintained as described in Fig. 22 until treatment was initiated. Cells were treated with 0.5 mM 8-Br-cAMP in the absence (●) or presence (□) of 0.5 mM aminoglutethimide. Control cultures without addition of cAMP were treated with (■) or without (○) aminoglutethimide. Hatched bar, enzyme activity in freshly isolated Leydig cells. 17α-Hydroxylase activity was determined on days indicated, as described in Fig. 5.

markedly greater than when steroid production was not inhibited. Addition of aminoglutethimide to control cultures had little, if any, effect on the microsomal *P*-450s. Since steroid production in the absence of cAMP is very low, no effect of aminoglutethimide would be expected.

To investigate whether oxygen tension would affect the induction process in the absence of increased steroid production, Leydig cell cultures were incubated at 19 or 1% O_2 in the presence of cAMP and aminoglutethimide. As shown in Fig. 28, even in the absence of steroid hormone synthesis, induction of 17α-hydroxylase in cultures maintained in air (19% O_2) is only 50% of that seen in cultures maintained at reduced oxygen tension (1% O_2). As discussed earlier in this article, oxygen-mediated damage of the microsomal *P*-450s occurs in cultures incubated at 19% O_2 in the absence of increased steroid hormone synthesis and this damage is markedly increased when steroid hormone synthesis is stimulated by the addition of LH or cAMP to the cultures (Fig. 13). It should be noted, however, that *in vivo* cells are not subjected to as high an oxygen tension

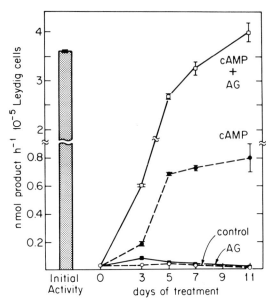

FIG. 27. Effect of inhibition of steroid biosynthesis on cAMP induction of C_{17-20} lyase activity. Experimental details are identical to those described in Fig. 26, except that the activity of C_{17-20} lyase was measured.

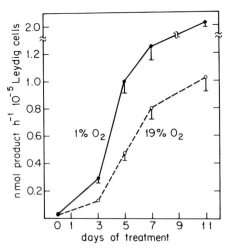

FIG. 28. Effect of oxygen tension and inhibition of steroid biosynthesis on cAMP induction of 17α-hydroxylase activity. Leydig cells were maintained in culture as described in Fig. 21. On day 6 (day 0 of treatment) cultures were either continued at 19% O_2 (○) or transferred to 1% O_2 (●). Cultures at both oxygen tensions were treated with 0.5 mM 8-Br-cAMP and 0.5 mM aminoglutethimide and 17α-hydroxylase activity was determined, on days indicated, as described in Fig. 5.

as when incubated in air (19% O_2). Therefore, oxygen-mediated damage to *P*-450 enzymes under physiologic conditions would be considerably less than that observed under normal culture conditions, but greater than that seen at 1% O_2. It is concluded from the data presented in Figs. 26–28, that inhibition of steroid hormone biosynthesis and incubation in a reduced oxygen tension markedly decreases degradation of the microsomal *P*-450 enzymes and thus allows a greater accumulation of newly synthesized 17α-hydroxylase and C_{17-20} lyase. Furthermore, these data demonstrate that cAMP induction of the microsomal *P*-450 activities is not a steroid- or substrate-mediated process.

In previous studies on ACTH-stimulated induction of 17α-hydroxylase activity in cultures of bovine adrenocortical cells, increases in 17α-hydroxylase activity of a short duration followed by decreases between 36 and 96 hours were reported (McCarthy *et al.*, 1983; Crivello and Gill, 1983). In Leydig cells, we have not observed a decrease in either 17α-hydroxylase or in C_{17-20} lyase activity in cultures treated with cAMP for as long as 13 days. As stated above, we demonstrated that the culture conditions used in our studies reduce or prevent degradation of newly synthesized enzymes. In the above studies in adrenocortical cells, cells were incubated in air, which, most likely, caused oxygen-mediated damage to the 17α-hydroxylase. With increasing time in culture, degradation may have exceeded ACTH-stimulated induction of 17α-hydroxylase, resulting in the observed decrease in enzyme activity that occurred between 36 and 96 hours. Continuous treatment with high concentrations of ACTH also could have caused down-regulation of ACTH receptors which could make continued treatment with ACTH less effective. Studies in adrenocortical cells, using different culture conditions, should resolve whether synthesis and degradation of 17α-hydroxylase in adrenal and Leydig cells are regulated in the same manner.

C_{17-20} lyase is expressed to only a minimal extent in adrenal cells. It has been suggested that 17α-hydroxylase and C_{17-20} lyase are the same protein, based on copurification of these activities from neonatal pig testis and adrenal microsomes (Nakajin and Hall, 1981; Nakajin *et al.*, 1981; Suhara *et al.*, 1984). An explanation for the low expression of C_{17-20} lyase in porcine adrenal cells was recently provided by Suhara *et al.* (1984). 17α-Hydroxyprogesterone is the substrate for 21-hydroxylase as well as C_{17-20} lyase in adrenal microsomes. These latter two enzymes compete for the same substrate, 17α-hydroxyprogesterone, and the amount of deoxycortisol and cortisol produced through the action of 21-hydroxylase, compared to the amount of C_{19}-androstenedione produced, through the action of C_{17-20} lyase, depends on the ratio of the activities of these two enzymes present. Suhara and colleagues, in an elegant study, demonstrated that when 17α-hydroxyprogesterone was incubated in a reconstituted hybrid system that contained equal amounts of testicular P-450$_{sccII}$ (17α-hydroxylase and C_{17-20} lyase) and adrenal P-450 $_{C21}$ (21-hydroxylase), androstenedione and 11-deoxycortisol were produced in an approximately equal molar ratio (Suhara *et al.*, 1984). However, when the hybrid system contained a 3:1 ratio of P-450$_{C21}$ to P-450$_{sccII}$, the metabolites closely resembled that of adrenal microsomes: 11-deoxycortisol was the major product and only small quantities of androstenedione were produced. These data indicate that the low production of C_{19} steroids in adrenal cells is probably not due to low expression of the enzyme, C_{17-20} lyase, but may be a result of rapid metabolism of substrate in alternative pathways.

In a recent study on regulation of adrenal steroidogenesis, DiBartolomeis and Jefcoate (1984) examined the effect of chronic ACTH stimulation on 17α-hydroxylase and C_{17-20} lyase activities in primary bovine adrenocortical cell cultures. Cultures incubated for 24 hours in the presence of ACTH showed a marked increase of ~9-fold, between 8 and 24 hours, in 17α-hydroxylase activity without showing any increase in C_{17-20} lyase activity. These data indicate that 17α-hydroxylase activity is regulated differently than C_{17-20} lyase activity in adrenal cells and, furthermore, suggest the possibility of two distinct enzymes. Our data on Leydig cell cultures demonstrate that both enzyme activities are induced by cAMP in a similar manner (Figs. 26 and 27), even though the extent of induction appears to be greater for C_{17-20} lyase than for 17α-hydroxylase. Additional studies are necessary to resolve the question of whether these two activities are associated with distinct proteins or the same protein.

IV. Conclusion

In conclusion, the data presented in this article provide new insights into the mechanism by which the microsomal cytochrome P-450 enzymes, 17α-hydroxylase and C_{17-20} lyase, of Leydig cells are maintained at a constant level under normal physiological conditions. The data are summarized in a schematic illustration in Fig. 29. Pulsatile stimulation of Leydig cells by LH *in vivo* increases cAMP levels which, by some as yet unknown mechanism, increases synthesis of the microsomal P-450 enzymes. In addition, cAMP increases steroid hormone production by increasing the availability of the precursor, cholesterol, for further metabolism to testosterone. The steroid products, present at elevated concentrations, can then act as pseudosubstrates for the P-450 enzyme, and in the presence of oxygen, a P-450–pseudosubstrate–O_2 complex is formed. Due to the inability of the pseudosubstrate to be hydroxylated, the complex breaks down, giving rise to reactive oxygen-free radical spe-

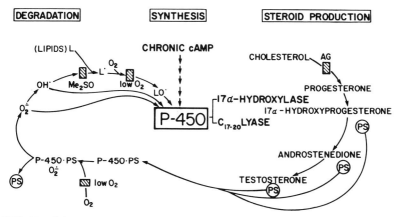

FIG. 29. Schematic diagram of regulation of synthesis and degradation of microsomal cytochrome *P*-450 enzymes in Leydig cells of cAMP and steroids. PS, Pseudosubstrate (products); O^-, oxygen radical; OH•, hydroxyl radical; LO•, lipoxy radical; AG, aminoglutethimide.

cies. The latter can then inactivate the *P*-450 directly or indirectly, by initiating peroxidation of membrane lipids in which these enzymes are embedded. Thus, the prolonged maximal stimulation of steroidogenesis in response to a desensitizing dose of LH or hCG results in accumulation of steroid products and increased degradation of the microsomal *P*-450 enzymes.

Our studies also provide data that explain why chronic treatment with LH or hCG results in marked increases in the *P*-450 activities in hypophysectomized animals, but only in relatively small increases in intact animals. Microsomal *P*-450s and testosterone synthesis rapidly disappear in the absence of LH, as seen following hypophysectomy. When these animals are treated with LH or hCG, the low levels of microsomal *P*-450 activities limit the amount of steroid product formation. The absence of high levels of steroid products facilitates a greater induction of these enzyme activities. Higher levels of these enzymes can then result in increased steroidogenesis, again initiating the process of pseudosubstrate-induced *P*-450 degradation, thus achieving homeostasis of microsomal *P*-450s. In contrast, in an intact animal, given chronic treatment of LH or hCG, there is not only an induction of *P*-450 synthesis, but also an increase in the production of steroids which can act as pseudosubstrates and cause degradation of the newly synthesized microsomal *P*-450, resulting in only small net increases in total amounts of 17α-hydroxylase and C_{17-20} lyase. The future availability of specific antibodies to the microsomal cytochrome *P*-450 enzymes should allow us to more precisely examine the rates of synthesis and degradation of these enzymes in cultured Leydig cells under various conditions.

ACKNOWLEDGEMENTS

The authors gratefully acknowledge the following collaborators whose experiments and discussions have contributed to the studies presented in this article: Peter J. O'Shaughnessy, Tamie Malaska, David J. Chase, John R. D. Stalvey, and Markos Georgiou. We are indebted to Mary R. Dockrill and Linda A. Whittingham for technical assistance and to Linda J. Johnson for preparation of the manuscript. Preparation of the manuscript and studies reported in this article were supported by National Institutes of Health Grants HD-08358 and HD-17915. Patrick G. Quinn was supported by the National Institutes of Health Training Grant HD-07048.

REFERENCES

Adashi, E. Y., and Hsueh, A. J. W. (1981). *Nature (London)* **293**, 737.

Ascoli, M. (1981). *J. Biol. Chem.* **256**, 179.

Benahmed, M., Dellamonica, C., Haour, F., and Saez, J. M. (1981). *Biochem. Biophys. Res. Commun.* **99**, 1123.

Brinkman, A. O., Leemborg, F. G., and van der Molen, H. J. (1981). *Mol. Cell. Endocrinol.* **24**, 65.

Brinkman, A. O., Leemborg, I., Rommerts, F., and van der Molen, H. J. (1982). *Endocrinology* **110**, 1834.

Brown, M. S., and Goldstein, J. L. (1976). *Science* **191**, 150.

Catt, K. J., Tsuruhara, T., and Dufau, M. L. (1972). *Biochim. Biophys. Acta* **279**, 194.

Chance, B., Sies, H., and Boveris, A. (1979). *Physiol. Rev.* **59**, 527.

Charreau, E. H., Calvo, J. C., Nozu, K., Pignataro, O., Catt, K. J., and Dufau, M. L. (1981). *J. Biol. Chem.* **256**, 12719.

Chasalow, F., Marr, H., Haour, F., and Saez, J. M. (1979). *J. Biol. Chem.* **254**, 5613.

Chen, Y-D. I., Kraemer, F. B., and Reaven, G. M. (1980). *J. Biol. Chem.* **255**, 9162.

Christensen, A. K., and Peacock, K. C. (1980). *Biol. Reprod.* **22**, 383.

Cigorraga, S., Dufau, M. L., and Catt, K. J. (1978). *J. Biol. Chem.* **253**, 4297.

Cigorraga, S. B., Sarrell, S., Bator, J., Catt, K. J., and Dufau, M. L. (1980). *J. Clin. Invest.* **65**, 699.

Cooke, B. A., Lindh, M. L., and Janszen, F. H. A. (1976). *Biochem. J.* **160**, 439.

Cooke, B. A., Lindh, L. M., and Janszen, F. H. A. (1977). *FEBS Lett.* **73**, 67.

Coon, M. J., White, R. E., and Blake, R. C., II (1982). *In* "Oxidases and Related Redox Systems" (T. E. King, H. S. Mason, and M. Morrison, eds.), pp. 857. Pergamon, Oxford.

Crivello, J. F., and Gill, G. N. (1983). *Mol. Cell. Endocrinol.* **30**, 97.

Crivello, J. F., Hornsby, P. J., and Gill, G. N. (1982). *Endocrinology* **11**, 469.

Crivello, J. F., Hornsby, P. J., and Gill, G. N. (1983). *Endocrinology* **113**, 235.

DiBartolomeis, M. J., and Jefcoate, C. R. (1984). *J. Biol. Chem.* **259**, 10159.

Dufau, M. L., Watanabe, K., and Catt, K. J. (1973). *Endocrinology* **92**, 6.

Dufau, M. L., Tsuruhara, T., Horner, R. A., Podesta, E. J., and Catt, K. J. (1977). *Proc. Natl. Acad. Sci. U.S.A.* **74**, 3419.

Dufau, M. L., Cigorraga, S. B., Baukal, A. J., Bator, J. M., Sorrell, S. H., Neubauer, J. F., and Catt, K. J. (1979). *J. Steroid Biochem.* **11**, 193.

Ernster, L., Lind, C., Nordenbrand, K., Thor, H., and Orrenius, S. (1982). *In* "Oxygenases and Oxygen Metabolism" (M. Nozaki, S. Yamomato, Y. Ishimura, M. J. Coon, L. Ernster, and R. W. Estrabrook, eds.), p. 357. Academic Press, New York.

Freeman, D. A., and Ascoli, M. (1982). *Proc. Natl. Acad. Sci. U.S.A.* **79**, 7796.

Guengerich, F. P. (1978). *Biochemistry* **17**, 3633.

Gunsalus, I. C., and Sligar, S. G. (1977). *Adv. Enzymol. Relat. Areas Mol. Biol.* **47**, 1.

Hall, P. F. (1970). *In* "The Testis" (A. J. Johnson, E. R. Gomes, and N. L. van Demark, eds.), p. 1. Academic Press, New York.

Hall, P. F., Charponnier, C., Nakamura, M., and Gabbiani, G. (1979). *J. Steroid Biochem.* **11**, 361.

Hauger, R. L., Chen, Y-D. I., Kelch, R. P., and Payne, A. H. (1977). *J. Endocrinol.* **74**, 57.

Hornsby, P. J. (1980). *J. Biol. Chem.* **255**, 4020.

Hornsby, P. J., and Crivello, J. F. (1983a). *Mol. Cell. Endocrinol.* **30**, 1.

Hornsby, P. J., and Crivello, J. F. (1983b). *Mol. Cell. Endocrinol.* **30**, 123.

Hsueh, A. J. W., Dufau, M. L., and Catt, K. J. (1976). *Biochem. Biophys. Res. Commun.* **72**, 1145.

Hsueh, A. J. W., Dufau, M. L., and Catt, K. J. (1977). *Proc. Natl. Acad. Sci. U.S.A.* **74**, 592.

Hunter, M. G., Magee-Brown, R., Dix, C. J., and Cooke, B. A. (1982). *Mol. Cell. Endocrinol.* **25**, 35.

Kuthan, H., and Ullrich, V. (1982). *Eur. J. Biochem.* **126**, 583.

Kuthan, H., Tsuji, H., Graf, H., Ullrich, V., Werringloer, J., and Estabrook, R. W. (1978). *FEBS Lett.* **91**, 343.

McCarthy, J. L., Kramer, R. E., Funkenstein, B., Simpson, E. R., and Waterman, M. R. (1983). *Arch. Biochem. Biophys.* **222**, 590.

Malaska, T., and Payne, A. H. (1984). *J. Biol. Chem.* **259**, 11654.

Mather, J. P. (1980). *Biol. Reprod.* **23**, 243.

Mather, J. P., Saez, J. M., and Haour, F. (1982). *Endocrinology* **110**, 933.

Melner, M. H., and Abney, T. D. (1980). *Endocrinology* **107**, 1620.

Moger, W. H. (1980). *Endocrinology* **106**, 496.

Murphy, P. R., and Moger, W. H. (1982). *Biol. Reprod.* **27**, 38.

Nakajin, S., and Hall, P. F. (1982). *J. Biol. Chem.* **256**, 3871.

Nakajin, S., Shively, J. E., Yuan, P.-M., and Hall, P. F. (1981). *Biochemistry* **20**, 4037.

Neumann, F., von Berswardt-Wallrabe, R., Elger, W., Steinbeck, H., Hahn, J. D., and Kramer, M. (1970). *Recent Prog. Horm. Res.* **26**, 337.

Nordblom, G. D., and Coon, M. J. (1977). *Arch. Biochem. Biophys.* **180**, 343.

Nozu, K., Dufau, M. L., and Catt, K. J. (1981a). *J. Biol. Chem.* **256**, 1915.

Nozu, K., Dehejia, A., Zawistowich, L., Catt, K. J., and Dufau, M. L. (1981b). *J. Biol. Chem.* **256**, 12875.

O'Shaughnessy, P. J., and Payne, A. H. (1982). *J. Biol. Chem.* **257**, 11503.

O'Shaughnessy, P. J., Wong, K. L., and Payne, A. H. (1981). *Endocrinology* **109**, 1061.

Payne, A. H., Wong, K. L., and Vega, M. M. (1980). *J. Biol. Chem.* **255**, 7118.

Purvis, J. S., Canick, J. A., Rosenbaum, J. H., Hologittas, J., and Latif, S. A. (1973a). *Arch. Biochem. Biophys.* **159**, 32.

Purvis, J. S., Canick, J. A., Latif, S. A., Rosenbaum, J. H., Hologittas, J., and Menard, R. H. (1973b). *Arch. Biochem. Biophys.* **159**, 39.

Quinn, P. G., and Payne, A. H. (1984). *J. Biol. Chem.* **259**, 4130.

Quinn, P. G., and Payne, A. H. (1985). *J. Biol. Chem.* **260**, 2092.

Quinn, P. G., Dombrausky, L. J., Chen, Y-D. I., and Payne, A. H. (1981). *Endocrinology* **109**, 1790.

Rani, C. S. S., Keri, G., and Ramachandran, J. (1983). *Endocrinology* **112**, 315.

Ruiz de Galarreta, C. M., Fanjul, L. F., Meidan, R., and Hsueh, A. J. W. (1983). *J. Biol. Chem.* **258**, 10988.

Saez, J. M., Haour, F., and Cathiard, A. M. (1978). *Biochem. Biophys. Res. Commun.* **81**, 552.

Schonfeld, G., Felski, C., and Howard, M. A. (1974). *J. Lipid Res.* **15**, 457.

Sharpe, R. M. (1976). *Nature (London)* **264**, 644.

Sharpe, R. M. (1977). *Biochem. Biophys. Res. Commun.* **76**, 956.

Suhara, K., Fujimura, Y., Shiroo, M., and Katagiri, M. (1984). *J. Biol. Chem.* **259**, 8729.

Tsuruhara, T., Dufau, M. L., Cigorraga, S., and Catt, K. J. (1977). *J. Biol. Chem.* **252**, 9002.

Valladares, L. E., and Payne, A. H. (1979). *Proc. Natl. Acad. Sci. U.S.A.* **76**, 4460.

Van der Vusse, G. J., Kalkman, M. L., and van der Molen, H. J. (1975). *Biochim. Biophys. Acta* **380**, 473.

Zipf, W. B., Payne, A. H., and Kelch, R. P. (1978). *Biochim. Biophys. Acta* **540**, 330.

DISCUSSION

J. L. Vaitukaitis: Why do the two subpopulations of rat Leydig cells have differential testosterone production rates in the face of having the same number of LH receptors per cell?

A. H. Payne: They have differential testosterone production, but the same number of LH receptor sites per Leydig cell. Under numerous conditions, such as desensitization or chronic stimulation with gonadotropin, we have never found a correlation between number of LH receptor sites and maximal capacity of Leydig cells for testosterone production.

The difference in testosterone production may be due to differences in the activities of the mitochondrial and the microsomal P-450s. We earlier reported that differences in testosterone production between population I and population II Leydig cells may, in part, be due to differences in the activities of 17α-hydroxylase and C_{17-20} lyase (O'Shaughnessy, P. J., and Payne, A. H., *J. Biol. Chem.* **257**, 11503, 1982). In a more recent study we used 25-hydroxycholesterol as a substrate for testosterone production in the two populations of Leydig cells. In these studies, we demonstrated that the difference in maximal testosterone production between the two populations of Leydig cells was similar whether the cells were maximally stimulated by cAMP or incubated with a saturating concentration of 25-hydroxycholesterol (M. Georgiou and A. H. Payne, unpublished data). This observation is consistent with cholesterol side-chain cleavage being the major contributing factor which determines the difference in maximal testosterone production between the two populations of Leydig cells.

Let me mention that we do not observe two populations of Leydig cells in the mouse. Mouse Leydig cells have a density in-between populations I and II of the rat. If there are two populations of Leydig cells in the mouse, their densities may be so close that we cannot detect them.

A. Segaloff: I wonder if you considered the possibility that isoprogesterone might very well be the natural pseudosubstrate. The reaction for that which is real easy for bacteria was first reported by Seymour Lieberman I believe about 45 years ago, but it is a well known reaction, and it may very well go.

A. H. Payne: What is the structure of isoprogesterone.

A. Segaloff: The side-chain is 17α.

A. H. Payne: We have not tried isoprogesterone.

A. Segaloff: And it should fit it beautifully as an inhibitor.

A. H. Payne: Yes, thank you for this suggestion.

D. R. Aquilano: Some other laboratories strongly believe that unresponsive or less responsive Leydig cells are actually damaged Leydig cells still having the capacity to bind the gonadotropins. I would like to know your opinion on this controversy.

A. H. Payne: We previously examined rat Leydig cells from both populations by electron microscopy (Payne, A. H. *et al., Ann. N.Y. Acad. Sci.* **383**, 174, 1982). Electron micrographs of Leydig cells from each population indicated that the Leydig cells were intact and not damaged and exhibited the morphological characteristics described for rat Leydig cells (Christensen, A. K., *Handbook Physiol.* **5**, 57, 1975). In a more recent study we demonstrated that cAMP-stimulated testosterone production in both populations of Leydig cells, after 24 hours in culture and a change in medium, was not different from that of freshly isolated Leydig cells (M. Georgiou and A. H. Payne, unpublished data). Since it has been reported earlier (Molenaar *et al., Int. J. Androl.* **6**, 211, 1983) that Leydig cells damaged during isolation procedure do not attach to plastic culture dishes and are removed with the first change of medium, our results argue against the difference in testosterone-producing capacity between the two populations being due to a preponderance of damaged Leydig cells in population I (the population with a lower capacity for testosterone production).

D. R. Aquilano: Do you have any evidence of how testosterone is released? Is it through secretory granules, or by simple diffusion?

A. H. Payne: I think it is simple diffusion. We have no evidence at all that testosterone is released in secretory granules.

K. Sterling: The first question deals with the *in vivo* injection of gonadotropin for 7 days. You contrasted daily versus single—does that mean a single dose for the whole week or what?

A. H. Payne: No. The single dose means we injected one high dose of gonadotropin and 72 hours later Leydig cells were isolated. The single dose was equivalent to the dose we gave over a 6-day period. For daily injections animals were injected for 6 days, and killed on the seventh day. Continuous administration of smaller doses resulted in an increase in microsomal *P*-450 enzyme activities, the same as we demonstrated in the culture system. In the mouse culture system, we demonstrated that the continuous presence of cAMP is necessary for a continuous increase in microsomal *P*-450 enzyme activity. When mouse Leydig cells in culture are subjected to a single high dose of cyclic AMP for 24 hours, then we observe increased degradation of the microsomal *P*-450 enzymes.

K. Sterling: In other words, the daily dosage was probably a pulsatile dose, whereas a single dose, was an abrupt huge dose.

A. H. Payne: Yes. I wish to point out that under normal or pathologic conditions Leydig cells are exposed to only small pulsatile LH discharges and not massive LH surges. The phenomenon of desensitization following the administration of a single high dose of LH or hCG only occurs when patients or animals are injected with a single high pharmacologic dose of gonadotropin.

K. Sterling: About the free oxygen radicals, the question is first, do we have any information as to what is the partial pressure of oxygen in the Leydig cells? We know it's originally arterial blood, but I would think the seminiferous tubules would be using up a lot of the oxygen and they may be quite a bit below the 19 or 20% we think of as ambient oxygen; and second, what do you conceive as the role of the dimethyl sulfoxide you use with the 1% oxygen?

A. H. Payne: The tissue oxygen is considerably lower than 19% O_2 but is probably greater than 1% O_2. In answer to your second question, dimethyl sulfoxide acts as a hydroxyl radical scavenger. Superoxide and hydrogen peroxide are generated during catalysis by microsomal P-450 enzymes and by autooxidation of P-450. The hydrogen peroxide is converted to hydroxyl radicals. Hydroxyl radicals can initiate lipid peroxidation and the resulting lipid hydroperoxides and lipoxy radicals can destroy the heme of the P-450 (Hornsby, P. J., and Crivello, J. F., *Mol. Cell Endocrinol.* **30**, 123, 1983). The addition of dimethyl sulfoxide together with low oxygen tension reduces the concentration of damaging hydroxyl radicals in the incubation medium.

J. D. Veldhuis: Do you have evidence that testosterone or one of the other steroidal products might directly influence cholesterol metabolism in these cells, such as rates of cholesterol ester turnover or *de novo* cholesterol biosynthesis?

A. H. Payne: We have not looked at that yet, so I can't answer your question.

M. A. Kirschner: Several years ago, we were looking at testosterone secretion in men with gonadotropin-producing choriocarcinomas, and found normal testosterone secretion despite high levels of gonadotropin, suggesting Leydig cell desensitization. It was subsequently shown that some of the sensitivity of the Leydig cell to hCG could be restored by administration of FSH. Therefore, I wonder whether or not you have looked at the possibility that some of the microsomal enzyme systems involved in the desensitization process might be restored by the coadministration of FSH?

A. H. Payne: We have never looked at the effect of FSH on the microsomal P-450 enzymes. We have administered FSH to adult, hypophysectomized animals. FSH administration had no effect, as regards maintaining or increasing the capacity for LH/hCG-stimulatable testosterone production. We have studied the effect of FSH administration by itself or together with LH on two other steroid biosynthetic enzymes. Administration of 50 μg twice daily of NIH-FSH-S11 for 14 days to hypophysectomized adult male rats had no effect on reversing the 72% loss in 3β-hydroxysteroid dehydrogenase-isomerase activity of isolated interstitial tissue. LH (NIH-LH-S19) administered as 20 μg twice daily to these hypophysectomized rats maintained enzyme activity at intact control values. When rats were injected with LH plus FSH, a synergistic effect of FSH and LH on 3β-hydroxysteroid dehydrogenase-isomerase activity was observed (Shaw, M. J., Georgopoulos, L. E., and Payne, A. H., *Endocrinology* **104**, 912, 1979). In another study, administration of a highly purified preparation of FSH (2 μg/day, G4-150C from Harold Papkoff) for 6 days to adult male, intact rats, no effect was observed, on aromatase (another microsomal P-450) activity (Valladares, L. E., and Payne, A. H., *Endocrinology* **105**, 431, 1979). We have not looked at the effect of FSH on the microsomal P-450 enzymes, 17α-hydroxylase and C_{17-20} lyase.

P. K. Donahoe: Have you attempted to correlate the morphological changes seen with pathological states seen in the testis with the presence of oxygen free radicals.

A. H. Payne: We have not. Our data would indicate that there is no general damage to the Leydig cell as a result of oxygen free radical generation. This conclusion is based on the observation that we observed no change in the activity of another microsomal enzyme, 3β-hydroxysteroid dehydrogenase-isomerase, either in cells that had been subjected to a desensitizing dose of cAMP or incubated under different culture conditions, i.e. 19% O_2, 1% O_2, 100 mM Me_2SO, or 1% O_2 plus Me_2SO. These observations indicate that the damaging effect of oxygen-derived free radicals is specific for P-450 enzymes and not a general effect on the membrane in which all of these enzymes are embedded.

P. K. Donohoe: It would be interesting to see if the injury seen with the undescendent testis, or in the ambiguous genitalia of babies with dysgenetic testes are due to oxygen free radical toxicity.

A. H. Payne: It could very well be, but we have not looked at it.

C. Monder: The relationship between the pseudosubstrate, iron and the hydrogen peroxide that you showed in one of your slides resembled the Fenton reaction (the oxidation of hydroxylic compounds by hydrogen peroxide in the presence of a ferrous salt). That would generate quite a substantial quantity of oxygen free radicals. I was wondering if that, in fact, was the mechanism. It would be an unusual mechanism under physiological conditions. Under these conditions, how would one control the level of oxygen free radicals without completely destroying the *P*-450?

A. H. Payne: You are correct that the reaction proposed for generation of hydroxyl radicals is via the Fenton reaction (Hornsby, P. J., and Crivello, J. F., *Mol. Cell Endocrinol.* **30**, 1, 1983). The oxygen tension in the Leydig cell *in situ* is considerably lower than the 19% oxygen of air, which was used in the incubation studies to demonstrate the damaging effect of oxygen derived free radicals on the microsomal *P*-450s of Leydig cells. However, even at 1% O_2 tension, one observes time related degradation of microsomal *P*-450s. I'll let Dr. Quinn answer how Leydig cells *in vivo*, in addition to being subjected to lower than 19% oxygen tension, are protected from completely destroying *P*-450s.

P. G. Quinn: Leydig cells, as well as adrenal and luteal cells, are found to contain rather high concentrations of natural antioxidants, such as vitamin E, which serve the role of protecting cells from this kind of damage *in vivo*.

C. Monder: There has been some question about the identity of 17-hydroxylation with C_{17-20} lyase. The data that you presented really do not allow one to resolve that question.

A. H. Payne: Our data on degradation and on induction of 17α-hydroxylase and C_{17-20} lyase do not resolve the question whether we are dealing with one protein with two activities or two distinct proteins.

S. Cohen: I have a question about enzymes. When I studied enzymes in biochemistry over 50 years ago, an enzyme was named by naming the substrate it acted on and then adding the suffix ase on it. Well obviously you don't do that now. And the hydroxylase, I wondered what that does. Strictly speaking, it should add a hydroxyl group to a carbon. If it changes a ketone to a hydroxyl group then it's a hydrogenase. Is that what you were referring to?

A. H. Payne: 17α-Hydroxylase does follow that convention. A hydroxyl group is introduced at C_{17} of progesterone yielding 17α-hydroxyprogesterone.

S. Cohen: This is a C_{21} compound, not a C_{19} compound.

A. H. Payne: Correct.

B. F. Rice: As an old worker with Leydig cells and paticularly Leydig cell tumors, I just feel compelled to ask you a question. In all of your studies have you run across any products that you were unable to identify? And the reason for asking that obviously is that there is this Leydig cell tumor preparation that produces lethal hypercalcemia in the host animal. The factor responsible for this has never been identified. These tumors do not produce any identifiable steroid hormones, but were responsive to hCG, raised calcium; it is lethal in the host animals.

A. H. Payne: In our studies we have not detected a nonidentifiable metabolite. When mouse Leydig cells are incubated with ^3H-labeled C_{21} substrates, we have been able to account for all the ^3H label in the expected identifiable products.

RECENT PROGRESS IN HORMONE RESEARCH, VOL. 41

The Defective Glucocorticoid Receptor in Man and Nonhuman Primates

Mortimer B. Lipsett, George P. Chrousos, Masako Tomita,
David D. Brandon, and D. Lynn Loriaux

*Developmental Endocrinology Branch, National Institute of Child Health and Human
Development, National Institutes of Health, Bethesda, Maryland*

I. Introduction

End-organ resistance to steroid hormones in man has been clearly described for androgens (Wilkins, 1957; Griffin and Wilson, 1980), cortisol (Chrousos *et al.*, 1982c), and vitamin D (Brooks *et al.*, 1978; Eil *et al.*, 1981) and there is presumptive evidence of resistance to aldosterone (Cheek and Perry, 1958) and progesterone (Keller *et al.*, 1979). For an extensive review see Verhoeven and Wilson (1979). There are no known examples of resistance to the action of estradiol, probably because estradiol is necessary for blastocyst implantation and early embryogenesis.

Since cortisol is essential for life in primates, end-organ insensitivity is compensated for and revealed by elevated plasma cortisol concentrations (Chrousos *et al.*, 1982b,c). This occurs because the affected individual has an intact hypothalamic–adrenal axis (HPA axis), with functioning feedback mechanisms, and apparently the tissue resistance is generalized and includes the pituitary gland and the hypothalamus.

Glucocorticoid resistance in primates has been described recently by us in a Dutch family (Vingerhoeds *et al.*, 1976; Chrousos *et al.*, 1982c, 1983) and several species of New World primates (Chrousos *et al.*, 1982b). Men or animals with this condition have high plasma free cortisol concentrations and no evidence of Cushing syndrome or other stigmata of hypercortisolism. Thus, by definition, they have "partial" or "compensated" end-organ resistance to cortisol. The purpose of this article is to review the examples of end-organ resistance to cortisol in primates and discuss the pathophysiologic and evolutionary mechanisms involved, as well as their implications for the structure of receptors.

199

II. Glucocorticoid Resistance in Man

A. THE CLINICAL SYNDROME

1. Clinical Presentation

Two patients, a father and son, with long-term "hypercortisolism" not associated with clinical manifestations of Cushing's syndrome were described by Vingerhoeds *et al.* (1976). The father (height 161 cm, weight 62.2 kg) was noted to have "hypercortisolism" at the age of 48 years during evaluation for hypertension (180–190/120–130 mm Hg) and hypokalemic alkalosis. Subsequent studies revealed markedly elevated plasma cortisol levels, increased 24-hour urinary 17-ketogenic steroids, and an increased cortisol production rate. There were no stigmata of Cushing's syndrome. The plasma renin activity was normal and 24-hour urinary aldosterone values on a 9 g NaCl diet were low.

When evaluated in 1982 at the National Institutes of Health the patient had none of the features of Cushing's syndrome (Chrousos *et al.*, 1982c). He had low serum potassium (2.2 mEq/liter) and elevated bicarbonate concentrations. The 24-hour urinary potassium ranged between 86 and 128 mEq during the period of hypokalemia. He was always normonatremic (141–146 mEq/liter). Renal function tests were normal. The hemoglobin was 15.2. Serum cholesterol and triglycerides were normal. An oral glucose tolerance test indicated carbohydrate intolerance (fasting blood glucose, 51 mg/dl, and serum insulin, 4.9 μU/ml, 2-hour glucose 266, and insulin 33). This test, however, was performed during hypokalemia severe enough to inhibit insulin release (Gorden *et al.*, 1972).

The son (height 173 cm, weight 84 kg) was found to have hypercortisolism at the age of 20 years during family studies stimulated by the unusual findings in his father. He was asymptomatic. The 17-ketogenic steroids and cortisol production rate were both elevated but to a lesser extent than those of his father. During his hospitalization at the National Institutes of Health he was normotensive and had normal serum electrolytes. Urinary potassium excretion ranged between 59 and 83 mEq/24 hours on a regular hospital diet.

Delayed hypersensitivity tests were normal in both patients and adrenal sonography showed normal size glands in both. There was neither clinical nor radiological evidence of osteoporosis. Both men worked as farm or construction laborers. Further family studies in which an additional 28 normotensive, asymptomatic blood relatives were examined revealed mild hypercortisolism in additional 8 members of the family (see Section II,A,3).

2. Biochemical Studies

a. Basal Function of the Hypothalamic–Pituitary–Adrenal (HPA) Axis. Although the circadian rhythm and episodic secretory patterns were normal in both patients (Fig. 1) (Chrousos *et al.*, 1982c), the mean of 49 consecutive total serum cortisol concentration values from samples drawn every 30 minutes over a period of 24 hours was 27.4 µg/dl in the father and 9.9 µg/dl in the son. The mean plasma cortisol in eight normal men was 7.52 ± 1.64 µg/dl (Fig. 1, Table I). The 24-hour urinary free cortisol measured on 4–5 consecutive days was also markedly increased in the father and mildly elevated in the son (Table I).

Plasma cortisol binding globulin (CBG) capacity and affinity were normal in both patients (Table I). The concentration of unbound free cortisol, however, was markedly increased in the father and twice normal in the son (Table I). Plasma ACTH measured at 0800 hours was elevated in both patients (Table I). Serum dehydroepiandrosterone sulfate and Δ^4-androstenedione were elevated in both father and son (Table I). Serum 17-hydroxyprogesterone values were within the normal range in both patients and 11-deoxycortisol was elevated in the father and normal in the son (Table I).

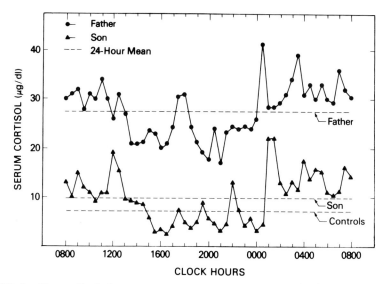

FIG. 1.   Plasma Cortisol secretory pattern over 24 hours for the propositus and his son. Interrupted lines indicate the mean plasma cortisol values for all the samples drawn every 30 minutes over 24 hours. Both had higher 24-hour mean plasma cortisol levels than the mean obtained from eight normal male controls. (From Chrousos *et al.*, 1982c.)

TABLE I

Characteristics of Hypothalamic–Pituitary–Adrenal Function in the Two Original Patients with Cortisol Resistance[a]

	Father (mean ± SE)	Son (mean ± SE)	Normal control (mean ± SD)
Mean serum cortisol,[b] μg/dl	27.4[c]	9.9	7.52 ± 1.64 ($n = 8$)[d]
Cortisol binding globulin (CBG)			
Binding capacity, μg/dl	21.1 ± 0.3 ($m = 3$)[d]	17.4 ± 1.5 ($m = 3$)	22.5 ± 1.3 ($n = 7$)
Binding affinity, $10^7 \, M^{-1}$	6.0 ± 0.5 ($m = 3$)	4.9 ± 0.5 ($m = 3$)	5.4 ± 0.3 ($n = 7$)
Serum-free cotisol concentration, μg/dl	1.76 ± 0.30[e] ($m = 4$)	0.70 ± 0.32 ($m = 4$)	0.27 ± 0.39 ($n = 7$)
Dehydroepiandrosterone sulfate, DHEAS, μg/dl	524 ± 88[e] ($m = 5$)	381 ± 83 ($m = 5$)	284 ± 97 ($n = 14$)
Δ^4-Androstenedione, ng/dl	470 ± 86[e] ($m = 5$)	241 ± 48 ($m = 5$)	198 ± 71 ($n = 14$)
17-Hydroxyprogesterone, ng/dl	118 ± 20 ($m = 4$)	67 ± 11 ($m = 4$)	138 ± 65 ($n = 14$)
11-Deoxycortisol, ng/dl	240 ± 50[e] ($m = 4$)	80 ± 16 ($m = 4$)	83 ± 52 ($n = 14$)
ACTH, pg/ml	155,123	175,76	<75
Urinary-free cortisol, μg/24 hours	1780 ± 70[c] ($m = 5$)	128 ± 7[e] ($m = 4$)	48 ± 22 ($n = 22$)
Sensitivity to dexamethasone suppression, ED_{50} in mg/dl[f]	3.0[c]	1.2[c]	0.4 ± 0.07 ($n = 5$)

[a] From Chrousos *et al.* (1982c).
[b] Measured in 49 samples drawn every 30 minutes for 24 hours.
[c] $p < 0.005$.
[d] *m*, Number of measurements; *n*, number of subjects.
[e] $p < 0.05$.
[f] ED_{50}, dose of demexamethasone required for 50% suppression of 0800 serum cortisol levels (see legend to Fig. 2).

These findings imply that these patients had a hypothalamic–pituitary–adrenal axis that had been reset to provide elevated levels of plasma cortisol. Qualititatively the HPA axis remained intact and retained its circadian variation. This is different from the situation in Cushing's disease where the circadian rhythm is usually abolished (Boyar *et al.*, 1979).

    b. *Suppressibility of the HPA Axis by Glucocorticoids.* The responsiveness of the hypothalamic–pituitary unit to exogenous glucocorticoids was tested with dexamethasone (Chrousos *et al.*, 1982c). Increasing doses of dexamethasone were given orally at midnight every other day (Fig. 2,

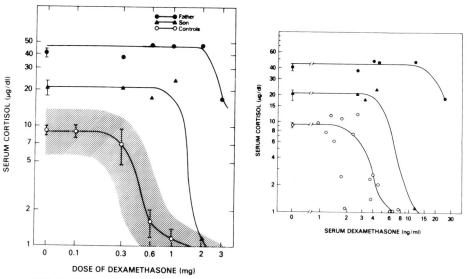

FIG. 2. The results of a midnight dexamethasone suppression test. Dexamethasone doses ranging from 0.1 to 3 mg were given per os at midnight to the patients (father and son) and five normal male controls. Serum cortisol and dose of dexamethasone (left) or serum dexamethasone (right) are plotted logarithmically. Higher doses and plasma levels of dexamethasone are required to obtain the same degree of cortisol suppression in both patients when compared with controls (Table I). (From Chrousos *et al.*, 1982c, modified.)

left). A serum sample was drawn at 0800 hours the next morning for the determination of serum cortisol and dexamethasone levels. The father required 3.0 mg and the son 1.2 mg of dexamethasone to effect a 50% suppression of the morning cortisol levels. This same degree of suppression was achieved with 0.4 mg of dexamethasone in five normal controls (Table I).

To exclude the possibility of increased metabolic clearance or decreased absorption of dexamethasone in the two patients, we also measured serum dexamethasone levels at 0800 hours (Meikle *et al.*, 1973). The same degree of resistance to dexamethasone suppression was noted when serum cortisol values were plotted against the morning serum dexamethasone concentrations from the same samples (Fig. 2, right).

Thus, the HPA axis is resistant to glucocorticoids. Such resistance is also known to exist in patients with Cushing's disease in whom there is also a shift of the dose–response curve to dexamethasone suppression to the right (Meikle *et al.*, 1975).

c. Mineralocorticoid Status.   Because of the hypertension and hypokalemic alkalosis in the father we measured also 24-hour urinary aldoster-

TABLE II

Patient Mineralocorticoid Status[a]

	Father (mean ± SE)	Son (mean ± SE)	Normal control (mean ± SD)
Urinary aldosterone, μg/24 hours	3.4 ± 0.3	2.4 ± 0.4	4.5 ± 2.2
	$(m = 5)^b$	$(m = 5)$	$(n = 19)^b$
Serum corticosterone, ng/dl	2870 ± 360*	1376 ± 326[c]	400 ± 116
	$(m = 5)$	$(m = 6)$	$(n = 15)$
Serum deoxycorticosterone, ng/dl	53.9,45.7	13.7,7.2	0–20[d]
			$(n = 81)$

[a] From Chrousos *et al.* (1982c).
[b] m, Number of measurements; n, number of subjects.
[c] $p < 0.001$.
[d] Range.

one and serum corticosterone and deoxycorticosterone (Table II) (Chrousos *et al.*, 1982c). Urinary aldosterone was in the low normal range in both patients. Serum corticosterone, however, was elevated in the son and markedly elevated in the father. Serum deoxycorticosterone was also increased in the father.

It is thus clear how the propositus became hypertensive, hypokalemic, and alkalotic. The plasma concentrations of the potent sodium-retaining corticoids, corticosterone and deoxycorticosterone, were increased due to excessive stimulation of the adrenal glands by the increased ACTH. The levels were similar to those seen in patients with hypertension and hypokalemic alkalosis due to the ectopic ACTH syndrome (Schambelan *et al.*, 1971).

3. Family Studies

To examine the inheritance pattern of this condition, 28 additional members of these patients' large kindred (Fig. 3) spanning four generations were studied by measuring the urinary free cortisol of at least 2–24 hour urine samples and by doing at least one standard dexamethasone suppression test (1 mg dexamethasone po given at midnight) (Chrousos *et al.*, 1983). Consanguinity was not apparent by history for seven generations.

Although the propositus presented with a florid clinical picture of mineralocorticoid excess, none of the other members of the family studied had hypertension. Two relatives (II_{11} and III_1) had a mild biochemical picture of hypercortisolism, similar to that of the propositus' son (III_{13}).

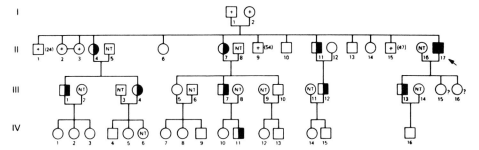

FIG. 3. Family pedigree. The propositus (arrows) had severe hypertension and hypokalemic alkalosis and markedly elevated plasma and urinary free cortisol concentration (■). His untested brother (II$_9$) had marked hypertension and died of a cerebrovascular accident at the age of 54. Another brother (II$_{11}$), his son (III$_{13}$), and a nephew (III$_1$) were asymptomatic but had definite biochemical evidence of hypercortisolism (◨). Another six members had at least one abnormal test of the pituitary adrenal axis (◨, ◑). Subjects III$_{15}$ and III$_{16}$ were asymptomatic and had normal urinary 17-ketogenic steroid excretion [1]. (From Chrousos et al., 1983.)

Six other relatives had a borderline biochemical picture of hypercortisolism. Thus, of the total of 32 blood relatives studied biochemically from 11 different sibships, one (or possibly by history, two, if we include subject II$_9$) had the disease expressed both clinically and biochemically, three had clear biochemical evidence, and six equivocal evidence of hypercortisolism.

HLA typing of this extended kinship showed no association between the transmission of the condition and the HLA haplotypes, suggesting that the gene responsible for the abnormality is not within or close to the HLA locus (unpublished data).

B. THE MOLECULAR BASIS OF THE DISEASE

1. Glucocorticoid Receptor Binding Characteristics

Glucocorticoid receptor content of intact mononuclear leukocytes or cultured skin fibroblasts measured by the methods of Murakami et al. (1979, 1980) and Eil et al. (1980) was normal in both patients (Fig. 4, Table III) (Chrousos et al., 1982c). When B-lymphocytes were transformed with the Epstein–Barr (EB) virus (Tomita et al., 1985a,b) glucocorticoid receptor content increased to a greater extent in normal cells than in those from the family (Table III, Fig. 5). The data from an additional study of a second asymptomatic, hypercortisolemic relative studied were in accord.

TABLE III
Patient Glucocorticoid Receptor Status[a]

	Father (mean ± SE)	Son (mean ± SE)	Normal controls (mean ± SD)
Whole cell			
Mononuclear leukocytes			
Binding capacity (R_o)	3190 ± 60	3371 ± 751	3251 ± 133
(sites/cell)	$(m = 2)^b$	$(m = 2)$	$(n = 10)^b$
Apparent dissociation	$7.4 ± 1.5^c$	$3.9 ± 0.1^d$	2.8 ± 0.44
constant (nM)	$(m = 2)$	$(m = 2)$	$(n = 10)$
Cultured skin fibroblasts			
Binding capacity (R_0)	171,300 ± 41,700	121,000 ± 30,900	133,400 ± 45,300
(sites/cell)	$(m = 3)$	$(m = 3)$	$(n = 6)$
Apparent dissociation	$10.5 ± 0.5^d$	5.4 ± 1.3	6 ± 1.3
constant (nM)	$(m = 3)$	$(m = 3)$	$(n = 6)$
EB-virus transformed lymphocytes			
Binding capacity (R_0)	$14280 ± 6780^d$	$14220 ± 4560^d$	28560 ± 10140
(sites/cell)	$(m = 3)$	$(m = 3)$	$(n = 9)$
Apparent dissociation	$4.5 ± 1.4^c$	1.5 ± 0.3	1.3 ± 0.3
constant (nM)	$(m = 3)$	$(m = 3)$	$(n = 9)$
Cytosol			
Mononuclear leukocyte			
Binding capacity (R_0)	26.0 ± 4.7	53.0 ± 8.6	191.0 ± 30
(fmol/mg protein)	$(r = -0.89)^e$	$(r = -0.93)$	$(r = -0.90)$
Dissociation constant	3.5 ± 1.2	3.2 ± 1.0	1.7 ± 0.7
(nM)			
Cultured skin fibroblasts			
Binding capacity (R_0)	35 ± 3.0	88 ± 27	94 ± 29.4
(fmol/mg protein)	$(m = 3)$	$(m = 3)$	$(n = 3)$
Dissociation constant	6.0 ± 1.5	2.8 ± 0.3	1.4 ± 0.34
(nM)	$(m = 3)$	$(m = 3)$	$(n = 3)$
EB-virus-transformed lymphocytes			
Binding capacity (R_0)	$90.2 ± 58^c$	$130.5 ± 42.5^c$	529 ± 68.7
(fmol/mg protein)	$(m = 4)$	$(m = 5)$	$(n = 3)$
Apparent dissociation	$8.7 ± 0.6^c$	3.6 ± 0.8	4.8 ± 1.4
constant (nM)	$(m = 4)$	$(m = 5)$	$(n = 3)$

[a] From Chrousos *et al.* (1982c) and Tomita *et al.* (1985b), modified.
[b] m, Number of measurements; n, number of subjects.
[c] $p < 0.005$.
[d] $p < 0.05$.
[e] r, Correlation coefficient of the Scatchard regression lines.

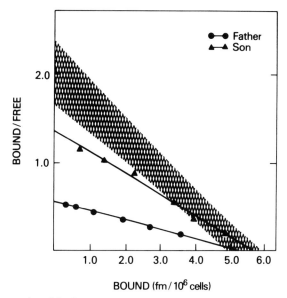

FIG. 4.   The results of the Scatchard analysis of dexamethasone binding to the glucocorticoid receptor of circulating mononuclear leukocytes in the two patients and 10 controls (8-hour incubation, 24°C). The shaded area represents the normal range. The number of receptors indicated by the x axis intercept is within the normal range. The apparent affinity indicated by the slope of the line (slope = $-1/K_D$) is clearly different in the father and outside the normal range in the son. (From Chrousos *et al.*, 1982c.)

The apparent dissociation constant (K_D) in all three assay systems was significantly increased in the propositus, implying a diminished affinity of the receptor for dexamethasone (Figs. 4 and 5, Table III). However, the affinity of the asymptomatic patient's receptors for labeled dexamethasone was not uniformly reduced in the various assay systems employed (Table III). This may reflect the inability of our assays to detect small changes in affinity at the range of 20–100%.

There was another unexpected difference between patients and controls when the receptor was assayed in cytosol. Whereas in intact mononuclear lymphocytes and cultured skin fibroblasts a normal number of receptors was found, the receptor concentration in the cell cytosols was significantly reduced in both the propositus and the asymptomatic son (Table III). Even in the EB virus-transformed cells where the patient cells had approximately half the number of receptors as control cells, the cytosol receptor concentration was approximately one-fifth or one-fourth of that of control cells, respectively, in the father and the son. These findings led us to hypothesize that relative instability of receptor, occurring during

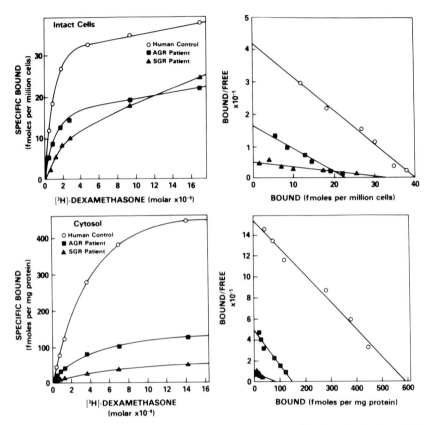

FIG. 5. Representative saturation curves (left) and respective Scatchard plots (right) from glucocorticoid receptor binding studies performed with Epstein–Barr virus-transformed cells from the propositus (SGR), and a mildly hypercortisolemic, asymptomatic member of the family (AGR). Top panels, intact cells; bottom panels, cytosol fractions. A decreased receptor concentration was found in the patients' cells in both assay systems. The apparent affinity was decreased only in the cells of the propositus. (From Tomita *et al.,* 1985b.)

the preparation of cytosol or during incubation, was compensated for by new receptor synthesis in whole cells (Chrousos *et al.,* 1982c). It should be noted that there were no alterations of the receptor in Cushing's syndrome (Kontula *et al.,* 1980).

2. Glucocorticoid Hormone–Receptor Complex Stability

As expected from the dissociation constants, the hormone–receptor complex was unstable in both patients studied, with excess loss of specific bound ligand during thermal activation of cytosol, in the absence of so-

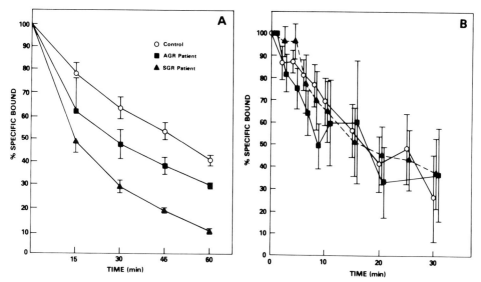

FIG. 6. (A) Specifically bound hormone during incubation of cytosol for 30 minutes at 28°C. Prior to thermal activation, equilibrium had been reached by incubation of cytosol with labeled dexamethasone for 2 hours at 0–4°C. Phosphocellulose chromatography of the steroid–receptor complex demonstrated that the ratio of activated to unactivated complex remained constant throughout the activation time. (B) Specifically bound hormone after previous incubation of cytosol for various time intervals at 28°C. (From Tomita *et al.*, 1985b.)

dium molybdate (Fig. 6A) (Tomita *et al.*, 1985a,b). Thus, using this procedure we could better appreciate the differences among receptor affinities than was possible by Scatchard plots (see Fig. 4). This may be the method of choice for discerning small differences in affinity not distinguished by a standard Scatchard analysis.

The ratio of activated to unactivated receptor remained stable when the cytosol receptor was examined by passage through small phosphocellulose columns which retain the activated fraction (see below and Fig. 7). This suggests that the "instability" of the complex was present in both the activated and unactivated receptors in our patients.

Because of the measured differences in affinity between the receptors of intact cells and cytosol we asked whether in addition to the increased hormone–receptor dissociation, there is also increased receptor loss in our patients, responsible for the differences observed during temperature activation. To examine this, we incubated cytosol from our patients and controls at 28°C, for various time intervals (0–30 minutes) and then assessed the remaining specific binding of labeled dexamethasone. We

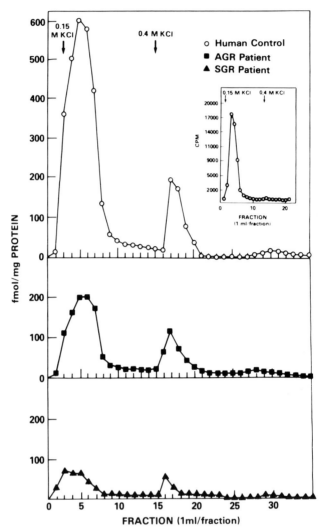

FIG. 7. Phosphocellulose chromatography after thermal activation. Approximately 25–30% of receptor is retained by phosphocellulose in both the severely and the biochemically only affected patient and controls. (From Tomita *et al.*, 1985b.)

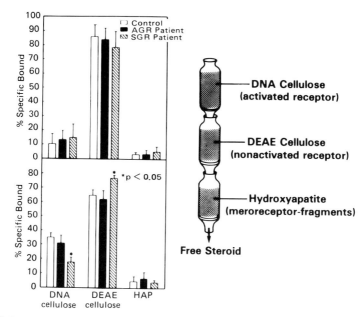

FIG. 8. *In vivo* activation of receptor by incubating cells at 37% for 30 minutes followed by fractionation and passage of cytosol through a DNA cellulose–DEAE cellulose and hydroxyapatite column series ("minicolumns") shown in the right. No excessive meroreceptor was found in our patients. Top, nonactivated cells; bottom, activated cells. (From Tomita *et al.*, 1985b.)

could not discern any differences between patients and controls (Fig. 6B) and this suggests these abnormal receptors are not excessively unstable under thermal stress.

3. Activation of the Glucocorticoid Hormone–Receptor Complex

We first examined the complex activation process *in vitro*, by elevating the temperature of cytosol and assessing the proportion of activated to unactivated receptors, by their ability to be retained by a polyanion (phosphocellulose) column (Tomita *et al.*, 1985a,b). We found that the ratio of activated to unactivated receptor was the same in patient and control cytosols (Fig. 7).

Thermal activation of the hormone–receptor complex *in vivo*, by incubating cells with radiolabeled dexamethasone at 37°C led to less activated receptor remaining in the cytosol of our propositus, after "nuclear translocation," but not in the cytosol of a biochemically only affected member (Fig. 8). Use of the "minicolumn" system described by Holbrook *et al.* (1983, 1984) allowed us to determine not only the activated to unactivated receptor ratio, but also the amount of generated meroreceptor. As shown in Fig. 8 we could not demonstrate excessive meroreceptor generation in our patients as it occurs with certain leukemic cell lines that have labile glucocorticoid receptors (Holbrook *et al.*, 1983, 1984).

In addition, the ratio of "nuclear" to "cytosolic" receptor was normal in both the severely affected propositus and the mildly affected individual (Fig. 9). The determination was done under saturating concentrations of dexamethasone (40 n*M*) and the result was expected since, in our patients, resistance to glucocorticoids is compensated for by elevated hormone concentrations, implying that nuclear binding must be sufficient for full hormone action. We should note that the absolute amount of specifically bound hormone to the nucleus was mildly decreased in both patient cells.

4. Glucocorticoid Receptor Complex Positive or Negative Modifiers

The low affinity of the glucocorticoid receptor of our patients for glucocorticoids and its putative instability, responsible for the differences observed between the intact cell and cytosol receptor concentrations, could be explained by extrareceptor modifiers. Inhibitory factors and positive modifiers of binding or stabilizers of the receptor have been described. For a review see Grody *et al.* (1982).

Mixing of cytosol, from either patient with cytosol from normal control B-lymphocytes followed by evaluation of the cytosol by the minicolumn gave no evidence for the presence of excess inhibitory factors or for deficiency of positive modifiers in the patients (Tomita *et al.*, 1985a,b) such as those described in the guinea pig (Hodgson and Funder, 1978; Kraft *et al.*, 1979) or in mouse strains that are resistant to induction of a cleft-palate by prenatal administration of glucocorticoids (Katsumata *et al.*, 1981) (Fig. 10).

5. Determination of the Molecular Weight of the Receptor Binding Subunit

The molecular weight of the glucocorticoid receptor from both the severely and a mildly affected patient determined by SDS–PAGE was similar to that of controls (~92,000) (Fig. 11) (Tomita *et al.*, 1985b).

C. IMPLICATIONS

1. Clinical

a. Pathophysiologic Rationale for Therapy. We have described a unique glucocorticoid receptor affinity defect that had profound pathophysiologic implications (Chrousos *et al.*, 1982c). In order to maintain

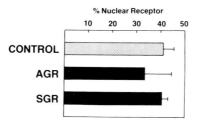

% Nuclear Receptor

FIG. 9. Percentage of [³H]dexamethasone found in the nucleus after activation of intact cells by incubating them for 2 hours at 37°C in the presence of 40 nM labeled dexamethasone. (From Tomita *et al.*, 1985b.)

sufficient nuclear acceptor bound cortisol–receptor complexes, the serum cortisol was maintained at a high level and this was achieved by increased ACTH secretion, leading to excessive secretion of the sodium-retaining corticoids, deoxycorticosterone and corticosterone.

The hypertension and hypokalemic alkalosis was treated satisfactorily by using a pharmacologic dose of dexamethasone of 3 mg/day, sufficiently high to overcome the glucocorticoid resistance and suppress ACTH and therefore deoxycorticosterone and corticosterone. No stigmata of Cushing syndrome have developed in this patient during the 3 years of his therapy and his hypertension has been controlled.

b. Genetics. Primary cortisol resistance appears to be a familial disease. Father-to-son transmission excludes X-linked inheritance and the entity appears therefore to be autosomal with two possible modes of inheritance: dominance with variable penetrance or recessive transmission, with the father (and possibly his brother II₉) representing the fully

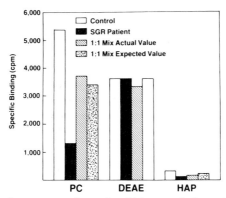

FIG. 10. Results from an experiment in which cytosols from the propositus and the control cells were mixed, then fractionated and studied by minicolumn chromatography. Expected and actual values were similar suggesting that there is no excess of inhibitors or deficiency of positive modifiers. Phosphocellulose (PC) was used instead of DNA cellulose. (From Tomita *et al.*, 1985b.)

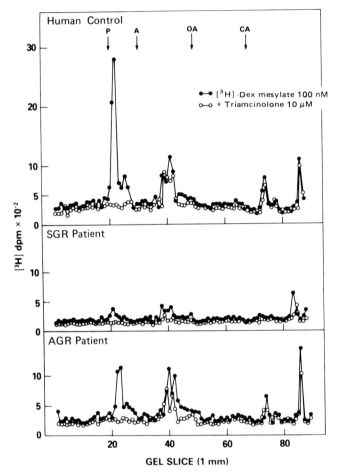

FIG. 11. SDS–PAGE of glucocorticoid receptor bound to dexamethasone mesylate. Both the propositus and the mildly affected patients glucocorticoid receptor had a molecular weight similar to that of controls. (From Tomita *et al.*, 1985b.)

expressed homozygous state and the son and the biochemically only affected relatives representing the heterozygous state (Chrousos *et al.*, 1983).

A mutation of the receptor might have silently occurred many generations prior to that of the propositus' parents and could explain a recessive pattern of inheritance. This implies that the parents of the propositus descend from families with consanguinity that occurred before the sixteenth century. This is not unlikely considering that both families have lived for a long time in close proximity.

This must be the rarest cause of hereditary hypertension yet described in man. Presumably, any patient with hypertension and hypokalemic alkalosis would be studied thoroughly for an aldosteroma and the high plasma and urinary cortisol levels would be discovered. The occurrence of the syndrome in a person with a mild affinity defect, as was present in the son, would not be noticed unless a urinary free cortisol or dexamethasone suppression test were carried out. A similar case with a mild affinity defect has recently been reported in an abstract (Nawata *et al.*, 1984).

2. Theoretical

The absence of any manifestation of glucocorticoid toxicity in our patients is explained by the assumption that the defect in glucocorticoid receptors is generalized. This has the important implication that glucocorticoids exert their effects in all tissues via specific receptors.

If we assume that the asymptomatic subjects represent the heterozygote state, then the clinical picture and the receptor findings could be explained by either a receptor mutation or by an abnormality in putative cytosolic factor(s) that may normally modify the cascade of events during glucocorticoid action. Mixing studies have not demonstrated the presence of excess inhibitor(s) or deficiency of positive modifier(s). Thus, a mutation of the receptor may be the case. However, nuclear receptor binding sites or control elements need to be considered.

Although the straight Scatchard regression line found in the mildly affected members would suggest mixing of receptor subunits rather than separate receptor molecules with different affinities, a slightly nonlinear Scatchard regression line may not have been detected.

III. Glucocorticoid Resistance in New World Primates

A. GENERAL CHARACTERISTICS OF NEW WORLD PRIMATES

Living primates are divided into three major evolutionary groups, with marked differences in their glucocorticoid hormone-target organ systems (Fig. 12): Old World primates (including man), New World primates, and prosimians (Napier and Napier, 1967). The last presumably are descendants of the common prosimioid ancestor of both Old and New World primates. They are considered subprimates and have been found living only in the Old World. Old and New World primates diverged from each other about 50 million years ago or, according to recent evidence, possibly even later (Sarich, 1970; Cronin and Sarich, 1978; Cichion and Chiarelli, 1980).

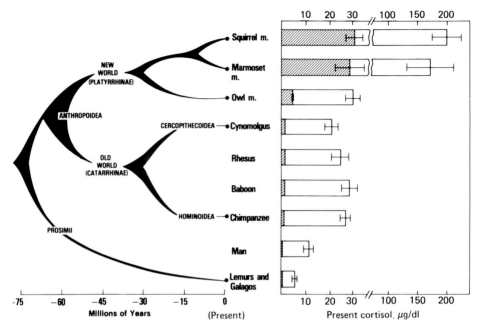

FIG. 12. An albumin and transferrin phylogeny tree for the primate taxa, in which the time scale is assigned with the assumption that their most common ancestor lived 60 million years ago (according to recent evidence it may be less), indicates phylogenetic relationships among the primate species studied. Total (whole bar) and free (hatched portion) plasma cortisol concentrations in primates. m, Monkey. (From Chrousos et al., 1982b.)

Brown et al. (1970), Yamamoto et al. (1977), and we have shown that New World primates studied to date have greatly elevated plasma cortisol levels. However, their life expectancy is similar to that of Old World primates. They have normal carbohydrate metabolism (Gallina and Ausman, 1979) and their arterial blood pressure and serum electrolytes are similar to those of Old World primates (Melby and Altman, 1976; New, 1968; Chrousos et al., 1984b) (Table IV).

The females during their reproductive cycle and pregnancy also have high plasma concentrations of progesterone, when compared to that of Old World primate females (Preslock et al., 1973; Abbot and Hearn, 1978; Bonney et al., 1979; Chrousos et al., 1982a, 1984a). In addition, less pronounced elevations of plasma concentrations of other steroid hormones are found in New World primates such as those of aldosterone (Chrousos et al., 1984b), estradiol (Preslock et al., 1973; Abbot and Hearn, 1978; Bonney et al., 1979; Chrousos et al., 1982a, 1984a), testos-

TABLE IV

Electrolyte Plasma Concentrations and Daily Urinary Excretion in Cynomolgus and Squirrel Monkeys[a]

	Plasma conc. (meq/liter)				24-hour urinary excretion (meq)	
	Na⁺	K⁺	Cl⁻	-HCO₃	Na⁺	K⁺
Cynomolgus monkey	146.2 ± 4.7(21)[b]	4.0 ± 0.77(21)	103 ± 6.8(21)	24.7 ± 2.3(21)	0.2 ± 0.23 [22.5 ± 16.9](6)	2.62 ± 2.06 [23.5 ± 11.3](6)
Squirrel monkey	149.9 ± 4.5(31)	4.2 ± 0.6 (31)	109 ± 6.2(31)	20.5 ± 3.0(25)	0.66 ± 0.65 [38.0 ± 25.4](6)	32.06 ± 18.8 [210.0 ± 49.5](6)

[a] From Chrousos et al. (1984b).
[b] Mean ± SD. The number of animals is in parentheses; the milliequivalents of electrolyte excreted per g creatinine are in brackets.

terone (Pugeat *et al.*, 1984b), and 1,25-dihydroxyvitamin D (Shinki *et al.*, 1983; Suda *et al.*, 1985).

We assumed that the high plasma cortisol levels resulted from a defective glucocorticoid receptor as shown above, but the associated findings raised a series of new questions.

1. What adjustments in the adrenal axis took place to permit such high plasma cortisol levels without concomitant increases in sodium-retaining corticoids?

2. How do the New World primates avoid sodium retention with plasma cortisols of 200 μg/dl? Cortisol is known to have mineralocorticoid (sodium-retaining) properties in Old World primates and other species (rats, dogs) (Ringler, 1964; Gaunt, 1971; Christi, 1971; Hayes and Larner, 1975; Baxter *et al.*, 1976; Gerrard and Palem-Vliers, 1980; Lan *et al.*, 1982). Elevation of plasma cortisol should lead to suppression of the renin–angiotensin–aldosterone axis, sodium retention and hypertension, hypokalemia, and alkalosis.

3. What are the reasons for the elevated plasma sex steroids in New World primates? Does progesterone have the aldosterone-antagonist properties that are well known in Old World primates (Landau and Lugibihl, 1958, 1961; Kagana, 1964).

4. Is there a common element responsible for the presumptive alterations of the six steroid hormone receptors (if we include vitamin D as steroid hormone) in New World primates?

5. How are the changes in affinity and capacity of cortisol-binding globulin related to steroid receptor alterations?

B. GLUCOCORTICOID PHYSIOLOGY

1. The Hypothalamic–Pituitary–Adrenal (HPA) Axis

a. Circulating Plasma ACTH and Cortisol.   Plasma concentrations of immunoreactive ACTH measured as described by Chrousos *et al.* (1984c), and β-endorphin measured by the method of Healy *et al.* (1983), are markedly elevated in the squirrel and owl monkey being 6- to 15-fold higher than the values observed in rhesus and cynomolgus monkeys studied in parallel (Chrousos *et al.*, 1984b) (Table V).

The free plasma cortisol concentration, determined by dialysis, is also increased in those New World primates that we have been able to study, i.e., the squirrel monkey, the marmoset, and the owl monkey (Fig. 12, Table VI). In corroboration of these findings, urinary free cortisol, a reflection of protein-unbound plasma cortisol, was markedly increased in squirrel monkeys and moderately increased in the owl monkey (Chrousos *et*

TABLE V
Comparative Plasma Concentrations of Immunoreactive ACTH and β-Endorphin

Monkey	n	ACTH (pg/ml)	β-Endorphin (pg/ml)
Cynomolgus	10	8.3 ± 1.0[a]	<12.5
Rhesus	10	12.4 ± 1.7	18.9 ± 5.4
Squirrel	10	58.2 ± 8.9[b]	51.5 ± 7.8[b]
Owl	10	110.2 ± 6.4[b]	191.4 ± 16.9[b]

[a] Mean ± SD.
[b] $p < 0.01$.

al., 1982b). The levels seen in New World primates, adjusted for weight and body surface area, were within and above the range seen in Cushing syndrome in man (Murphy, 1968).

   b. Plasma Cortisol Transport.   The increased percentage of protein-unbound free plasma cortisol (Chrousos *et al.*, 1982b; Siiteri *et al.*, 1982) in the face of the normal serum albumin concentrations in the New World primates is associated with a cortisol-binding globulin (CBG) of low con-

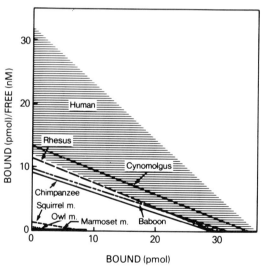

FIG. 13.   Scatchard plots of representative studies of [³H]cortisol binding to CBG from various primate species. The moles of binding sites contained in 100 μl plasma are indicated by the *x* intercept. The CBG binding affinity is indicated by the slope of the line. The shaded area indicates the range of human values. See Table VI for the mean ± SD. Correlation coefficients (*r*) were greater than 0.9 for all regression lines. (From Pugeat *et al.*, 1984a.)

TABLE VI

Circulating Cortisol Forms and Plasma CBG Binding Capacity and Affinity in Primates[a]

Species	n	Plasma cortisol		n	Plasma CBG	
		Total (μg/dl)	Free (μg/dl)		Capacity (μg/dl)	Affinity (10^{-7} M)
Prosimians						
Lemurinae	13	5.7 ± 1.0	0.48 ± 0.08	13	12.8 ± 3.6	33.8 ± 3.0
Galaginae	5	5.0 ± 1.5	0.20 ± 0.06	6	17.9 ± 3	29.2 ± 2.0
Old World primates						
Man	11	11.5 ± 2.0	0.29 ± 0.06	9	22.2 ± 3.0	83.8 ± 31
Chimpanzee	10	26.5 ± 2.0	0.76 ± 0.06			
Rhesus	5	24.5 ± 3.5	1.20 ± 0.16	3	17.9 ± 2.1	33.8 ± 6.6
Cynomolgus	5	21.0 ± 2.5	0.90 ± 0.10	4	12.9 ± 3.6	34.6 ± 3.9
Baboon	5	28.5 ± 3.5	1.02 ± 0.14	4	21.8 ± 3.4	32.0 ± 8.7
New world primates						
Owl monkey	8	30.0 ± 3.0	4.30 ± 0.42	4	0.2 ± 0.1	3.2 ± 2.8
Squirrel monkey	10	199.0 ± 24.0	30.60 ± 3.70	4	2.3 ± 2.2	18.2 ± 3.6
Marmoset monkey						
Callithrix	6	171.0 ± 34.0	28.40 ± 5.64	3	I[b]	I
Saguinus	9	197.0 ± 30.0	ND[c]		ND	ND

[a] From Chrousos *et al.* (1982c) and Pugeat *et al.* (1984a).
[b] I, Not quantifiable binding parameters, although some CBG is evidently present.
[c] ND, not done.

centration and low affinity for cortisol as measured by the method of Nisula and Dunn (1979) and Pugeat *et al.* (1981). (Fig. 13, Table VI). Thus although the owl monkey has a total cortisol concentration at the upper limits of the normal range, the plasma free cortisol is elevated many fold. The CBG in each species was found to be glycosylated, as judged from lectin interactions, and to exhibit an electrophoretic mobility similar to that of human CBG (Fig. 14) (Pugeat *et al.*. 1984a).

c. *Resistance to Dexamethasone Suppression.* The hypothalamic–pituitary–adrenal axis of squirrel monkeys is resistant to dexamethasone suppression (Chrousos *et al.*, 1982c). Squirrel monkeys require 460 μg of dexamethasone per kg of body weight for a 50% suppression of the 8:00 AM total plasma cortisol concentration. The cynomolgus monkey requires only 10 μg/kg (Fig. 15). To exclude the possibility that this might be an artifact due to differences in absorption or clearance of dexamethasone between the two species, concurrent measurements of plasma dexamethasone were made (Fig. 15, insert). The same doses of dexamethasone produced similar dexamethasone levels in both species, indicating no major differences in the bioavailability or rate of metabolism. The level of

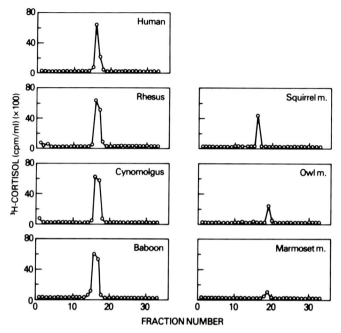

FIG. 14.   Polyacrylamide gel electrophoresis of [³H]cortisol-containing plasma from various primate species. A single peak was evident in fractions 15–19 in all species examined (m = monkey). The panels on the left are for Old World primates, and those on the right are for New World primates. (From Pugeat *et al.*, 1984a.)

plasma dexamethasone required for 50% suppression of plasma cortisol was 66-fold higher in the squirrel monkey than in the cynomolgus.

   d.   Production Rate (PR) and Metabolic Clearance Rate (MCR) of Cortisol.   The production rate of cortisol in the squirrel monkey is about 6-fold higher than that of the cynomolgus and the MCR about 2-fold less (Table VII) (Cassorla *et al.*, 1982). This is one of several mechanisms that permit the New World primates to sustain their high cortisol levels in the plasma. The lower MCR observed in the squirrel monkey may be ascribed presumptively to the rate-limiting step of 5α-reduction of cortisol (Siiteri, 1985).

   e.   Intraadrenal Adaptations.   The adrenal glands in squirrel monkeys are increased in size and histologically have an enlarged *zona fasciculata* (Cassorla *et al.*, 1982). In addition to the morphological changes of the adrenal glands, two enzymes, 21- and 11-hydroxylase have increased activities whereas, 17,20-desmolase activity is decreased in squirrel monkeys, as compared with an Old World monkey (Table VIII). (Cassorla *et*

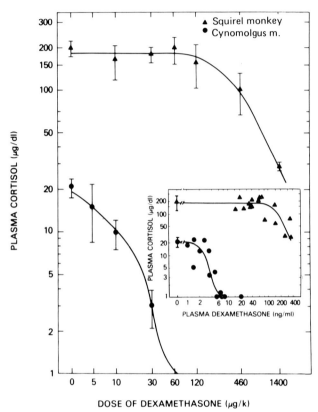

FIG. 15.   Responsiveness of the hypothalamic-pituitary-adrenal axis to dexamethasone suppression in squirrel (▲) and cynomolgus (●) monkeys. Dose-response curves of total plasma cortisol (taken at 7:00 to 8:00 am) to intramuscular dexamethasone given at 8:00 pm on the previous evening. Squirrel monkeys required 46-fold more dexamethasone for 50% suppression of plasma cortisol value, when compared with cynomolgus monkeys. Insert: The plasma concentration of dexamethasone required for 50% suppression was 66-fold higher in the squirrel monkey. (From Chrousos *et al.*, 1982.)

TABLE VII

Adrenal Weights and Cortisol PR and MCR in Squirrel and Cynomolgus Monkeys[a]

	Adrenal weight (mg/kg body weight)	Cortisol PR (mg/m²/day)	Cortisol MCR (liters/M²/day)
Cynomolgus monkey	197 ± 10 (10)[b]	32 ± 6 (3)	123 ± 3
Squirrel monkey	320 ± 22 (4)	199 ± 21 (3)[c]	65 ± 3[c]

[a] From Cassorla *et al.* (1982).
[b] Mean ± SD; *n* in parentheses.
[c] $p < 0.001$.

TABLE VIII

Adrenal Enzyme Activities in Squirrel and Cynomolgus Monkeys[a]

	21-Hydroxylase (nmol-min/mg protein)	17,20-Desmolase (pmol-min/mg protein)	17-Hydroxylase (nmol-min/mg protein)	3β-Hydroxysteroid dehydrogenase-Δ^5,Δ^4 isomerase (nmol-min/mg protein)	11-Hydroxylase (pmol/min/mg mitochondrial protein)
Cynomolgus monkey	6.4 ± 0.23[b]	37.5 ± 1.86	10.5 ± 0.09	10.2 ± 0.09	27.5 ± 4.2
Squirrel monkey	23.9 ± 0.26[c]	24.7 ± 1.98[c]	9.8 ± 0.52	10.5 ± 0.15	197.8 ± 14.4[c]

[a] From Cassorla et al. (1982) and Albertson et al. (1985).
[b] Mean ± SE.
[c] $p < 0.01$.

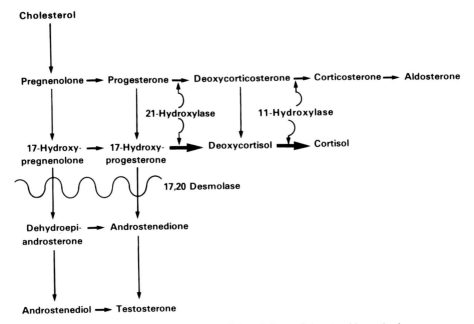

FIG. 16. Alterations in the enzyme activity of three of the steroidosynthesis enzymes (increased: 21-hydroxylase and 11-hydroxylase; decreased: 17,20-desmolase) would lead to funnelling of steroid precursors toward the production of C_{21}-hydroxylated steroids.

al., 1982; Albertson et al., 1985). These alterations would funnel steroid precursors toward the production of C-21-hydroxylated steroids, including cortisol and aldosterone (Fig. 16).

2. The Glucocorticoid Target Tissues

a. Glucocorticoid Receptor Binding Characteristics. We have examined the glucocorticoid receptor of intact circulating mononuclear leukocytes and cultured skin fibroblasts (Chrousos et al., 1982b) and B-lymphocytes transformed with the Epstein–Barr virus (Tomita et al., 1985b). A general characteristic is that the affinity of the glucocorticoid receptor for dexamethasone is decreased in New World primates compared to Old World primates. However, although the glucocorticoid receptor concentration in white cells (Fig. 17) and fibroblasts is similar in New and Old World primates, transformed B-lymphocytes from marmoset monkeys contain a much lesser amount of glucocorticoid receptor than human transformed cells (Fig. 18). This decreased induction of glucocorticoid receptor by viral transformation mirrors that seen in the study of human transformed B-lymphocytes from the two patients. The marmoset was used here because the EB virus transformed its B-lymphocytes but not those of the squirrel monkey.

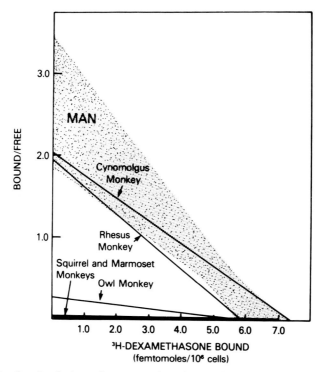

FIG. 17. Scatchard plots of representative glucocorticoid receptor studies on intact mononuclear leukocytes from various primate species (16-hour incubation at 24°C). The number of receptors per cell, indicated by the x intercept, is statistically the same in all species. The affinity of the receptor for dexamethasone, reflected by the slope of the line, is different. The shaded area indicates the human range ($n = 6$). The affinity for dexamethasone of the owl monkey glucocorticoid receptor is moderately decreased and that of the squirrel monkey is markedly decreased. In the latter, special analysis was required to define the affinity and number of receptors. (From Chrousos *et al.*, 1982b.)

We also examined the glucocorticoid receptor in the cytosol fraction from marmoset transformed B-lymphocytes (Fig. 18). The findings were similar with those in the intact cells, i.e., a low number of receptors and a decreased affinity for labeled dexamethasone. However, the differences in both receptor concentration and affinity were more marked than with the intact cells (Table IX).

b. Glucocorticoid Hormone–Receptor Complex Stability. The absolute amount of cytosolic receptor is generally less than expected based on the intact cell data. This again raised the question of instability during the preparation of cytosol or incubation. We examined the stability of the glucocorticoid receptor–steroid complex by measuring specific bound ligand at different time points during thermal activation (Tomita *et al.*, 1985b). As expected from the lower affinity of the receptor in the marmo-

TABLE IX

Glucocorticoid Receptor Status in EB Virus Transformed Lymphocytes from Human Controls and a Glucocorticoid Resistant Primate[a]

	Intact cell studies			Cytosol studies		
	R_0 (receptor sites/cell)	K_D (10^8 M^{-1})	n^b	R_0 (fmol/mg protein)	K_A (10^8 M^{-1})	n
Human controls	28560 ± 10140^c	7.7 ± 1.8	9	529.2 ± 68.7	2.1 ± 0.6	3
Marmoset	4920 ± 840^d	4.3 ± 2.1^e	3	58.2 ± 15.9^d	0.32 ± 0.1^d	3

[a] From Tomita et al. (1985b).
[b] n, Number of measurements.
[c] Mean $\pm$ SD.
[d] $p < 0.005$.
[e] $p < 0.05$.

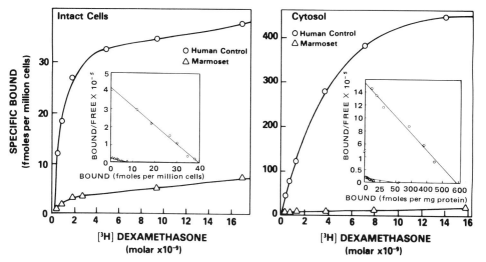

FIG. 18. Saturation curve and Scatchard plot of representative glucocorticoid receptor studies on Epstein–Barr-transformed B-lymphocytes. Not only the affinity but also the receptor concentration is decreased in the marmoset cells. (From Tomita *et al.*, 1985b.)

set there was greater loss of specific bound ligand in the marmoset than human control, probably a result of increased dissociation (Fig. 19A).

However, determination of receptor concentration at 0–4°C after heating the unoccupied cytosolic receptor for various time intervals indicated that the marmoset receptor was not more thermolabile than the human control run in parallel (Fig. 19B), a finding identical to that seen in the cortisol-resistant humans.

c. Activation of the Glucocorticoid Receptor. We examined the thermal activation pattern of the glucocorticoid receptor by heating cytosol *in vitro* and by incubating cells at 37°C *in vivo* (Tomita *et al.*, 1985b). When we incubated cytosol at 25–28°C with saturating concentrations of dexamethasone and then examined specific bound counts retained on phosphocellulose chromatography columns, we found that the ratio of activated to unactivated receptor was similar to the ratio of human control cytosol run in parallel (data not shown). Thus, activation, as defined by these studies was normal.

We incubated intact cells at 37°C and then examined the cytosolic glucocorticoid receptor by passage through the minicolumn described by Holbrook *et al.* (1983, 1984). The ratio of activated to unactivated receptor was similar to the ratio found in human control cells run in parallel. There was no excess of meroreceptor (Fig. 20). These data were compati-

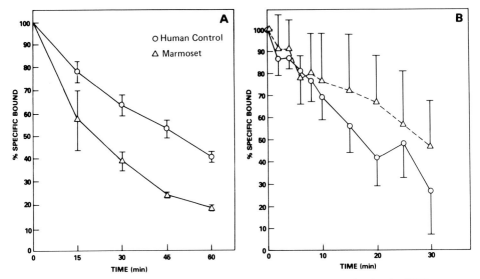

FIG. 19. (A) Specific-bound labeled dexamethasone during thermal activation 28°C over time. There is greater loss in the marmoset cytosol. (B) Specifically bound hormone alter previous incubation of cytosol for various time intervals at 28°C. See also legend to Fig. 6 for experimental details. (From Tomita *et al.*, 1985b.)

ble with the normal nucleus to cytosol receptor ratio found in the marmoset cells after incubation at saturating concentrations dexamethasone (40 n*M*).

d. Glucocorticoid Receptor Positive or Negative Modifiers. As in the previous studies, we mixed labeled marmoset and human cytosol, incubated them, and then assayed glucocorticoid receptor. The actual and expected values for specific finding were similar, suggesting that an excess of inhibitors or deficiency of positive modifiers may not be responsible for the low binding seen in the marmoset cells (Fig. 20).

e. Molecular Weight of the Glucocorticoid Receptor. We measured the molecular weight of the marmoset glucocorticoid receptor by using SDS–PAGE electrophoresis of receptor bound to an irreversible ligand, dexamethasone mesylate (Tomita *et al.*, 1985a). The molecular weight of the receptor is similar to that of the human receptor (data not shown).

We can now summarize our attempts to understand the differences between receptors. To anticipate later studies, we note that the glucocorticoid receptors of the transformed B-lymphocytes of the marmoset had the same pattern of experimental findings as did the receptor from the transformed patient lymphocytes. Except for a grossly similar molecular size, the glucocorticoid receptor had a lower affinity than controls in both

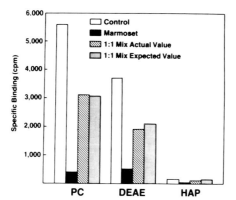

FIG. 20. Minicolumn chromatography of cytosol obtained from cells previously incubated with [³H]dexamethasone and heated for 30 minutes at 23°C. See also legends to Figs. 8 and 10. (From Tomita *et al.*, 1985b.)

the human syndrome and the animal model and we had no evidence of thermal instability or excess generation of meroreceptors in either. We could show no involvement of cytosolic factors and in both conditions we observed a decreased receptor content in the EB virus-transformed cells compared to controls.

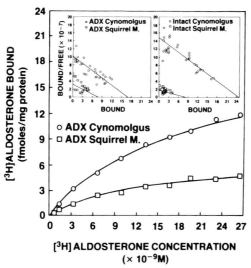

FIG. 21. Representative saturation curves for binding of [³H]aldosterone to kidney aldosterone receptor from squirrel and cynomolgus monkeys (18 hours at 0–4°C). Insets: The results of Scatchard analysis of [³H]aldosterone binding to the renal cytosol mineralocorticoid receptor of adrenalectomized (ADX; left) and intact (right) squirrel and cynomolgus monkeys. (From Chrousos *et al.*, 1984b.)

C. MINERALOCORTICOID PHYSIOLOGY

1. The Renin–Angiotensin–Aldosterone Axis

From studies in rodents and man, cortisol is known to interact with the mineralocorticoid receptor and exert sodium-retaining effects (Ringler, 1964; Gaunt, 1971; Christi, 1971; Hayes and Larner, 1975; Baxter *et al.*, 1976; Gerrard and Palem-Vliers, 1980; Lan *et al.*, 1982). Thus, we would expect New World primates to have low aldosterone concentrations. However, cortisol, at concentrations greater than 150 μg/dl, did not cause sodium retention, potassium loss, alkalosis, or hypertension in these New World primates, and immunoreactive aldosterone measured by the procedure of Ito *et al.* (1972) circulates at concentrations similar or slightly higher (mean value is 2-fold higher than that of cynomolgus) than those of Old World primates (Table X) (Chrousos *et al.*, 1984b).

In addition, no changes in plasma immunoreactive aldosterone levels are observed during the reproductive cycle or pregnancy, when the levels of progesterone are 10- to 20-fold higher than those seen in women, in whom aldosterone concentrations change accordingly (Table XI) (Chrousos *et al.*, 1984b).

2. The Mineralocorticoid Target Tissues

a. Renal Aldosterone Receptors.   Renal cytosol aldosterone receptor concentrations measured by a modification of the Grekin and Sider technique (1980) are about 2- to 3-fold lower in the squirrel monkey than in the cynomolgus, whereas the receptor affinities for [³H]aldosterone are similar in the two species (Fig. 21) (Chrousos *et al.*, 1984b).

b. Cross-reactivity with Cortisol.   Higher plasma concentrations of cortisol are needed to displace [³H]aldosterone from the mineralocorticoid receptor in the squirrel monkey than from the renal receptor in the cynomolgus ($K_i = 7.8 \times 10^{-7}$ vs $2.9 \times 10^{-8}M$, respectively) (Chrousos *et al.*, 1984b). Thus, the salt-retaining potency of cortisol is low in this species, presumably because of a decrease in the affinity of the aldosterone receptor for glucocorticoids.

Although we have no direct evidence of decreased cross-reactivity of progesterone for the mineralocorticoid receptor in New World primates, in a fashion analogous to cortisol, it appears to be at the present time the most plausible hypothesis. Since plasma 11-deoxycorticosterone has not been measured during pregnancy in the squirrel monkey, we are unable to assess its possible role in the regulation of plasma aldosterone. It is nevertheless clear that a necessary adaptive mechanism in the kidney to the high ambient cortisol concentrations is the relative failure of this receptor to respond to cortisol.

TABLE X

Comparative Plasma Concentrations of Some C-21 Steroids, CBG, Albumin, and PRA[a]

	Cortisol (μg/dl)	Albumin (g/dl)	Corticosterone (ng/dl)	11-Deoxy-cortisol (ng/dl)	17-Hydroxy-progesterone (ng/dl)	PRA (ng/ml/hour)	Aldosterone (ng/dl)
Cynomolgus monkey	20.2 ± 1.5(15)[b]	2.9 ± 0.61(16)	1390 ± 301(13)	196 ± 45.6(9)	31.6 ± 11.5(9)	10.8 ± 1.00(25)	25.9 ± 2.7(25)
Squirrel monkey	187.2 ± 16.2(22)	3.98 ± 0.36(26)	2166 ± 346(15)	1906 ± 252(10)	844 ± 265(10)	6.4 ± 1.5(18)	41.1 ± 10.5(24)

[a] From Chrousos et al. (1984b).
[b] Mean ± SE. The number of animals sampled is in parentheses.

TABLE XI

Comparative Plasma Concentrations of Progesterone and Aldosterone during the Reproductive Cycle and Pregnancy[a,b]

	Progesterone (ng/ml)					Aldosterone (ng/dl)		
	M	F repro	F quies	F preg	F ovx	F repro	F quies	F preg
Cynomolgus monkey	0.2 ± 0.03[c] (n = 5)	<15		<15	0.17 ± 0.07 (n = 3)			32.0 ± 5.6 (n = 6)
Squirrel monkey	1.1 ± 0.3 (n = 5)	[57–510] (n = 3; m = 51)	$8.22 + 1.9$ [0.2–34.2] (n = 15; m = 28)	[49–490] (n = 2; m = 28)	1.2 ± 0.2 (n = 7)	29.3 ± 7.13 (n = 12)	30.5 ± 18.6 (n = 8)	38 ± 8.0 (n = 9)

[a] From Chrousos et al. (1984b).

[b] M, Male; F, female; repro, reproductive cycle; quies, quiescent ovaries, during nonmating season; preg, pregnancy; ovx, ovariectomy; n, number of subjects studied; m, number of serial samples measured; range in brackets.

[c] Mean ± SE.

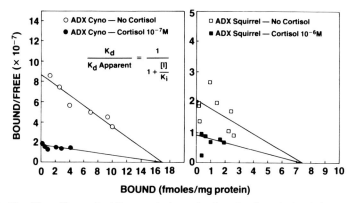

FIG. 22. The effects of adding cortisol on the Scatchard analysis of [³H]aldosterone binding to the renal cytosol aldosterone receptor of adrenalectomized cynomolgus (ADX Cyno) and squirrel monkeys (18 hours at 0–4°C). The apparent K_d increased with cortisol addition in both species. The K_i of cortisol for the squirrel aldosterone receptor (7.8×10^{-7} M) was about 30-fold higher than that found in the cynomolgus monkey (2.9×10^{-8} M). (From Chrousos et al., 1984b.)

D. SEX STEROID PHYSIOLOGY

1. Plasma Sex Steroid Transport

We studied many primate species, including Old and New World primates and prosimians for the presence of testosterone–estradiol binding globulin (TeBG) (Pugeat et al., 1984b). In all species tested, TeBG was found to be a glycoprotein as judged by absorption to lectins, and to have similar mobility in polyacrylamide gel electrophoresis.

In New World primates the TeBG binding capacity was higher than in Old World primates or prosimians. The affinity however for testosterone or estradiol was lower in New World primates, resulting in higher free plasma testosterone or estradiol concentrations (Pugeat et al., 1984b; Chrousos et al., 1984a). The majority of circulating progesterone should also be in the free form, if one takes into account the very low capacity of CBG in New World primates and the very high concentrations of circulating cortisol.

2. Circulating Levels of Sex Steroids

The females of the squirrel monkey and other New World primate species have markedly elevated plasma progesterone concentrations during their seasonal reproductive cycles, being 2- and as much as 20-fold higher than the maximum luteal values observed in Old World primates (Fig. 23) (Preslock et al., 1973; Abbot and Hearn, 1978; Bonney et al.,

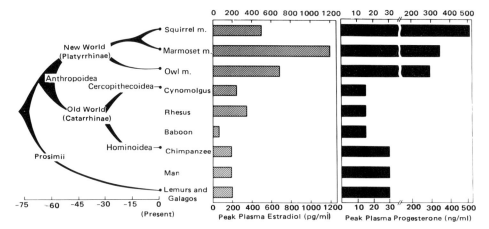

FIG. 23. Middle, mean plasma preovulatory peak estradiol concentrations in primates. Right, mean plasma luteal peak progesterone concentrations. Left, an albumin and transferrin phylogenetic tree for the primate taxa, in which the time scale (in million years) is assigned with the assumption that their most common ancestor lived about 60 million years ago). Recent reports suggest a more contracted time scale. See also legend to Fig. 12. (From Chrousos *et al.*, 1984a.)

1979; Chrousos *et al.*, 1982a, 1984a). Also, plasma progesterone levels in pregnant squirrel monkeys are markedly elevated compared to those in pregnant cynomolgus monkeys, but are similar to those in humans during the third trimester of pregnancy (Fig. 24) (Chrousos *et al.*, 1982a). In addition, plasma estrogen levels are higher in squirrel monkeys than in cynomolgus and rhesus monkeys during both the reproductive cycle and pregnancy (Fig. 23). When compared to the human, however, plasma estradiol concentrations are higher in the squirrel monkey only during the reproductive cycle. They are similar in the two species during pregnancy.

The elevations of plasma progesterone and estradiol concentrations in New World primates are associated with large, markedly luteinized ovaries (Castellanos and McCombs, 1968). In these species, the reproductive cycle ranges between 8 and 16 days and is seasonal.

3. Sex Steroid Target Tissues

Since progesterone receptors depend upon both estrogen and progesterone concentrations and change throughout the reproductive cycle, and since timing of reproductive cycle events is difficult in New World primates, in which handling or procedures such as laparoscopy disturb ovulation, we studied progesterone receptors in a controlled fashion.

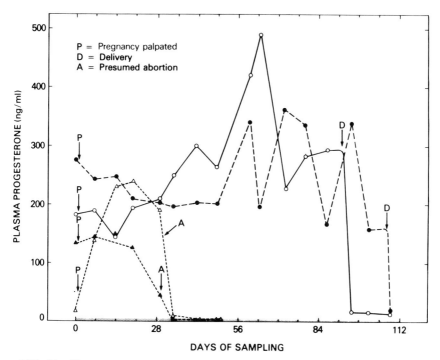

FIG. 24. Plasma progesterone levels in four pregnant squirrel monkeys. Two of them aborted during the first third of pregnancy. The shaded area represents the normal range of plasma progesterone in pregnant rhesus and cynomolgus monkeys. (From Chrousos *et al.*, 1982a.)

Animals from a representative New World (squirrel monkeys) and Old World primate (cynomolgus macaques) species were ovariectomized, allowed to convalesce, and then given pharmacologic amounts of estrogen (estradiol in sesame oil, 10 μg/kg body weight im) for 2–14 days. Uterine and hypothalamic–pituitary progesterone and estrogen receptors were then examined using either a dextran-coated charcoal assay (Rifka *et al.*, 1976) or an LH-20 assay (MacLusky *et al.*, 1984). Both receptor affinity and binding capacity were determined. All experiments were done in parallel. Histology of the endometrium and vagina were obtained also.

Uterine cycosolic progesterone receptor concentrations were generally 4- to 8-fold lower in squirrel monkeys than in cynomolgus monkeys (Fig. 25). However, both receptors had similar affinities (Chrousos *et al.*, 1984a). Pituitary receptors were also 2-fold lower in squirrel monkeys than in cynomolgus monkeys, suggesting that the hypothesized target-organ insensitivity to progesterone includes the pituitary gland. However,

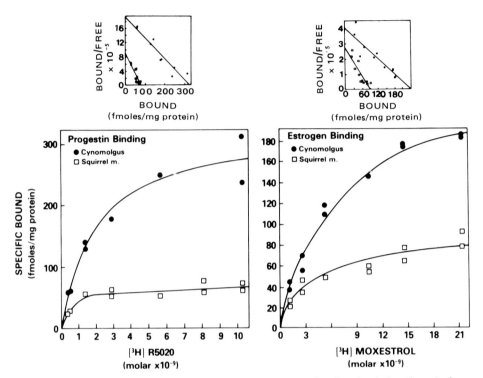

FIG. 25. Representative saturation curves and corresponding Scatchard plots (insets) of [³H]R5020 or [³H]moxestrol binding from ovariectomized squirrel and cynomolgus monkeys after treatment with estradiol for 2 days. (From Chrousos *et al.*, 1984a.)

no differences in receptor concentrations were observed in the hypothalamic–preoptic area between the two species (MacLusky *et al.*, 1984).

Cytosolic estrogen receptors were also examined in the same tissues. The differences observed were smaller than those of the progesterone receptors, as would be expected also from the plasma estrogen concentrations (Fig. 25). Although the uterus contained ~3-fold lower estrogen receptor concentrations in the New World primates, no differences were observed in the pituitary and hypothalamic receptors (MacLusky *et al.*, 1984, and unpublished data).

The New World primates' decreased pituitary sensitivity to progesterone might lead to increased LH concentrations and hyperstimulation of the corpus luteum. However, the relationships between the progesterone and gonadotropin secretion are unclear and, unfortunately, the available radioimmunoassays for LH do not cross-react with New World monkey

LH. Thus, at this point this hypothesis remains unanswered. In a woman with progesterone resistance and decreased endometrial progesterone receptor concentration (Keller *et al.,* 1979), plasma LH and progesterone were not increased. However, this woman may have had an isolated endometrial anomaly and a normal hypothalamic–pituitary sensitivity to progesterone.

Androgen receptors appear to be only slightly decreased in cultured skin fibroblasts from squirrel monkeys (Siiteri *et al.,* 1982). In addition, extremely reduced target-organ 5α-reductase activity has been described in this species (Siiteri, 1985), which would preclude conversion of testosterone to 5α-dihydrotestosterone (DHT), a hormone of importance in several target tissues in Old World primates. However, the external genitalia have a normal appearance in adult New World primates and DHT may not play the role it does in Old World primates.

E. "GENERALIZED" STEROID HORMONE RESISTANCE IN NEW WORLD PRIMATES

Adaptive Evolutionary Changes: Implications

In summary, the following steroid hormone–receptor systems appear to be altered in New World primates in the form of end-organ resistance: (1) glucocorticoid resistance, associated with high free plasma cortisol concentrations and low affinity glucocorticoid receptors; (2) aldosterone resistance, associated with high plasma aldosterone and low renal aldosterone receptor concentrations (also characterized by diminished crossreactivity for cortisol); (3) progesterone resistance, characterized by high levels of plasma progesterone and low concentrations of uterine cytosol progesterone receptors; (4) estrogen resistance, characterized by high levels of estradiol in plasma and low uterine cytosol estrogen receptors; (5) androgen resistance characterized by high free plasma testosterone concentrations and possible changes of the androgen receptors, and associated with low 5α-reductase activity at the target tissues; and (6) vitamin D resistance characterized by high levels of 1,25-dihydroxyvitamin D (Shinki *et al.,* 1983) and low concentrations of intestinal vitamin D receptors (Suda *et al.,* 1985).

If we assume that the glucocorticoid receptor alteration was the first mutation, we can consider the following changes as adaptive: high plasma ACTH, increased adrenal size, increased *zona fasciculata* size, increased cortisol production rate, increase cortisol biosynthetic enzyme activity, decreased cortisol binding globulin capacity and affinity, and decreased crossreactivity of the aldosterone receptor for cortisol. We have no physiologic link to connect the sex steroid or vitamin D changes with a putative initial glucocorticoid receptor mutation.

Since it is difficult to hypothesize a random simultaneous occurrence of 6 different mutations affecting all 6 steroid hormone–receptor–acceptor systems, we believe that it is possible that the concurrent alterations of the glucocorticoid, mineralocorticoid, sex steroid, and vitamin D receptor systems reflect some fundamental change in the chromatin proteins or DNA sequences involved in steroidal regulation of gene transcription, putatively common (nonclass specific) to the different steroid hormones. The changes in affinity of TeBG and of affinity and amount of CBG suggest additional linkages between receptors and carrier proteins.

The estrogen "resistance" of squirrel monkeys and other New World primates appears to be the first such example in nature. Unquestionably, in contrast to the human steroid resistance syndromes, this condition in monkeys is a well-adapted evolutionary change that represents a variant of normal. We believe that noncompensated estrogen resistance has not yet been found in individuals or species because of the probably indispensable role of estrogens in blastocyst implantation and early embryogenesis.

We do not understand the possible selective advantages that increased circulating sex steroids could offer the New World primates. The fact that most major New World primate representative species that we and others have been able to study have the "syndrome" of generalized steroid hormone resistance suggests that tolerated genetic drift (Eldredge and Cracraft, 1980) is not the case.

ACKNOWLEDGMENTS

We would like to acknowledge the intellectual and practical contribution of many of our collaborators in these studies. We are greatful to Drs. B. Albertson, F. Cassorla, M. DeVroede, C. Eil, C. Foster, D. Fowler, N. Holbrook, P. Munson, B. Nisula, M. Pugeat, D. Renquist, D. Rodbard, S. Taylor, R. Vigersky, and A. Vingerhoeds. We would like to thank Ms. Janice Day Robinson for her expert secretarial assistance.

REFERENCES

Abbott, D. H., and Hearn, J. P., (1978). *J. Reprod. Fertil.* **53,** 155.
Albertson, B., Chrousos, G. P., Loriaux, D. L., and Lipsett, M. B. (1985). In preparation.
Baxter, J. D., Schambelan, M., Matulich, D. T., Spindler, B. J., Taylor, A. A., and Bartter, F. C. (1976). *J. Clin. Invest.* **58,** 579.
Bonney, R. C., Dixson, A. F., and Fleming, D. (1979). *J. Reprod. Fertil.* **56,** 271.
Boyar, R. M., Witkin, M., Carruth, A., and Ramsey, J. (1979). *J. Clin. Endocrinol. Metab.* **48,** 363.
Brooks, M. H., Bell, N. H., Love, L., Stern, P. H., Orfei, E., Queener, S., Hamstra, F., and Deluca, H. (1978). *N. Engl. J. Med.* **298,** 996.

Brown, G. M., Grota, L. J., Penney, D. P., and Reichlin, S. (1970). *Endocrinology* **86**, 519.

Cassorla, F., Albertson, B., Chrousos, G. P., Booth, J., Renquist, D., Lipsett, M. B., and Loriaux, D. L. (1982). *Endocrinology* **111**, 448.

Castellanos, H., and McCombs, H. L. (1968). *Fertil. Steril.* **27**, 1256.

Cheek, D. B., and Perry, J. W. (1958). *Arch. Dis. Child.* **33**, 252.

Christy, N. P., ed. (1971). *In* "The Human Adrenal Cortex," p. 395. Harper, New York.

Chrousos, G. P., Renquist, D., Brandon, D., Barnard, D., Fowler, D., Loriaux, D. L., and Lipsett, M. B. (1982a). *J. Clin. Endocrinol. Metab.* **55**, 364.

Chrousos, G. P., Renquist, D., Brandon, D., Eil, C., Cutler, G. G., Vigersky, R., Loriaux, D. L., and Lipsett, M. B. (1982b). *Proc. Natl. Acad. Sci. U.S.A.* **76**, 2036.

Chrousos, G. P., Vingerhoeds, A., Brandon, D., Eil, C., Pugeat, M., DeVroede, M., Loriaux, D. L., and Lipsett, M. B. (1982c). *J. Clin. Invest.* **69**, 1261.

Chrousos, G. P., Vingerhoeds, A. C. M., Loriaux, D. L., and Lipsett, M. B. (1983). *J. Clin. Endocrinol. Metab.* **56**, 1243.

Chrousos, G. P., Brandon, D., Renquist, D. M., Tomita, M., Johnson, E., Loriaux, D. L., and Lipsett, M. B. (1984a). *J. Clin. Endocrinol. Metab.* **58**, 516.

Chrousos, G. P., Renquist, D., Brandon, D., Tomita, M., Loriaux, D. L., and Lipsett, M. B. (1984b). *Endocrinology* **115**, 25.

Chrousos, G. P., Schulte, H. M., Oldfield, E. H., Gold, P. W., Cutler, G. P., Jr., and Loriaux, D. L. (1984c). *N. Engl. J. Med.* **310**, 622.

Cichion, R. L., and Chiarelli, A. B., eds. (1980). "Evolutionary Biology of the New World Monkeys and Continental Drift." Plenum, New York.

Cronin, J. E., and Sarich, V. M. (1978). *Prim. Med.* **10**, 12.

Eil, C. E., Lippmann, E. M., and Loriaux, D. L. (1980). *Steroids* **35**, 389.

Eil, C., Liberman, U. A., Rosen, J. F., and Marx, S. J. (1981). *N. Engl. J. Med.* **304**, 1588.

Eldredge, N., and Cracraft, J. (1980). *In* "Phylogenetic Patterns and the Evolutionary Process," p. 298. Columbia Univ. Press, New York.

Gallina, D. L., and Ausman, L. M. (1979). *In* "Primates in Nutritional Research" K. C. Hayes, ed., p. 225. Academic Press, New York.

Gaunt, R. (1971). *In* "The Human Adrenal Cortex" (N. P. Christy, ed.), p. 273. Harper, New York.

Gerrard, P., and Palem-Vliers, M. (1980). *J. Steroid. Biochem.* **13**, 1299.

Gorden, P., Sherman, B. M., and Simopoulos, A. P. (1972). *J. Clin. Endocrinol. Metab.* **34**, 235.

Grekin, R. J., and Sider, R. S. (1980). *J. Steroid. Biochem.* **13**, 835.

Griffin, J. E., and Wilson, J. D. (1980). *N. Engl. J. Med.* **302**, 198.

Grody, W. W., Schrader, W. T., and O'Malley, B. W. (1982). *Endocrine Rev.* **3**, 141.

Hayes, R. C., and Larner, J. (1975). *In* "The Pharmacological Basis of Therapeutics" (L. S. Goodman, and A. Gilman, eds.), p. 1472. Macmillan, New York.

Healy, D. L., Hodgen, G. D., Schulte, H. M., Chrousos, G. P., Loriaux, D. L., Nicholas, R. H., and Goldstein, H. L. (1983). *Science* **222**, 1353.

Hodgson, A. J., and Funder, J. W. (1978). *Am. J. Physiol.* **235**, R115.

Holbrook, N. J., Bloomfield, C. D., and Munck, A. (1983). *Cancer Res.* **43**, 4478.

Holbrook, N. J., Bloomfield, C. D., and Munck, A. (1984). *Cancer Res.* **44**, 407.

Ito, T., Woo, J., Haning, R., and Horton, R. (1972). *J. Clin. Endocrinol. Metab.* **34**, 106.

Kagana, C. M. (1964). *Methods Horm. Res.* **3**, 351.

Katsumata, M., Baker, M. K., and Goldman, A. S. (1981). *Biochim. Biophys. Acta* **676**, 245.

Keller, D. W., Wiest, W. G., Askin, F. B., Johnson, L. W., and Strickler, R. C. (1979). *J. Clin. Endocrinol. Metab.* **48**, 127.

Kontula, K., Pelkonen, R., Andersson, L., and Sivula, A. (1980). *J. Clin. Endocrinol. Metab.* **51**, 654.

Kraft, N., Hodgson, A. J., and Funder, J. W. (1979). *Endocrinology* **104**, 344.

Lan, N. C., Graham, B., Bartter, F. C., and Baxter, J. D. (1982). *J. Clin. Endocrinol. Metab.* **54**, 332.

Landau, R. L., and Lugibihl, K. (1958). *J. Clin. Endocrinol. Metab.* **18**, 1237.

Landau, R. L., and Lugibihl, K. (1961). *Recent Prog. Horm. Res.* **17**, 249.

MacLusky, N. J., Chrousos, G. P., Brandon, D., Renquist, D. M., Loriaux, D. L., Lipsett, M. B., and Naftolin, F. (1984). *Int. Congr. Endocrinol. 7th, Quebec* Abstr. 1325, p. 923.

Meikle, A. W., Lagerquist, L. G., and Tyler, F. H. (1973). *Steroids* **22**, 193.

Meikle, A. W., Lagerquist, L. G., and Tyler, F. H. (1975). *J. Lab. Clin. Med.* **86**, 472.

Melby, A., and Altman, E., eds. (1976). *Handb. Lab. Anim. Sci.* **3**, 49.

Murakami, T., Brandon, D., Rodbard, D., Loriaux, D. L., and Lipsett, M. B. (1979). *Endocrinology* **104**, 500.

Murakami, T., Brandon, D., Loriaux, D. L., and Lipsett, M. B. (1980). *J. Steroid Biochem.* **13**, 1125.

Murphy, B. E. P. (1968). *J. Clin. Endocrinol. Metab.* **28**, 343.

Napier, J. R., and Napier, P. H. (1967). "A Handbook of Living Primates." Academic Press, New York.

Nawata, H., Sekiva, K., Higuchi, K., Yanase, T., Kato, K., and Ibayashi, H. (1984). *Int. Congr. Endocrinol. 7th, Quebec* Abstr. 1605. p. 1063.

New, A. (1968). *In* "The Squirrel Monkey" (L. A. Rosenbloom and R. W. Cooper, eds.), p. 417. Academic Press, New York.

Nisula, B. C., and Dunn, J. F. (1979). *Steroids* **34**, 771.

Preslock, J. P., Hampton, S. H., and Hampton, J. K., Jr. (1973). *Endocrinology* **92**, 1096.

Pugeat, M. M., Dunn, J. F., and Nisula, B. C. (1981). *J. Clin. Endocrinol. Metab.* **53**, 69.

Pugeat, M. M., Chrousos, G. P., Nisula, B. C., Loriaux, D. L., Brandon, D., and Lipsett, M. B. (1984a). *Endocrinology* **115**, 357.

Pugeat, M., Rocle, B., Chrousos, G. P., Dunn, J. F., Lipsett, M. B., and Nisula, B. C. (1984b). *J. Steroid. Biochem.* **20**, 473.

Rifka, A. M., Pita, J. C., Jr., and Loriaux, D. L. (1976). *Endocrinology* **99**, 1091.

Ringler, I. (1964). *Methods Horm. Res.* **3**, 227.

Sarich, V. M. (1970). *In* "Old World Monkeys: Evolution, Systematics and Behaviour" (J. R. Napier and P. H. Napier, eds.), p. 177. Academic Press, New York.

Schambelan, M., Slaton, P. E., Jr., and Biglieri, E. G. (1971). *Am. J. Med.* **51**, 299.

Shinki, T., Shiina, Y., Takahashi, S., Tanioka, Y., Koizumi, H., and Suda, T. (1983). *Biochem. Biophys. Res. Commun.* **114**, 452.

Siiteri, P. K. (1985). *In* "Mechanisms and Clinical Aspects of Steroid Hormone Resistance" (G. P. Chrousos, D. L. Loriaux, and M. B. Lipsett, eds.). Plenum, New York, in press.

Siiteri, P. K., Murai, J. T., Hammond, G. L., Nisher, J. A., Raymoure, W., and Kuhn, R. W. (1982). *Recent Prog. Hormone Res.* **38**, 457.

Suda, T., Takahashi, N., Shinki, T., Yamaguchi, A., and Tanioka, (1985). *In* "Mechanisms and Clinical Aspects of Steroid Hormone Resistance" (G. P. Chrousos, D. L. Loriaux, and M. B. Lipsett, eds.). Plenum, New York, in press.

Tomita, M., Chrousos, G. P., Brandon, D., Ben-Or, S., Foster, C., DeVougn, L., Taylor, S., Loriaux, D. L., and Lipsett, M. B. (1985a). *Horm. Metab. Res.* (in press).

Tomita, M., *et al.* (1985b). In preparation.

Verhoeven, G. F. M., and Wilson, J. D. (1979). *Metabolism* **28**, 253.

Vingerhoeds, A. C. M., Thijssen, J. H. H., and Schwarz, F. (1976). *J. Clin. Endocrinol. Metab.* **43**, 1128.

Wilkins, L. (1957). *In* "The Diagnosis and Treatment of Endocrine Disorders in Childhood and Adolescence," 2nd Ed., p. 276. Thomas, Springfield, Illinois.

Yamamoto, S., Utsu, S., Tamioka, Y., and Ohsawa, N. (1977). *Acta Endocrinol.* **85**, 398.

DISCUSSION

C. W. Bardin: One of the things that struck me about the family patients that you have reported is the heterogeneity of the phenotype. The same thing occurs in families with androgen resistance. I think this has puzzled people in the field. In addition we have wondered how a small change in receptor number or binding affinity can result in such a marked change in phenotype. To look for reasons for this we have examined the effect of androgens on the expression of the β-glucuronidase (Gluc), ornithine decarboxylase (ODC), and kidney androgen regulated protein (KAP) genes in mouse kidney when a large dose of testosterone is given that will cause maximal association of receptor as in chromatin, the lag time for the onset of mRNA accumulation and the peak levels of mRNA from all three genes is different. Furthermore, KAP mRNA is maximally induced by the number of active androgen receptors bound in nuclei of intact males. By contrast, maximal accumulation of ODC and Gluc mRNAs requires many more androgen receptors. These and other data suggest that each gene in a given cell may have a differential response in a given quantity of receptors. They each could also respond differentially to abnormal receptors. Since the phenotype in steroid resistance represents the composite response of multiple genes to a stimulus and each gene responds in a dose–response to a variable amount of receptor it is easy to understand how a small change in receptor quantity or quality could produce a large change in phenotype which could vary from one family member to another.

W. F. Crowley: Did you happen to have the opportunity to give either of your two patients spironolactone?

G. P. Chrousos: No, we did not give spironolactone. We used a different therapeutic rationale. Since the hypertension and hypokalemic alkalosis were due to ACTH-stimulated secretion of sodium-retaining corticoids, treatment should consist of supressing ACTH with a non-sodium-retaining corticoid. Dexamethasone did this and at 3 mg/day controlled the hypertension without causing Cushing's syndrome.

W. F. Crowley: One could sort of argue it the other way, that you're presumably using for this patient a pharmacologic dose of dexamethasone to suppress him, even though the curve is far shifted to the right, you still over the long-term might have some of the worries such as decreased bone density, particularly by using 3 mg in the son.

G. P. Chrousos: We only treated the father.

W. F. Crowley: But since the only clinical problem was hypertension and hypokalemic alkalosis would not spironolactone have all you needed to give?

G. P. Chrousos: We chose the dose of 3 mg from our dose–response studies because at this dose, we were able to bring the corticosterone levels down to the levels of the son, who was not hypertensive. Thus, we did not cause a complete suppression of the hypothalamic–pituitary axis. Furthermore, over a 3-year period of observation, he has remained well without stigmata of Cushing's syndrome.

M. Lipsett: I think the real question is, are you giving excess glucocorticoids. At 3 mg of dexamethasone per day we weren't. We didn't give it to the son because he was asymptomatic.

K. Sterling: My question has to do with the evolution of platyrrhine and catarrhine monkeys. My understanding is that the New World monkeys are much more primitive, that they're doubtless· ancestral to the Old World monkeys and ourselves ultimately; so my question is, why assume, looking at it from a human standpoint, that these New World primates have an abnormal mutation affecting the receptor. Why not assume that the change in the receptor is a recent development of the Old World primates and ourselves; I think the answer would be given if you were to study the still earlier group, the prosimians, including the lemuroids. Can you answer that?

M. Lipsett: Dr. Chrousos discussed the question whether we have taken an anthropocentric view of these data. We really believe that there was a mutation in the New World primates because the prosimioids have plasma cortisols that are in the same range as that of the Old World primates. Thus, I think it's a relatively safe assumption that this mutation happened sometime after the separation. The really interesting question from the evolutionary standpoint is the survival advantage conferred by this mutation. We wondered if high cortisol levels might inhibit the growth of some sort of parasite present only in the New World, but we have no evidence for this.

I. Callard: My question follows the evolutionary thrust of Dr. Sterling's question. First let me congratulate you on a really beautiful comparative study. It was nice you were able to do all of those things, with all of those species, in one place with one group of hands so that you can eliminate a lot of variables. If you look back beyond primates to the nonmammalian forms such as reptiles, one finds fairly typically that the estrogen receptor, for example, is an order of magnitude lower in affinity, and the plasma estrogen levels tend to be in order of magnitude higher in the nanogram range. Although I am not sure about the glucocorticoid or mineralocorticoid receptors in amphibia, the levels of glucocorticoids and mineralocorticoids, aldosterone and corticosterone are similar and they are in the microgram range per 100 ml. Thus, the New World monkeys may be closer to some nonmammalian species and we should possibly consider that the Old World monkeys have adapted by evolving a higher affinity receptor and consequently lower steroid levels. In contrast, the New World monkeys are more in line with the phylogenetically more ancient groups. It is also possible that the New World monkeys represent a secondary return to an ancestral condition with regard to the affinity of their steroid receptors.

G. Chrousos: You may be right. We followed an ancient Greek saying which says that "man is a measure of all things." So we compared everything to man and just kept going back in the evolutionary scale and the furthest back we went was the rat. Assuming that New and Old World primates and the living prosimians are descendants of a common ancestor we had to conclude that the mutations occurred in the New World primates. There may have been other changes in steroid hormone receptors and levels depending on the selective advantages that they offered. Even just a tolerated genetic drift is a possibility.

T. G. Muldoon: Given the relatively high degree of ligand promiscuity of glucocorticoid receptors I was a little surprised not to see a cross-sectional analysis of steroidal specificity. Have you done those studies? They could very well be involved with what you are looking at as a defect or a difference among groups in steroid responsiveness.

G. Chrousos: That might have been an interesting study; however even with dexamethasone or triamcinolone acetonide which are very good ligands for glucocorticoid receptors we had very little specific binding. In fact, it was necessary for Drs. David Rodbard and Peter Munson to devise a new analysis using pooled data to obtain a K_d. If we used other steroids, such as cortisol or corticosterone, we would not be able to measure any specific binding because of the very low affinities. Now with the transformed cell lines it might be possible to do these studies.

I. Callard: I certainly think we have to put everything in the framework of adaptive advantage, which is something that we haven't always done. Let me encourage you to go back beyond the mammals in your comparative studies of glucocorticoid receptors because I think you have a real contribution to make. Thank you.

J. H. Clark: With respect to the evolutionary pathway which led to the differences in New and Old World monkeys, I suspect that high blood steroids and decreased responsiveness resulted from mutational events which occurred 60 million years ago and coincides with the adaptive radiation of these primates. The lower serum steroid levels and higher receptor concentrations and/or higher affinity is characteristic of mammals in general and thus represents the more primitive state. Since primates evolved from "lower mammals," they would be expected to retain this steroid level receptor sensitivity state and the status in the New World monkey must then be considered a more recent development—not a primordial one.

I might add my theory concerning the cause of this adaptation: 60 million years ago when South America separated from the land mass now known as Africa, it scared the hell out of the monkeys as they floated away and we all know what happens to stressed monkeys.

The relationship between the increased free steroid and the decrease in affinity of the receptor shows very good agreement and is very satisfying to see; however, Dr. Siiteri would argue that the true affinity has been underestimated because you have not used an equilibrium assay. If this were the case then your relationships between increased serum levels of steroid and decreased affinity do not look as good. I feel your data are excellent and I believe your interpretation, but I felt this point should be made.

G. Chrousos: We have measured the apparent affinity properly. Adrenalectomized animals were used as controls to rule out effects on the apparent affinity. In addition, we have used transformed cells with no glucocorticoid in the medium. Thus, the steroid environment was well controlled and there was no endogenous cortisol to produce the artifact to which you allude.

M. Lipsett: Jim, I know you are filling in for Dr. Siiteri and I am sorry he wasn't here because he told me at our last meeting all of the questions he had for us. I think you are referring to his paper in *Science*. I think that the conclusions from that study are only pertinent when you are dealing with extremely low concentrations of the steroid. In that case, and he was dealing with estradiol, not measuring the amount of estradiol that you used to bind to the receptor makes a big difference. In our situation where the cortisol levels are so high, the specific activity or amount of labeled ligand is not pertinent.

J. H. Clark: The point that Dr. Siiteri has made in those papers is simple: one does not get an accurate measurement of free steroid in most receptor assays because these assays are done under dissociating conditions (nonequilibrium). Much of the steroid that is judged to be free is really bound to nonspecific sites at equilibrium and dissociates during the assay. Thus the amount of free steroid is overestimated and this leads to an error in the establishment of the true affinity.

G. Chrousos: We measured the total bound and nonspecific bound hormone. The free hormone was calculated from the total amount of ligand used minus the bound ligand. Nonspecific binding was linear. The difference between calculated and actual free hormone must be small.

J. H. Clark: But you have a degree of nonspecific binding which is impossible to estimate properly and therefore you never know the true free. Therefore, your binding affinity is actually higher than what you think it is.

M. Lipsett: We certainly agree that these are not absolute values but only apparent K_Ds. We are, of course, comparing in each case a relative change in apparent K_D between normal and the affected humans or between one animal species and another.

J. H. Clark: Yes and I understand we have all done this. However, there is a discrepancy which is difficult to reconcile. As I said earlier, I feel your interpretation of this circumstance is correct; it just seems to me that not all of the pieces of the puzzle fit as nicely as they might.

B. F. Rice: I think the data also make a great deal of sense and the entire study is a classical example of how a single case or a single family being carefully studied can lead to a whole new area of research in endocrinology and I congratulate the authors on this. I have one question: in the past decade or so there have been these occasional reports of families with dexamethasone suppression, suppressible hypertension that have come from Genest's laboratory and a few other places. Do you think that that is what they were reporting, the same time problem?

G. Chrousos: As you know, there is a syndrome that is called dexamethasone suppressible hyperaldosteronism. Current theory of its pathophysiology is that it is due to some promiscuity in the action of ACTH. The ACTH stimulates not only the fasciculata but the glomerulosa as well. So as soon as you suppress ACTH the syndrome is corrected.

B. F. Rice: Are the levels of ACTH or cortisol increased?

G. Chrousos: They don't have increased levels of plasma ACTH or cortisol. The abnormality lies in the excess stimulation of the glomerulosa by normal amounts of ACTH.

B. F. Rice: Am I correct that in your patients you corrected the problem with dexamethasone?

G. Chrousos: Right, but our patients had high plasma ACTH and cortisol levels. This is a major difference between the syndrome that we described here and dexamethasone suppressible hyperaldosteronism.

N. A. Samaan: Mort, after this elegant study we may find this syndrome is not as rare as we thought. You showed in the families that there is probably autosomal dominant inheritance; have you done any chromosomal or genetic studies on this family?

M. Lipsett: We have performed HLA typing and that is all. Certainly, glucocorticoid receptor defects may be more common because you will not pick up the asymptomatic individuals unless you happen to measure a 24-hour urine free cortisol or do a dexamethasone suppression test. On the other hand, the hypertension must be very rare because in any modern medical center hypokalemic alkalosis would stimulate many studies that would reveal hypercortisolism.

D. Keefe: These two patients had high levels of ACTH and presumably high CRF secretion. These substances have been shown to cause behavioral abnormalities when given centrally to animals, and have been implicated in some of the mental status changes in Cushing's disease. Of course interpretation of such studies is always complicated by the cortisol excess in this disease. It seems that a patient with defective glucocorticoid receptors would provide an optimal system to study the behavioral changes associated with high ACTH and CRF secretion in the absence of end-organ response to cortisol. I understand it would probably be hard to know what baseline behavior is for a farmer from the Dutch countryside, but did you notice any history of psychologic disturbances or abnormal behavior in the two patients you studied?

M. B. Lipsett: As far as we can tell, they are perfectly normal citizens of South Holland and part of their communities. What may be more interesting is when you look at the squirrel monkey with consistently high plasma β-endorphins. I have no idea how a squirrel monkey behaves if the β-endorphin is low or high, but at least the squirrel monkeys behave normally in the squirrel monkey environment.

S. Cohen: I recall when I first read that orientals had a higher estriol production than Caucasians, and I wondered at that time, whether it wasn't something genetically determined. But that proved false because when the orientals moved to the Causacian environment the difference disappeared. I wonder, has this been tried with these New World animals?

G. P. Chrousos: The majority of the New World primate species that we studied had been caught in the wild and brought to the United States. Most of the animals that we studied were housed at the N.I.H. primate facilities. Some of them have been bred in this particular colony.

S. Cohen: I was thinking more of temperature differences. I think the fluctuations and temperature may be something that is not readily thought of.

G. P. Chrousos: The temperature, the humidity, and the light intensity and schedule are strictly controlled in the primate unit. These conditions are the same for the Old World and the New World primates, so that their differences cannot be attributed to the environment.

J. Cidlowski: In terms of your studies with resistance you've studied dexamethasone suppression as the primary resistance and you've studied receptors in lymphoid cells. I was wondering whether or not the lymphoid cells themselves with the abnormal receptors displayed any signs of resistance. For example, are they less susceptible to killing by glucocorticoids or do they not respond to the same dose of glucocorticoids as a human peripheral lymphocyte with reduced leucine or uridine incorporation?

M. B. Lipsett: Of course, in the primate, lymphocytes are not killed by cortisol. Squirrel monkeys and the father had normal white cells essentially.

J. Cidlowski: Were there any responses, or did you check for any physiological responses?

G. P. Chrousos: We tried to determine the effects of dexamethasone on 2-deoxyglucose utilization and on uridine uptake. Unfortunately, we were unable to obtain consistent results and could not derive comparative dose–response curves. We could see clear-cut results using rat thymocytes, these differences may be due to the lesser sensitivity of the lymphoid system of the primates to glucocorticoids.

J. Cidlowski: Did you try it in the EBV-transformed cells?

G. P. Chrousos: Yes, we did, and we just couldn't see the effects—we didn't see it in the controls.

G. D. Aurbach: You raised the question of whether there might be a common subunit among the several steroid receptors that might account for the abnormality in the New World monkeys. One could put this in context, in terms of benefit to the monkey being resistant to 1,25-dihydroxyvitamin D. The reason for this is that there are some plants that contain glycosides of 1,25-dihydroxyvitamin D, and when these plants are eaten, animals get vitamin D toxicity with hypercalcemia. A difference in distribution of the above flora, in the Old World versus the New World, would represent a distinct advantage in developing resistance to 1,25-dihydroxyvitamin D. Perhaps this is reflected in a common subunit mutation producing resistance to other steroids as well. There are investigators who have antibodies to the 1,25-dihydroxyvitamin D receptor; I don't know whether there are any studies yet on cross-reactivity among these receptors.

M. Lipsett: I believe such studies are underway both in Japan and in Bethesda.

K. L. Barker: My question is a follow-up of Dr. Aurbach's comment. You implied that the adaptation to the various receptors in New World primates may have been sequential adaptations. It seems more likely that they would have been derived from a coincidental event. If so, this would suggest that a common gene sequence may exist for steroid receptors or binders in general, perhaps even including the CBG transport protein. Have you done characterization experiments with some of these other receptor systems, such as determining the electrophoretic mobility in isoelectric focusing systems, to see if there may be a common shift in isoelectric point of the various receptors relative to that seen of the receptors in Old World primates. A common shift in pI by all receptors would suggest a common adaptation event and the presence of a common sequence in the series of steroid binding proteins.

G. P. Chrousos: Let me say that first of all I agree with you. The probability of having six simultaneous but independent mutations is so small, that one must believe there is a common link among the steroid receptors and even CBG. With Dr. Sara Ben-Or we performed isoelectric focusing of the glucocorticoid receptor, and saw no differences between the marmoset receptor and the human control.

M. R. Walters: I have to say that I feel like the third soldier on the march. My question also relates to whether the basic underlying mechanism was an individual mutation in either a common subunit (and of course we know that a number of people now think that there is a 90K nonsteroid binding subunit that may be common to many of the steroid receptors), or perhaps to some other common factor that acts on the receptor resulting in the change in affinity. As someone who has worked across a number of systems, I was struck by the possibility of such a common origin, as you pointed out in one of your slides. But to perhaps take you a little bit further in terms of analogies, I wonder whether you have looked at the levels of peptide hormones and the affinity for peptide receptors, because I'm also beginning to be struck by some similarities across these two very different apparent classes of receptor mechanisms.

G. P. Chrousos: We have tried to measure several peptide hormones, such as plasma LH, but many of the peptide hormones of New World primates could not be measured by our radioimmunoassays. We cannot measure insulin, LH, or FSH, although we do attain apparently reasonable values for ACTH, TSH, and prolactin.

R. N. Anderson: In a recent paper by R. Harrison, C. Woodward, and E. Thompson (*Biochem. Biophys. Acta* **759**, 1, 1983), a study of the effect of *p*-chloromercuriphenyl sulfonate (PCMPS) on glucocorticoid receptors showed that binding activity was reduced but not abolished. With Scatchard analysis of triamcinolone acetonide binding to the treated cytosol, it was shown PCMPS caused a reduction of binding affinity with little or no effect on the apparent number of binding sites. Their study suggests that it may be the free sulfhydryl, which is common to all steroid receptors, I believe, that is the common element that has been modified.

G. P. Chrousos: It's possible. In the majority of our cytosol studies we've used dithiothreitol to protect the sulfhydryl groups of the receptors.

R. N. Anderson: But if there were a genetic alteration in the cysteine residue, dithiothreitol would not affect that. Jim Clark's comments reminded me that Dr. Siiteri made a presentation recently at this conference in which he proposed that the serum steroid binding proteins may serve to transport steroids into cells rather than to hold them in the circulation as was generally considered to be their role. I believe that he used a New World monkey and TeBG and testosterone as his model. Is it possible that you were looking at binding proteins that were serving as intracellular receptors? Or, are the affinities an order too high to make that a possibility?

G. P. Chrousos: It's difficult to accept this theory because many of the very potent steroids like dexamethasone do not bind to the transport proteins, and still are very active.

M. Birnbaumer: Along these same lines, I wish to point to the fact that in the monkey you see a general defect. All the steroid hormones are elevated in the blood and you interpret this finding as an apparent generalized resistance to all of them. One of the factors that we know very little about is how steroids enter the cells. Recently, S. Bourgeois (Johnson, D. M., Newby, R. F., and Bourgeois, S., *Cancer Res.* **44**, 2435, 1984) has reported that some lymphoid cell lines that have been selected by survival to dexamethasone could be killed by triamcinolone acetonide, showing that steroids that do not bind to known carrier proteins of steroids do seem to enter the cells by different mechanisms, still unknown. You could be looking in the monkey at a defect in the general permeability of the cells to steroid hormones, that has been compensated by an increase in the level of all circulating steroid hormones. Also you could be looking at a little bit of this phenomenon in your patient. I noticed that the differences between control and the patient values were much more marked when you made your measurements in whole cells than when you prepared cytosol from those cells. It looks as if by breaking the cells you have removed a barrier and made the two systems much more similar.

G. P. Chrousos: This is a very fine suggestion—the putative common mechanism of "generalized steroid resistance" may be there.

K. Sterling: I have a question for Dr. Lipsett with regard to his remark that he accepts the view and data of Green and Gorski that in life all receptors reside in the nucleus and that the cytosolic receptors are some sort of artifact after you kill the animal. My question is how do you reconcile this with the prevailing dogma?

M. Lipsett: I don't have to defend Gorski or Green; I think their studies represent a paradogmatic shift in a way we think of steroid receptors. I think their data are good; fortunately, placing the receptors in the nucleus will not change much of our thinking.

G. Callard: I have a general question for Dr. Lipsett. At the beginning of the talk you showed a slide listing the various steroid resistant syndromes. Notably missing from that list was estrogen resistance. Can you tell us whether there is any report?

M. Lipsett: We don't know of any report; of course the question of a deficient estrogen receptor has been raised in the past. However, since estrogen seems to be important in blastocyst implantation, it seems likely that an estrogen receptor defeat would be incompatible with development of the embryo.

D. T. Krieger: I would like to go back to the comment on the behavioral effects of endorphins. There is evidence that in patients with Cushing's and Nelson's syndrome there are high circulating levels of endorphins; the question is what is the behavioral significance of this; this has been open to great question. If you take these patients and do psychological profiles and then give them an opiate receptor antagonist, you get absolutely no change in the behavioral profiles, and there is also no real evidence that the circulating endorphin will be able to cross the blood–brain barrier to provide sufficient CNS concentrations to have an effect on central opiate receptor mechanisms which would be the locus of action, that one would expect would produce behavioral abnormalities.

M. Lipsett: All we could really say is we see these high peripheral endorphins. Essentially they have no meaning, whether that was because of the phenomenon you describe or because they have no meaning physiologically.

D. T. Krieger: I would like to make another comment on a different model of glucocorticoid resistance which we have been interested in, namely the specific tissue resistance seen in intermediate lobe in which, unlike anterior lobe, there is marked resistance to glucocorticoid effects such as suppression of POMC synthesis; this has been attributed to absence of the receptor rather than the presence of a receptor with a different affinity from the "normal" receptor. We decided to take a look at this on the basis of the observations of neural regulation of the intermediate versus the absence of such regulation of the anterior lobe, mainly with regard to the neural influences on intermediate lobe expression of POMC synthesis and release. We have preliminary evidence, based purely on immunocytochemical observations with polyclonal and monoclonal antibodies to the glucocorticoid receptor, that if you remove the intermediate lobe from what we call "neural" influences, namely by stalk transection or by grafting the intermediate lobe under the kidney capsule or by culturing the intermediate lobe, in this tissue in which you cannot see the glucocorticoid receptor, you observe, after these procedures, appearance of glucocorticoid receptors. We haven't yet identified whether these are functional receptors. In view of other reports of neural influences on glucocorticoid and other steroid receptors in brain and in other tissues, this may be one mechanism influencing the expression of the glucocorticoid receptor.

RECENT PROGRESS IN HORMONE RESEARCH, VOL. 41

Progestin Action and Progesterone Receptor Structure in Human Breast Cancer: A Review

KATHRYN B. HORWITZ, LISA L. WEI, SCOT M. SEDLACEK, AND CAROLYN N. D'ARVILLE

Department of Medicine and Division of Endocrinology, University of Colorado Health Sciences Center, Denver, Colorado

I. Introduction

In 1975 we showed that human breast tumors have progesterone receptors (PR), and suggested that these proteins would serve as markers of hormone dependence (1,2). This idea has been confirmed by extensive clinical trials which show, not only that PR-rich tumors are highly likely to respond to endocrine therapies, but also, that patients with such tumors have longer disease-free periods and a better prognosis than patients whose tumors are PR-poor (3). While the status of PR as predictive markers is firm, the functional significance of PR is unknown. The relationship between PR content and response to progestin treatment has also not been properly explored, even though there is increasing evidence that progestins are effective and well-tolerated drugs for treatment of the disseminated disease. That the crucial role of progestins and PR in the biology of human breast cancer has not been precisely defined is due to lack of experimental models. Structural analysis of mammalian PR has been difficult because the receptors are extremely labile, low in abundance, and require estrogen priming. The biological actions of progestins have not been adequately studied since even PR-positive human tumor cells have failed to respond to progestins *in vitro* and hormone antagonists have been unavailable. The purpose of this review is to analyze the current information about progestin action, and PR structure and function, especially as it relates to breast cancer. We will also review recent data from our laboratory, in which a progestin-responsive human breast cancer cell line has been used to study the biochemical mechanisms involved in progesterone action.

249

II. The Role of Progestins and Progesterone Receptors in the Treatment of Breast Cancer

A. PROGESTINS IN NORMAL MAMMARY GLAND DEVELOPMENT AND GROWTH

Progesterone is essential for human breast alveolar gland development and growth. It is not a mitogenic hormone alone, but acts in synergy with estradiol to prime the mammary gland to respond to mitogens like prolactin, glucocorticoids, and growth hormone (4).

At puberty, estradiol induces mammary duct formation. As the hypothalamic-pituitary–ovarian axis matures, there is a brief phase of anovulatory cycles during which the mammary gland is influenced principally by estrogens. Once ovulation is established, progesterone is produced by the corpus luteum and stimulates growth of the lobuloalveolar structures (5). During the reproductive years, progesterone promotes differentiation of alveolar cells into secretory cells, and dilation of the ductal system. In conjunction with prolactin and other metabolic hormones, progesterone stimulates lipid droplet formation, and secretory activity. While prolactin and growth hormone are the most important pituitary hormones affecting growth of the mammary gland during pregnancy, it is estradiol and progesterone which prevent the full expression of their secretory effects on the mammary epithelium (5). At parturition, the sudden withdrawal of these two hormones permits the breast to respond to the lactogenic hormones.

B. PROGESTINS IN EXPERIMENTAL ANIMAL TUMOR MODELS

1. Carcinogenesis

In 1959, Huggins et al. (6) published a report describing the induction of mammary carcinoma in a rat model with the single intragastric instillation of the aromatic hydrocarbon 3-methylcholanthrene. Though this observation was first made by Lacassagne in 1932 (7), Huggins' report was most significant because of the novel observation that the tumors were hormone dependent. Later studies most commonly used 7,12-dimethylbenz-[a]anthracene (DMBA) in the albino female Sprague–Dawley (SD) strain of rats. This strain was chosen because of its high spontaneous rate of mammary tumor formation. One hundred percent of SD rats fed DMBA between days 50 and 65 of life develop mammary carcinomas (8), thus providing an excellent animal model to study hormone-dependent breast cancer.

Progestins have been studied extensively in the DMBA model to deter-mine its effect on tumor induction, as well as its effect on growth of established tumors. In studies of tumor induction, two distinctly different responses to progestins have been observed, depending on the time of progestin administration in relation to the time of DMBA administration. When the progestin is given either after the day of DMBA instillation or no more than 2 days prior to DMBA, the development of tumors is en-hanced; there is a shorter latency period, a greater number of tumors per rat, and an increase in tumor size (8–11). This effect of progesterone as a cocarcinogen is dependent on the presence of estrogens, and fails to occur in ovariectomized animals.

In contrast to its tumor-promoting effects when administered together with estradiol and DMBA, early treatment with progesterone protects the mammary gland. When progesterone is administered 7 to 25 days before DMBA, tumor development is inhibited. The latency period is prolonged and fewer rats develop tumors, with fewer tumors per rat (12–14).

The mechanism by which progesterone produces this protective effect was thought to be due to its promotion of terminal differentiation, thus protecting lobuloalveolar glands from the carcinogen (12). However, when DMBA is applied topically by dusting a single mammary gland, malignancy develops only in that gland, and this process is unaffected by the administration of progesterone 25 days prior to the DMBA. This study suggests that progesterone exerts its inhibitory effect on carcinogenesis outside the breast, possibly in the liver, by promoting metabolism of DMBA to an inactive product (11).

Similar conclusions are drawn from thymidine-labeling studies which show that there is no interaction between DMBA and progesterone on mammary epithelial cell DNA synthesis (15). However, this area clearly requires further study, since it influences our understanding of oral con-traceptive use and breast cancer risk.

2. Tumor Growth and Progression

The effects of progestins on established tumors are more clearcut: pro-gesterone alone cannot maintain tumor growth. In ovariectomized and adrenalectomized rats bearing growing DMBA tumors, estradiol alone or an estradiol/progesterone combination can sustain continued tumor growth, but progesterone alone cannot and tumors regress (16). Asselin *et al.* (17) studied regressing tumors in castrated rats and found similar results. Estradiol alone but not progesterone alone restored tumor growth. However, progesterone enhanced the effect of estradiol. In con-trast, Danguy *et al.* (18) have more recently shown that progestins can have dual effects in castrated rats depending on their concentrations: low doses of medroxyprogesterone acetate (MPA) (1 mg/kg) displayed growth stimulatory activity whereas at high doses (100 mg/kg) it was strongly inhibitory. They suggest that growth inhibition is mediated at the level of the hypothalamus and not at the tumor. The actual site of progesterone action in tumorigenesis and growth remains unclear, though the breast, liver, and hypothalamic/pituitary axis are possible targets.

3. In Vitro Models

Cell culture has been used to evaluate more directly the effects of progesterone and other hormones using lines derived from DMBA-induced tumors (RBA line) or N-nitrosomethylurea-induced tumors (NMU line). Both cell lines contain glucocoticoid (GR) and androgen receptors (AR), but are deficient in PR (19). By [^{3}H]thymidine incorporation, dexamethasone (Dex) proved to be the most potent mitogen, while dihydrotestosterone (DHT) was weaker; progesterone inhibited the effects of both hormones. The increased DNA synthesis was most likely mediated through GR because Dex > Prog > DHT in enhancing [^{3}H]thymidine labeling. Progesterone alone showed no effect on the RBA cell line but was partially stimulatory in the NMU cell line. Thus, progesterone displayed properties of a growth promoter (stimulating NMU cell growth) and an antagonist (inhibiting the stimulatory effect of Dex in both cell lines). These findings suggest that in the treatment of breast cancer, progestins may cause remissions directly, or indirectly because they can function as estrogen, glucocorticoid, or androgen antagonists.

Other parameters besides tumor development and growth have been monitored in progesterone-treated rats. Enzyme induction has been studied in explants from DMBA-induced tumors (20). Estrogen induces p-nitrophenyl phosphatase, β-glucuronidase, glucose-6-phosphate dehydrogenase, 6-phosphogluconate dehydrogenase, pyruvate kinase, aldolase, and lactate dehydrogenase, and progesterone inhibits these estrogenic effects.

4. Progestins and Steroid Receptors

DMBA-induced tumors are well differentiated and express receptors for many hormones including ER and PR. Since receptor content is thought to relate to hormone dependence of tumors, this relationship has been studied in hormone treated animals (16,17,21). We showed (16) that if animals bearing ER$^+$, PR$^+$ tumors are castrated and adrenalectomized tumors regress and PR levels fall. Estradiol administration prevents tumor regression and PR loss, or restores PR in regressed tumors, but progesterone alone fails to sustain tumor growth, despite the presence of PR. Estrogen-responsive tumor growth, and estrogen-induced PR, are not inexorably linked. Some tumors are autonomous and grow in the absence of estradiol, yet their PR fall with estrogen withdrawal, making them estrogen dependent. This suggests some dissociation between estrogen-controlled tumor growth and estrogen-controlled PR synthesis. Similarly, there is a persistent basal level of PR in estradiol-deprived tumors and in some tumors that fail to respond to estradiol, suggesting that at least some PR are estrogen independent, which confirms similar observations in human tumors.

C. USE OF PROGESTINS IN THE TREATMENT OF ADVANCED BREAST CANCER

In 1896, Beatson reported the positive results of ovariectomy in a patient with advanced breast cancer (22). Since that time, the hormone dependence of breast cancer has been exploited in the treatment of patients with inoperable and/or disseminated disease. The first reported use of progesterone in advanced breast cancer involved 18 patients (23). Three patients (17%) showed an objective response to the treatment thus adding another agent to the armamentarium of the cancer therapist.

Five different progestins have been used historically: progesterone, 17α-hydroxyprogesterone, norethisterone acetate, medroxyprogesterone acetate (MPA), and megestrol acetate (MA), in a variety of concentrations, routes of administration, schedules, and lengths of treatment. Criteria for responses cite World Health Organization (WHO), Eastern Cooperative Oncology Group (ECOG), EORTC Clinical Screening Cooperative Group, or Cooperative Breast Cancer Group standards. A positive response includes either a complete response regarded as total disappearance of all known disease and/or a partial response which is at least a 50% reduction in tumor size, or a 50% decrease in the sum of the products of the perpendicular diameters of all measurable lesions.

A review of the clinical use of progestins in the treatment of advanced breast disease suggests that the data should be subclassified into studies using low doses versus those using high doses of progestins. We have arbitrarily chosen >500 mg/day of progestins as "high-dose" therapy.

Using low-dose progestins in 15 studies, 839 patients have been accrued, and the total objective positive response rate is 27% (23–37). Survival ranges from 2 to 23+ months with a median of 7.0 months.

Pannuti et al. in 1978 (38) reported results of a study using high-dose MPA to treat metastatic breast cancer which was prompted by a pilot study in 17 patients, showing that intramuscular injection of 1500 mg/day was well tolerated. We have compiled the results of 9 centers (Table I), with 673 patients, showing that the overall objective response rate to high-

TABLE I
Treatment Response to High-Dose Progestins

Reference	Positive response	
Mattsson, 1978 (39)	7/25	(28%)
DeLena, 1979 (40)	6/28	(21%)
	17/53	(32%)
Mattsson, 1980 (41)	14/26	(54%)
Madrigal, 1980 (42)	9/21	(43%)
Izuo, 1981 (43)	7/20	(35%)
Morgan, 1983 (44)	15/25	(60%)
Pannuti, 1983 (45)	82/205	(40%)
	15/32	(47%)
Funes, 1983 (46)	13/46	(28%)
	15/43	(35%)
Cavalli, 1983 (47)	9/73	(12%)
	27/76	(36%)
Total	236/673	(35%)
	Duration 5 → 13.1 months	
	(7.0 median)	

dose progestins is 35% (39–47). With MPA given intramuscularly, patients have developed induration and sterile abscesses at the sites of injection thus limiting the duration and ultimately the amount of drug administered. However, the oral route has proven to be equally effective and as much as 5000 mg/day (45) have been given with no greater side effects than found with low-dose therapy. At high concentrations, progestins are well tolerated, have no serious side effects (45), and their efficacy compares favorably with antiestrogens, the hormones currently in widest use (48).

That antiestrogens and progestins may be equally useful for the treatment of breast cancer is suggested not only from separate clinical trials reporting similar response data for each (39–48), but also from a number of studies in which progestin therapy has been directly compared with tamoxifen in the same clinical trial (Table II). The combined results of 7 studies in which 357 patients were treated with progestins and 320 were treated with tamoxifen show 31% responding to the progestins and 29% responding to tamoxifen (Table II) (41,49–54). All of these women were postmenopausal. In many of these studies, the patients had been previously treated with cytotoxic chemotherapy (41,49,50) yet this did not preclude response to subsequent progestins or tamoxifen.

This brings us to a consideration of combination antiestrogen/progestin therapy, and the role of progestins in the treatment of antiestrogen-resis-

TABLE II

Tamoxifen vs Progestins in the Same Clinical Trials

	Tamoxifen		Progestin		
Mattsson, 1980 (41)	15/32	(47%)	14/26	(54%)	MPA[a]
Morgan, 1980 (49)	17/48	(36%)	14/46	(30%)	MA[b]
Ingle, 1982 (50)	7/27	(26%)	4/28	(14%)	MA[b]
Pannuti, 1982 (51)	7/26	(27%)	10/27	(37%)	MPA
Johnson, 1983 (52)	14/49	(28%)	20/49	(41%)	MA[b]
Van Veelen, 1983 (53)	17/58	(29%)	18/45	(40%)	MPA
Alexieva-Figusch, 1983 (54)	17/80	(21%)	31/136	(23%)	MA[b]
Total	94/320	(29%)	111/357	(31%)	

[a] MPA, Medroxyprogesterone acetate; MA, megestrol acetate.
[b] Low-dose progestin.

tant tumors. Our studies (described further below) with antiestrogen-resistant and ER negative cultured human breast tumor cells (T47D$_{co}$) show that progestins can still inhibit growth in this setting. Similarly, there are clinical data showing that progestins can be of benefit in patients who fail to respond to, or become resistant to other hormonal agents including antiestrogens, or whose tumors are estrogen-receptor negative. Several studies report that 34% of patients responded to high-dose progestins whose tumors had been antiestrogen resistant, or had failed or relapsed from previous hormonal therapy (39,40,43,45–47).

Based on these clinical, as well as our experimental data, we propose that antiestrogens and progestins act by different mechanisms to promote remission. Therefore, two treatment strategies using progestins are conceivable, and these are outlined in Fig. 1. Antiestrogens are successful in estrogen-receptor positive tumors (Fig. 1, top). In addition, due to the estrogenic properties of antiestrogens, tumors treated for short periods with these agents have increased PR levels (55–57). Thus simultaneous or brief pretreatment with antiestrogens may increase the sensitivity of ER-positive tumors to subsequent progestins; the latter should then promote regression by other pathways thereby conferring synergistic therapeutic effects. There are some clinical data to support this model: a total of 177 postmenopausal women with advanced breast cancer have been treated with a combination of tamoxifen and progestins (58–62), given either simultaneously or sequentially. The response rate was 11% complete and 34% partial remissions or a total objective response of 45%. This level of response is as good as, if not better than, the response rates for tamoxifen or progestins when used singly: 29 and 31%, respectively. Of note was the study by Trodella *et al.* (60) whose patient population was heavily

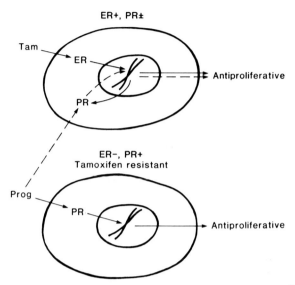

FIG. 1. A model describing possible roles of progestins in the treatment of breast cancer. See the text for details. ER, Estrogen receptors; PR, progesterone receptors; Tam, tamoxifen; Prog, progestin. Reprinted with permission. See reference 220.

pretreated with chemotherapy and/or hormonal therapy (61 and 83%, respectively). They still found a 44% objective response rate with combined tamoxifen/progestin, which included 22% complete remissions.

These results using combination therapy warrant further study in an attempt to increase the response rates of present day conventional hormonal therapy. Though the two hormones can probably be administered together, theoretically, the antiestrogen should precede the progestin by 1 to 2 weeks in order to maximally induce PR. Excessively prolonging the interval between the antiestrogen and the progestin could result in loss of PR altogether, leaving a hormone-insensitive cell population (57). Only one study has explored the value of repeatedly alternating the two hormones (62). Clearly, more extensive clinical trials of these well-tolerated hormonal agents are warranted.

The second strategy for use of progestins is shown in Fig. 1, bottom. Our studies with ER-negative, PR-positive, antiestrogen-resistant T47D$_{co}$ cells show that progestins can inhibit growth of such cells. Small clinical studies using high doses of MPA or MA support the idea that a similar set of patients, whose tumors have become resistant to antiestrogen treatment, or whose tumors have no ER but are PR positive, may achieve further benefit from progestin therapy. Such tumors are usually not con-

TABLE III
Tamoxifen vs Progestin Cross-Over: Same Center Studies

Mattsson, 1980 (41)	Tam fail → MPA	6/10	(60%)
	MPA fail → Tam	0/10	(0%)
Ingle, 1982 (50)	Tam fail → MA[a]	2/16	(12%)
	MA[a] fail → Tam	2/18	(11%)
Van Veelen, 1983 (53)	Tam fail → MPA	5/14	(36%)
	MPA fail → Tam	0/14	(0%)
Alexieva-Figusch, 1983 (54)	Tam fail → MA[a]	14/83	(17%)
	MA[a] fail → Tam	12/132	(9%)
Total	Tam fail → Prog	27/123	(22%)
	Prog fail → Tam	14/174	(8%)

[a] Low-dose progestin.

sidered to be candidates for endocrine therapies, but four trials based on 123 patients show that 22% respond to progestins after relapse from tamoxifen (41,50,53,54). In contrast, tumors rarely respond to tamoxifen (8%) if they have failed to respond to progestins (Table III).

That progestins and antiestrogens inhibit the growth of breast tumor cells by different paths has important clinical implications, and we propose that, by targeting different cell populations, the complementary therapeutic actions of these two agents can be used to advantage in the design of treatment protocols.

Finally, an area in which progestins have also been used is in combination with cytotoxic chemotherapy. Similar studies have been performed comparing chemotherapy vs chemotherapy combined with tamoxifen. Four recent randomized studies (63–66) have been reported, with two studies showing no benefit after tamoxifen addition and two showing a significant benefit of combination chemotherapy/tamoxifen. Few data are available on progestins.

The use of progestins in conjunction with chemotherapy was first reported by Stott *et al.* in 1973 (67). Since then randomized and nonrandomized studies have been performed with response rates varying from 27 to 75% (68–72). In 6 studies, 218 of 402 (54%) patients on combined progestin/chemotherapy obtained an objective response. However, the 3 studies (68,70,71) that compared chemotherapy alone, with chemoprogestin therapy, were unable to show a statistically significant difference between treatment arms. Nevertheless, the patients treated with the progestin seemed to have an increased performance status, increased sense of well being, less pain, weight gain, and a protective effect on the bone marrow (70,72–74). Since MPA has been shown to protect patients against the neutropenia induced by vincristine, adriamycin, and cyclophosphamide (75), it is possible that with reduced marrow toxicity due to the presence of a progestin, patients could receive more intensive chemotherapy, and be more likely to stay on the planned schedule of therapy.

D. PROGESTERONE RECEPTORS AS MARKERS OF HORMONE-DEPENDENT TUMORS

Estrogen receptors (ER) have been used since 1971 (76) as a guide to therapy and correctly predict a positive response in 50–55% of patients (77). However, assessment of tumor PR (1,2,35,36,78–89) is even more useful as Table IV shows, improving predictive accuracy by an additional 15–20%. In contrast, receptor-negative tumors rarely respond to endocrine therapies and such patients should be considered candidates for alternate treatments. Not surprisingly, few tumors are ER⁻, PR⁺ though some of these may be falsely negative due to methodological reasons (90). Others may have ER that are either sequestered in an unmeasured compartment or nonfunctional, and may resemble the variant $T47D_{co}$ subline that is antiestrogen resistant but progestin sensitive. Such tumors should be considered candidates for progestin therapy (see above).

Progesterone receptors have also proven to be more accurate than ER in predicting prognosis of limited stage (I and II) breast cancer (3,91–94); patients with PR⁺ tumors are 3 to 4 times less likely to develop metastases than those with PR⁻ ones (91). In more advanced grade III disease, PR are an independent prognostic variable, and more useful for predicting disease-free survival than either clinical or pathological staging (92). Clark

TABLE IV
Receptor Content and Response to Endocrine Therapies[a]

		Positive response	
ER⁺		312/586	(53%)
ER⁻		33/264	(13%)
PR⁺		240/352	(68%)
PR⁻		108/498	(22%)
ER⁺	PR⁺	230/323	(71%)
ER⁺	PR⁻	85/263	(32%)
ER⁻	PR⁺	10/29	(34%)
ER⁻	PR⁻	23/235	(10%)

[a] Cumulative data 14 series 1978–1983 (refs. 35, 36, 78–89).

et al. (3) reported similar results in patients with stage II breast cancer who were undergoing adjuvant therapy. An earlier study (95) had failed to detect these relationships, perhaps due to the small number of patients evaluated.

III. The Structure of Progesterone Receptors

A. REVIEW OF RECEPTOR STRUCTURE

A common molecular mechanism of action has been proposed for all steroid hormones, in which binding of the hormones to soluble receptors increases the affinity of receptor–hormone complexes for the genome, resulting in the expression of inducible genes. A common structural basis may underlie this mechanism of action, but the structural characterization of steroid receptors remains a complex and poorly understood subject for many reasons: receptors are regulatory proteins present in low concentrations in cells; they are themselves subject to regulation so that their intracellular location and activity-state vary; they are soluble in complex cell extracts where they are substrates for a variety of modifying enzymes; their oligomeric structure is modified by the extraction and purification procedures needed to study them; and their presence has only been detectable with radioactive ligands that fail to reveal associated non-hormone-binding proteins.

Despite these problems the general picture suggests that each steroid receptor is an oligomer composed of identical subunits, with one hormone binding site per polypeptide chain. A consensus on the size or molecular weight of the subunits for each receptor is developing, showing that regardless of the cell or tissue of origin, the subunit for glucocorticoid (GR), estrogen (ER), and androgen receptors (AR) is a unique protein for that steroid. Progesterone receptors are an exception. Structural data from chick oviduct and human breast cancer PR show that they are oligomers composed of at least two, dissimilar proteins. Despite differences in primary structure of the constituent polypeptides, analysis of steroid holoreceptors, as well as proteolytic fragmentation patterns of the native subunits, show remarkable uniformity among all steroid receptors. It is possible that at the tertiary level, all steroid receptors are similarly organized, and share highly conserved functional domains. The evidence is reviewed further below.

1. Glucocorticoid Receptors

Glucocorticoid receptors from rat hepatoma (HTC) cells, photoaffinity labeled *in vitro* with R5020, have a single polypeptide of M_r 87,000 (96).

This value is in agreement with the M_r 85,000 protein isolated from HTC cells covalently linked *in vivo* to dexamethasone-21-mesylate (97), and is slightly smaller than the M_r 90,000 of rat liver GR determined by electrophilic affinity labeling and immunochemistry (98). This protein is missing in glucocorticoid-resistant mouse lymphoma S49 (r$^-$) cells, while mutant S49 (nt$^-$) cells, exhibiting normal steroid binding activity but decreased receptor-complex binding to nuclei, have photolabeled receptors of M_r 39,000 (96). The latter observation suggests either that a mutation has occurred in the GR structural gene, resulting in the formation of a truncated protein, or that a posttranscriptional modification prevents accumulation of a fully functional protein, perhaps by rendering it sensitive to site-specific proteolysis.

The mutants developed for study of GR are extremely powerful tools since they can be used to dissect the receptors into their structural and functional domains. Receptor monomers probably subserve several functions. At the very least these are their hormone binding capacity, and their chromatin and/or DNA binding capacity. Immunologic probes, limited proteolysis, and receptor mutants are now beginning to be used to detect and characterize these functional segments. Three domains separated by two protease-sensitive regions have been identified in native, activated GR of A$_t$T-20 cells: a hormone binding region (domain A of M_r 24,000), a DNA-binding region (domain B of M_r 29,000), and a third, domain C, of unknown function, but containing the epitopes for all anti-GR antibodies so far obtained (98,99), that appeared to be missing in naturally occurring variants (nt^i) of the S49 mouse lymphoma cell line (100). The missing domain resulted in apparently truncated receptors of M_r 39,000 that rendered the cells resistant to the lethal effects of glucocorticoids despite the fact that nuclear uptake of GR was enhanced. However, recently Gruol *et al.* (101) measured the size of these GR by radiation inactivation in intact cells and found their mass to be normal. They postulate that the truncated size of the mutant S49 (nt^i) receptors in cell-free extracts is an artifact, due to enhanced *in vitro* protease sensitivity of the C domain, and that the primary function of this domain is interaction with "acceptor" proteins in nuclei.

Untransformed, sodium molybdate-stabilized GR are proposed to exist as tetramers with molecular weights ranging from 317,000 to 350,000 that vary somewhat depending on protein sources, storage conditions, or analytical methods (102–104). Although the existence of oligomers *in vivo* has not yet been established, an intermediate, activated form, composed of a homodimer of monomeric subunits of GR has been reported in both the Syrian hamster MF-2 cell line (M_r 198,000) (102) and the mouse A$_t$T-20 pituitary tumor cell line (M_r 176,000) (103) in the presence of 0.3 M KCl and sodium molybdate, suggesting that the dissociation of the multimeric receptor into dimers of identical subunits could be a possible mechanism for receptor activation. This appears to be a process promoted by sulfhydryl groups but blocked by molybdate ions, the latter preventing exposure of the DNA-binding sites on the receptors.

2. Androgen Receptors

The situation for androgens is complicated by the possibility that these receptors may exist as two different classes, one that binds testosterone, and one that binds dihydrotestosterone. Gel filtration and ultracentrifugation studies show untransformed receptors of 280,000 to 365,000 MW that are converted to a 117,000 MW form by salt (105). Other values for AR range from M_r 113,000 to 167,000 in different tissues (106,107). Smaller molecular-weight forms probably result from proteolysis of the native receptors during purification, since they are prevented by serine protease inhibitors (106). This artifact does not explain why, with DNA-cellulose chromatography and isoelectric focusing, two hormone-labeled species are seen that bind predominantly one or the other of the two active androgens (108,109). It is not known whether these represent different receptors or dissimilar subunits.

3. Estrogen Receptors

In most studies, ER consist of a single subunit with one estrogen-binding site whose molecular mass is 60,000 to 70,000 daltons (110–114). This value has been obtained by conventional chromatographic techniques, and with affinity labeled receptors. However, recently, two molecular species of M_r 60,000 have been demonstrated in hen oviduct, that differ in their net charge: one focuses at pH 6.8, the other at pH 7.3 (115,116). Like other steroid receptors, undissociated and untransformed ER appear to be oligomers of smaller subunits with molecular weights ranging between 240,000 and 290,000 (117).

In sum, steroid receptors probably consist of several subunits assembled into a large asymmetric complex, the holoreceptor, whose physicochemical properties are conserved for the various classes of steroids (118). Whether these subunits are dissimilar or identical is not entirely clear. Evidence for dissimilar subunits is strong only for PR (see below); the subunits for AR, GR, and ER appear to consist of a single polypeptide chain. However if, as seems to be the case for PR (119), the two subunits subserve different functions in nuclei, then one must conclude either (1) that progestins are unique among steroids and that quite different nuclear binding and activation mechanisms have evolved for the other three classes of steroid receptors, or (2) that different functional subunits do

exist for the other three, but that the methods used to study these receptors have failed, as yet, to disclose them. This could conceivably occur if
one of the subunits of the holoreceptor is not a hormone binding protein,
or if subtle posttranslational covalent modifications involving, for example, protein glycosylation or phosphorylation, actually create two functionally different subunits from the same primary polypeptide.

B. THE STRUCTURE OF CHICK OVIDUCT AND MAMMALIAN PROGESTERONE RECEPTORS

While GR, AR, and ER appear to be multimers of one protein, extensive data are now available from chick oviduct and human breast cancer
cells showing that PR consist of two dissimilar polypeptides present in
equimolar amounts. Analysis of purified chick oviduct PR by chromatographic, electrophoretic, and photoaffinity labeling methods show that
they consist of at least two hormone binding proteins of M_r 79,000 and
108,000. These are, respectively, proteins A and B. Protein A has high
affinity for DNA while protein B binds well to chromatin, but only weakly
to DNA (119,120). The two chick oviduct proteins have been extensively
purified and analyzed in an effort to determine their structural relationships. Both subunits can be covalently photoaffinity labeled at a high-
affinity hormone-binding site (121) and both contain a second low-affinity
hormone-binding site of unknown function (122). When the native proteins are subjected to mild proteolysis by a variety of enzymes, fragments
from both A and B are indistinguishable for all peptides of M_r less than
60,000, indicating that they share considerable homology in the native
state. However, after extensive protease digestion, autoradiographic two-
dimensional peptide maps of denatured ^{125}I-labeled purified A and B show
similarities as well as significant differences in their primary amino acid
sequence (123,124). Taken together these data suggest that A and B have
different amino acid structure and probably are products of different
genes, but that they share common tertiary structural features upon folding, and that certain segments of the primary structure of each remain
highly conserved. Furthermore, the conformational homologies suggest
that a close genetic relationship exists between the two proteins, and that
successive nucleotide mutations in the respective genes may have occurred subject to the constraint that the overall three-dimensional archi-
tecture of the proteins be preserved. Monoclonal antibodies have been
produced against the B subunit (125) that do not cross-react with A under
denaturing conditions, strengthening the argument that the two proteins
differ in some segments of their primary structure.

The functional domains of the two chick receptor subunits have been partially mapped using chymotrypsin, trypsin, and *S. aureus* V8 protease. Both subunits are first clipped from the carboxyl-terminal end to an M_r 43,000 peptide fragment (called Form IV) that retains hormone binding as well as DNA binding activity. Additional protease digestion yields an M_r 23,000 meroreceptor which binds hormone but lacks DNA-binding activity; the DNA-binding domain is released in an M_r 15,000 "D fragment" that is nearer the carboxyl-terminal of the original 43K molecule (123,126,127). Since both A and B subunits have a DNA binding domain, this segment may be occluded in the native B protein—a poor DNA binder. The 23K meroreceptor can be fragmented further to a limit digest of M_r 9500 close to the NH_2 terminal of the intact protein, that still binds hormone (the H fragment). An *in vitro* phosphorylation site has been located in a 4.8K peptide near the carboxyl-terminal end of protein B (128), and the amino terminus is blocked by acetylation (125), a property that permits orientation of proteolytic fragments.

While there appears to be little dispute about the existence of distinct subunits in chick oviduct PR, their organization into the native receptor complex, and the role of other, non-hormone-binding proteins in this complex, are far from clear. Based on studies with bifunctional cross-linking reagents, and on reconstitution studies with the purified subunits, Schrader and co-workers (129) postulate that equimolar amounts of A and B are involved in dimer formation. In contrast, Dougherty and Toft (130) have shown that sodium molybdate stabilizes two forms of 8 S untransformed PR that can be separated chromatographically: the two forms have either the A subunit or the B subunit, but not both. They conclude that A and B are not found together in a dimer. These are clearly opposing conclusions whose resolution awaits analytical probes that are already being developed.

Using hormone affinity resins, two groups of investigators have purified molybdate-stabilized, untransformed PR, and shown that they contain not only the A and B subunits, but an additional protein of M_r 90,000 (131,132) that does not bind progesterone (133). Since this protein copurifies with PR it has been proposed to be an integral component of the native PR complexes, and in fact, since it also copurifies with other steroid receptors, that it is a protein common to all steroid receptors (162). On the other hand, Birnbaumer *et al.* (133) argue that this 90K protein is unrelated to PR and is an artifact of the affinity purification method, that it is too abundant to be stoichiometrically complexed to A or B, and that immunochemical studies show it to be localized in PR poor cells of the chick oviduct. The resolution of this question will probably require *in vitro* reconstitution of fully active receptors from their isolated and purified components.

Until recently, two subunits have not been demonstrable in mammalian PR, due to problems with receptor stability, proteolysis, aggregation, and concentration. Smith *et al.* (134,135) using chromatography and photoaffinity labeling reported that human uterine PR consist of a single protein of M_r 42,000, and that rabbit uterine PR had a single protein of M_r 70,000. These results raised the possibility that the dual subunit structure of PR described in the chick was an anomaly and not typical of PR in mammals. We have developed a method, described further below, to photoaffinity label PR of human cells *in situ,* and have used it to demonstrate the dual subunit structure of mammalian PR under conditions that avoid *in vitro* protein degradation. With these methods we have shown (Fig. 2) that untransformed human breast cancer PR have two dissimilar proteins (M_r 115,000 and 83,000) present in equimolar amounts (136, and Table V). They thus resemble chick PR with the exception (Fig. 2) that the human A and B proteins are 4000 to 7000 daltons heavier than their chick counterparts, when photolabeled PR from the two species are compared on a single electrophoretic gel. Figure 2 also shows that the same two subunits, with apparently unmodified mass, can be demonstrated in nuclei of human breast tumor cells after receptors have been activated and transformed by progestin treatment, suggesting that receptor acquisition of tight nuclear binding capacity does not require proteolytic processing of subunits or other major structural modifications (137). Our data taken together with those from the chick oviduct should lay to rest the persistent speculation that the dual subunits of PR are artifactual, and we can now proceed to study the differential nuclear functions of these two intriguing hormone-binding and gene regulatory proteins.

C.   THE USE OF ANTIBODIES IN STUDIES OF STEROID RECEPTORS

That our knowledge of steroid receptor structure is still so clouded is due in part to lack of some key experimental tools. Heading the list has been the absence of receptor-recognizing antibodies; a gap that is rapidly being filled as libraries of monoclonal antibodies become available. Development of these reagents is important because ligand-dependent assay systems probably fail to recognize nascent or proreceptor forms, receptors occupied by unusual ligands, processed or other nuclear receptors, proteolytic fragments, denatured receptors, mutant or abnormal receptors, and non-hormone-binding subunits and domains.

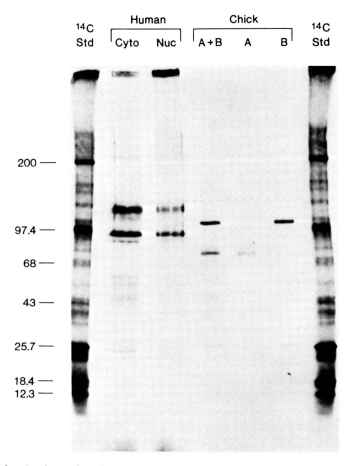

FIG. 2.   An electrophoretic comparison of cytoplasmic and nuclear human PR subunits, with the purified chick A and B PR subunits. Human PR: T47D$_{co}$ cells were grown to confluence in petri dishes, then treated for 5 minutes at 37°C with 80 nM [^{3}H]R5020 to label receptors in nuclei (nuc), or treated for 2 hours at 0°C with 80 nM [^{3}H]R5020 to label untransformed cytoplasmic receptors (cyto). Cells were then washed with ice-cold buffer, the buffer was removed, and the uncovered petri dishes were inverted for 2 minutes at 0°C on the surface of a 300 nm UV transilluminator. Cells were dislodged and homogenized; nuclei were sedimented and extracted for 1 hour at 0°C with 0.4 M KCl-containing buffer. The nuclear extract was concentrated with ammonium sulfate. Cytosol was prepared from the postnuclear supernatant. This and the redissolved nuclear extracts were heated in SDS at 100°C, subjected to SDS–PAGE, and visualized by fluorography. Chick PR: Photolabeled chick oviduct receptor subunits were a gift of M. Birnbaumer and W. Schrader. They were separately purified and photoaffinity labeled as described in Birnbaumer et al. (127), heated in SDS, and then pooled (A + B) and/or separately chromatographed.

1. Antibodies to Estrogen Receptors

Polyclonal antibodies have been produced to human breast cancer ER (138), and to human (139), porcine (140), and calf (141), uterine ER. In general, they cross-react with cytoplasmic and nuclear ER from a variety of tissues and species, and have been used to show that the hormone binding site differs from at least one immunoreactive site, and to show that ER and receptors for other steroids are antigenically distinct proteins.

Monoclonal antibodies produced against calf uterine ER (142,143) seem to be more specific, cross-reacting only with ER from calf tissues, suggesting that species-specific variations in ER exist, but that the modifications do not compromise hormone binding or receptor action (142). However, not all monoclonal antibodies exhibit such specificity (143). A library of monoclonal antibodies directed against human ER purified from MCF-7 breast cancer cells is now available (144). They are being used for immunochemical and immunocytochemical mapping of the receptors. Antibodies reacting with different epitopes of the receptor molecule, coupled with controlled proteolytic cleavage, have been used to identify separate steroid and DNA-binding domains on the receptor protein. The antigenic determinants that are conserved across all species appear to be close to either the steroid-binding or the DNA-binding domains, while an intermediate region confers mammalian or primate specificity (144). A common, highly conserved core for all ER has also been postulated by others (140).

In addition to their use in structural analyses of ER, antibodies are being used to compare the antiestrogen with the estrogen binding site on the molecule. However, preliminary data are conflicting with some finding similar, and others different, hormone binding sites. The contradictions result not only from the use of different antibodies, but from unresolved technical details, such as the order in which reagents should be added (145–148).

Finally, preliminary studies have employed immunohistochemical techniques to study ER distribution in tissues, as well as intracellular ER localization. Although tissue heterogeneity is accepted, there is as yet no consensus on the intracellular location of ER (138) although there exist compelling data showing that even hormone-free ER may be intranuclear proteins in intact cells (149,150).

2. Antibodies to Glucocorticoid Receptors

Progress with the immunochemical structural analysis of GR has been similar to that with ER. Polyclonal anti-GR antibodies have been used, first, to confirm the identity of the M_r 90,000 moiety as the receptor (151,152), second, to show that GR consist of a unique protein differing from other glucocorticoid-binding and steroid binding proteins, and third, to show that species specificity but not tissue specificity exists among GR (153,154). At least three functional/structural domains have been deduced by the ability of ligand and DNA to bind receptors that have been precomplexed to antibodies (155). The existence of these three regions has been confirmed by limited proteolysis: trypsin and α-chymotrypsin split purified 90K receptors (Stokes radius 6.1 nm) into a 39K (3 to 3.6 nm) fragment that binds hormone (domain A) and DNA (domain B), and a second 2.6 nm fragment (domain C), that contains all the immunological determinants observed so far. Domain C is missing in some glucocorticoid resistant lymphomas, and appears to be involved in the interaction of receptors with nuclear chromatin (see above). Further digestion of the 39K fragment yields a 25 to 27K (1.9 nm) fragment that only contains the steroid binding site (domain A).

Rat liver GR have recently been used to generate monoclonal antibodies (156,157). Although 10 or more different antibodies have been produced, both of the IgM and IgG subclasses, that recognize different regions of the M_r 90,000 protein, all the epitopes are located on domain C. Polyclonal antibodies are similarly discriminant, but the reason for this unusual antigenicity of GR is unknown.

3. Antibodies to Progesterone Receptors

The generation and use of antibodies for structural analysis of PR have been exceptionally difficult. Though chick oviduct PR have been purified since 1975 (119) they have proven to be poor immunogens (158). Polyclonal (159) and monoclonal (160) antibodies reportedly raised against molybdate-stabilized chick oviduct holoreceptors appear, instead, to be directed against an M_r 90,000 non-hormone-binding protein (90K) whose function and relationship to PR subunits A and B remain speculative (161,162). This protein copurifies with other steroid receptors as well (see above).

Two groups now report production of polyclonal (163,161) and monoclonal (125) antibodies to the authentic, M_r 108,000, B protein. The polyclonal antibody (163) IgG-RB$_2$ has extensive cross-reactivity: it binds chick subunits B and A (but not the 90K protein), nuclear PR, PR meroreceptors, 8S molybdate-stabilized PR, human and rabbit PR, and chick ER. The monoclonals (125), 9G10 and 3E8, recognize strictly the B protein. However, they bind only the denatured hormone-free protein and not native, hormone-bound B. The monoclonal antigenic site has been mapped to a 3000-Da segment between M_r 31,000 and 34,000 from the amino-terminal end of the molecule. This epitope differs from that of the polyclonal antibody which binds to the smaller 23K meroreceptor at the amino-terminal end.

Some of the properties of the two monoclonal antibodies are puzzling: 9G10 can shift denatured subunit B on sucrose gradients, if the protein has been internally labeled with radioactive phosphate. However, no such sedimentation shift is observed if the covalent label on the denatured protein is provided by $[^3H]R5020$ at the hormone binding site. That steroid binding might interfere with the binding of the antibody due to an antigenic determinant at the hormone binding site, has also been ruled out. It seems therefore, that the native, hormone-binding B protein, is distinct from the immunoreactive M_r 108,000 antigen; the latter is a highly abundant protein, found in many cells, and may be among other things, a nonfunctional proreceptor. The antigen and B protein are closely related, since they have identical size, charge, and proteolytic peptide maps.

Antibody 9G10 has been used to screen the proteins expressed by recombinant bacterial clones containing selected chick oviduct plasmid cDNA, that had been synthesized from a template of poly(A)$^+$ mRNA of the size expected for B protein mRNA (164). The cDNA is being used as a probe to screen a chick genomic library, to assess the factors involved in the regulation and distribution of the B subunit in chick oviduct cells, and, assuming sufficient cross-reactivity to identify the related gene in a human DNA library. Unfortunately, the finding that polyclonal and monoclonal antibodies to rabbit PR cross-react with other mammalian PR but not with chick oviduct receptors (165,166), and our finding that the human and chick B protein differ considerably in size (Fig. 2), suggest that the avian and human proteins, and the respective genes, have diverged to some extent.

D. COVALENT MODIFICATIONS

Most proteins undergo some reversible covalent modifications after their synthesis, that serve to regulate their activity. A common example is the phosphorylation/dephosphorylation of hydroxyl groups at serine, threonine, or tyrosine amino acid residues. There is now strong evidence that steroid receptors are phosphoproteins, and considerable speculation that other modifications exist as well. The estrogen, glucocorticoid, and progestin-binding capacity of cytosols (167–169) is modulated by phosphorylation/dephosphorylation, and all three receptors have been shown to be phosphoproteins (169–171). These studies are reviewed briefly below; we will not address the multiple other factors and reagents that have been implicated in receptor activation/inactivation, transformation, and translocation (172).

1. Estrogen Receptors

A series of studies by Auricchio and co-workers (169,173,174) have led to the conclusion that translocated ER complexes are dephosphorylated by a nuclear phosphatase, and that a protein kinase in cytoplasm rephosphorylates ER. The nuclear phosphatase has been demonstrated by inactivation of cytoplasmic ER complexes, and by dephosphorylation of ^{32}P-labeled receptors, after their *in vitro* incubation with nuclei; a loss that is prevented by phosphatase inhibitors. Of interest is the fact that antiestrogen–receptor complexes are not inactivated by nuclei. Since these effects on ER and antiestrogen receptor complexes are analogous to those seen for nuclear receptor processing, it is tempting to speculate that dephosphorylation is involved in this effect.

The inactivated estrogen-binding activity can be reactivated by a cytoplasmic kinase. In the presence of kinase, [^{32}P]ATP, Ca^{2+}, and calmodulin, the protein can be labeled, and then visualized on SDS–PAGE as a single band of M_r 69,000. On sucrose density gradients the sedimentation of this ^{32}P-labeled protein is shifted by an anti-ER antibody.

2. Glucocorticoid Receptors

The data for GR differ somewhat from those for ER. Apparently only the hormone-free receptors are sensitive to inactivation by exogenously added phosphatase, while the steroid-bound receptors are unaffected (167). More recent data suggest that purified GR are autophosphorylated by an endogenous protein kinase (170).

3. Progesterone Receptors

Weigel *et al.* (171) first showed that purified PR proteins A and B can act as substrates for a cAMP-dependent protein kinase. They found no evidence for endogenous kinase activity intrinsic to the receptors. A similar conclusion was reached by Ghosh-Dastidar *et al.* (175) who showed that proteins A and B can be phosphorylated by a tyrosine kinase on the EGF receptor. Though they denied that autophosphorylation occurred, some labeling of the receptors was seen in the absence of EGF receptors (175), and Garcia *et al.* (176) report that the purified B protein has intrinsic kinase activity and can phosphorylate either itself or histones added to the reaction mixture. Clearly, these questions require further investigation—there is as yet no evidence that either of the two PR subunits is phosphorylated *in vivo*. However, the M_r 90,000 protein, that copurifies with molybdate-stabilized steroid receptors, is apparently a phosphoprotein *in vivo* (177).

IV. Biological Actions of Progestins in Cultured Breast Tumor Cells

The evidence that steroid hormones act primarily at the level of DNA transcription is considerable. Steroid receptors bind preferentially to specific sequences in the 5′-flanking region of steroid inducible genes. Functional tests have been established for these steroid control regions, by transfecting receptor-containing cells with *in vitro* mutagenized sequences, and showing that appropriate messages and proteins accumulate (albeit at low efficiency) in response to hormone treatment, only if the receptor recognition sequences are intact. To define the mechanisms of progesterone's actions in breast cancer, it would be useful if similar steps were defined for growth-promoting and growth-inhibitory cellular proteins under progesterone control, and for tissue specific markers of hormone dependence. Virtually no such proteins are known. The milk proteins are the only breast-specific proteins that have been studied to any extent, but these are unlikely candidates to be growth regulators or tumor markers.

Although a functional approach would be most rational in searching for hormone-regulated proteins, the approach usually taken is to describe sets of intracellular or secreted inducible proteins first, and look for function second. As a result a series of estrogen-inducible proteins have been demonstrated, they have been purified, monoclonal antibodies have been generated, their mRNAs have been isolated, and some of the genes cloned (178–182). Double stranded cDNA from one such protein, pS2, has been cloned and the cDNA used as a probe to show that pS2 mRNA is induced by estradiol in MCF-7 cells, but not in T47D cells. The message is found in some biopsies of human breast tumors but not, apparently in other human cells (182). The function of pS2 protein is not known, but like the other estrogen-inducible proteins, the hope has been that it will be somehow involved in estrogen-controlled growth regulation. M. Lippman (personal communication) finds, however, that in the LY2 antiestrogen-resistant cell line, antiestrogens have no effect on growth, though they still inhibit pS2 mRNA synthesis, suggesting the pS2 protein is not involved in growth regulation.

The same shotgun approach that has been used for estrogens is now being used to isolate progestin-responsive proteins, and T47D have proven to be the best cells for such studies. An M_r 48,000 protein is released into the medium bathing T47D cells following 2 days of R5020 treatment, and an M_r 250,000 protein is seen in cell lysates. Synthesis of the 48K protein is inhibited by the antiprogestin RU38 486 (183–185). Another protein, M_r 60,000 is not directly regulated by progestins; it is induced by estradiol and the increase is inhibited by R5020 in its antiestrogenic capacity.

Studies of progestin regulated breast tumor cell proteins are in their infancy. T47D$_{co}$ cells in our laboratory have several progestin-specific responses: these are growth inhibition, increases in insulin receptors, lipid accumulation, and ultrastructural changes, which are described further below.

V. Progesterone Receptors and Progestin Action in T47D$_{co}$ Human Breast Cancer Cells

A. THE MODEL

It is generally agreed that in appropriate target cells, PR are synthesized in response to estrogens acting through ER. This relation has been demonstrated in a variety of experimental systems, including human breast cancer cells in culture, and led us to suggest several years ago that the presence of PR in human breast tumor biopsies could be used to deduce the integrity of the ER and of the estrogen-response system, and would serve as a marker of hormone-dependent tumors (1,2).

It was therefore of considerable interest to us that while measuring the steroid receptor content of a series of cultured human breast cancer cells, one cell line, T47D, had no cytoplasmic ER by sucrose density gradient analysis, yet had the highest PR levels of any breast cancer cell line surveyed (186). We decided to characterize these receptors in 1981 and established a cell line from frozen stocks that initially had very low plating efficiency (<5%). However, the cells proliferated, and were passaged 20 to 30 times in medium that differed slightly from the recommmended one by having decreased serum and insulin concentrations, and no hydrocortisone. After 30 passages the cells had less than 3 fmol/mg protein (<0.04 pmol/mg DNA) of specific, unfilled ER in cytosols and none in nuclear extracts (187). Human breast tumor biopsies with these levels of ER are classified as ER-negative. However, not only did the cells have large amounts of cytoplasmic PR (2.7 pmol/mg cytosol protein; 16.5 pmol/mg DNA) (Fig. 3), but a KCl extract of the nuclear pellet, showed that a considerable number of PR sites were associated with the crude nuclei. This compartment contained an additional 2.3 pmol of receptor/mg of extracted protein (14.6 pmol of PR/mg of DNA). Thus, under the culture conditions described, T47D cells have more than 300,000 total PR sites

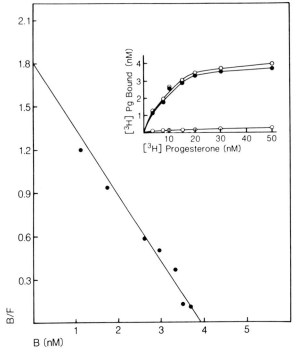

FIG. 3.   Binding of progesterone to T47D$_{co}$ cytosol. Triplicate aliquots of cytosol (1.4 mg protein/ml) were incubated with [^{3}H]progesterone concentrations ranging from 0.5 to 54 nM (picomoles per ml). Parallel sets contained a 100-fold excess of unlabeled progesterone. The inset shows total (○; top), specific (●), and nonspecific binding (○, bottom). Data were plotted according to the method of Scatchard after subtraction of nonspecific binding. The number of receptor sites calculated from the X intercept is 14.6 pmol/mg DNA; the K_d is about 2 nM. Points represent the average of triplicate determinations.

per cell. This is 5- to 10-fold greater than is usually seen, even in estradiol-stimulated tissues.

T47D cells were established from the pleural effusion of a patient with breast cancer; they have mammary epithelial characteristics and synthesize casein (188). Various sublines have now been established (see above) with different ER content and estrogen responsiveness. We have therefore designated ours as T47D$_{co}$. It is likely that these are epigenetic variants rather than true mutations of the parental cells.

1.   T47D Estrogen Receptors and "Processing Reversal"

Are these really ER-negative cells? Figure 4 shows that these cells are not entirely devoid of ER. With protamine sulfate precipitation we find

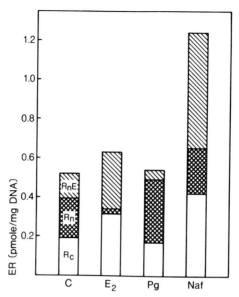

FIG. 4. Effect of estrogen, progesterone, and nafoxidine on ER distribution showing "processing-reversal" by the antiestrogen. Triplicate T75 flasks containing confluent cells were treated with growth medium only (C), or with medium containing 10 nM estradiol (E$_2$), 0.1 μM progesterone (Pg), or 1 μM nafoxidine. Cells were harvested and homogenized, and triplicate aliquots of the cytosol and nuclear extracts were incubated with [^{3}H]estradiol only, or together with a 100-fold excess of diethylstilbestrol. Binding was measured by the protamine sulfate exchange assay after a 0 or a 30°C incubation. R$_c$, unfilled cytoplasmic sites; R$_n$, unfilled nuclear sites; R$_n$E, filled nuclear sites.

some cytoplasmic ER, but these sites cannot be depleted by estradiol (Rc, Fig. 4) and are therefore a basal, nontranslocatable, possibly nonfunctional, receptor fraction. We see approximately the same irreducible minimum cytoplasmic ER in MCF-7 cells after 90–95% of sites have been translocated by estradiol. Protamine sulfate also precipitates some (0.1 to 0.2 pmole/mg DNA) hormone filled (RnE) and unfilled (Rn) nuclear ER. These values approximate the steady-state levels of nuclear ER seen after receptor translocation and down-regulation following chronic estrogen treatment of MCF-7 cells. This "processed" level is an activated state; continuous protein synthesis is required for its maintenance and PR are induced (189,190).

We therefore postulate that in T47D cells, ER are in a persistent activated state in the nucleus. We have several indications that this is the case. First, when protein synthesis is inhibited, 65% of nuclear ER are lost in 18 hours. Thus, continuous protein synthesis may be required to keep ER in the nucleus. Second, the antiestrogen, nafoxidine, has an unusual effect: it doubles ER levels in 6 hours (Fig. 4), and the new sites are virtually all intranuclear. The rate of this increase is similar to the rate of nuclear ER processing. We believe this increase represents a reversal of some step involved in ER processing. Such a reversal can be brought about in MCF-7 cells when estrogen treatment is followed by antiestrogen treatment, and is too rapid to be explained by new receptor synthesis. Third, processing reversal, like processing, is independent of protein synthesis and cannot be blocked by cycloheximide (187). It would seem that the nafoxidine-induced increase in ER represents recruitment of pre-formed receptor protein from a previously unmeasured receptor pool.

These ER require further study using the new probes now available—electroaffinity labeling and immunochemical analysis. It would not be surprising if these receptors contain a mutant chromatin binding domain, analogous to domain C of GR in nt^i lymphoma cells, that accounts for chronic nuclear binding and chronic PR gene activation. These receptors may be estrogen insensitive because the mutation has dispensed with the only step that requires estrogen—the initial transformation step.

2. Biological Actions of ER

To show whether the ER can mediate estrogenic or antiestrogenic effects we measured cell growth and PR levels after hormone treatment. First, the growth of $T47D_{co}$ was unaffected by presence of estradiol (10 nM), or by concentrations of nafoxidine that are cytotoxic in ER-positive breast cancer cells (189). Insensitivity to the killing effects of antiestrogens is characteristic of cell lines that have no ER (191). Second, prolonged treatment (5 to 7 days) of the cells with estradiol, with nafoxidine, or with steroid-depleted serum had little appreciable effect on the very high PR levels. Thus we conclude that the nuclear ER in these cells cannot respond to exogenously added estrogens in the usual way.

3. The Progesterone Receptors

The PR appear to be normal by several criteria: the receptors are heat-labile, they sediment at 7–8 S on sucrose gradients, they bind only progestins specifically and with high affinity (187,192), and they can only be translocated by progestins (193). If the cells are treated with progesterone for 5 minutes, the PR acquire tight nuclear binding capacity. With longer progesterone treatment (10 minutes) nuclear receptor levels begin to fall and as many as 85% of the sites are lost in 1 hour in a step analogous to ER processing. Removal of progesterone leads to new receptor synthesis, that includes a cycloheximide-sensitive step; total replenishment requires about 24 hours. Replenishment is neither stimulated by estradiol nor inhibited by antiestrogens, showing again that these PR are estrogen independent (194). Some of these steps are characterized further below.

We have indirect evidence that PR synthesis remains under some regulation and is not simply constitutive, based on studies with 5-bromodeoxyuridine (BUdR) and sodium butyrate. The thymidine analog BUdR selectively inhibits the expression of some specialized functions in differentiated cells, but has relatively little effect on proteins of more general use and distribution (195). The ER from rabbit uterus have an enhanced affinity for BUdR-substituted DNA (196), and in human breast tumor cells this compound inhibits the synthesis of estrogen-induced PR and of an estrogen-induced 46-kDa protein (197). Butyrate preferentially inhibits the steroid-inducible component of transferrin and ovalbumin transcription, while only moderately inhibiting the constitutive synthesis of these mRNAs (198). This compound alters the level of histone acetylation (199) and has stimulating (200) as well as inhibitory (198) effects on gene induction.

We therefore used BUdR and butyrate to distinguish between constitutive transcription and an inductive process involving the PR gene. Both compounds suppress PR extensively, even though at early time points they have little effect on overall DNA and protein synthesis (Figs. 5 and 6). Thus PR retain characteristics of inducible proteins, and it is tempting to speculate that the persistent nuclear ER chronically stimulate transcription of the PR gene, in the absence of exogenous estrogen.

B. REGULATION OF PR LEVELS BY PROGESTINS

1. Ligand Exchange

To study the kinetics of PR translocation, nuclear turnover, and replenishment, we needed to establish that the receptors could be assayed quantitatively in both cytoplasm and nucleus and when hormone filled or unfilled, and that receptors could be measured equally well whether they are occupied by progesterone or a synthetic progestin.

To quickly assess exchange, we devised a "mixing" assay in which half of a cytosol is incubated with unlabeled ligand to fill the receptors, and the other half is left untreated. After adsorption of both cytosols with charcoal, the two preparations are mixed in different proportions and then assayed for [³H]R5020 binding at either 0 or 10°C, with incubation times ranging from 4 to 24 hours. Under conditions of complete exchange, we would expect to see similar [³H]R5020 binding whether or not sites were previously hormone filled. Under conditions in which no exchange occurs, we would expect to see no binding of [³H]R5020 to previously hor-

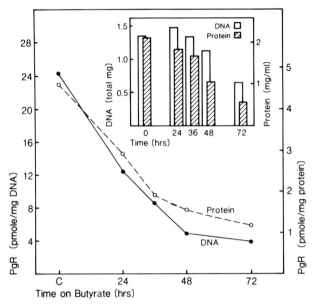

FIG. 5. Effect of 10mM sodium butyrate on PR, soluble proteins, and growth of T47D$_{co}$. Each point represents the average of triplicate determinations from three pooled T75 flasks. Cells were treated with the experimental media for the times indicated. Controls contained no addition. Starts were staggered and time points were harvested simultaneously. Data are shown as PR/mg protein (protein), or PR/mg DNA (DNA) in main figure.

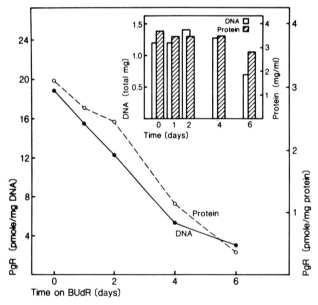

FIG. 6. Effect of 20 μg/ml bromodeoxyuridine on PR levels, soluble proteins, and total cellular DNA. Each point represents the average of triplicate determinations from three pooled T75 flasks. Cells were treated with the experimental media for the times indicated. Controls contained 20 μg/ml thymidine. Starts were staggered and all time points were harvested together. Data are shown as PR/mg protein (protein) or PR/mg DNA (DNA) in main figure.

mone-filled sites, and progressively more binding as the number of un-filled sites increase. Partial exchange would fall between these two extremes.

We have tested progesterone, and several synthetic progestins includ-ing R5020, medroxyprogesterone acetate, megestrol acetate, and the syn-thetic antiprogestin RU38 486. Progesterone-occupied sites exchange completely for [^{3}H]R5020 under all conditions. In contrast the synthetic progestins exchange only 50%, regardless of the conditions used. In prac-tice this means that half of all sites can be measured when PR are occu-pied by synthetic progestins and that doubling the measured value gives a good estimate of the actual number of sites. Progesterone-occupied sites can always be accurately measured.

2. Translocation and Nuclear Processing

If translocation is a specific response to the action of one class of steroid hormones, then only those hormones should decrease soluble cytoplasmic receptors. To measure the specificity of PR translocation, T47D$_{co}$ cells were treated for 5 minutes at 37°C with a variety of steroids, and residual soluble PR were measured in cytosols (Fig. 7). Progesterone

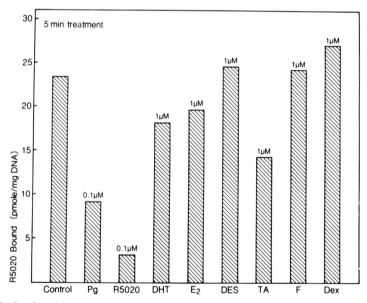

FIG. 7. Steroid specificity of cytoplasmic PR translocation in T47D$_{co}$ human breast cancer cells. Intact cells were treated for 5 minutes at 37°C with the hormones indicated, then rapidly cooled and homogenized. Residual unoccupied cytoplasmic PR were measured with 20 nM [^{3}H]R5020 in the presence or absence of unlabeled R5020. Pg (progesterone), DHT (dihydrotestosterone), E$_2$ (estradiol), DES (diethylstilbestrol), TA (triamcinolone ace-tonide), F (hydrocortisone), Dex (dexamethasone).

and synthetic progestins cause rapid decreases in PR; 65–70% of sites are depleted by progesterone and 90 to 95% by all synthetic progestins. At 10-fold higher concentrations, androgens and estrogens have little effect. The glucocorticoids, hydrocortisone and dexamethasone also have no effect, but triamcinolone acetonide depleted 55% of PR, consistent with its known progestational properties (201,202). These and similar data prompt us to recommend strongly that PR be masked by an unlabeled progestin when [³H]triamcinolone is used to measure GR. In our opinion [³H]dexamethasone is a far superior ligand for GR determinations.

Although nuclear accumulation of PR is stoichiometric, an unusual and very rapid nuclear turnover, or processing step, characterizes the high affinity binding of nuclear PR when they are occupied by progesterone (Fig. 8). After PR are translocated by 0.1 μM progesterone, they can be quantitatively recovered from nuclei only in the first few minutes. Thereafter, rapid nuclear processing results in loss of 50–80% of the newly translocated sites. Rapid processing may be inherent to PR; it also occurs in PR of MCF-7 cells. The extent of receptor translocation and of nuclear receptor processing is increased at higher progesterone concentrations (193).

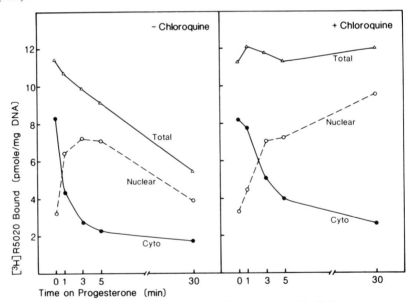

FIG. 8.   Effect of chloroquine on the processing of nuclear PR. Cells were pretreated with chloroquine (100 μM) for 30 minutes at 37°C before 0.1 μM progesterone was added for 1 to 30 minutes. Cells were cooled and homogenized and cytoplasmic and nuclear PR were measured by [³H]R5020 exchange. Total receptors are the sum of sites in the two compartments.

Nuclear PR turnover is more difficult to study if cells are treated with synthetic progestins, because the exchange assay underestimates PR. However, we can measure nuclear PR labeled with [³H]R5020 that have been covalently photolinked *in situ* with ultraviolet light at the end of the incubations. Under these conditions labeled nuclear receptors persist for several hours before they disappear from all cellular compartments, suggesting that nuclear PR processing is slowed when receptors are occupied by this synthetic hormone. A similar result is seen in time-course studies of subcellular [³H]R5020 distribution (194).

Interestingly, covalently labeled subunits A and B disappear from nuclei simultaneously and no small-molecular-weight fragments replace them, which means either (1) that during processing the receptors are clipped close to or at the hormone binding site, leaving a large receptor fragment that cannot bind hormone, or (2) that receptors are degraded into fragments smaller than the resolving capacity of 7.5 to 19% gradient gels (~10,000 daltons).

3. Inhibition of Nuclear PR Processing

We have shown that processing of nuclear ER can be entirely blocked by the G-C specific DNA intercalators, chromomycin A_3 and actinomycin D, but not by many other DNA binding agents including chloroquine, and that the inhibitory effects of actinomycin probably result from a direct disturbance of estrogen receptor–DNA interactions (203,204). To see if nuclear PR "loss" and ER processing are analogous, we tested a variety of DNA intercalators for their ability to interfere with the changes in nuclear PR levels. Ethidium bromide and chromomycin A_3 did not significantly prevent this loss (only 26–30% of translocated PR remain) and actinomycin is only minimally effective (40% of translocated PR remain). The most effective inhibitor is chloquine (Fig. 8), which prevents the loss of 70 to 100% of nuclear PR (193).

Since chloroquine is both a DNA intercalator and an inhibitor of lysosomal enzymes, it raised the possibility that inhibition of PR turnover by chloroquine was due to an effect of proteolytic enzymes and not due to interference with receptor–DNA interactions. We therefore tested other enzyme inhibitors and chloroquine analogs. Leupeptin and antipain, which prevent the proteolytic breakdown of PR to meroreceptors (205), were ineffective inhibitors of nuclear PR processing, as was carbobenzoxy-L-phenylalanine, a chymotrypsin-like enzyme inhibitor that stabilizes glucocorticoid receptors (206). However, primaquine and quinacrine were as effective as cholorquine in preventing PR loss. These compounds are A-T specific intercalators that yield characteristic banding patterns on chromosomes (207,208). However, primaquine, unlike quinacrine and chloroquine, is a poor (one-fifth as potent) lysosomotropic agent. These experiments suggest that the actions of these three agents on PR turnover result from their DNA-binding properties and that it is PR interactions at A-T containing DNA regions that are involved. Recently two groups (209–211) have provided direct evidence for an interaction of PR with A-T-rich sequences upstream from PR-inducible genes. It would be interesting to see if their *in vitro* receptor–DNA interactions are blocked by the addition of chloroquine.

The mechanisms involved in processing of steroid–receptor complexes in the nucleus are unknown. However, its course is not inexorable, because processing can be rapidly and entirely (193,203,204) prevented by agents which intercalate into and modify the structure of DNA. Since some gene-regulatory proteins slide from nonspecific to specific DNA target sites and undergo conformational changes in the process (212), it is possible that the intercalators prevent the movement of receptors from one intranuclear binding site to another. In the end, a critical step in steroid–receptor processing involves recognition of base specific sites, since PR processing appears to be inhibited by A-T specific intercalators, while ER processing is only inhibited by G-C intercalators, and intercalators that have no base-sequence specificity have no inhibitory effects on either PR or ER.

4. Progesterone Receptor Replenishment

Current mechanisms of steroid receptor action postulate that receptors are site-specific gene regulatory proteins that are transformed to high affinity chromatin-binding molecules by the hormone. It is further assumed, though no direct evidence exists, that after the transcriptional effects are elicited, the nuclear signal shuts off. How receptors are then reactivated is also unknown, but replenishment of hormone-free sites resulting from receptor recycling, from covalent modifications, or from new protein synthesis, probably restores cellular sensitivity to hormone. Thus, in progesterone target cells, the replenishment of PR following their transformation and nuclear processing may be essential if the cells are to regain responsiveness to progesterone. We have studied the replenishment of PR in T47D$_{co}$ cells to determine both the rate and the extent of this process (194).

A typical result is shown in Fig. 9, in which T47D$_{co}$ cells were treated for 1 hour with progesterone or R5020, then the hormones were removed, and the cells were washed and reincubated in hormone-free medium, to measure the restoration rate of "cytoplasmic" untransformed PR. If progesterone is removed from the cells, complete replenishment occurs in 24–36 hours. In contrast, the synthetic progestin R5020 suppresses PR

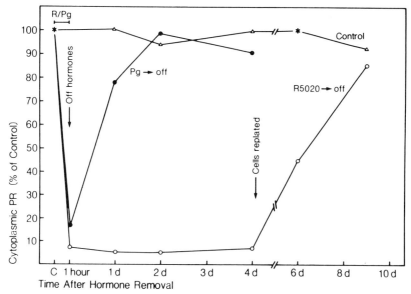

FIG. 9.   Effect of a 1 hour R5020 or progesterone pulse on long-term cytoplasmic PR levels. Duplicate 75-cm² flasks containing preconfluent T47D cells were treated 1 hour at 37°C with medium containing 0.1 μM unlabeled progesterone (Pg, ●) or R5020 (R, ○). Control cells received no hormone additions (*). The medium was then removed, the cell surface was washed, and cells were reincubated with hormone-free medium for 24, 48, or 96 hours. (For the 96 hour sets, spent medium was removed and replaced with fresh medium at 48 hours.) For the control and R5020-treated cells, parallel sets were harvested at 96 hours, washed, and replated at a 1:4 split ratio into fresh flasks. Specific progesterone receptor levels were measured in triplicate by [³H]R5020 exchange and charcoal adsorption. Data are shown as percentage of controls, which were 12.3 pmol/mg of DNA initially and 20.6 pmol/mg of DNA after replating.

replenishment even 96 hours after its removal from the medium, and an additional 6 days is required to restore PR to control values despite the transfer of cells to fresh flasks. This property is not restricted to R5020; every synthetic progestin that we have tested, including RU38 486, medroxyprogesterone acetate, and megestrol, gives similar results. In fact, the block to replenishment cannot be prevented even in cells replated immediately after the 1-hour pulse, or in cells flooded with progesterone in an attempt to displace the intracellular progestin. It must be due either to true inhibition of new receptor synthesis, or to the presence of a long-acting, tightly bound, intracellular pool of hormone that chronically retranslocates newly replenished receptors. Unlike progesterone, which is very rapidly metabolized ($t_{\frac{1}{2}}$ 2–4 hours) and ultimately converted to 5α-pregnan-3β,6α-diol-20-one by these cells (unpublished) the synthetic progestins are not degraded. This may account for their long-acting effects. If metabolism of progesterone is prevented by providing an alternative enzyme substrate (i.e., androgens) or with enzyme inhibitors, then replenishment is also slowed.

It has been known for several years that demonstration of PR in breast tumor biopsies is often difficult in premenopausal women with normal circulating progesterone levels, because progesterone sequesters receptors in nuclear compartments, where they are not measured by current assay procedures or because receptors are down-regulated or "processed." This can result in false-negative assays. Our data provide a molecular explanation for these clinical findings by showing that under continuous progesterone stimulation, total cell PR levels can be chronically suppressed. The data also suggest that in women treated with synthetic progestins (for example women taking oral contraceptives), accurate measurement of available PR may be especially difficult. Finally, it is possible that some synthetic progestins have a much longer intracellular duration of action, than simple blood hormone clearance measurements indicate.

C. THE STRUCTURE OF PR IN HUMAN BREAST CANCER CELLS

1. Chromatography and DNA Binding

T47D$_{co}$ cells are the best available source from which to purify and characterize human PR. First, the receptors are present in relatively high abundance (2 to 5 pmol/mg protein), and constitute 0.05% of total cellular proteins. Second, the receptors are unusually resistant to degradation in cell-free extracts because endogenous protease activity is low. One can therefore eliminate some chromatographic steps designed specifically to remove proteases, and still obtain intact proteins.

When [^{3}H]R5020 photolabeled cytosol is applied to DEAE, a characteristic elution pattern is seen (Fig. 10). The broad peak of specific binding (peak 1, fractions 80–110) eluting between 0.1 and 0.2 M KCl is followed by a second smaller peak eluting at 0.3 M KCl (peak 2, fractions 130–145). The average concentrations of KCl required to elute these peaks in six separate experiments is 0.17 and 0.27 M. The smaller trailing peak 2 is not seen if the cytosol is precipitated with ammonium sulfate, resuspended, and diluted before DEAE chromatography and probably consists of a small percentage of receptors that either did not dissociate into monomers or dissociated late. Monomer separation is completed after fractions are eluted and pooled, since samples from both peaks sediment at about 4.1 S

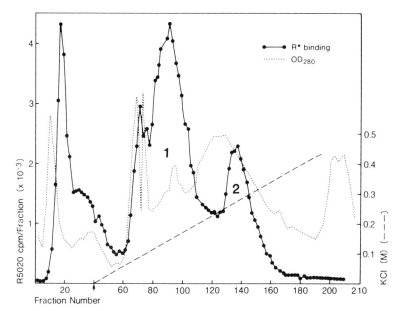

FIG. 10.   DEAE-cellulose column chromatography of human breast cancer PR. A cytosol from T47D_{co} cells was incubated with 40 nM [^{3}H]R5020 and the hormone–receptor
complexes were then covalently photolinked *in vitro* by a 300 nm UV pulse. A 2 ml sample
of cytosol prepared in TESH buffer was chromatographed on a 2.4 × 2.5-cm DEAE-cellulose column. The column was washed with 20 ml buffer, then eluted with a gradient of 0 to
0.5 M KCl in 150 ml TESH; 1 ml fractions were collected, and 50-μl aliquots from alternate
tubes were counted. KCl concentration (dashed line) was measured by conductivity; protein
(dotted line) was monitored by absorbance at 280 nm.

on sucrose density gradients. When aliquots from peaks 1 and 2 are concentrated and subjected to SDS–PAGE, equimolar amounts of A and B
proteins are found in each peak.

Pooled fractions from peak 1 were ammonium sulfate precipitated, and
the redissolved concentrate was applied to DNA-cellulose in 0.05 M salt.
After extensive washing the column was eluted with a gradient of 0.05 to
0.4 M salt, and sequential fractions were collected, concentrated, and
analyzed by SDS–PAGE. We find that both subunits A and B bind to
DNA-cellulose, albeit with different affinity. The B protein elutes from
the column at a salt concentration of 0.08 M, while the A protein is
retained on the column until the salt concentration reaches 0.15 M. This
differs somewhat from recent findings with rabbit uterine PR in which two
major PR proteins analogous to the A and B proteins of chick oviduct,
could not be distinguished on the basis of their DNA-binding characteristics (213).

2. In Situ Photoaffinity Labeling of PR

Although we were able to show, by *in vitro* photoaffinity labeling (136,137), that human breast cancer PR consist of at least two hormone-binding proteins of dissimilar size, it was possible that they were formed *in vitro* by proteolytic cleavage of a larger protein, or that A is generated from B. We showed that A and B are always present in equimolar amounts, and that treatment of cytosols with a variety of thiol, serine, and metallopeptidase inhibitors [iodoacetamide (5 mM), PMSF (2 mM), o-phenanthroline (5 mM), 1-chloro-3-tosylamido-7-amino-L-2-heptanone (200 μM), N-ethylmaleimide (500 μM), ovomucoid trypsin inhibitor (100 μg/ml), and leupeptin (20 mM)] does not alter this stoichiometry (137).

Since such studies are still not conclusive, we developed an *in situ* photoaffinity labeling method for PR that permits study of their subunits with minimal *in vitro* incubations. The strategy is to use [³H]R5020, a synthetic photoactive progestin (214), and suitable incubation temperatures to place receptors into their precise intracellular sites in intact cells. The cells, still intact, are then irradiated with UV at 300 nm for 2 minutes. A spectrophotometric scan of R5020 had shown that it maximally absorbs UV at 304 nm. We therefore used a 300 nm output UV lamp, rather than one emitting 360 nm radiation described by Dure *et al.* (214). With this lamp we increased the yield of specifically photolabeled receptors 10-fold, and decreased the irradiation time at least 15-fold (from 30–120 minutes irradiation, to 2 minutes irradiation). This method efficiently (~15%) yields covalently linked hormone–receptor complexes at any intracellular location, in the unbroken cells.

Cells are then rapidly ruptured, nuclei are separated, and receptors are extracted with salt, and/or solubilized with detergents before the subunits are displayed on denaturing gels. The time and temperature at which [³H]R5020 is incubated with the cells determine the intracellular location of the receptors: if incubation is at 0°C (2 hours) 80–90% of receptors are recovered in the cytosol; if incubation is at 37°C (5 minutes), more than 90% of receptors are transformed and recovered in a salt extract of nuclei (see Fig. 2). Figure 11 shows the latter. Clearly, activated and translocated nuclear PR consist of two subunits present in equimolar amounts. Their mass equals that of holoreceptor subunits from untreated cells and equals the mass of the small fraction (7%) of residual receptors that fail to translocate. From these and time-course studies, we conclude that A and B are synchronously translocated by R5020.

To completely eliminate even the short *in vitro* incubation required by salt extraction of *in situ* photolinked nuclear PR, the nuclear pellets from a low-speed 5-minute centrifugation were immediately solubilized with

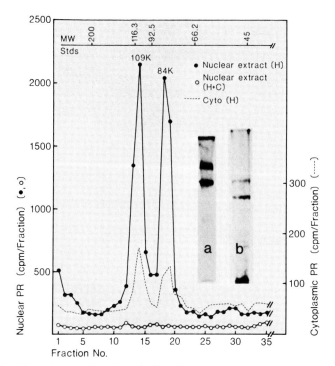

FIG. 11.   The subunits of nuclear PR identified by *in situ* photoaffinity labeling. SDS-PAGE and scintillation counting of nuclear salt extract. Intact cells grown in petri dishes were incubated 5 minutes at 37°C with 40 n*M* [³H]R5020 (H) or together with 100-fold excess unlabeled R5020 (H + C). Cells were cooled to 0°C and irradiated for 2 minutes with UV at 300 nm. Cells were harvested, homogenized, nuclei were sedimented, and the receptors extracted with 0.4 *M* KCl. Cytosol was prepared from the postnuclear supernatant. Ammonium sulfate precipitated cytosol and nuclear receptors were redissolved, solubilized, and subjected to SDS–PAGE. Gel lanes were sliced and counted. Standard proteins of known molecular weight were electrophoresed in parallel lanes and stained. Inset a: The same as the figure, but fluorographed. Inset b: SDS–PAGE and fluorography of nuclear PR subunits photolinked *in situ* and solubilized directly from intact nuclei. Nuclei prepared as in main figure, were incubated 30 minutes at room temperature in 1% SDS, and PMSF. Debris was pelleted and the proteins released into the supernatant were electrophoresed. The stained gel containing nuclear PR was then impregnated with PPO–DMSO. The PPO was crystalized with water, the gel was dried, and used to expose Kodak X-Omat AR-5 film at −70°C for 10 days.

detergent. The extracts were then separated on SDS–PAGE, and the radioactive bands were visualized by fluorography (Fig. 11, inset b). Again, only two, specifically labeled bands (MW 116,000 and 85,000) were present. Other solubilized minor R5020-binding proteins were nonspecifically labeled.

TABLE V

Mass and Stoichiometry of Human Breast Cancer Progesterone Receptor Subunits Determined by in situ Photoaffinity Labeling at T47D$_{co}$

	MW ($\times 10^3$)			
	Subunit B	Subunit A	50K protein	B/A[a]
Cytoplasmic[b]	114.8 ± 1.2 (32)[c]	81.1 ± 0.7 (32)	50.8 ± 0.4 (27)	0.97 ± 0.03 (21)
Nuclear, salt extracted	112.6 ± 1.9 (18)	83.2 ± 1.0 (18)	Absent	1.01 ± 0.03 (14)
Whole nuclei, solubilized	110, 118, 116	85, 82, 84	Absent	

[a] Calculated from the area under each peak after subtraction of nonspecific binding.

[b] Combined data from *in vitro* photolabeled PR and from *in situ* photolabeled 0°C untranslocated and 37°C residual cytoplasmic PR.

[c] Values are the mean ± SEM; the number of studies is in parentheses.

The data from a series of experiments are summarized in Table V and show (1) that the subunit molecular weights of cytoplasmic and nuclear PR are identical, and (2) that the subunits are present in both compartments in equimolar amounts, so that only their intracellular compartmentalization is altered by progestin treatment, and no other detectable modification occurs. We conclude that major subunit proteolysis does not accompany the acquisition of nuclear binding capacity.

In order to entirely avoid exposure of the receptors to cell-free conditions, even those created by homogenization, an experiment was performed in which [³H]R5020-treated and irradiated cells were solubilized directly with detergent while still intact. This lysate was then analyzed by SDS–PAGE. Figure 12 shows that both subunits can be demonstrated by this method, and that they are identical to those extracted from nuclei by the more conventional method. We conclude that the A and B proteins are integral intracellular proteins and that they are not artifactually formed *in vitro*. The peptide mapping studies of chick oviduct PR show that endogenous proteases cannot generate A from B intracellularly. It remains possible that A and B form part of a larger pro-receptor protein that is processed posttranslationally to generate the 2 subunits, or alternatively, that they are the products of two genes. This question will be answered rapidly since the mRNA for the B protein has now been isolated.

Figure 13 shows that the nuclear receptors retain the hormone specificity expected of authentic PR. They bind R5020 (and all other synthetic progestins) and progesterone, but not estradiol, dihydrotestosterone,

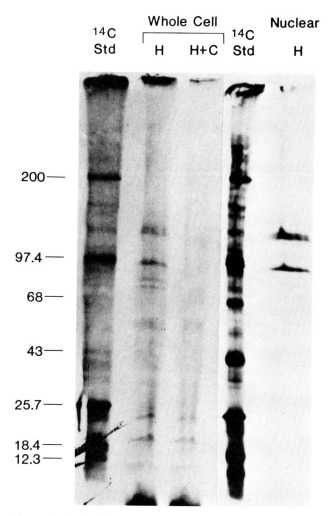

FIG. 12. The two PR subunits solubilized from intact cells after *in situ* labeling with [³H]R5020. T47D$_{co}$ cells growing in petri dishes were treated 5 minutes at 37°C with 80 nM [³H]R5020 only (H) or with labeled R5020 plus a 100-fold excess of unlabeled R5020 (H + C). The cells were then cooled and irradiated 2 minutes at 0°C with 300 nm UV. The whole cells were then lysed from the dishes with a solubilization buffer containing 1% SDS, 0.4 M KCl, and protease inhibitors. The lysate was heated at 100°C for 2 minutes and resolved on 7.5 to 19% gradient gels. The standard salt extracted nuclear receptors (see Figs. 10 and 11) are shown on the right for comparison.

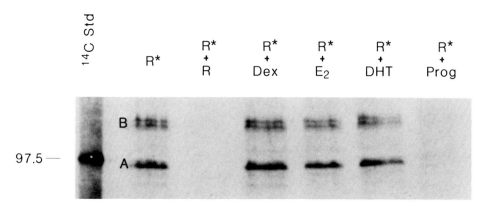

FIG. 13. Binding specificity of nuclear subunits A and B demonstrated by *in situ* photoaffinity labeling. T47D$_{co}$ cells were incubated 5 minutes at 37°C with 40 nM [^{3}H]R5020 only (R*) or with [^{3}H]R5020 plus a 100-fold excess of unlabeled R5020 (R), dexamethasone (Dex), estradiol (E$_2$), dihydrotestosterone (DHT), or progesterone (Prog). The cells were then cooled and irradiated 2 minutes at 0°C with 300 nm UV. Cells were harvested, homogenized, nuclei were precipitated, washed, and extracted 1 hour with 0.4 M KCl-containing buffer. Extracted proteins were concentrated with ammonium sulfate, solubilized, and heated in detergent, resolved on 7.5 to 19% acrylamide gradient SDS–PAGE gels, and fluorographed. ^{14}C Standards were run in parallel lanes and the position of the M_r 97,500 phosphorylase B standard is shown. The doublet "split" of the B subunit is a characteristic finding on gradient gels, and is discussed in the text.

dexamethasone, or (not shown) hydrocortisone. They do bind triamcinolone acetonide which, as we discussed above, is known to be progestational. The data in Fig. 13 address the frequently asked question, whether PR and GR share a common subunit. This is raised by studies with R5020 for example, since this compound is used to measure PR, but can also interact with GR (215), and has been used to photoaffinity label both classes of receptors (214,215). When used as a marker for GR in hepatoma or lymphoma cells, R5020 covalently labels a single protein of M_r 87,000–90,000. As a marker for PR in human breast cancer cells, R5020 covalently labels two other proteins of M_r 115,000 and 83,000. Presumably R5020 labels either the receptor class that is present, or if both are present, the more abundant class. In T47D cells, the levels of PR exceed GR by more than 100-fold, and addition of unlabeled glucocorticoid to the cells has no effect on R5020 binding, or on PR transformation (Fig. 7). The failure of dexamethasone to compete for binding of R5020 to PR subunit A (the M_r 83,000 protein), strongly suggests that the A subunit of PR and the M_r 90,000 subunit of GR are two different proteins. The B subunit of PR is also not bound by dexamethasone, and is probably too large to be the common protein.

Figure 13 also shows the characteristic "doublet" structure of the B subunit following 5 minutes of R5020 treatment. This structural heterogeneity is still under investigation. However, we believe that it represents an intranuclear covalent modification of the protein that results from hormone binding, which increases the apparent molecular weight of the B protein by 2000 to 3000 Da. If hormone treatment is extended for longer periods before UV irradiation, the B protein is entirely converted to the heavy form. The nuclear A protein becomes similarly modified about 30 minutes after B. Such shifts in denaturing gels have been described when proteins become phosphorylated (216), and we are examining this, as well as other protein modifying reactions. It is interesting to note that such chemical modifications usually serve to regulate the biological activity of proteins, and that in the case of PR, the changes occur after the proteins have acquired tight nuclear binding capacity.

3. A New, Nuclear, Progestin-Binding Molecule?

Following [^{3}H]R5020 treatment and UV irradiation, the two PR subunits are extracted from nuclei with 0.4 M KCl-containing buffer. If the residual, salt-resistant pellet is then solubilized with SDS, analyzed by PAGE, and the gels are fluorographed, a heavily labeled specific [^{3}H]R5020 binder is seen that has a mass of 28,000 daltons. This molecule has several interesting properties: (1) It is not solubilized by 2 M salt and resists proteolytic digestion under conditions that destroy PR. It is, however, digested by exhaustive protease treatment, and we speculate that it is either a tight DNA-binding protein or a nuclear matrix protein. (2) The molecule can be [^{3}H]R5020 labeled by direct incubation of purified nuclei from untreated cells. Under these conditions there are few PR in nuclei and the 28K molecule is apparently not formed from them. This is also suggested by the fact, (3) that the 28K molecule is not "processed" by prolonged R5020 treatment, as are the PR. (4) The 28K molecule binds [^{3}H]R5020 with 10-fold lower affinity than do PR, but the binding is entirely competed by excess unlabeled R5020 and by certain other synthetic progestins; however, it does not bind progesterone, or any nonprogestational steroid. It is possible that the natural endogenous ligand for this molecule is yet to be discovered, and tempting to speculate that 28K is analogous to the nuclear type II estrogen binding sites, whose natural ligand should soon be described (217).

D. BIOLOGICAL ACTIONS OF PROGESTINS IN T47D$_{co}$

As reviewed above, there is renewed interest in the use of synthetic progestins to treat men and women who have advanced breast cancer.

First, clinical results using pharmacologic progestin concentrations have been very encouraging. However, it is not known whether progestins act directly on the regressing tumors, or indirectly through other hormones. Second, PR are the single best marker for predicting both the hormone dependence of tumors, and the disease-free survival of patients. This has led to speculation that PR-rich tumors would be especially sensitive to progestin treatment. Third, in small series of studies, positive responses to progestins have been obtained in tumors that have failed to respond to, or have become resistant to antiestrogens or other endocrine therapies, or in tumors lacking (ER). This suggests that some of the mechanisms responsible for the antitumor effects of progestins and antiestrogens must differ.

There is little experimental evidence underlying any of these assumptions. It has been difficult to study the direct biological actions of progestins separate from those of estrogens, because estrogen priming is required to maintain elevated—and presumably functional—levels of PR. Thus, the contaminating presence of estradiol in the system under study has precluded accurate assessment of true progestin effects *in vivo,* and prevented separation of the progestational from the antiestrogenic properties of these hormones. Furthermore, for reasons that are not clear, progesterone action has been difficult to study *in vitro,* where conditions can usually be more carefully controlled. As a result, there are several established cell lines that contain estrogen-inducible PR, but in which direct responses to progesterone have not been demonstrable.

Since $T47D_{co}$ contain high levels of PR that are independent of estrogen controls, lack ER, and are antiestrogen resistant, they can be used in estrogen-free conditions, to assess the direct biological actions of progestins, distinct from their antiestrogenic ones. We find that progestins have multiple effects on these cells.

1. Lipid Accumulation and Ultrastructural Changes

R5020 stimulates lipid accumulation as shown by staining of cells with Oil Red O (Fig. 14). The effect is extremely heterogeneous, with some cells showing extensive lipid droplet formation and others showing no change when compared to untreated controls. Whether this heterogeneity reflects the PR distribution in these cells is not known. Judge and Chatterton had previously reported that progesterone stimulates incorporation of [^{14}C]acetate into triglycerides in T47D cells (218). Interestingly, the same effect occurs when the cells are treated with prolactin or growth hormone (219), suggesting that all these hormones influence a common pathway involved in lipid biosynthesis.

Electron micrographs show that R5020-treated cells contain large numbers of lipid droplets and other inclusions, which are not found in the

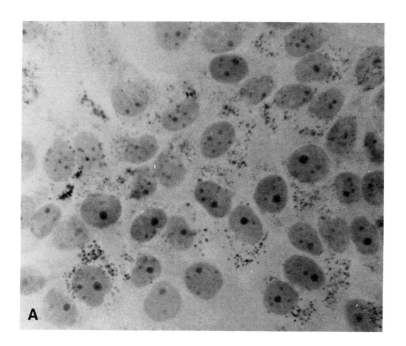

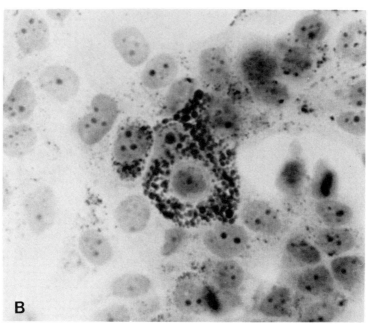

FIG. 14.   Staining of lipid droplets by Oil Red O in untreated and R5020 treated T47D$_{co}$. (A) Untreated cells. (B) Cells treated with 0.1 μM R5020 for 4 days (with thanks to G. J. Miller).

control cells. In addition, many R5020-treated cells are entirely filled with cytoskeletal elements, particularly bundles of tonofilaments (Fig. 15). We do not know the significance of this, although filamentous accumulation may be a sign of regressive and degenerative changes in amitotic or terminally differentiated cells. This may be the morphological reflection of the cytostatic or antipromotional effects of progestins described further below. It would be interesting to see if similar ultrastructural changes are seen in tumors regressing after progestin therapy.

2. Growth Inhibition of T47D$_{co}$ Cells

We have shown that, in the absence of estradiol or ER, physiologic concentrations of progestins directly inhibit proliferation of these anties-

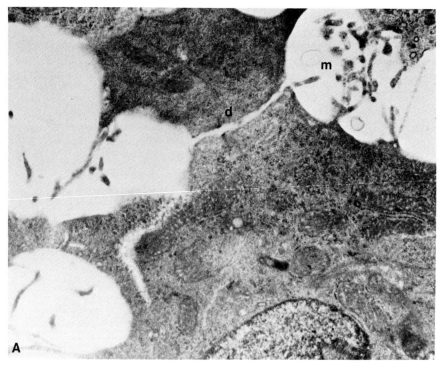

FIG. 15. The ultrastructure of untreated and R5020-treated T47D$_{co}$. (A) Control, untreated cell; showing epithelial morphology including desmosomes (d), microvilli (m), and unremarkable cytoplasmic organization. ×25,000. (B) Four day R5020-treated; showing lipid droplets surrounded by mitochondria; occasional tonofilaments (t). ×17,500. (C) Four day R5020-treated; showing some lipid droplets (1) and extensive tonofilament accumulation; tonofilaments are also seen in cross-section at left. ×25,000 (with thanks to L. E. Gerschenson)

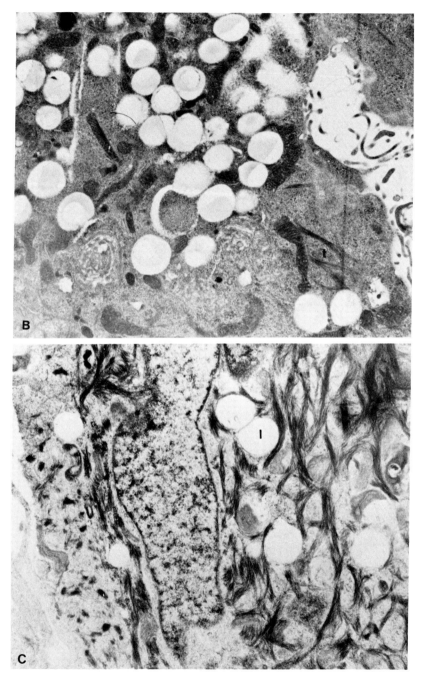

FIG. 15B,C.

trogen-resistant cells (220). Ten days of treatment with 1 or 10 nM R5020 suppresses cell growth approximately 50 to 60%, consistent with the concentrations that either partially (approximately 10%), or more extensively (>60%), translocate cytoplasmic PR; growth suppression by 0.1 μM R5020 is shown in Table VI. Even a brief 1-hour pulse of R5020 inhibits cell growth for at least 4 days which coincides with the time that PR replenishment is blocked (Fig. 16). Other synthetic progestins also inhibit cell growth, as does progesterone, whose effects are attenuated because, unlike the synthetic progestins, it is rapidly metabolized in the medium. At physiological concentrations (0.01 μM), estradiol, androgens, glucocorticoids, and 1,25-dihydroxyvitamin D_3 have no effect on cell growth. Our data indicate that the effects of progestins on mammary tumor cell proliferation can be direct, and independent of estrogen, and that antiestrogens and progestins can target different cell populations. This may explain the clinical efficacy of progestins in otherwise hormone-resistant tumors; the implications for endocrine therapy were outlined in Section IIC.

3. Progestins and Insulin Receptors

Cell proliferation in culture is under complex regulation involving not only exogenous factors added to the growth medium, but growth stimula-

TABLE VI

Effect of R5020 on Insulin Receptors and Cell Growth[a]

Treatment time (days)	[^{125}I]insulin bound (% per μg DNA)		DNA (μg/flask)	
	−R5020	+R5020	−R5020	+R5020
0	1.0	—	45	45
1	1.5	2.2	ND	ND
2	1.4	5.7	ND	ND
3	1.8	5.1	102	45
5	1.0	3.7	202	100
7	1.0	2.1	310	190
9	1.0	2.2	510	240

[a] Duplicate 75-cm^2 flasks were plated at a 1:5 ratio. Twenty-four hours later (day 0) cells were switched to medium containing charcoal-stripped insulin-free serum only, or with 0.1 μM R5020 added. Cells were fluid-changed daily. Cells from each flask were harvested separately after the treatment time shown. Four aliquots were taken for DNA analysis, and triplicate aliquots/flask were used for assay of specific insulin binding as described in Ref. (220). Binding was normalized to DNA content of the cells, and is shown as % insulin bound/μg DNA.

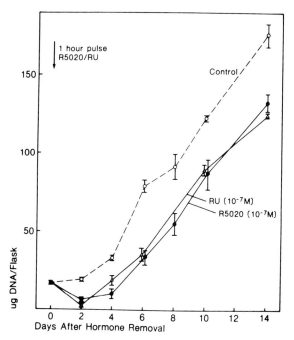

FIG. 16.   Chronic effect of a 1-hour pulse of R5020 or RU38 486 on $T47D_{co}$ proliferation. Cells were plated in 25-cm^2 flasks at a 1:7 split ratio. Twenty-four hours later (day 0), the medium was replaced for 1 hour with medium containing either 0.1 μM R5020 (●), RU38 486 (△), or hormone-free medium (○). The cell surface was then washed 3 times with RPMI and the cells were reincubated in hormone-free medium for 14 days. Flasks were fluid changed every 48 hours. At the indicated time points the cells from triplicate flasks were suspended in Ca^{2+}/Mg^{2+}-free Hanks'-EDTA and triplicate 1-ml aliquots/flask were taken for DNA analyses. Each point represents the average of 9 determinations ± SEM.

tory and inhibitory factors that can be synthesized by the cells themselves. Insulin is a common medium supplement and is required for the continuous serum-free growth of all human breast cancer cell lines in which it has been tested (221–223). Moreover, insulin and steroid hormones can reciprocally regulate each others actions (224–227). We have shown that in $T47D_{co}$ cells, progestins are among the heterologous hormones that regulate insulin receptor levels, an effect that seems to be closely related to the simultaneous cell-growth inhibition (220, and Table VI). In untreated cells, the number of insulin binding sites/cell increase slightly during the first round of cell division (days 1 to 3) then settle down to control levels. In contrast, during the first 3 days, when little if any growth is demonstrable in R5020-treated sets, the number of insulin binding sites/cell increases 4- to 5-fold and peaks on days 2 to 3. Thereafter, slow cell proliferation is paralleled by a fall in insulin receptor levels to about twice control values, where a new steady state is established.

Scatchard analysis shows that the increased binding is due to a real increase in the number of insulin binding sites/cell and not due to a change in binding affinity. At steady state (days 5 to 9) there are 18,000 insulin-binding sites/cell compared to 3000 in untreated cells (220).

To determine the hormone specificity of the increase in insulin receptors, cells were incubated for 5 days with several classes of steroid hormones or analogs, at concentrations sufficient to bind and translocate their respective receptors, but below pharmacological levels. The increase in insulin receptors was specific to R5020; neither estradiol nor dihydrotestosterone had any effect, consistent with reports in other systems. The synthetic glucocorticoid dexamethasone decreased the number of insulin binding sites by 50%. Glucocorticoids are known to modulate insulin receptor levels, and their effects are variable depending on the cell type and the conditions used in the studies. RU38 486, a synthetic steroid with antiglucocorticoid and antiprogestin actions (see below) had no effect on insulin receptor levels when it was added to the cells alone; together with R5020, it partially blocked receptor induction by R5020. We are testing the possibility that regulation of insulin receptors (or any other inducible protein) may be a useful marker to distinguish progestins from antiprogestins in T47D$_{co}$. Other hormones that had no effect on insulin receptors were 1,25-dihydroxyvitamin D$_3$ (0.1 μM), testosterone (10 nM), 21-hydroxyprogesterone (0.1 μM), and the antiestrogen nafoxidine (1 μM).

4. The Antiprogestin, RU38 486

Despite the theoretical promise of synthetic antiprogestational agents— as anticancer agents, as experimental tools, as mid-cycle contraceptives and implantation inhibitors—none has been available for either basic or clinical studies. However, a candidate antiprogestin, RU38 486 [17β-hydroxy-11β(4-dimethylaminophenyl)-17α-(1-propynl)-estra-4,9-dien-3-one] has recently been described that has antiprogestational and antiglucocorticoid activity in early clinical trials (228,229). Its mechanisms of action are unclear. Furthermore, development of this drug underscores an old bioassay problem: that biological screening of progestins and antiprogestins is complex because of the physiological requirement that progestational effects must be superimposed upon an estrogenized system. This has made it difficult to distinguish among progestational, antiprogestational, and antiestrogenic properties of unknown agents, a problem that can be entirely circumvented when T47D$_{co}$ are used for screening. These cells have therefore been used to contrast the agonist and antagonist actions of this interesting drug (220,230).

We find that like R5020, RU38 486 absorbs UV at approximately 300 nm, and this wavelength can be used to covalently photolink the drug to PR *in situ*. Like the synthetic progestin, low concentrations (10 nM) of [³H]RU38 486 bind two PR subunits in nuclei of T47D$_{co}$; glucocorticoid receptors are not bound. In competition studies, unlabeled RU38 486 is a potent inhibitor for *in situ* [³H]R5020 binding to both nuclear subunits A and B. RU38 486 has a high affinity for PR in vitro (K_d approximately 2 nM at 0–4°C) and in intact cells, low concentrations (6 to 8 nM) transform more than 95% of PR to a high-affinity nuclear binding state. Like the other synthetic progestins, the compound is not metabolized, so that it chronically (3 to 6 days) suppresses PR replenishment. These biochemical properties of RU38 486 are typical of synthetic progestins, and distinguish it from pure glucocorticoids. To bioassay RU38 486 both growth and insulin receptors were measured, with interesting results. RU38 486 is as potent as the other synthetic progestins in growth inhibition; as little as 1 nM concentration suppresses growth by 55%. When R5020 and RU38 486 are combined, cell growth remains inhibited. Since a 1-hour pulse of RU38 486 blocks receptor replenishment, we asked whether this would have a long-term effect on cell growth. As Fig. 16 shows, compared to hormone-free controls, the growth of 1 hour RU38 486-pulsed cells is suppressed for at least 4 days, after which the cells resumed growth at a rate similar to that of the controls. Other synthetic progestins are similarly long acting, as shown here for R5020.

Thus, using cell growth as a biological marker, we would conclude that RU38 486 has agonist progestin-like properties, with no evidence of antagonist effects. This is, however, not the case when the biological endpoint measured is the level of insulin receptors. T47D$_{co}$ were incubated 60 hours with medium containing R5020 alone, RU38 486 alone, or the two hormones together. R5020 increased the number of insulin binding sites as expected, but RU38 486 at concentrations sufficient to translocate PR and alter cell growth rate, had no effect on these proteins. When the two hormones were added to cells together, RU38 486 blocked 20 to 50% of the R5020-induced increase, depending on the concentration of each hormone. Thus, if insulin receptor levels are used as a biological marker, RU38 486 displays some of the properties expected of an antagonist (230).

The dual action of RU38 486 is a classic property of synthetic steroid antagonists, and it is likely that *in vivo* RU38 486 will prove to have similar biphasic effects. Its actions as an antiglucocorticoid in some systems may well prove to be due to its progestational nature since pharmacologic levels of progestins have been known for more than a decade to antagonize glucocorticoid action by binding to GR.

Undoubtedly, RU38 486 is only the first in a long line of steroidal analogs that, in the next few years, will be synthesized and found to have clinically useful antiprogestational activity. The problems with past biological screening methods have been 2-fold. First, it has been difficult to find markers that distinguish between progestin and antiprogestin actions; and second, it has been impossible to demonstrate pure and direct progestin and/or antiprogestin effects in systems that, of necessity, also contain estradiol. We propose that T47D$_{co}$ may be used to circumvent both problems.

VI. Summary and Future Prospects

The model in Fig. 17 schematically summarizes some of our data dealing with the role of progestins and PR structure in T47D$_{co}$ cells. The availability of these cells for studies of human PR biochemistry and function comes at a time when we are emerging from the technological dol-

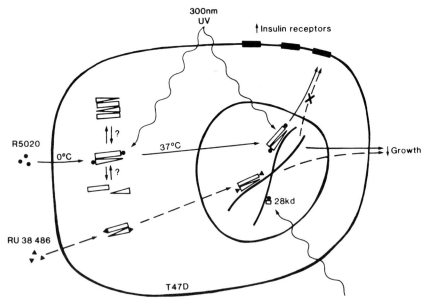

FIG. 17. Schematic representation of the progestin effects studied in T47D$_{co}$. *In situ* photoaffinity labeling with 300 nm UV demonstrates two progestin-binding proteins in either cytosols or nuclei of the cells, depending on the hormone incubation temperature. How the two proteins are organized into the native holoreceptors is unknown. UV irradiation also covalently links progestins to a nuclear 28-kDa progestin-binding protein of unknown function; the protein is unrelated to PR. Progestins can inhibit growth and increase insulin receptors, but the antiprogestin RU38 486 can only effect growth; it antagonizes insulin receptor stimulation.

drums that stifled steroid–receptor research for half a decade. Although ligand binding assays provided the critical impetus for the large and innovative body of work on steroid receptors that appeared in the early 1970s, the limitations of these assays were becoming evident by the end of the decade. The pace of research did not resume until new methods in molecular biology, and the availability of covalent ligands, provided the technological tools that have led to the recent spate of papers dealing with receptor purification, structure, and antibody production. The availability of these reagents now virtually assures (1) that receptors will be purified to homogeneity and then sequenced, and that the messages for these proteins will be isolated, and their genes cloned. (2) *In vitro* translation assays and expression vectors will be used to search for proreceptors and to study posttranslational modification. We will find that the primary proteins are chemically modified in several ways, and that reversible changes influence receptor activation and processing. (3) We will find unexpected functions for receptors and receptor-like proteins, possibly unrelated to hormone binding, forcing us in some cases to dispense with the word "receptor." (4) The accurate description of receptor structure will lead very quickly to deduction of the evolutionary relationships among these proteins. Conserved structural features for all steroid receptors will suggest that they share functional homologies, especially for intranuclear sites of action. (5) We predict, based on the position of progesterone in the metabolic scheme of steroid hormones, that PR are the ancestral receptors, and that at least two structurally different subunits will be demonstrated for all steroid receptors. (6) Our historic forebears found hormones first and their receptors later; this sequence will be reversed, and strange receptors will be discovered before their natural ligands are known. (7) This prompts the question: Is there a natural antagonist for every steroid hormone? (8) And finally, what about steroids and cancer? We suspect that the link among epidermal growth factor receptors, insulin receptors, and PR is not accidental. At this time there are reports (231) of the fusion of MMTV regulatory sequences containing a receptor binding element, to the coding sequence of the *c-myc* gene. Transgenic female mice bearing this fusion gene develop hormone-promoted breast cancers.

ACKNOWLEDGMENTS

We are grateful to the NIH, the NSF, and the National Foundation for Cancer Research who supported the studies from our laboratory described here. Dr. Horwitz holds a Research Career Development Award from the NCI. The expert past and present technical work of Sue Alexander, Rebecca Sheridan, and Mary Francis is also acknowledged, as is the secretarial help of Linda Babcock.

REFERENCES

1. Horwitz, K. B., McGuire, W. L., Pearson, O. H., and Segaloff, A. (1975). *Science* **189**, 726–727.
2. Horwitz, K. B., and McGuire, W. L. (1975). *Steroids* **25**, 497–505.
3. Clark, G. M., McGuire, W. L., Hubay, C. A., Pearson, O. H., and Marshall, J. S. (1983). *NEJM* **309**, 1343–1347.
4. Houdebine, L. M., Teyssot, B., Devinoy, E., Olliver-Bousguet, M., Djiane, J., Kelly, P. A., Deloris, C., Kann, G., and Fevre, J. (1983). *In* "Progesterone and Progestins" (C. W. Bardin, E. Milgrom, and P. Mauvais-Jarvis, eds.), pp. 297–319. Raven, New York.
5. Reyniak, J. V. (1978). *In* "The Breast" (H. S. Gallager, H. P. Leis, Jr., R. K. Snyderman, and J. A. Urban, eds.), pp. 23–32. Mosby, St. Louis.
6. Huggins, C., Briziarelli, G., and Sutton, H., Jr. (1959). *J. Exp. Med.* **109**, 25–42.
7. Lacassagne, A. (1932). *C.R. Acad.* **195**, 630.
8. Huggins, C., Moon, R. C., and Morii, S. (1962). *Proc. Natl. Acad. Sci. U.S.A.* **48**, 379–386.
9. Jabara, A. G. (1967). *Br. J. Cancer* **21**, 418–429.
10. McCormick, G. M., and Moon, R. C. (1973). *Eur. J. Cancer* **9**, 483–486.
11. Jabara, A. G., Marks, G. N., Summers, J. E., and Anderson, P. S. (1979). *Br. J. Cancer* **40**, 268–273.
12. Welsch, C. W., Clemens, J. A., and Meites, J. (1968). *J. Natl. Cancer Inst.* **41**, 465–471.
13. Kledzik, G. S., Bradley, C. J., and Meites, J. (1974). *Cancer Res.* **34**, 2953–2956.
14. Gottardis, M., Erturk, E., and Rose, D. P. (1983). *Eur. J. Cancer Clin. Oncol.* **19**, 1479–1484.
15. Jabara, A. G., Toyne, P. H., and Fisher, R. J. (1972). *Br. J. Cancer* **26**, 265–273.
16, Horwitz, K. B., and McGuire, W. L. (1977). *Cancer Res.* **37**, 1733–1738.
17. Asselin, J., Kelly, P. A., Caron, M. G., and Labrie, F. (1977). *Endocrinology* **101**, 666–671.
18. Danguy, A., Legros, N., Devleeschouwer, N., Heuson-Stennon, J. A., and Heuson, J. C. (1980). *In* "Role of Medroxyprogesterone in Endocrine-related Tumors" (S. Iacobelli and A. DiMarco, eds.), pp. 21–28. Raven, New York.
19. Joly, E., Vignon, F., and Rochefort, H. (1981). *Breast Cancer Res. Treat.* **1**, 381–389.
20. Nicholson, R. I., and Boyns, A. R. (1974). *J. Endocrinol.* **63**, 57.
21. Leung, B. S., and Sasaki, G. H. (1973). *Biochem. Biophys. Res. Commun.* **55**, 1180–1187.
22. Beatson, G. T. (1896). *Lancet* **ii**, 104–107.
23. Escher, G. C., Heber, J. M., Woodard, H. Q., Farrow, J. H., and Adair, F. E. (1951). *Symp. Steroids Exp. Clin. Practice* pp. 375–402.
24. Muggia, F. M., Cassileth, P. A., Ochoa, M., Jr., Flatow, F. A., Gellhorn, A., and Hyman, G. A. (1968). *Ann. Intern. Med.* **68**, 328–337.
25. Goldenberg, I. S. (1969). *Cancer* **23**, 109–112.
26. Jones, V., Joslin, C. A. F., Jones, R. E., Davies, D. K. L., Robests, M. M., Gleave, E. N., Campbell, H. F., and Forrest, A. P. M. (1971). *Lancet* **i**, 1049–1050.
27. Edelstyn, G. A. (1973). *Cancer* **32**, 1317–1320.
28. Ansfield, F. J., Davis, H. L., Jr., Ellerby, R. A., and Ramirez, G. (1974). *Cancer* **33**, 907–910.
29. Rubens, R. D., Knight, R. K., and Hayward, J. L. (1976). *Eur. J. Cancer* **12**, 563–565.

30. Klaassen, D. J., Rapp, E. F., and Histe, W. E. (1976). *Cancer Treat. Rep.* **60**, 251–253.
31. Ansfield, E. J., Davis, H. J., Jr., Ramirez, G., Davis, T. E., Borden, E. C., Johnson, R. O., and Bryan, G. T. (1976). *Cancer* **38**, 53–55.
32. Teulings, F. A. G., van Gilse, H. A., Henkelman, M. S., Portengen, H., and Alexieva-Figusch, J. (1980). *Cancer Res.* **40**, 2557–2561.
33. Alexieva-Figusch, J., van Gilse, H. A., Hop, W. C. J., Phoa, C. H., Blonk-van der Wijst, J., and Treurniet, R. E. (1980). *Cancer* **46**, 2369–2372.
34. Ross, M. B., Buzdar, A. U., and Blumenschein, G. R. (1982). *Cancer* **49**, 413–417.
35. Clavel, B., Pichon, M. F., Pallud, C., and Milgrom, E. (1982). *Eur. J. Cancer Clin. Oncol.* **18**, 821–826.
36. Johnson, P. A., Bonomi, P. D., Anderson, K. M., Wolter, J. M., Bacon, L. D., Rossof, A. H., and Economou, S. G. (1983). *Cancer Treat. Rep.* **67**, 717–720.
37. Alexieva-Figusch, J., Blankenstein, M. A., Hop, W. C. J., Klijn, J. G. M., Lamberts, S. W. J., DeJong, F. H., Docter, R., Adlercreutz, H., and van Gilse, H. A. (1984). *Eur. J. Cancer Clin. Oncol.* **20**, 33–40.
38. Pannuti, F., Martoni, A., Lenaz, G. R., Diana, E., and Nanni, P. (1978). *Cancer Treat. Rep.* **62**, 499–504.
39. Mattsson, W. (1978). *Acta Radiol. Oncol.* **17**, 387–400.
40. DeLena, M., Brambilla, C., Valagussa, P., and Bonadonna, G. (1979). *Cancer Chemother. Pharmacol.* **2**, 175–180.
41. Mattsson, W. (1980). *In* "Role of Medroxyprogesterone in Endocrine-Related Tumors" (S. Iacobelli and A. Di Marco, eds.), pp. 65–71. Raven, New York.
42. Madrigal, P. L., Alonso, A., Manga, G. P., and Modrego, S. P. (1980). *In* "Role of Medroxyprogesterone in Endocrine-Related Tumors" (S. Iacobelli and A. Di Marco, eds.), pp. 93–96. Raven, New York.
43. Izuo, M., Iino, Y., and Endo, K. (1981). *Breast Cancer Res. Treat.* **1**, 125–130.
44. Morgan, L. R., Donley, P. J., and Savage, J. (1983). *Proc. Am. Assoc. Cancer. Res.* **24**, 134, Abst. 529.
45. Pannuti, F., Gentili, M. R. A., DiMarco, A. R., Martoni, A., Giambiasi, M. E., Battistoni, R., Camaggi, C. M., Burroni, P., Strocchi, E., Iafelice, G., Piana, E., and Murari, G. (1983). *In* "Role of Medroxyprogesterone in Endocrine-Related Tumors" (L. Campio, G. Robustelli Della Cuna, and R. W. Taylor, eds.), Vol. 2, pp. 95–104. Raven, New York.
46. Funes, H. C., Madrigal, P. L., Mangas, G. P., and Mendiola, C. (1983). *In* "Role of Medroxyprogesterone in Endocrine-Related Tumors" (L. Campio, G. Robustelli Della Cuna, and R. W. Taylor, eds.), Vol. 2, pp. 77–83. Raven, New York.
47. Cavalli, F., Goldhirsch, A., Jungi, F., Martz, G., Alberto, P. for the Swiss group for Clinical Cancer Research (SAKK) (1983). *In* "Role of Medroxyprogesterone in Endocrine-Related Tumors" (L. Campio, G. Robustelli Della Cuna, and R. W. Taylor, eds.), Vol. 2, pp. 69–75. Raven, New York.
48. Horwitz, K. B., and McGuire, W. L. (1978). *In* "Breast Cancer: Modern Approaches to Therapy and Research (W. L. McGuire, ed.), Vol. 2, pp. 155–204. Plenum, New York.
49. Morgan, L. R., and Donley, P. J. (1980). *Rev. Endocrine Related Cancer Suppl.* **9**, 301–310.
50. Ingle, J. N., Ahmann, D. L., Green, S. J., Edmonson, J. H., Creagan, E. T., Hahn, R. G., and Rubin, J. (1982). *Am. J. Clin. Oncol.* **5**, 155–160.
51. Pannuti, F., Martoni, A., Fruet, F., Burroni, P., Canova, N., and Hall, S. (1982). *In*

302 KATHRYN B. HORWITZ ET AL.

"The Role of Tamoxifen in Breast Cancer" (S. Iacobelli, ed.), pp. 85–92. Raven, New York.

52. Johnson, P. A., Bonomi, P. D., Wolter, J. M., Anderson, K. M., Economou, S. G., and DePeyster, F. A. (1983). *Proc. Am. Assoc. Cancer Res.* **24,** 172, Abstr. 680.

53. Van Veelen, H., Roding, T. J., Schweitzer, M. J. H., Sleijfer, D. T., Tjabbes, T., and Willemse, P. H. B. (1983). *J. Steroid Biochem.* **19,** (Suppl.), 86, Abstr. 259.

54. Alexieva-Figusch, J., Klijn, J. G. M., Blonk-van der Wijst, J., and van Putten, W. L. J. (1983). *J. Steroid Biochem.* **19,** (Suppl.), 87, Abstr. 260.

55. Horwitz, K. B., Koseki, Y., and McGuire, W. L. (1978). *Endocrinology* **103,** 1742–1751.

56. Namer, M., Lalanne, C., and Baulieu, E. E. (1980). *Cancer Res.* **40,** 1750–1752.

57. Waseda, N., Kato, Y., Imura, H., and Kurata, M. (1981). *Cancer Res.* **41,** 1984–1988.

58. Mouridsen, H. T., Ellemann, K., Mattsson, W., Palshof, T., Daehnfeldt, J. L., and Rose, C. (1979). *Cancer Treat. Rep.* **63,** 171–175.

59. Forastiere, A. A., Braun, T. J., Wittes, R. E., Hakes, T. B., and Kaufman, R. J. (1981). *Int. Congr. Chemother., 12th, Florence July 19–24* Abstr. 265.

60. Trodella, L., Ausilli-Cefaro, G. P., Turriziani, A., Saccheri, S., Venturo, I., and Minotti, G. (1982). *Am. J. Clin. Oncol.* **5,** 495–499.

61. Bruno, M., Roldan, E., and Diaz, B. (1983). *J. Steroid Biochem.* **19,** (Suppl.), 87, Abstr. 261.

62. Garcia-Giralt, E., Jouve, M., Palangie, T., Bretandeau, B., Magdelenat, H., Asselain, B., and Pouillart, P. (1984). *Proc. Am. Soc. Clin. Oncol.* **3,** 129, Abstr. C-504.

63. Link, H., Ruckle, H., Waller, H. D., and Wilms, K. (1981). *Dtsch. Med. Wochenschr.* **106,** 1260–1262.

64. Tormey, D. C., Falkston, G., Crowley, J., Falkson, H. C., Voelkel, J., and Davis, T. E. (1982). *Am. J. Clin. Oncol.* **5,** 33–39.

65. Krook, J. E., Ingle, J. N., Green, S. J., and Bowman, W. D., Jr. (1983). *Proc. Am. Soc. Clin. Oncol.* **2,** 106.

66. Cocconi, G., DeLisi, V., Boni, C., Mori, P., Malacarne, P., Amadori, D., and Giovanelli, E. (1983). *Cancer* **51,** 581–588.

67. Stott, P. B., Zelkowitz, L., and Tucker, W. G. (1973). *Cancer Chemother. Rep.* **57,** 106, Abstr. 66.

68. Brunner, K. W., Sonntag, R. W., Alberto, P., Senn, H. J., Martz, G., Obrecht, P., and Maurice, P. (1977). *Cancer* **39,** 2923–2933.

69. Buzdar, A. U., Tashima, C. K., Blumenschein, G. R., Hortobagyi, G. N., Yap, H. Y., Krutchik, A. N., Bodey, G. P., and Livingston, R. B. (1978). *Cancer* **41,** 392–395.

70. Rubens, R. D., Begent, R. H. J., Knight, R. K., Sexton, S. A., and Hayward, J. L. (1978). *Cancer* **42,** 1680–1686.

71. Robustelli Della Cuna, G., and Bernardo-Strada, M. R. (1980). *In* "Role of Medroxyprogesterone in Endocrine-Related Tumors" (S. Iacobelli and A. DiMarco, eds.), pp. 53–64. Raven, New York.

72. Wander, H. E., Bartsch, H. H., Blossey, H. C., and Nagel, G. A. (1983). *In* "Role of Medroxyprogesterone in Endocrine-Related Tumors" (L. Campio, G. Robustelli Della Cuna, and R. W. Taylor, eds.), Vol. 2, pp. 85–93. Raven, New York.

73. Pellegrini, A., Massidda, B., Mascia, V., Lippi, M. G., Ionta, M. T., Muggiano, A., and Carboni-Boi, E. (1980). *In* "Role of Medroxyprogesterone in Endocrine-Related Tumors" (S. Iacobelli and A. DiMarco, eds.), Vol. 2, pp. 29–51. Raven, New York.

74. Robustelli Della Cuna, G., Cuzzoni, Q., Preti, P., and Bernardo, G. (1983). *In* "Role of Medroxyprogesterone in Endocrine-related Tumors" (L. Campio, G. Robustelli Della Cuna, and R. W. Taylor, eds.), Vol. 2, pp. 131–140. Raven, New York.

75. Wils, J., Borst, A., Bron, H., and Scheerder, H. (1983). *J. Steroid Biochem.* **19**, (Suppl.), 85s.

76. Jensen, E. V., Block, G. E., Smith, S., Kyser, K., and DeSombre, E. R. (1971). *Natl. Cancer Inst. Monogr.* **34**, 55–70.

77. McGuire, W. L. (1980). *In* "Hormones and Cancer" (S. Iacobelli *et al.*, eds.), pp. 337–343. Raven, New York.

78. Matsumoto, K., Ochi, H., Nomura, Y., Takatani, O., Izuo, M., Okamoto, R., and Sugano, H. (1978). *In* "Hormones, Receptors and Breast Cancer" (W. L. McGuire, ed.), pp. 43–58. Raven, New York.

79. Bloom, N. D., Tobin, E., Schreibman, B., and Degenshein, G. A. (1980). *Cancer* **45**, 2992–2997.

80. von Maillot, K., Gentsch, H. H., and Gunselmann, W. (1980). *J. Cancer Res. Clin. Oncol.* **98**, 301–313.

81. Degenshein, G. A., Bloom, N., and Tobin, E. (1980). *Cancer* **46**, 2789–2793.

82. Manni, A., Arafah, B., and Pearson, O. H. (1980). *Cancer* **46**, 2838–2841.

83. Osborne, C. K., Yochmowitz, M. G., Knight, W. A., III, and McGuire, W. L. (1980). *Cancer* **46**, 2884–2888.

84. King, R. J. B. (1980). *Cancer* **46**, 2818–2821.

85. McCarty, K. S., Jr., Cox, C., Silva, J. S., Woodard, B. H., Mossler, J. A., Haagensen, D. E., Jr., Barton, T. K., McCarty, K. S., Sr., and Wells, S. A., Jr. (1980). *Cancer* **46**, 2846–2850.

86. Nomura, Y., Takatani, O., Sugano, H., and Matsumoto, K. (1980). *J. Steroid Biochem.* **13**, 565–566.

87. Skinner, L. G., Barnes, D. M., and Ribeiro, G. G. (1980). *Cancer* **46**, 2939–2945.

88. Young, P. C. M., Ehrlich, C. E., and Einhorn, L. H. (1980). *Cancer* **46**, 2961–2963.

89. Holdaway, I. M., and Skinner, S. J. M. (1981). *Eur. J. Cancer Clin. Oncol.* **17**, 1295–1300.

90. Sarrif, A. M., and Durant, J. R. (1981). *Cancer* **48**, 1215–1220.

91. Pichon, M.-F., Pallud, C., Brunet, M., and Milgrom, E. (1980). *Cancer Res.* **40**, 3357–3360.

92. Saez, S., Pichon, M. F., Cheix, F., Mayer, M., Pallud, C., Brunet, M., and Milgrom, E. (1983). *In* "Progesterone and Progestins" (C. W. Bardin, E. Milgrom, and P. Mauvais-Jarvis, eds.), pp. 355–366. Raven, New York.

93. Saez, S., Cheix, F., and Asselain, B. (1983). *Breast Cancer Res. Treat.* **3**, 345–354.

94. Schuchter, L., Bitran, J., Rochman, H., Desser, R. K., Michael, A., and Recant, W. (1984). *Proc. Am. Soc. Clin. Oncol.* **3**, 111, Abstr. 432.

95. Stewart, J. F., Rubens, R. D., Millis, R. R., King, R. J. B., and Hayward, J. L. (1983). *Eur. J. Cancer Clin. Oncol.* **19**, 1381–1387.

96. Nordeen, S. K., Lan, N. C., Showers, M. O., and Baxter, J. D. (1981). *J. Biol. Chem.* **256**, 10503–10508.

97. Simons, S., Jr., and Thompson, E. B. (1981). *Proc. Natl. Acad. Sci. U.S.A.* **78**, 3541–3545.

98. Eisen, H., Schleenbaker, R. E., and Simons, S. S. (1981). *J. Biol. Chem.* **256**, 12920–12925.

99. Carlstedt-Duke, J., Okret, S., Wrange, O., and Gustafsson, J.-A. (1982). *Proc. Natl. Acad. Sci. U.S.A.* **79**, 4260–4264.

100. Yamamoto, K. R., Stampfer, M. R., and Tomkins, G. M. (1974). *Proc. Natl. Acad. Sci. U.S.A.* **71**, 3901–3905.

101. Gruol, D. J., Kempner, E. S., and Bourgeois, S. (1984). *J. Biol. Chem.* **259**, 4833–4839.

102. Norris, J. S., and Kohler, P. O. (1983). *J. Biol. Chem.* **258**, 2350–2356.
103. Vedeckis, W. V. (1983). *Biochemistry* **22**, 1983–1989.
104. Sherman, M. R., Moran, M. C., Tuazon, F. B., and Stevens, Y. W. (1983). *J. Biol. Chem.* **258**, 10366–10377.
105. Wilson, E. M., and French, F. S. (1979). *J. Biol. Chem.* **254**, 6310–6319.
106. Lea, O. A., Wilson, E. M., and French, F. S. (1979). *Endocrinology* **105**, 1350–1360.
107. Chang, C. H., and Tindall, D. J. (1983). *Endocrinology* **113**, 1486–1493.
108. Wieland, S. J., and Fox, T. O. (1979). *Cell* **17**, 781–787.
109. Fox, T. O., and Wieland, S. J. (1983). *Endocrinology* **109**, 790–797.
110. Katzenellenbogen, J. A., Carlson, K. E., Heiman, D. F., Robertson, D. W., Wei, L. L., and Katzenellenbogen, B. S. (1983). *J. Biol. Chem.* **258**, 3487–3495.
111. Oosbree, T., Kim, U. H., and Mueller, G. C. (1984). *Anal. Biochem.* **136**, 321–327.
112. Sica, V., and Bresciani, F. (1979). *Biochemistry* **18**, 2369–2378.
113. Redeuilh, G., Secco, C., Bauleiu, E.-E., and Richard-Foy, M. (1981). *J. Biol. Chem.* **256**, 11496–11502.
114. Monsma, F. J., Katzenellenbogen, B. S., Miller, M. A., Ziegler, Y. S., and Katzenellenbogen, J. A. (1984). *Endocrinology* **115**, 143–153.
115. Kon, O. L., Webster, R. A., and Spelsberg, T. C. (1980). *Endocrinology* **107**, 1182–1191.
116. Ericksson, M., Upchurch, S., Hardin, J. W., Peck, E. J., and Clark, J. H. (1978). *Biochem. Biophys. Res. Commun.* **81**, 1–7.
117. Al-Nuaimi, N., Davis, P., and Griffiths, K. (1979). *J. Endocrinol.* **81**, 119–130.
118. Sherman, M., and Stevens, J. (1984). *Annu. Rev. Physiol.* **46**, 83–105.
119. Schrader, W. T., Birnbaumer, M., Hughes, M. R., Weigel, N., Grody, W., and O'Malley, B. (1981). *Recent Prog. Horm. Res.* **37**, 583–633.
120. Gschwendt, M. (1980). *Mol. Cell. Endocrinol.* **19**, 57–67.
121. Dure, L. S., Schrader, W. T., and O'Malley, B. W. (1980). *Nature (London)* **283**, 784–786.
122. Maggi, A., Schrader, W. T., and O'Malley, B. W. (1984). *J. Biol. Chem.* **259**, 10956–10966.
123. Birnbaumer, M., Schrader, W. T., and O'Malley, B. W. (1983). *J. Biol. Chem.* **258**, 7331–7337.
124. Gronemeyer, H., Harry, P., and Chambon, P. (1983). *FEBS Lett.* **156**, 287–292.
125. Edwards, D. P., Weigel, N. L., Schrader, W. I., O'Malley, B. W., and McGuire, W. L. (1984). *Biochemistry* **23**, 4427–4435.
126. Sherman, M. R., Atienza, S. B. P., Shansky, J. R., and Hoffman, L. M. (1974). *J. Biol. Chem.* **249**, 5351–5363.
127. Birnbaumer, M., Schrader, W. T., and O'Malley, B. W. (1983). *J. Biol. Chem.* **255**, 1637–1644.
128. Weigel, N. L., March, C. J., Schrader, W. T., and O'Malley, B. W. (1983). *Endocrine Soc. Abstr.* No. 576, p. 224.
129. Birnbaumer, M. E., Schrader, W. T., and O'Malley, B. W. (1979). *Biochemistry* **181**, 201–213.
130. Dougherty, J. J., and Toft, D. O. (1982). *J. Biol. Chem.* **257**, 3113–3119.
131. Puri, R. F., Grandics, P., Dougherty, J. J., and Toft, D. O. (1982). *J. Biol. Chem.* **257**, 10831–10837.
132. Renoir, J. M., Yang, C. R., Formstecher, P., Hustenberger, P., Wolfson, A., Redeuilh, G., Mester, J., Richard-Foy, H., and Baulieu, E.-E. (1982). *Eur. J. Biochem.* **127**, 71–79.

133. Birnbaumer, M., Bell, R. C., Schrader, W. T., and O'Malley, B. W. (1984). *J. Biol. Chem.* **259**, 1091–1098.
134. Smith, R. G., d'Istria, M., and Van, N. T. (1981). *Biochemistry* **20**, 5557–5565.
135. Holmes, S. D., Van, N. T., Stevens, S., and Smith, R. G. (1981). *Endocrinology* **109**, 670–672.
136. Lessey, B. A., Alexander, P. S., and Horwitz, K. B. (1983). *Endocrinology* **112**, 1267–1274.
137. Horwitz, K. B., and Alexander, P. S. (1983). *Endocrinology* **113**, 2195–2201.
138. Raam, S., Nemeth, E., Tamura, H., O'Brian, D. S., and Cohen, J. L. (1982). *Eur. J. Cancer Clin. Oncol.* **18**, 1–12.
139. Coffer, A. I., and King, R. J. B. (1981). *J. Steroid Biochem.* **14**, 1229–1235.
140. Jungblut, P. W., Hekim, N., Meyer, H. H. D., and Szendro, P. I. (1983). *J. Steroid Biochem.* **19**, 87–94.
141. Green, G. L., Class, L. E., Fleming, H., DeSombre, E. R., and Jensen, E. V. (1979). *J. Steroid Biochem.* **11**, 333–341.
142. Greene, G. L., Fitch, F. W., and Jensen, E. V. (1980). *Proc. Natl. Acad. Sci. U.S.A.* **77**, 157–161.
143. Moncharmont, B., Su, J. L., and Parikh, I. (1982). *Biochemistry* **21**, 6916–6921.
144. Greene, G. L., Nolan, C., Engler, J. P., and Jensen, E. V. (1980). *Proc. Natl. Acad. Sci. U.S.A.* **77**, 5115–5119.
145. Tate, A. C., DeSombre, E. R., Greene, G. L., Jensen, E. V., and Jordan, V. C. (1983). *Breast Cancer Res. Treat.* **3**, 267–277.
146. Tate, A. C., Greene, G. L., DeSombre, E. R., Jensen, E. V., and Jordan, V. C. (1984). *Cancer Res.* **44**, 1012–1018.
147. Garcia, M., Greene, G., Rochefort, H., and Jensen, E. V. (1982). *Endocrinology* **110**, 1355–1361.
148. Borgna, J. L., Fauque, J., and Rochefort, H. (1984). *Biochemistry* **23**, 2162–2168.
149. King, W. J., and Greene, G. L. (1984). *Nature (London)* **307**, 745–747.
150. Welshons, M. V., Lieberman, M. E., and Gorski, J. (1984). *Nature (London)* **307**, 747–749.
151. Eisen, H. J., Schleenbaker, R. E., and Simons, S. S. (1981). *J. Biol. Chem.* **256**, 12920–12925.
152. Govindan, M. V. (1979). *J. Steroid Biochem.* **11**, 323–332.
153. Eisen, H. J. (1980). *Proc. Natl. Acad. Sci. U.S.A.* **77**, 3893–3897.
154. Okret, S., Carlstedt-Duke, J., Wrange, O., Carlstrom, K., and Gustafsson, J.-A. (1981). *Biochim. Biophys. Acta* **677**, 205–219.
155. Carlstedt-Duke, J., Okret, S., Wrange, O., and Gustafsson, J.-A. (1982). *Proc. Natl. Acad. Sci. U.S.A.* **79**, 4260–4264.
156. Grandics, P., Gasser, D. L., and Litwack, G. (1982). *Endocrinology* **111**, 1731–1733.
157. Okret, S., Wikstrom, A. C., Wrange, O., Andersson, B., and Gustafsson, J. A. (1984). *Proc. Natl. Acad. Sci. U.S.A.* **81**, 1609–1613.
158. Weigel, N. L., Pousette, A., Schrader, W. T., and O'Malley, B. W. (1981). *Biochemistry* **20**, 6798–6803.
159. Renoir, J. M., Radanyi, C., Yang, C. R., and Baulieu, E. E. (1982). *Eur. J. Biochem.* **127**, 81–86.
160. Radanyi, C., Joab, I., Renoir, J. M., Richard-Foy, H., and Baulieu, E. E. (1983). *Proc. Natl. Acad. Sci. U.S.A.* **80**, 2854–2858.
161. Renoir, J. M., and Mester, J. (1984). *Mol. Cell. Endocrinol.* **37**, 1–13.
162. Joab, I., Radanyi, C., Renoir, J. M., Buchou, T., Catelli, M. G., Binart, N., Mester, J., and Baulieu, E. E. (1984). *Nature (London)* **308**, 850–853.

163. Tuohimaa, P., Renoir, J. M., Radanyi, C., Mester, J., Joab, I., Buchou, T., and Baulieu, E. E. (1984). *Biochem. Biophys. Res. Commun.* **119**, 433–439.
164. Zarucki-Schulz, T., Kulomaa, M. S., Headon, D. R., Weigel, N. L., Baez, M., Edwards, D. P., McGuire, W. L., and O'Malley, B. W. (1984). Proc. Natl. Acad. Sci. U.S.A. **81**:6358–6362.
165. Logeat, F., Hai, M. T. V., and Milgrom, E. (1981). *Proc. Natl. Acad. Sci. U.S.A.* **78**, 1426–1430.
166. Logeat, F., Hai, M. T. V., Fournier, A., Legrain, P., Buttin, G., and Milgrom, E. (1983). *Proc. Natl. Acad. Sci. U.S.A.* **80**, 6456–6459.
167. Nielsen, C. J., Sando, J. J., and Pratt, W. B. (1977). *Proc. Natl. Acad. Sci. U.S.A.* **74**, 1398–1402.
168. Grody, W. W., Compton, J. G., Schrader, W. T., and O'Malley, B. W. (1980). *J. Steroid Biochem.* **12**, 115–120.
169. Auricchio, F., Migliaccio, A., and Rotondi, A. (1981). *Biochem. J.* **194**, 569–574.
170. Kurl, R. N., and Jacob, S. T. (1984). *Biochem. Biophys. Res. Commun.* **119**, 700–705.
171. Weigel, N. L., Tash, J. S., Means, A. R., Schrader, W. T., and O'Malley, B. W. (1981). *Biochem. Biophys. Res. Comm.* **102**, 513–519.
172. Dahmer, M. K., Housley, P. R., and Pratt, W. B. (1984). *Annu. Rev. Physiol.* **46**, 67–81.
173. Auricchio, F., Migliaccio, A., Castoria, G., Lastoria, S., and Rotondi, A. (1982). *Biochem. Biophys. Res. Commun.* **106**, 149–157.
174. Auricchio, F., Migliaccio, A., Castoria, G., Rotondi, A., and Lastoria, S. (1984). *J. Steroid Biochem.* **20**, 31–35.
175. Ghosh-Dastidar, P., Coty, W. A., Griest, R. E., Woo, D. D., and Fox, C. F. (1984). *Proc. Natl. Acad. Sci. U.S.A.* **81**, 1654–1658.
176. Garcia, T., Tuohimaa, P., Mester, J., Buchon, T., Renoir, J.-M., and Baulieu, E.-E. (1983). *Biochem. Biophys. Res. Commun.* **113**, 960–966.
177. Dougherty, J. J., Puri, R. K., and Toft, D. O. (1982). *J. Biol. Chem.* **257**, 14226–14230.
178. Masiakowski, P., Breathnach, R., Bloch, J., Gannon, F., Kriest, A., and Chambon, P. (1982). *Nucleic Acids Res.* **10**, 7895–7903.
179. Chalbos, D., Vignon, F., Keydar, I., and Rochefort, H. (1982). *J. Clin. Endocrinol. Metab.* **55**, 276–283.
180. Adams, D. J., Hajj, H., Bitor, K. G., Edwards, D. P., and McGuire, W. L. (1983). *Endocrinology* **113**, 415–417.
181. Iacobelli, S., Scambia, G., Natoli, V., and Sica, G. (1984). *J. Steroid Biochem.* **20**, 747–752.
182. Chambon, P., Dierich, A., Gaub, M.-P., Jakowlev, S., Jongstra, J., Kriest, A., Le-Pennec, J.-P., Oudet, P., and Reudelhuber, T. (1984). *Recent Prog. Horm. Res.* **40**, 1–42.
183. Vignon, F., Bordon, S., Chalbos, D., and Rochefort, H. (1983). *J. Clin. Endocrinol. Metab.* **56**, 1124–1130.
184. Chalbos, D., and Rochefort, H. (1984). *J. Biol. Chem.* **259**, 1231–1238.
185. Rochefort, H., and Chalbos, D. (1984). *Mol. Cell. Endocrinol.* **36**, 3–10.
186. Horwitz, K. B., Zava, D. T., Thilagar, A. K., Jensen, E. M., and McGuire, W. L. (1978). *Cancer Res.* **38**, 2434–2437.
187. Horwitz, K. B., Mockus, M. B., and Lessey, B. A. (1982). *Cell* **28**, 633–642.
188. Keydar, I. Chen, L., Karbey, S., Weiss, F. R., Delarea, J., Radu, M., Chaitcik, S., and Brenner, H. J. (1979). *Eur. J. Cancer* **15**, 659–670.
189. Horwitz, K. B., and McGuire, W. L. (1978). *J. Biol. Chem.* **253**, 2223–2228.

190. Horwitz, K. B., and McGuire, W. L. (1978). *J. Biol. Chem.* **253**, 8185–8191.
191. Lippman, M., Bolan, K., and Huff, K. (1976). *Cancer Res.* **36**, 4595–4601.
192. Mockus, M. B., Lessey, B. A., Bower, M. A., and Horwitz, K. B. (1982). *Endocrinology* **110**, 1564–1571.
193. Mockus, M. B., and Horwitz, K. B. (1983). *J. Biol. Chem.* **258**, 4778–4783.
194. Horwitz, K. B., Mockus, M. B., Pike, A. W., Fennessey, P. V., and Sheridan, R. L. (1983). *J. Biol. Chem.* **258**, 7603–7610.
195. Stellwagen, R. H., and Tomkins, G. M. (1971). *J. Mol. Biol.* **56**, 167–182.
196. Kallos, J., Fasy, T. M., Hollander, B. P., and Bick, M. D. (1978). *Proc. Natl. Acad. Sci. U.S.A.* **75**, 4896–4900.
197. Garcia, M., Westley, B., and Rochefort, H. (1981). *Eur. J. Biochem.* **116**, 297–301.
198. McKnight, G. S., Hager, L., and Palmiter, R. D. (1980). *Cell* **22**, 469–477.
199. Samuels, H. H., Stanley, F., Casanova, J., and Shao, T. C. (1980). *J. Biol. Chem.* **255**, 2499–2508.
200. Leder, A., and Leder, P. (1975). *Cell* **5**, 319–322.
201. Hagino, N. (1972). *J. Clin. Endocrinol. Metab.* **35**, 716–721.
202. Zava, D. T., Landrum, B., Horwitz, K. B., and McGuire, W. L. (1979). *Endocrinology* **104**, 1007–1012.
203. Horwitz, K. B., and McGuire, W. L. (1978). *J. Biol. Chem.* **253**, 6319–6322.
204. Horwitz, K. B., and McGuire, W. L. (1980). *J. Biol. Chem.* **255**, 9699–9705.
205. Sherman, M. R., Pickering, L. A., Rollwagen, F. M., and Miller, L. K. (1978). *Fed. Proc., Fed. Am. Soc. Exp. Biol.* **37**, 167–173.
206. Stevens, J., Stevens, Y. W., Rhodes, J., and Steiner, G. (1978). *J. Natl. Cancer Inst.* **61**, 1477–1485.
207. Lurquin, P. F. (1974). *Chem. Biol. Interact.* **8**, 303–313.
208. Packman, V., and Rigler, R. (1972). *Exp. Cell Res.* **72**, 602–608.
209. Compton, J. G., Schrader, W. T., and O'Malley, B. W. (1982). *Biochem. Biophys. Res. Commun.* **105**, 96–104.
210. Compton, J. G., Schrader, W. T., and O'Malley, B. W. (1983). *Proc. Natl. Acad. Sci. U.S.A.* **80**, 16–20.
211. Mulvihill, E. R., LePennec, J.-P., and Chambon, E. R. (1982). *Cell* **24**, 621–632.
212. Berg, O. G., Winter, R. B., and von Hippel, P. H. (1982). *Trends Biochem. Sci.* **7**, 52–55.
213. Lamb, D. J., and Bullock, D. W. (1984). *Endocrinology* **114**, 1833–1840.
214. Dure, L. S., Schrader, W. T., and O'Malley, B. W. (1980). *Nature (London)* **283**, 784–785.
215. Nordeen, S. K., Lan, N. C., Showers, M. O., and Baxter, J. D. (1981). *J. Biol. Chem.* **256**, 10503–10508.
216. Wegener, A. D., and Jones, L. R. (1984). *J. Biol. Chem.* **259**, 1834–1841.
217. Markaverich, B. M., Roberts, R. R., Alejandro, M. A., and Clark, J. H. (1984). *Cancer Res.* **44**, 1575–1579.
218. Judge, S. M., and Chatterton, R. T. (1983). *Cancer Res.* **43**, 4407–4412.
219. Shiu, R. P. C., and Paterson, J. A. (1984). *Cancer Res.* **44**, 1178–1186.
220. Horwitz, K. B., and Freidenberg, G. R. (1985). *Cancer Res.* **45**:167–173.
221. Allegra, J. C., and Lippman, M. E. (1978). *Cancer Res.* **38**, 3823–3829.
222. Barnes, D., and Sato, G. (1979). *Nature (London)* **281**, 388–389.
223. Barnes, D., and Sato, G. (1980). *Cell* **22**, 649–655.
224. Butler, W., Kelsey, W. H., and Green, N. (1981). *Cancer Res.* **41**, 82–88.
225. Knutson, V. P., Ronnett, G. V., and Lane, M. D. (1982). *Proc. Natl. Acad. Sci. U.S.A.* **79**, 2822–2826.

226. Moore, M. R. (1981). *J. Biol. Chem.* **256**, 3637–3640.
227. Osborne, C. K., Monaco, M. E., Kahn, R., Huff, K., Bronzert, D., and Lippman, M. E. (1979). *Cancer Res.* **39**, 2422–2428.
228. Herrmann, W., Wyss, R., Riondel, A., Philibert, D., Teutsch, G., Sakiz, E., and Baulieu, E. E. (1983). *C.R. Acad. Sci. (Paris)* **294**, 933–938.
229. Jung-Testas, I., and Baulieu, E. E. (1983). *Exp. Cell Res.* **147**, 177–182.
230. Horwitz, K. B. (1985). *Endocrinology.* In press.
231. Stewart, T. A., Pattengale, P. K., and Leder, P. (1984). *Cell* **38**:627–637.

DISCUSSION

W. Leavitt: I would like to ask you a question related to the similarity between your A and B subunits and the subunits that have been studied in the chick oviduct system. Originally, as I recall, Bert O'Malley's group showed that A and B subunits had differential binding specificity for chromosomal acid protein and DNA. Tom Spelsberg and Bill Schrader worked this out in some detail. Have you had a chance to test your A and B components for binding in these kinds of systems?

K. Horwitz: We have not done this exactly the way Spelsberg's group has, because we have not purified A and B separately, and then done binding studies with the separated proteins. What we have done, is to partially copurify these proteins using ordinary chromatographic techniques, by sequentially taking cytosol through phosphocellulose and DNA cellulose drop-through columns, ammonium sulfate, and DEAE cellulose. We usually obtain two specific binding peaks on DEAE cellulose, one larger than the other. It we photolabeled the receptors before the start of the purification protocols, we can take individual fractions from the columns and run them on gels to see what we have under each of those peaks. It turns out that both A and B are present in each of the DEAE cellulose peaks. If we then take the larger DEAE peak and apply it to DNA cellulose, much of the labeled material binds to the DNA column. When that column is eluted with a salt gradient, we find that both B and A have stuck to the DNA, but with apparently different affinities, because if you take sequential fractions from the eluted peak and look at each fraction electrophoretically the B protein elutes at a lower salt concentration than does the A. However, both proteins stick to DNA under the conditions we used.

W. Leavitt: These are all under reducing conditions, right.

K. Horwitz: Yes that's right.

T. G. Muldoon: I would like to address the issue of this very prolonged lack of replenishment of the R5020 complexes mainly because I felt from your tone of voice that you were not very happy with what you were speculating as a long-lived pool of R5020.

K. Horwitz: Unfortunately, my explanation seems somewhat plebian. I would like to think it is more interesting than that.

T. G. Muldoon: What about the possibility that this is something like an "aggravated" processing; that is, a prolonged and very extensive degradation of nuclear receptor. What do you know about the nuclear dynamics during those periods and do you know if there is a great deal of processing going on?

K. Horwitz: The last slide showed what happens if you treat the cells with R5020 for 24 hours continuously, and monitor the amount of each subunit by SDS–PAGE. The receptors disappear from the nucleus despite the continuous presence of R5020. Now those are not exactly the same conditions under which we did the replenishment experiments, because in the replenishment studies, we removed R5020 after 1 hour, and then looked for restoration of cytoplasmic receptors. There was none. We have not done the experiment you suggest, that is to treat the cells for an hour with R5020 then wash them well, and look at the nuclear receptors by photoaffinity labeling. My guess is that we would see exactly the same thing that we see with continuous R5020 treatment; that is, nuclear labeling for a period of time and then total disappearance of the label from the nucleus, or "normal" nuclear receptor processing. I did not mention it in my talk to avoid complications, but you may have noticed that processing of the R5020-bound receptors is much slower than processing of progesterone-bound receptors. That too may be related to the suppression of replenishment.

J. H. Clark: In relation to the vanishing receptor subunits, where does the label go?

K. Horwitz: In the studies that showed the nuclear receptor bands disappearing in 8 to 16 hours, the bottom of the gels remained very heavily labeled for at least 24 hours. That label at the bottom represents either free hormone, or hormone bound to very small peptide fragments. It is very difficult to separate the fraction of free hormone that came from the original incubation, from the free or small peptide-bound fraction, that may have been generated from the "processed" receptors.

J. H. Clark: Is anything being secreted in the medium?

K. Horwitz: I think that too is possible. You know that those experiments are hard to do, because what you have to do is take cells, treat them with a radioactive hormone, then wash them extensively, assume that after washing nothing remains in the medium, and then reincubate the cells in fresh medium to see if any radioactivity comes out. Those experiments are difficult to control because you never know whether the radioactivity that comes out in the medium is due to nonspecific sticking of label to the outside of the cells or to the cell membrane, is due to extrusion of nonspecifically bound radioactivity from inside the cells, or is due to radioactivity that actually had been bound to receptors.

J. H. Clark: You suggested that progesterone treatment should cause the regression of estrogen dependent breast tumors based upon your studies with T47D cells. Does progesterone also inhibit the growth of MCF-7 cells? It seems that it should if this is to be a concept which can be generalized.

K. Horwitz: No. That's a problem; we have been unable to demonstrate any of these responses in MCF-7 cells, even though they too have progesterone receptors. I cannot explain why not, but it is important to remember that MCF-7 cells have to be estrogenized to raise progesterone receptor levels, but T47D cells do not. It is quite possible that estradiol prevents the growth inhibitory effects of the progestins. The value of the T47D cells is that one can study progestin effects free from estradiol interference. I also want to point out that our hypothesis is based not only on our work with T47D cells, but is also based on new clinical data showing that progestins, especially at high doses, are indeed very effective in the treatment of breast cancer.

J. H. Clark: Several years ago, we also thought that progesterone would suppress growth of estrogen dependent tumors; however, when we did those experiments progesterone did not cause regression but instead caused more tumors to appear. This was done in the rat so there may be differences here. Also, the older literature indicates that progesterone therapy is ineffective.

K. Horwitz: The clinical literature that I am talking about has been published in the last 3–4 years. It has come mostly from clinical studies in Denmark and Italy, and reports the use of high doses of medroxyprogesterone acetate to obtain remissions.

J. H. Clark: I know it works in the endometrial cancer but I was not familiar with the breast cancer.

G. Gibori: R5020 causes an increase in number of insulin receptors and at the same time causes an accumulation of lipid droplet in the cell. It is possible that the accumulation of lipid is due to insulin present in the cell culture and not to R5020.

K. Horwitz: We did those experiments in insulin-free medium.

P. Kelly: Just a follow up on that question about lipid droplets; I was interested in the heterogeneity of distribution with the cells grown in the presence of R5020 or was it progesterone?

K. Horwitz: It was R5020.

P. Kelly: Were you able to correlate the accumulation of lipid with the level of receptors and second were you able to counteract the accumulation of lipid using the antiprogesterone, RU 38486?

K. Horwitz: Both are good experiments, neither of which we have done. Obviously the correlation of lipid accumulation with receptors is difficult because you have to have a cell sorting mechanism to separate these different subclasses of cells and we have not attempted to do that. Someone suggested to me recently that we might be able to separate the lipid-rich cells from the lipid-poor cells by just floating the lipid-rich ones in medium and I think that might be a good idea. Obviously since we have not separated the cells, we have not been able to measure their receptors, so I don't know what the relationship is between positive lipid accumulation and receptor content. We have not done the experiment with the anti-progestin to see if the R5020 effect is suppressible.

P. Kelly: The last question I have concerns the small shift in the size of the molecular B and A forms of the receptor. Have you done anything to control or try to block those changes in molecular size during your incubation?

K. Horwitz: Phosphatase experiments to eliminate the doublets are in progress. They have been a little difficult to do because the phosphatase we were using was protease contaminated and degraded our receptors. We think we now have well purified phosphatase, and we are doing precisely that experiment to see if we can convert the doublet to a singlet. The other experiment that is in progress is one in which we have treated these cells with epidermal growth factor, because a recent paper suggested that the progesterone receptor might be a substrate for the EGF receptor kinase. Since T47D cells have EGF receptors, we are hoping that by treating them with EGF, we can show the same doublet formation on the progesterone receptors that progestins seem to generate.

J. Weisz: Just a simple minded question from someone who does not work in receptorology. You have said that in your system the efficiency of photoaffinity labeling is low, that is, that in the whole cell you are labeling only about 15% of the total receptor present. You appear to attribute this to technical problems, that is, to the conditions under which the labeling is carried out. But might not the differential labeling be due to heterogeneity of the receptor within the cell? If that were the case, focusing on the affinity labeled receptor might not give the whole picture. We might be looking only at what the method allows for, that is a subpopulation of receptors that is not necessarily representative for the population as a whole.

K. B. Horwitz: I think that we have to keep these kinds of caveats in mind. I do want to point out that radioactive R5020, as far as we know, binds nearly 100% of those proteins before photolabeling. So then when we pulse with UV, we are looking at the same cohort of receptors that we look at when we do a regular receptor binding assay. It's possible that R5020 has to sit in the binding site perfectly in order for efficient photolabeling to occur, and that if it sits slightly askew, one can still generate normal hormone binding assays, and a normal biological response, but that photolabeling becomes inefficient. I agree with you, we are clearly looking at only 10 or 15% of all the receptors in these cells, and we really do not know what is happening to the other 90 or 85%. We assume that what we are saying for the photolabeled receptors holds true for the others. But we have no direct proof of that.

J. Weisz: Just another point in relation to this fascinating observation of the lipid accumulation: it reminds me of this fascinating recent observation that the lipid cells, the brown fat cells are bona fide targets of progestins, that they are regulated in the same way, and I wonder whether it is a throwback on that kind of phenomenon, but looking at this question of whether your receptor is situated in the same cells as the one that accumulates so beautifully, couldn't one do a more simple old-fashioned experiment with autoradiography and maybe with photo affinity labeled cell populations and see the correspondence in intact cells as you plate them?

K. B. Horwitz: Yes, I think that would be technically possible and we would not have to separate cell types in order to do that.

K. L. Barker: You indicated that RU38,486 was an anti-progestin based on its ability to suppress the R5020 induction of insulin receptors in T47D cells. You also indicated that both RU38,486 and dexamethasone caused the levels of insulin receptors in these cells to be reduced relative to untreated cells. Have you ever tested dexamethasone for its antiprogestational effects by giving it R5020?

K. B. Horwitz: No, we have not. Since RU38,486 is also an antiglucocorticoid, it may be mediating this effect through the glucocorticoid receptor.

C. Monder: King and Green [*Nature (London)* **307**, 745, 1984] and Welshon *et al.* [*Nature (London)* **307**, 747, 1984] have placed the position of the estrogen receptor in the nucleus. In your presentation you indicated your willingness to generalize from that observation to at least the progesterone receptor, I'd like to know whether you feel that that type of generalization is justified at this point?

K. B. Horwitz: Well, I always assume the worst, and the worst is that we've been studying an inaccurate model for a long period of time. That is the bad news. The good news is that it probably makes no difference. As far as I'm concerned it does not matter whether the receptors are in the cytoplasm or loosely bound to nuclei, because functionally they behave the same way in either place. That is, receptors are loosely bound or have low affinity for nuclei in the absence of hormone, and have high affinity for nuclei in the presence of hormone, and that's really the major point that we want to make.

J. H. Clark: In relation to the localization of receptors, it seems likely that the nuclear localization concept can be generalized to other steroid hormones. The most recent work of Welshon, Lieberman, and Gorski (unpublished) shows that steroid receptors are found predominantly in the nucleus whether they are occupied or not.

S. Cohen: I'm interested in the relationship between estrogen and progestin: does the estrogen cause an increase in receptors, and/or of progesterone or of just one or both?

K. B. Horwitz: In typical estrogen target cells where this has been studied, estrogen increases the levels of progesterone receptors. In this particular cell line that I have been talking about, estrogen does not, but this is an anomalous case.

S. Cohen: And the reverse, progesterone inhibits the production of estrogen receptors and/or estrogen itself?

K. B. Horwitz: Yes, the reverse also appears to be true. This is work from Dr. Leavitt's group showing that progestins decrease the levels of estrogen receptors in normal estrogen target cells.

S. Cohen: I am interested in the myometrium, the human myometrium, during pregnancy in this case we have a strange relationship because the blood estradiol level is about 25 ng/ml whereas that of the human myometrium in the nuclei is only 4 ng/ml and the only explanation I can have to give for that is the high progesterone levels.

W. W. Leavitt: We have studied myometrial and decidual cells and find that receptor regulation in the two cell types is quite different. Progesterone is the main factor which down-regulates the estrogen receptor and we think that progesterone action occurs primarily in the nucleus (Leavitt *et al.*, "Biochemical Actions of Hormones," Vol X, p. 324, Academic Press, New York, 1983). In the decidual cell which is remarkably similar to the T47D cell in terms of the estrogen independence of progesterone receptors, and also the low level of estrogen receptor, progesterone is the hormone which maintains decidual cell differentiation (MacDonald *et al., Biol Reprod.* **28,** 753, 1982) and at the same time it down-regulates estrogen receptor. This probably explains why decidual tissue is a progestin-responsive tissue, and why estrogens have relatively little effect.

S. Cohen: How you account for the lower, much lower level in the nuclei than in the blood stream if all membranes are permeable to the estrogen?

W. W. Leavitt: I would interpret it as the difference in estrogen binding protein concentration.

S. Cohen: Does that mean only bound estrogens get into the nucleus, because that has been questioned before.

W. W. Leavitt: No, there is an equilibrium between the two compartments and the one with the higher concentration of binding protein is going to concentrate the hormone.

C. W. Bardin: I would like you to relate processing and replenishment of receptors to biological activity during chronic progestin action. In most of your studies on biological activity the time frame was days, and in most of your studies on binding it was hours. If you treat with a progestin and then look at receptor levels at 8 days, do you get a replenishment?

K. B. Horwitz: Yes, as I showed, the extent and rate of replenishment is dependent on the progestin used. In progesterone-treated cells, one observed rapid turnover or "processing," and then, despite the continuous presence of progesterone, the receptors return to control levels within 24 hours. With R5020 or with some of the other synthetic progestins, receptor replenishment takes many days. I did not show you the replenishment data on continuous progesterone treatment, but it is identical to the effect of a 1-hour pulse of progesterone. This is due to extensive progesterone metabolism. At $10^{-7} M$, progesterone is metabolized with a half-life of 2 to 3 hours. It is therefore difficult to perform experiments that require continuous progesterone treatment, since one has to feed cells 2 to 3 times a day in order to keep the progesterone levels up, and one has to do this for several days. On the rare occasions when we have done this, we obtain biological responses and replenishment patterns like those seen with synthetic progestins. To get back to your initial question which asked whether we can correlate or quantitate the extent of processing with the biological response, we have not done that for progesterone receptors. However, several years ago we did similar studies with estrogen receptors, and showed that there was a correlation between the extent of estrogen receptor processing and the amount of progesterone receptor induction in MCF-7 cells.

R. N. Andersen: You introduced very exciting data concerning the structure of receptors. To continue the discussion about the possible forms of receptors, with your permission and Dr. Leavitt's, I would like to show two slides.

We have been interested in possible differences between uterine leiomyoma and myometrium. As an approach to this question, we compared the sedimentation behavior of occupied and unoccupied receptors from endometrial, myometrial, and leiomyoma cytosols. The data in the top panel of Fig. A are for the occupied receptors and the data in the lower panel are for the unoccupied receptors: A and D are data from endometrium; B and E are data from myometrium; and C and F are data from leiomyoma. The data from each tissue substantiate the same point. Consequently, only the data from the endometrium will be discussed (A and D). The occupied receptors (A) are predominantly 8 S and to a lesser degree 4 S. With an added excess of R5020, binding to the 8 S receptor was almost totally displaced while that to the 4 S was displaced very little. This indicates that the 8 S binding is specific and that to the 4 S is probably nonspecific binding to albumin. Data on the unoccupied receptors are shown with and without leupeptin added to the cytosol preparation. With the endometrial preparation (D) there is a large 9–10 S peak, and again, most of this was displaced by excess R5020 and therefore was specific binding. Basically the same findings were made with the cytosols from myometrium and leiomyoma except that there was a lot more nonspecific binding and leupeptin was important for maintaining the integrity of the receptor. From these data, we thought there was a possibility that ligand binding to the unoccupied receptor converted it from a 9–10 S entity to a 7–8 S entity. We subsequently showed that this effect was concentration and time dependent and was blocked by molybdate.

To try to put these data into perspective with the literature (I realize that our findings are somewhat different from those of Dr. Buchi and Dr. Keller, *J. Steroid Biochem.* **20**, 433, 1984, who found unoccupied receptor for myoma and myometrium to be 8 S), I have prepared a diagram of data from the literature. A diagramatic representation of the 8 S cytosolic receptor is shown to the right of the center of Fig. B. This can be converted by 0.4 *M* KCl or 5′-pyridoxal phosphate to the typical 4 or 4.5 S native receptor. The native 4 S receptor can be converted by a calcium-dependent protease to a modified 4 S receptor which can be further degraded to the so-called mero-receptor. Murayama has presented evidence for what he calls an 8 S forming factor for both estrogen and progesterone receptors (Murayama *et al., J. Biochem.* **88**, 1305, 1980). The 8 S forming factor is depicted in the top center. The 8 S forming factor is composed of 2 subunits which can dissociate and recombine with native 4 S receptor to form 5 S and 6 S forms of the receptor. The intact 8 S forming factor can combine with native 4 S receptor to produce the 8 S receptor. Once native 4 S receptor was converted to the modified 4 S receptor; it was no longer able to combine with the 8 S forming factor. Murayama's data, therefore, account for most of the major forms of receptor that have been observed and reported in the literature.

Our data are shown on the right of Fig. B. Again, our basic finding is that ligand binding converts an unoccupied 9–10 S form of receptor to an occupied 7–8 S form. We believe that there are at least two possibilities for the effect of ligand binding on the large-molecular-weight unoccupied form. One possibility is simply a conformational change which is inhibited by molybdate. The other possibility that we wish to suggest is that there is another non-steroid-binding component associated with the 9–10 S form of unoccupied receptor. This concept is based on Murayama's data in which he showed that the 8 S forming factor is a 6.8 S dimer which can combine with a 4.5 S native receptor to form an 8 S receptor. If one sums the sedimentation coefficient of the 8 S forming factor with that of the native 4 S receptor, the sum is 11.3 S. The observed sedimentation coefficient of 8.0 S is only 0.7 of the "theoretical" sum of the two, 11.3 S. If we make the same type of calculation using 9.7 S as a value for the observed sedimentation coefficient of the unoccupied receptor, the apparent arithmetic sum (if another component were present and had the same relationship as that described above) would be 13.9 S. The difference between this calculated value of 13.9 S and the observed value of 9.7 S means that an entity on the order of 4.2 S may be a component of the unoccupied receptor which is dissociated by ligand binding. Molybdate, acting through an undefined mechanism, would prevent dissociation of this postulated component. In addition, there is a possibility that a low-molecular-weight component is involved in the makeup of the high-molecular-weight form of receptor. A recent paper on glucocorticoid receptors showed that the low-molecular-weight component was necessary to observe the molybdate effect on stabilization of the large-molecular-weight form.

So in summary, we feel that there is a considerable degree of complexity to the receptors that one finds in cytosol. Whether cytosolic receptors are an artifact of the preparation due to disruption of the nucleus or dissociation of nuclear receptors is a separate question.

K. Horwitz: I would tend to agree with your conclusion. I think there is a great deal of evidence, as you suggest, that non-hormone-binding proteins are involved in the structure of steroid receptors, and in fact in the structure of all receptors. There certainly is strong evidence for insulin receptors, for example, that the larger α subunit is a hormone binding

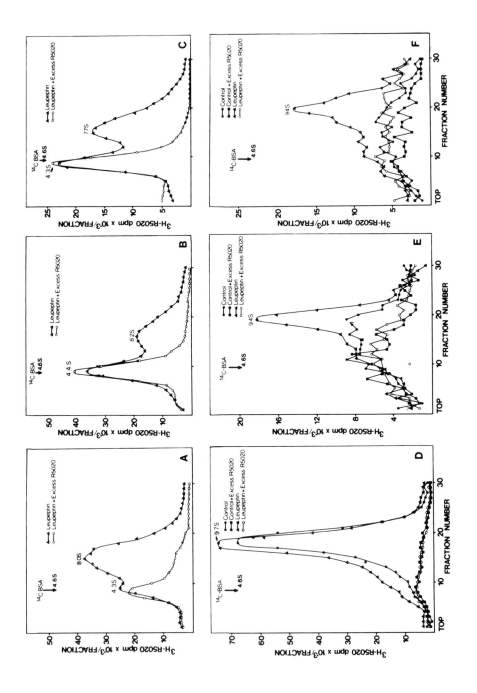

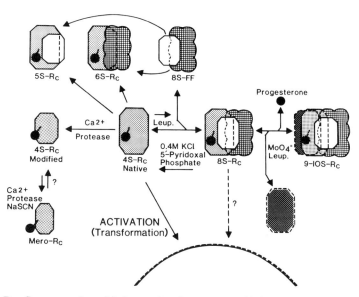

FIG. B.   Summary of possible interactions between steroid binding and nonbinding components of steroid receptors.

protein, but the smaller β subunit is not. For steroid receptors, to date we have only been able to measure the hormone binding proteins. Now we are beginning to use immunological methods, and preliminary data for progesterone receptors suggest that their structure may indeed be very complex; that non-hormone-binding proteins, closely related to the hormone binding proteins, are also present in cells. Molybdate stabilization is a big problem. This compound has been both useful and harmful for research in steroid receptors because we do not really know how it works. Dave Toft's group and Etienne Baulieu's group have both attempted to purify molybdate stabilized progesterone receptors by affinity chromatography and obtained 85–90K proteins against which they have made antibodies. More recently, Mariel Birmbaumer has shown that this protein does not bind to hormone and is structurally unrelated to the hormone-binding A or B subunits. However, the 85K protein copurifies with receptors from affinity columns, and may have some unknown relationship to receptors,

FIG. A.   Effect of ligand binding on sedimentation of cytosplasmic progestin receptors. Cytosols were prepared from human uterine endometrium, myometrium, and leiomyoma. One portion of each was prelabeled and analyzed by sucrose density gradient ultracentrifugation. (A) Endometrial cytosol with and without a 100-fold excess of radioinert R5020; (B) same as A, but myometrial cytosol; (C) cytosol from leiomyoma. A second protion of each cytosol was centrifuged on sucrose density gradients and the fractions were postlabeled after adsorption with protamine sulfate. (D) Endometrial cytosol with and without leupeptin and with and without a 100-fold excess of radioinert R5020; (E) same as D, but myometrial cytosol; (F) same as D, but cytosol from a leiomyoma. The arrow at the top of the figures indicate the position of the ¹⁴C-labeled BSA marker protein (4.6 S). (ElDeib, M. R., Costlow, M. E., and Andersen, R. N., *Steroids,* in press; reproduced with the permission of the authors and publishers of *Steroids.*)

since molybdate stabilizes its association to receptors. Clearly, there is a great deal of complexity to the structure of the receptors that we are only now discovering, as our techniques are changing.

T. Chen: Just to add to more confusion, I think there is some recent evidence that suggests that at least in the estrogen receptors, some agonist or antagonist bind to different receptors, they are structurally different; would you comment on that, is this another example of the "pet cell theory"?

K. Horwitz: My understanding for estrogen receptors has been that the same molecule(s) is bound by estrogen and by antiestrogens. Jim looks like he has more to say about this.

J. H. Clark: Are you addressing the data of Tom and Mary Ruh with a compound called H-1285. They did show that there was some differential binding and it looked as though that compound was binding to one "subunit" of the estrogen receptor and not the other. This turned out to be the result of dissociation of the compound from one of the peaks. When postlabeling techniques were used, H-1285 bound to both peaks. Other slight differences have been reported but most investigators do not observe differences on estrogen receptor binding of antiestrogens. There are, of course, other binding sites which are specific for antiestrogens but those are not estrogen receptors and at the present their function is not known.

B. A. Littlefield: I was interested that a 1-hour pulse of R5020 would cause an 8 to 10 day decrease in progesterone receptors. I was wondering how many cell doublings the cells have gone through during that time, and if it was surprising that after, I assume, 3 to 4 doublings you still see such low progesterone receptor levels in the progeny cells.

K. Horwitz: The inhibition to replenishment does seem to cross the cell cycle barrier; the cells are dividing while this is happening.

Creation of Transgenic Animals to Study Development and as Models for Human Disease

R. M. EVANS,* L. SWANSON,* AND M. G. ROSENFELD†

The Salk Institute, La Jolla, California, and †School of Medicine, University of California, San Diego, La Jolla, California

I. Hormonal Regulation of Gene Expression

Physiological processes are coordinated with the aid of both nerves and hormones. Each of these mechanisms has special characteristics that may be suited to the needs of the particular process involved and they often both operate together. How cells regulate gene expression is a question of great importance in modern biology because the unique features of each cell and ultimately complex tissues are by in large determined by their unique patterns of gene expression. Hormones contribute directly to the control of differentiation and growth of the embryo and behavioral and physiological processes in the adult. The control of metamorphosis in amphibians is a unique and dramatic example of how endocrines can influence development but they also contribute more ubiquitously especially to growth and sexual differentiation, in all groups of vertebrates. Hormones play an important role in these processes as regulators of gene expression.

II. Regulation of Growth Hormone Gene Expression

Growth hormone is a pituitary polypeptide important during adolescence but produced throughout the life span of all mammals. It is necessary for normal growth and development, and abnormal production is associated with numerous disease states including various forms of dwarfism and normal variant short stature syndromes. Overproduction of growth hormone results in diseases termed acromegaly and gigantism. To begin a molecular analysis, experiments were initiated resulting in the isolation of clones of the entire growth hormone gene and gene products (1–3). These growth hormone clones have been used as molecular probes to study the complex mechanisms associated with the expression and hormonal regulation of this gene. Normally, expression of the GH gene in

317

animals is restricted to the somatotrophic cells of the anterior pituitary, and we have shown that this expression is regulated by glucocorticoid hormones, thyroid hormone, and the hypothalamic peptide growth hormone releasing factor (GRF) (4,5). The development of new technology to reintroduce cloned genes back into cells provides a particularly powerful approach to the study of gene regulation and the genetic basis of development, work that could lead to a better understanding of human disease.

III.   Creation of Transgenic Animals

To address questions concerning the genetic basis of development and differentiation, we and others have explored the technique of genetically transforming entire mammalian organisms (6–8). The technique, very broadly, is literally to inject the foreign gene into a very early mouse embryo (the single cell fertilized egg) and then return the embryo to a foster mother mouse to complete its development. Animals that develop from eggs microinjected with foreign DNA that becomes incorporated into their genomes are referred to as transgenic (6). The growth hormone gene whose product has profound developmental effects provides a particularly convenient and biologically potent molecule to model this approach. This approach was initiated by the construction of a novel hybrid growth hormone gene which involved the fusion of the structural portion of the GH gene to the promoter of the mouse metallothionenin gene (Fig. 1) (9). Approximately 2000 copies of the fused gene were injected into each of 170 fertilized mouse eggs, which were then inserted into female

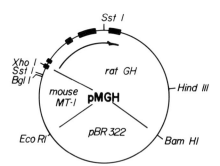

FIG. 1.   Schematic diagram of the construction of fusion gene containing a moust metallothionein I (MT-I) promoter region and the rat growth hormone gene. The fused gene contains 68 bases of the MT-I promoter and the entire rat growth hormone gene beginning at nucleotide 7 of the coding sequence and terminating 5 kb downstream at the *Bam*HI site. Growth hormone exons are represented as black boxes. Arrow indicates direction of transcription. The *Bgl*I to *Bam*HI fragment was injected into eggs.

mice serving as foster mothers. From these injected eggs, 21 mice were born. They appeared normal, but within a few weeks, some began to grow more rapidly than their littermates (Fig. 2).

Analysis of the DNA of the young mice showed that 7 animals carried the rat growth hormone genes, in 1–35 copies per cell. The reason the mice with the transferred GH gene are larger than normal was revealed by additional biochemical studies. These studies demonstrated efficient expression of the transferred gene resulting in the production of high levels of messenger RNA molecules and the subsequent synthesis and release of comparably high levels of growth hormone into the serum of these mice (Fig. 3). In fact, the largest genetically engineered mice contain more than 1000 times the normal levels of growth hormone giving rise to a physiological state similar to the human clinical condition called gigantism. Some of the biggest transgenic mice are infertile, although others are able to mate. These fertile mice are called "founders" and one male founder mouse has transmitted the rat growth hormone gene to approximately 50% of its offspring (Fig. 4). In this case, the genes appear to be stably integrated into one of the mouse chromosomes and, thus, gigantism represents a dominant heritable trait.

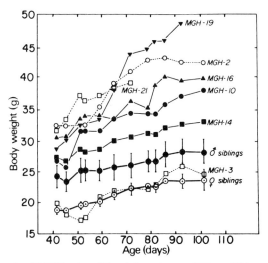

FIG. 2. Growth of MGH mice. Microinjected eggs (SJL × C57) were transferred to oviducts of foster mothers and animals were born 3 weeks later. At 33 days old they were weaned and growth measurements begun at 40 days. The body weights of the males are shown as solid symbols. The mean weight (±SD) of 11 siblings not containing MGH sequences is also shown. The female are represented by open symbols.

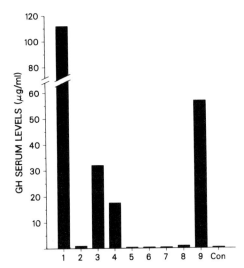

FIG. 3. Blood GH levels in transgenic mice. Animals 1, 3, and 9 represent the three animals showing the most accelerated growth and highest content of GH mRNA in their lives. Control mice contain approximately 0.15 μg/ml.

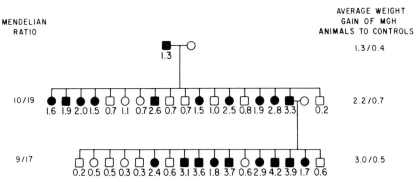

FIG. 4. Pedigree chart of offspring from MGH-10 [see Palmiter *et al.* (9)]. Solid symbols: individuals that carry the MGH genotype and the gigantism phenotype. Squares represent males and circles represent females. Numbers below each symbol indicate weight gain in grams per week from 5 to 11 weeks of age. The relative increase of weight of the transgenic mouse to the average normal littermate is its growth rate. The number of transgenic mice relative to total mice in the litter is the Mendelian ratio. Animal number 17, a control female, died before body weights were taken and was therefore excluded from the pedigree chart.

IV. Cadmium-Induced MGH Transcription

To test directly whether the expression of the fusion gene in animals can be regulated, we assayed its transcription rate in isolated liver nuclei before or after 1 hour of heavy metal treatment. Transcription rates of the fusion gene and the endogenous mouse metallothionein-I gene were determined by hybridization to growth hormone cDNA or metallothionein-I genomic clones. The results, shown in Fig. 5, indicate that the fusion gene exhibits a readily detectable basal rate of transcription which is inducible by cadmium treatment. There was no detectable level of GH transcription in the livers of control mice (data not shown). The induction of MGH transcription is rapid and nearly identical in fold to that of the endogenous metallothionein gene. This result demonstrates that the property of cad-

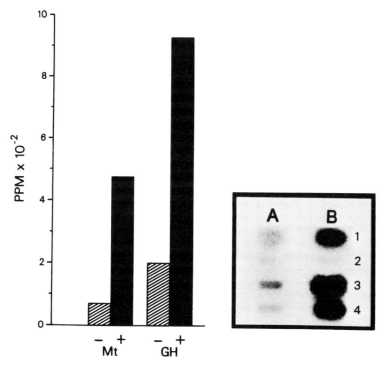

FIG. 5. The MGH gene is transcriptionally regulated in animals. (A) Comparative analysis of the transcription rate of the endogeneous metallothionein gene and the MGH transgene in liver before (−) and after (+) treatment with cadmium. (B) Regulation of liver MGH RNA levels by cadmium. Animal number 2 contains only 0.2 copies of the MGH gene, does not express or regulate MGH mRNA, and did not grow larger than control littermates. Animals 1, 3, and 4 are all larger (1.5- to 2.1-fold) then normal littermates.

mium inducibility of the metallothionein promoter is retained in the fusion gene of transgenic animals.

Based on these results RNA from the livers of MGH animals was isolated by partial hepatectomy before and following cadmium sulfate treatment (1 mg/kg body weight; 18 and 4 hours before hepatectomy) and analyzed for its content of growth hormone mRNA sequences. In three out of four MGH animals large mRNA inductions following cadmium treatment are observed (Fig. 3). Animal number 2, although transgenic, contains 0.2 copies of the fusion gene per cell, did not grow larger than normal littermates, and produced no detectable GH RNA before or after induction. This mouse could either be mosaic or contain a fragment of the orginial plasmid.

V. Regulation of Serum Growth Hormone Levels

A direct correlation between circulating growth hormone levels and fusion gene activity would provide a convenient means for assaying gene expression as well as creating a novel control for the serum levels of a physiologically important polypeptide hormone. Zinc treatment had no effect on serum concentrations of growth hormone in control animals. However, zinc treatment increased serum growth hormone levels 10-fold in animals that carried the fusion gene (Table I). The addition of zinc to the drinking water did not alter growth in animals that carried the MGH gene even though serum levels of growth hormone were elevated. In addition, the levels of serum growth hormone as well as growth rate showed some variation among the progeny.

TABLE I

Effect of Zinc Water on Weight Gain and Serum Growth Hormone Levels[a]

Animals	ZnH$_2$O	Weight gain (g)	GH (μg/ml)	Fold GH induction
Control ($n = 3$)	−	3.3 ± 1.0	0.41 ± 0.17	—
Control ($n = 5$)	+	5.0 ± 0.5	0.33 ± 0.12	0.85
MGH ($n = 5$)	−	14.0 ± 2.1	1.25 ± 0.21	—
MGH ($n = 5$)	+	11.6 ± 1.0	12.5 ± 3.6	10

[a] Effect of zinc water on weight gain and serum growth hormone in mice carrying the MGH fusion gene. Mice are from two litters from MGH-10 born 7 days apart (6). Animals were treated with 76 mM ZnSO$_4$ in their water starting at 5 weeks of age for 6 weeks. Serum growth hormone levels were determined by radioimmunoassay of duplicate serum samples after 3 weeks of zinc treatment. Weight gain was for the entire 6 weeks of zinc treatment.

VI. Developmental Expression of GH Fusion Genes

The ability to introduce functional growth hormone fusion genes into mice by injection of DNA into fertilized eggs allows us to ask questions about the sequence requirements that control its expression and allows us to investigate the potential developmental expression of these genes. Because tissues generally contain a number of specialized cell types, determination of developmental specificity should be examined at the cellular level. Interestingly, when the entire growth hormone gene, including 5 kb of flanking chromosomal sequences, was introduced into mice, no expression was apparent, although it was stably incorporated. Thus, even if sequences within the GH gene influence its normal developmental expression, they do not appear to be sufficient to activate the GH promoter. To examine the potential functions of GH sequences in dictating developmental expression of the GH gene, the tissue specific expression of the GH fusion gene was examined. As discussed above the fusion gene was expressed in the liver of all transgenic animals examined, consistent with the fact that liver is one of the primary sites of metallothionein biosynthesis.

Tissues such as the brain express the MT-I gene at levels 40-fold (or more) lower than the liver (see Fig. 6A). The growth hormone gene in adult mammals appears to be expressed entirely within somatotrophic cells, which constitute approximately 40% of the anterior pituitary. It was therefore unexpected to find exceptionally high levels of the fusion gene expressed in the brain of transgenic animals (see Fig. 6B). These findings lead us to examine in more detail the cellular distribution of fusion gene

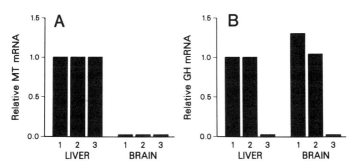

FIG. 6. Unexpected MGH expression in the brains of transgenic animals. (A) Relative amount of MT RNA in livers and brains of transgenic (animals 1 and 2) and normal control (3) mice as detected by slot hybridization with nick translated MT-I cDNA as probe. (B) Relative levels of GH RNA in livers and brains of the same animals. Rat growth hormone cDNA was used as probe.

expression in transgenic animals, and to determine if this specificity is a consequence of sequences in the gene.

VII. The MGH Fusion Gene Is Expressed in the Liver

The liver is the major site of heavy metal detoxification in animals and is also the major site of MT synthesis, which occurs primarily in hepatocytes. In all transgenic MGH animals synthesis of the mRNA encoding growth hormone is found in the liver, where expression of the fusion gene is transcriptionally regulated by heavy metal treatment. Thus, regulatory sequences conferring responsiveness to heavy metals are functional in transgenic animals. Although the presence and regulation of GH mRNA in liver are evidence for appropriate tissue specific expression, it does not demonstrate that the RNA is produced by MT-synthesizing cells. Because the liver is composed of several specialized cell types, it becomes necessary to assess whether the MGH gene is expressed in all, or only subsets, or liver cells. If the metallothionein regulatory region alone confers the pattern of developmental expression on the MGH gene, then the fusion gene will be active only in the same cell types as the endogenous MT gene. The availability of antisera to both MT and GH allowed us to evaluate this question be determining the precise cellular distribution of each gene product (Fig. 7A and B). In accord with previously published data MT appears to be synthesized in all hepatocytes, although, based on staining intensity, levels in different cells can be quite variable. It is concluded that the expression of high levels of the fusion gene in a restricted cell population of the liver is a consequence of metallothionein promoter sequences in the fusion gene.

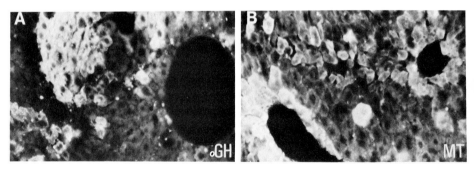

FIG. 7.   Cellular localization with GH expression in livers of transgenic mice. (A) Immunofluorescence with antiserum to mouse growth hormone. (B) Immunofluorescence with antiserum to mouse metallothinmein. Both sections ×330.

VIII. Expression in the Brain

Based upon the pattern of coexpression of MT and GH gene products in liver, and the fact that MT expression in brain is much lower relative to levels in the liver, the high levels of MGH mRNA in the brains of transgenic animals (Fig. 6) were an unexpected result. Although MT has not been reported to be highly localized in regions of the brain, histochemical analysis revealed that the fusion gene gave a highly restricted pattern of expression in several anatomically defined areas. The most obvious pattern of GH cell staining in transgenic mice was observed in the hypothalamus (Fig. 8). A detailed examination of eight animals representing offspring from five generations of a single transgenic parent (MGH-10) showed an identical distribution of GH-stained neuronal cell bodies in seven of the animals. GH-stained cells were concentrated in three parts of the hypothalamus. The most obvious group of cells consisted of large neurons in the paraventricular (PVH) and supraoptic (SO) nuclei (Fig. 8A and B), which synthesize oxytoxin and vasopressin, project to the posterior pituitary, and are involved in the integration of neuroendocrine and autonomic responses. In all case, neuronal staining was blocked by the addition of rGH to both of the anti-GH sera used. No glial or vascular cell types were stained. These results demonstrate that GH is consistently expressed in specific subpopulation of neurons in the brain.

In accord with the prominent but highly restricted expression of the GH fusion gene in the hypothalamus, specific expression was observed in several areas outside the hypothalamus, including regions of the neocortex, hippocampus, and olfactory cortex in the MGH-10 pedigree. All animals examined showed a similar pattern of GH immunostaining that was greatly enhanced by colchicine pretreatment, which blocks anoxal transport. Immunoactive pyramidal cells restricted to layer V of the neocortex (Fig. 8D) were found in all animals expressing the fusion gene in liver and hypothalamus. This cortex is broadly divided into six layers with unique cell types that are morphologically and physiologically distinct. Bright immunostaining in this region is highly localized and does not appear to enter other layers. Specific immunostaining is also seen in the pyramidal cells of hippocampal field CA_3 (Fig. 8C), which is a region that is dominated by mossy fiber afferents from the adjacent dentate gyrus. Although pyramidal cells in the other hippocampal fields (CA1, 2, and 4) were negative, some interneurons were stained here, as well as in the hilus of the dentate gyrus.

To determine whether the site of chromosomal integration of the fusion gene is critical in determining the pattern of MGH expression in neurous, six other integrations of the MT-rGH gene, and two integrations of the

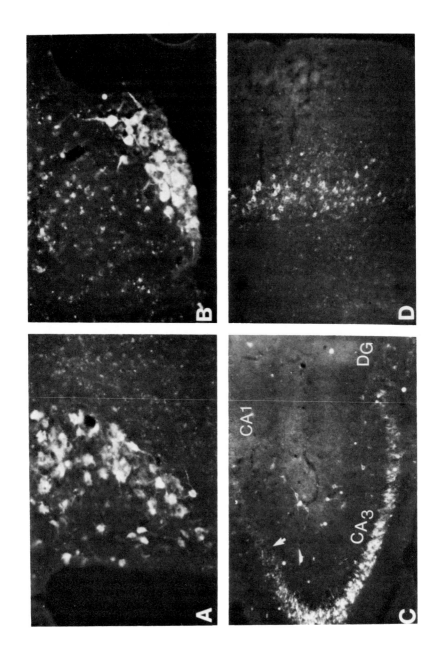

MT-hGH gene, were examined in a total of 11 animals. In each brain, the pattern of GH immunostaining in the hypothalamus was examined in detail, and was identical to that described for the MGH-10 peidgree, although the intensity of staining was variable.

In summary, 16 of the 18 transgenic mice analyzed, representing nine different integrations of the rGH and hGH fusion genes, showed the same cellular distribution of GH in the liver brain, while for unknown reasons, no immunostaining was observed in two other animals. An identical pattern of GH immunostaining was seen in males and females, as well as in albino, agouti, and black strains of mice. These data strongly suggest that the precise site of integration into the genome may not play a critical role in determining which neurons in the brain express the fusion gene, but may well modulate the absolute level of gene expression in these cells.

IX. Metallothionein (MT) Distribution in Brain

If sequences in the MT promoter determine the specific pattern of expession of the MGH fusion gene in the brain of transgenic mice then one might predict that the endogenous MT-I gene would be expressed with an identical distribution. An antiserum to rat liver MT-I was used to identify the pattern of MT-I immunostaining in normal and transgenic mice. This antiserum consistently stained small cells with the appearance of astrocytes in all parts of the white and gray matter, both in normal and transgenic animals (Fig. 9B). This tentative identification was confirmed in double immunostaining experiments with a monoclonal antibody (15,16) to the astrocyte marker, S-100, and the polyclonal MT-I antiserum (raised in rabbit). Essentially all cells were doubly labeled in this material (Fig. 9A and B), and no evidence for MT staining of neurons was obtained. These results indicate that although the fusion gene and MT-I appear to be coexpressed in hepatocytes, their expression is independently and differently regulated in the brain.

FIG. 8. Cellular localizaton of GH expression in the brains of transgenic mice. Frontal sections through the hypothalamus of an MGH-10 animal. Large neurons in the paraventricular (A) and supraoptic (B) nuclei stained with an antiserum to mouse growth hormone. ×150. (C) Growth hormone immunostaining in cell bodies in the hippocampus are confined to the pyramidal cell layer in field CA3, and to the region of interneurons in the hilus of the dentate gyrus (DG), and in fields CA1 and CA3, and to the region of interneurons in the hilus of the dentate gyrus (DG), and in fields CA1 and CA3. The arrowhead shows the boundary between fields CA1 and CA2; the fimbria is in the lower left hand corner. ×75. (D) Stained pyramidal cell bodies in layer V of the junctional region between the somatic sensory (upper half) and motor (lower half) cortex on the left side of the brain. The corpus collosum is to the far left (under the "C") and the pial surface is to the right. ×75.

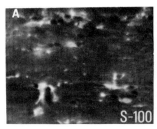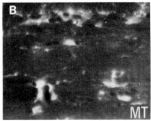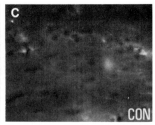

FIG. 9.   In the brain MT is expressed in nonneuronal cells. Colocalization of metallothionein (MT) and the astocyte-specific marker protein S-100 in the same section through the corpus callosum (a fiber tract) of an MGH-10 animal. The section was incubated in a mixture of a rabbit antiserum to MT and a mouse monoclonal antibody to S-100. The MT was shown with a fluorsescein-conjugated secondary antiserum and the S-100 was shown with a rhodamine-conjugated secondary antiserum. The control (CON) panel on the right shows the corpus callosum after incubation in anti-MT serum that was blocked by the addition of MT. ×400.

X. Discussion

These data strongly suggest that the altered phenotype of the mice is a direct result of the integration and expression of the metallothionein–growth hormone fusion gene. The elevated level of GH present in some of these mice corresponds to a high level of MGH mRNA in the liver (up to 3000 molecules per cell). The high level of MGH gene expression in transgenic mice will greatly facilitate direct comparison of MGH and MT-I mRNA production in different tissues, thus allowing us to determine whether chromosomal location has an important effect on tissue-specific expression of the MT-I promoter.

Growth hormone levels in some of the transgenic mice were as much as 800-fold higher than in normal mice, resulting in animals nearly twice the weight of their unaffected littermates. This greater than normal accumulation of GH undoubtedly reflects both the lack of normal feedback mechanisms and expression of this gene in many large organs including liver, kidney, and intestine. The effect of chronic exposure to high levels of GH is well documented (10), resulting in the clinical condition referred to as gigantism. This condition in humans is usually associated with pituitary adenomas (10) and more rarely with ectopic expression of GH by lung carcinomas (11,12).

Some of the diverse effects of GH are mediated directly by the hormone (13–15). However, it is generally believed that the major effect of GH is stimulation of somatomedin production in the liver (13,14).

The results of the transcription rate experiment demonstrate a rapid induction of the MGH gene by cadmium, and furthermore shows that high levels of gene expression can be achieved. In fact, the transcription rate of the fusion gene in the animal examined is higher than that of the endogenous metallothionein-I gene. We speculate that this may be the consequence of a gene dosage effect due to the presence of approximately 8 copies of the MGH gene per cell. If these results were normalized for the size of the hybridization probe, GH transcription would be even more elevated (1.7-fold). Furthermore, the animals are heterozygous for the fusion gene locus in somatic cells. Therefore, if all 8 genes were expressing at the same rate, each gene would retain approximately 90% of the transcriptional activity of the endogenous MT-I gene. The fold induction of the fusion gene is close to that of the endogenous metallothionein-I gene which is consistent with coordinate regulation of all of the expressed MGH genes.

Although it is likely that the combination of high gene activity in the liver along with constitutive growth hormone secretion gives rise to the unusually high circulating GH levels observed in the animals, there is no direct correlation between these levels and growth rates. Recently we have obtained transgenic mice that contain more than 250 μg/ml of growth hormone in the sera, approximately 2000-fold greater than normal. These exceptionally high levels of circulating growth hormone do not result in proportionately larger mice. There seems to be a maximum growth hormone-dependent growth rate and final size which are achieved at a relatively modest increase in their circulating GH levels.

In addition to changes in size and body weight, examination of the viscera of the gigantic mouse reveals dramatically enlarged liver, kidney, spleen, and heart. The longitudinal bones are proportionately increased as is the spinal cord, although the brain is virtually unchanged.

Interestingly, when the entire growth hormone gene, including 5 kb of flanking chromosomal sequences, was introduced into mice, no expression was apparent, although it was stably incorporated. Thus, even if sequences within the GH gene influence its normal developmental expression, they do not appear to be sufficient to activate the GH promoter. The fusion gene, however, was consistently expressed in the liver of all transgenic animals examined, consistent with the fact that liver is one of the primary sites of metallothionein biosynthesis. Immunohistochemistry demonstrates the production of growth hormone in clusters of liver parenchymal cells, a cell type that has been previously shown to produce metallothionein.

Unexpectedly, while MT is localized to glial cells (astrocytes) in the brain, expression of the MGH fusion gene is confined to neurons. Furthermore, detectable neuronal expression is restricted to several highly localized regions that include pyramidal cells in layer V of the neocortex

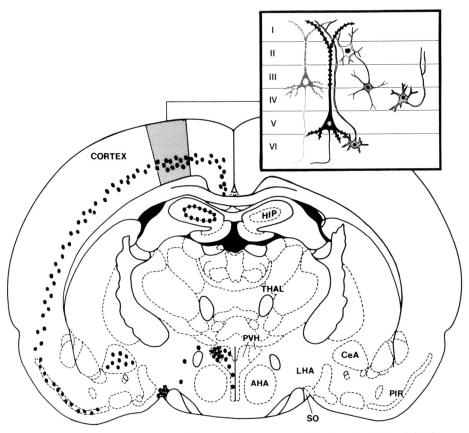

FIG. 10. This diagram summarizes the discrete neuronal localization (dots) of GH immunostaining in a frontal section through the forebrain of a rodent. The insert shows that while the cerebral cortex contains many cell types that are distributed through six layers, GH staining is confined to large pyramidal cells (dark) in layer V. AHA, Anterior hypothalamic area; CeA, central nucleus of the amygdala; HIP, hippocampus; LHA, lateral hypothalamic area; PIR, piriform cortex; PVH, paraventicular nucleus; SO, supraoptic nucleus; THAL, thalamus.

and field CA3 of the hippocampus, magnocellular neurosecretory cells of the hypothalamus, the suprachiasmatic nucleus, the central nucleus of the amygdala, the compact zone of the substantia nigra and adjacent parts of the ventral tegmental area, and the dorsal motor nucleus of the vagus (Figs. 9 and 10). Because these areas are not known to share common developmental influences, do not appear to use a common neurotransmitter, and do not manifest functional or cytological similarities, there is at

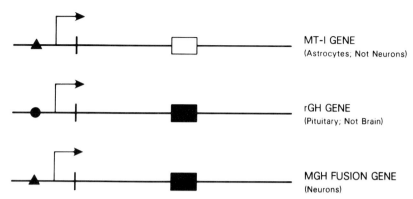

FIG. 11. Model of developmental synergism of GH and MT chromosomal regions. Symbols represent putative genetic elements capable of influencing gene expression. Horizontal lines schematically represent genes, vertical lines represent sites of gene fusion, and arrows represent transcription initiation sites.

present no obvious explanation for why the fusion gene is coordinately expressed in these particular neurons. Because metallothionein expression in the brain fails to colocalize with expression of the fusion gene it is tempting to propose a model that requires sequences within both the 5' flanking 3' structural region of the fusion gene for the observed cellular specificity (Fig. 11). According to this hypothesis, sequences present in the growth hormone chromosomal fragment are capable of promoting expression outside of the anterior pituitary, which appears to be the only location for endogenous growth hormone gene expression. This would further suggest that specific developmental expression of the growth hormone gene might require interaction between 5' flanking chromosomal sequences and those present in downstream regions of the gene. Chromosomal position of the fusion genes as a means to control growth hormone specificity is essentially excluded because of the identical pattern of expression of the fusion gene in the brains of unrelated transgenic animals.

It is also possible that the effect of sequences in the fusion gene might be modulated further by chromosomal position since the absolute level of GH expression appears to vary in different integrations. Whatever the explanation, the results presented here suggest a model in which combinations of sequence components might give rise to observed developmental and tissue specificities (Fig. 10). According to this model, the determination of the developmental specificity in some genes (such as rGH) may be due to the effects of several distinct regulatory elements. The separation of these elements may alter or abolish specificity whereas their linkage of elements from other genes may generate novel specificities such as that observed with the MGH gene. If this is true, it may be possible to introduce specific gene products into the brains of transgenic mice, providing a potential means to manipulate genetically CNS function.

It is currently is not possible to determine whether the observed pattern of MGH gene expression in the nervous system is novel or corresponds to as yet undescribed endogenous gene products. Nonetheless, the acquisition of a specificity distinct from either parent gene suggests another level at which the genome may expand its developmental diversity.

ACKNOWLEDGMENTS

We acknowledge the invaluable contributions of Marcia Barinaga, Neil Brinberg, Estelita Ong, Donna Simmons, Joan Vaughn, Wylie Vale, Ralph Brinster, and Bob Hammer. We thank these colleagues and Geof Wahl and Kelly Mayo for valuable discussions. We thank Carrie Humphrey for expert secretarial assistance. Experiments were supported by grants from the National Institutes of Health.

REFERENCES

1. Harpold, M., Dobner, P., Evans, R. M., and Bancroft, F. C. (1982). *Nucleic Acids Res.* **5**, 2039–2053.
2. Harpold, M. M., Dobner, P. R., Evans, R., Bancroft, F. C., and Darnell, J. D. (1979). *Nucleic Acids Res.* **6**, 3133–3144.
3. Doehmer, J., Barinaga, M., Vale, W., Rosenfeld, M. G., Verma, I. M., and Evans, R. M. (1982). *Proc. Natl. Acad. Sci. U.S.A.* **79**, 2268–2272.
4. Evans, R. M., Birnberg, N. C., and Rosenfeld, M. G. (1982). *Proc. Natl. Acad. Sci. U.S.A.* **79**, 7659–7663.
5. Barinaga, M., Yamamoto, G., Rivier, C., Vale, W., Evans, R., and Rosenfeld, M. (1983). *Nature (London)* **306**, 84.
6. Gordon, J. W., Scangos, G. A., Plotkin, D. J., Barbosa, J. A., and Ruddle, F. (1980). *Proc. Natl. Acad. Sci. U.S.A.* **77**, 7380–7384.
7. Brinster, R. L., Chen, H. Y., Trumbauer, M., Senear, A. W., Warren, R., and Palmiter, R. D. (1981). *Cell* **27**, 223–231.
8. Constantini, F., and Lacy, E. (1981). *Nature (London)* **295**, 92–94.
9. Palmiter, R. D., Brinster, R. L., Hammer, R. E., Trumbauer, M. E., Rosenfeld, M. G., Birnberg, N. C., and Evans, R. M. (1982). *Nature (London)* **330**, 611–615.
10. Richmond, J. L., and Wilson, C. B. (1978). *J. Neurosurg.* **49**, 163–167.
11. Steiner, H., Dahlback, O., and Waldenstarm, J. (1968). *Lancet* **1**, 783–785.
12. Greenberg, P. B., Beck, C., Martin, T. J., and Burger, H. G. (1972). *Lancet* **1**, 350–352.
13. Daughaday, W. H., Herrington, A. C., and Phillips, L. S. (1975). *Rev. Physiol.* **37**, 211–244.
14. Kostyo, J. L., and Isaksson, O. (1977). *Int. Rev. Physiol.* **13**, 255–274.
15. Morikawa, M., Nixon, T., and Green, H. (1982). *Cell* **29**, 783–789.
16. Danielson, K. G., Ohi, S., and Huang, P. C. (1982). *Proc. Natl. Acad. Sci. U.S.A.* **79**, 2301–2304.
17. Danielson, K. G., Ohi, S., and Huang, P. C. (1982). *Histol. Cytol.* **30**, 1033–1039.

DISCUSSION

M. A. Kirschner: Could you comment on the percentage of takes that you get with these transgenic injections?

R. Evans: Approximately 25–35% of the animals that develop are transgenic, that is, have incorporated the growth hormone gene. This percentage is a highly variable number and is dependent on who is doing the injections. It is this type of technique that gets better with time; time is measured in years; people who begin to develop this technology as we have at Salk generally start with a low percentage such as 1% of the animals being positive. People such as Ralph Brinster, with whom we collaborated in these studies, obtain the highest percentages of positive animals. I should simply mention that the way this is done is that you take the injected eggs and you implant them into pseudopregnant mice, and they develop normally after that. There's nothing really special after the injection process.

M. A. Kirschner: Do you have any matings of transgenic animals and can you comment on the growth characteristics if you do. Finally, do you have any data on the life span of these animals.

R. Evans: The presence of high levels of growth hormone is somewhat inhibitory to fertility, primarily in females, although very high levels of growth hormone can be tolerated in males, which is why we generally use males as the transgenic parent, although we have mated females with nontransgenic males, and you still get transgenic progeny. Another interesting related issue is that Bob Hammer also injected this gene into the dwarf strain of mice, it's "little" and when this gene is expressed, a couple of things happen. First of all, the mice grow up to be the size of normal transgenic animals, that is they are big; they are about four times the size of a dwarf mouse. Dwarf mice are very difficult to breed; the fertility of the transgenic animals goes way up in the males although not the females. With regard to the life span, it is relatively normal. We have carried some of these mice for quite an extensive period of time, for example, we have gone through approximately 6 generations.

T. Chen: Have you looked at the receptors for growth hormone in those transgenic mice? The reason I ask is, when endocrinologists look at this astronomical level of growth hormone, the first thing they think about is down-regulation, and the loss of responsiveness to the hormone.

R. Evans: We have not looked at growth hormone receptors; there has been one report that has looked at the effect on prolactin receptors in the liver, and there is some effect there.

M. B. Lipsett: I ought to tell you and all of the other people here about a new threat to this sort of research: recently Jeremy Rifkin, whom some of you may know, wrote a letter to the DNA Recombinant Advisory Committee (RAC) at the N.I.H. in which he asked the Committee to ban all research which consisted of taking DNA or genetic material from one species to another. I don't think that the RAC will take that very seriously but they will have to publish it in the Federal Register for comment. I wrote to some of the societies that work closely with us that if they thought that this would hamper research that it might be worthwhile to write to the RAC and make their wishes known.

R. Evans: This shouldn't become a political forum for that, but I've received a number of calls from committees that are investigating the potential outcome of what happens if these mice escape. There have been a number of individuals that have been worried about the potential outcome of this sort of experiment, assuming that some of these animals, once a number of people are doing the experiments, could possibly get out into the wild. Could this change the gene pool? What would be the consequence if it got into the gene pool of essentially wild mice? And there are ethical questions that are worthwhile to address. What is the right thing to do? If scientific societies can support the basic concept of this type of approach I think it is an important and potent way to influence public opinion. It is easy for the press and individuals to generate emotional issues among the public which is not thinking of the potential benefits and what we are trying to accomplish. We are not just trying to make big mice; but as this technology opens up a concept, a new conceptual area, you can begin to address questions in a different way that you were not able to address before, and you can begin to answer new questions and also answer long-standing biological issues. It also raises the potential for gene therapy which is another important new area that is developing.

B. F. Rice: I couldn't help thinking as you were giving your marvelous talk about Mr. Reagan's Starwars and this almost sounded like Genewars or something like that; but the real question I have for you is that, are these mice simply larger than normal mice or do they have some of the metabolic abnormalities that we normally see in people that have excessive growth hormone levels such as diabetes, bone malformations, and things of that nature?

R. Evans: Well you are asking the wrong person. We are not studying these questions. We are offering these mice to people who are interested in studying any type of physiological effects, the feedback mechanisms, processing, how other cell types handle gene products that are not normally present, how they secrete it, what mechanism exists to store protein, etc. There are a number of questions that are of interest to study. We have not approached any of these important types of issues.

B. F. Rice: Are their blood sugars elevated?

R. Evans: We do not know.

N. A. Samaan: I think my question may be a little similar to Dr. Rice. You mentioned that you examined the viscera of these animals. Have you examined the pancreas or have you examined the insulin level in these animals?

R. Evans: No.

N. A. Samaan: You followed these animals during their growth. Did they all continue to grow or did some of them grow and then stop growing? Did some of these animals lose weight because I expect some of them may have developed diabetes.

R. Evans: We have no evidence that suggests diabetes at all. They grow to about twice the size of a normal mouse, and then they stop growing. They reach that size in varying ways depending on which animal you're dealing with, but when they get there to a maximal size, they don't grow more than 2-fold bigger; that seems to be a limitation, genetic limitation of the effect of growth hormone. Therefore, there are obviously other factors that determine that limit. It is probably not too dissimilar from limits that are seen in humans, even in giantism; I don't think people get much more than twice the size. That is a big change. But that's where they stop. We don't know anything about diabetes. These animals occasionally develop nonmalignant growths in their liver, and occasionally in their lungs. That's about all we see that is abnormal.

P. Rayford: I have not been in the area of pituitary endocrinology for quite some while and maybe my question might be a little bit naive. In gastrointestinal endocrinology, the area of research that I am involved in, we find levels of hormones in picogram quantities and we feel that those levels are physiologic and even in some instances pathologic. You said levels of growth hormone in your studies were about 0.3 μg or did I understand correctly?

R. Evans: No, 0.3 mg.

P. Rayford: 0.3 mg, that's even higher; that means that you are looking at a level that is almost 0.1 or 0.2% the body weight of your animals—that is absolutely enormous and I wonder if you are measuring something that is not really growth hormone, if you are measuring something else, or have you looked at that, have you looked at any types or kinds of forms of growth hormone. You know your values are just enormous.

R. Evans: It is definitely growth hormone.

P. Rayford: Have you looked at it in terms of its biological activity?

R. Evans: You mean have we tried to purify it out of the serum of these mice?

P. Rayford: Yes, because if those are the levels of growth hormone, you could possibly purify it and then look at it in some kind of biologic activity or bioassay.

R. Evans: No, but what we have done is we have characterized the messenger RNA and we have established that indeed the RNA is being produced in tissues that are immunopositive and the RNA product is the complete and predicted RNA that would encode full length growth hormone. I should say that we can regulate the RNA levels in these cells by giving heavy metals like I showed you; furthermore, you can regulate the serum circulating growth hormone levels exactly in parallel, so we can induce these animals in the order of 10- to 12-fold, simply by feeding them a dietary supplement of zinc sulfate which apparently has no other effects with the exception of inducing the metallothionein gene and the fusion gene.

P. Kelly: I would like to point out that the animal in question is probably the best control for the biological activity of what is being secreted. Second, I would like to ask has there been any attempt to correlate somatomedin levels with growth hormone levels in these animals?

R. Evans: Yes there was a relatively brief study done by Ralph Brinster that looked at somatomedin levels and there is an elevation on the order of 2- to 3-fold.

B. Littlefield: I believe that glucocorticoids also regulate metallothionein. I was wondering if glucocorticoids have any effect on growth hormone production since the metallothionein promoter was used in the fusion gene.

R. Evans: Glucocorticoids do not appear to affect the expression of this fusion gene at all. The only thing that regulates it is heavy metals, although I should say that metallothionein is responsive to steroids in the animal, even in cell culture never is responsive to steroids.

B. Littlefield: I have a second question. Do you have any information about the copy number of the fusion gene that you are putting into these animals.

R. Evans: Yes it is a variable number that somewhat depends on the number of copies that you introduce into the fertilized egg; it goes from about 0.4 which is obviously a nonfunctional gene. We occasionally get fragments, as in the animal that you saw that did not grow but carried the gene; that animal had a portion of the gene. So from fragments of the gene all the way up to 100 to 200 copies, and generally all at the same chromosomal location.

B. Littlefield: Per cell in the transgenic animal?

R. Evans: Per cell.

P. Kelly: You mentioned that you injected 2000 copies of the GH gene. Is there a critical number of copies which needs to be injected to attain more than one copy number?

R. Evans: No, it is not a well stated parameter; basically the number was arrived at empirically. Some people inject 10,000, others inject a few hundred, it is not a hard number basically; that was just the final number that we injected, it is not really known what the variables are there.

H. Grotjan: My question is a follow-up to the one previously asked. Do you have any information on how the DNA which you inject is incorporated into the genetic material that is passed from the embryo into the other cells of the body and then subsequently passed by germ cells into a new generation? Is it randomly distributed or is it incorporated into specific chromosomal locations and passed on in a nonrandom fashion?

R. Evans: It is passed on nonrandomly; the mechanism for incorporation is not understood. It seems that DNA that is injected into the nucleus can, at a low percentage, be incorporated by unknown recombination of mechanisms. That is a question of interest to a number of people, i.e., what are the mechanisms that are involved in incorporating the DNA into chromosomes. Once it is in the chromosome then it is no problem because it is carried on as part of the genetic material, from the time that it is incorporated. There is some variability in time—it doesn't all get incorporated before the first cell division; sometimes it is free and becomes incorporated at later cell divisions; therefore not every cell in the embryo needs to have that DNA and you can get mosaic animals.

D. Keefe: Have you done frequent determinations to determine whether the growth hormone release is pulsatile?

R. Evans: It almost certainly is not; we are producing growth hormone now, in many different areas. Pulsatile regulation is very specific and probably relates to the neural control of the pituitary gene while the fusion gene is almost certainly just chronically expressed from the time the gene is activated and maintains very high levels. Whenever we look at mice from a particular pedigree, they are all expressing, within some variation that is relatively low, the exact same levels of growth hormone. In subsequent generations the growth hormone levels are always the same, so that we have never seen any variation at that level.

C. Nicoll: I have three questions. First, at what stage of development does the excess growth hormone appear in the circulation of the animals? Is it pre- or postnatally? Second, when do they start showing accelerated growth?

R. Evans: That is a good question which I cannot answer. I don't know when the growth hormone begins to be expressed, so I can't answer that question. It is probably expressed shortly after the liver develops, thus neonatally. The second part of the question is interesting. You cannot tell the transgenic mice from the normal mice when they are born. However, shortly before they are weaned there is a marked difference and you can begin to tell which ones are transgenic and which ones are not.

C. Nicoll: Do the tissues that are expressing growth hormone which do not normally do so, such as the heart or liver, show growth hormone secretion granules, or are they secreting it by an extragranular mechanism?

R. Evans: It certainly is constitutively secreted and there is no evidence for storage granules.

J. Stalvey: Since one of your objectives is to study the effects of inserting a gene into different known genetic backgrounds, have you tried different strains of mice and if so, do they show a difference in distribution of expression in the brain or a difference in amounts of growth hormone produced?

R. Evans: We have tried many different strains of mice, including the dwarf strains of mice, various types of inbred strains, and they all respond the same, the distribution is always the same, males, females, different strains, mutants, it always comes out the same. We have looked at about 19 different mice.

R. Osathanondh: I noticed in your pedigree study that you mixed a transgenic male animal with a normal female animal. Did you have any trouble mating the transgenic male with a transgenic female animal? The reason I ask this question is because women with acromegaly seem to have trouble with ovulation.

R. Evans: Yes, the female mice do not appear to be very fertile; we assume that that is a consequence of the expression of growth hormone, although we haven't done a formal analysis; but that is almost certainly the reason why they have reduced fertility and that is why we used males to generally propagate and transfer the gene to the next generation; however in the little mice the females regain complete fertility and so do the males.

R. Osathanondh: Could it be due to elevated serum prolactin or androgens? I don't know much about reproduction in mice but some women with acromegaly also have slightly elevated prolactin and androgens.

R. Evans: I don't know.

M. Thorner: I enjoyed the presentation very much. I have one comment and one question. The comment is that I was surprised that you said that you were perhaps surprised that your mice with the implanted GRF genes had high growth hormone levels and grew, because of the possibility of down-regulation. If that was the case the patient would never have presented with acromegaly and we would never have gotten to this stage.

R. Evans: That is true and of course Michael's point is that the way this cloning has started it obviously is that a patient presented with acromegalic conditions because of a tumor that was secreting growth hormone releasing factor, therefore it says that ectopic release of this factor can cause growth or elevation of growth hormone levels. However, the infusion of GRF into rodents did not have demonstrable growth effects. There it was not clear that the hormonal response in humans could be generalized to other animals.

M. Thorner: The second point is that we have observed that in another patient who has the same syndrome that the GRF levels remain very high (the normal level is undetectable, i.e. <100 pg/ml; this particular patient had levels running between 5 and 15 ng/ml over a 24-hour period being sampled every 20 minutes. In spite of those very high GRF levels, the patient secreted growth hormone in a pulsative fashion. My question to you is did your mice, who had the implanted GRF gene, grow even greater than the ones with the growth hormone gene because they may indeed still have pulsatile growth hormone secretion because their somatostatin system is still intact?

R. Evans: No, they don't; in fact they grow on average a little bit less, not dramatically less but they are averaging about 1.3- to 1.7-fold larger than the normal mouse whereas the growth hormone mice average 1.7 to 2.

R. Edgren: Have you ever measured the food intake in these animals; what is the food efficiency?

R. Evans: I don't know. One might expect that they might be more efficient but we haven't looked at fat and we haven't looked at food utilization.

Neuropeptides: Interactions and Diversities

FLOYD E. BLOOM, ELENA BATTENBERG, ANDRE FERRON,
JORGE R. MANCILLAS, ROBERT J. MILNER, GEORGE SIGGINS,
AND J. GREGOR SUTCLIFFE*

*Division of Preclinical Neuroscience and Endocrinology and *Department of Molecular Biology, Scripps Clinic and Research Foundation, La Jolla, California*

I. Introduction

Progress in cellular neurobiology has advanced most rapidly in three areas of discovery: (1) *new potential transmitter substances,* such as the rapidly expanding families of neuropeptides; (2) *newly recognized neuronal circuitry,* often recognized only because of the molecular markers created through the search for new transmitters; and (3) *the newly recognized molecular mechanisms* that may mediate the transmission of information by these circuits and transmitters to their target cells. Our laboratories have concentrated on the use of multidisciplinary methods to combine knowledge based on transmitter localization, transmitter circuitry, and transmitter mechanisms (see Siggins and Bloom, 1982; Foote *et al.,* 1983; Bloom, 1984).

This communication will highlight two areas of our recent exploration: (1) interactions between the transmitters of convergent synaptic inputs on their presumed common target cells. In particular, we have studied interactions between norepinephrine, the transmitter of the globally directed coeruleo-cortical projection (Morrison *et al.,* 1979; Foote *et al.,* 1983) and vasoactive intestinal polypeptide (VIP), one of the peptides attributed to the intrinsic local interneurons of the rodent cerebral cortex, the bipolar neurons (see Morrison *et al.,* 1984); we have also studied, in a similar manner, interactions in hippocampus between somatostatin, a peptide found within several neuronal elements of the limbic system (Morrison *et al.,* 1983), and acetylcholine, long a presumptive transmitter for the septo-hippocampal pathway. (2) The use of molecular genetic approaches to define those neuropeptides which have not yet been discovered. Toward this end, we summarize briefly our strategy to discover brain specific molecules (Milner and Sutcliffe, 1983; Milner *et al.,* 1984; Sutcliffe *et al.,* 1983a,b, 1984; Sutcliffe and Milner, 1984; Bloom, 1982a, 1984). We interpret our early findings with this strategy to exemplify some potentially important new directions in the quest to unravel more completely the chemical and functional organization of the nervous system. Given the historical lesson that the nervous system and the endocrine system use many of the same messenger molecules interchangeably (Bloom, 1984; Krieger, 1983; Guillemin, 1978) regardless of the functional system in which the molecules were first discovered, it is our view that these same principles will be as relevant to endocrinologists as they may be to neuroscientists.

II. Interactions between Vasoactive Intestinal Polypeptide and Norepinephrine in Rat Cerebral Cortex

Several lines of evidence support a role for vasoactive intestinal poly-peptide (VIP) as a neuronal messenger in cerebral cortex. Biochemical data support its presence, release, binding, and at best one possible action (see Morrison and Magistretti, 1983 for references). Immunocytochemical data have localized VIP to cortical bipolar neurons (Morrison et al., 1984). Single unit recording studies show that iontophoretically applied VIP excites some cortical neurons (Phillis et al., 1978) but in an inconsistent manner. Other cellular actions reported for VIP in cortex include the ability to stimulate cyclic AMP formation (Quik et al., 1979; Etgen and Browning, 1983; Magistretti and Schorderet, 1984) and glycogenolysis (Magistretti et al., 1981) in cortical slices. It is somewhat more potent in these actions than norepinephrine (NE).

Cytochemically, VIP and NE containing circuits show a contrasting but complementary cortical anatomy (see Morrison and Magistretti, 1983): VIP neurons are intrinsic, bipolar, radially oriented, intracortical neurons; the NE innervation arises only from locus ceruleus and innervates a broad expanse of cortex in a horizontal plane. The two fiber systems may have the same targets, the pyramidal cells. Identified cortical pyramidal neurons are depressed in spontaneous firing by iontophoresis of either NE or cyclic AMP (Stone et al., 1974; also see Foote et al., 1983). The recent findings of Magistretti and Schorderet (1984) suggest that VIP and NE can act synergistically to increase cyclic AMP in cerebral cortex. Therefore, we tested VIP and NE on rat cortical neurons to evaluate this interaction at the cellular level using iontophoresis. Analysis of more than 100 cortical neurons suggests definitively that there are significant interactions: application of VIP during subthreshold NE administration causes pronounced inhibitions of cellular discharge regardless of the effect of VIP prior to NE (Ferron et al., 1984).

In our hands, the direct effects of VIP on the spontaneous firing rate of sensorimotor cortical neurons was not very impressive. VIP depressed 24%, excited 20%, and had biphasic effects on 2%; maximal currents (200 nA) passed through the VIP barrel had no effect on 54% of these cells. The direction of the response and the proportion of responding neurons were similar for identified pyramidal neurons and for all cortical neurons. The direct effects of NE were predominantly depressant actions in the cortex, as previously reported (Siggins and Bloom, 1982; Foote *et al.*, 1983). Therefore, in order to examine possible interactions between VIP and NE effects on single neurons, ejection currents of NE were reduced until they had little or no direct effect on neuronal firing (1–5 μA). After testing a cell for direct effects (if any) of VIP, subthreshold currents of NE were then applied continuously for several minutes while VIP was repeatedly retested. Tests on approximately 50 neurons studied in this way showed that ejection of VIP during subthreshold NE administration now produced consistent inhibition of firing. Such synergistic inhibitions were seen in more than half the cells regardless of whether VIP alone had elicited excitatory, inhibitory, or negligible effects on the test neuron (Ferron *et al.*, 1984). When VIP alone had a depressant action, administration of subthreshold NE markedly enhanced this depressant effect. Even in cases where VIP alone gave excitatory effects, concurrent subthreshold NE treatment reversed the VIP effect from excitation to inhibition (6 of 9 cells).

Magistretti and Schorderet (1984) showed that the synergism of VIP by NE was blocked by phentolamine, an α-adrenergic receptor antagonist, and mimicked by phenylephrine, an α receptor agonist. Therefore, we examined the effect of phenylephrine as well as NE pretreatment on neuronal responses to VIP. In 10 cells showing an interaction between VIP and NE, 9 revealed equivalent interactive synergisms of depressant responses with phenylephrine (Ferron *et al.*, 1984). Thus, the interaction of VIP and NE at the cellular level may also involve α receptor activation, although further testing is required.

Our electrophysiological indications of a VIP–NE interaction at the cellular level may arise from their biochemical effects *in vitro* on cyclic AMP generation. Such parallel findings strengthen the suggestions that cyclic AMP may mediate both NE and VIP evoked depressions of neuronal firing in cortex. The reported enhancement by NE of synaptic and other transmitter responses (including inhibitory ones) may be related phenomena (see Foote *et al.*, 1983; Bloom, 1984). An apparently similar, cAMP-mediated enhancement by β receptors of noradrenergic target cell responsiveness to α-adrenergic agonists has been reported for pineal (Klein *et al.*, 1983). Furthermore, in rat hepatocytes, increased cAMP levels induced by glucagon enhance binding of α-adrenergic agonists to these cells (Morgan *et al.*, 1984). Two modes of indirect amplification of postsynaptic target cell mechanisms may be involved in these interactions, namely a cAMP-mediated activation of protein kinases (as with β-adrenergic and other responses) and a calcium activation of protein kinases (as with α_1-adrenergic and other transmitter or hormone responses; see Nestler and Greengard, 1984). However, it is not yet clear how these metabolic and electrophysiologic events actually interact. If NE- and VIP-containing fibers do indeed converge on the same cortical target cell, it is feasible that cyclic AMP is the intracellular mediator of their synergistic interaction.

III. Interactions between Somatostatin and Acetylcholine Actions in Rat Hippocampus

Although the oligopeptide somatostatin was discovered and named for its ability to impair the release of growth hormone from somatotropes (see Guillemin, 1978), the same peptide is ubiquitous through the central, peripheral, and diffuse gastrointestinal nervous systems and the endocrine pancreas. Among the nonendocrine regions of the rat and primate central nervous system where this peptide has been localized to large numbers of neurons are the hippocampus and cerebral cortex (see Morrison *et al.*, 1982, 1983 for references). In rat hippocampus, tests of neurons *in vitro* (Pittman and Siggins, 1981) and in vivo (French *et al.*, 1984) suggest that the peptide has many of the qualities of action of so-called "classical" inhibitory messenger molecules, depressing spontaneous discharge rate, hyperpolarizing the postsynaptic membrane, and increasing membrane conductance (but see Dodd and Kelly, 1978; Olpe *et al.*, 1980 for different results and interpretations).

We recently began additional studies on hippocampal neuronal responses to somatostatin when we observed some unexpected interactions between the effects of systemic ethanol on responsiveness to transmitter substances thought to act in the hippocampus (Mancillas *et al.*, 1984). What began as an attempt to determine the causes for apparent shifts in responsivity to afferent inputs after ethanol, then led to a series of experiments to map possible transmitter interactions without the confusion of systemic ethanol. While these tests are far from complete, tests on approximately 35 pyramidal neurons in CA1 or CA3 fields have indicated some consistent patterns of response interactions.

In general, somatostatin produces apparently direct depressant actions on spontaneous discharge rate. Often these effects were delayed in onset and offset by several seconds relative to the iontophoretic current pulses.

When neurons are tested with brief pulses of acetylcholine, which itself produces facilitation of firing, the effects of somatostatin on the acetylcholine-induced changes were dose dependent. At doses that had little or no direct effect on spontaneous discharge rate, somatostatin only depressed the basal firing between acetylcholine pulses that produced increased firing and did not affect the magnitude of the ACh-induced rate increases. This sort of effect could be regarded as "enhancing the signal-to-noise ratio" of afferent versus basal discharge rates, similar to one interpretation of noradrenergic synaptic transmission action (see Foote *et al.*, 1983).

At higher doses of somatostatin, the most notable effect was an increased responsiveness of the test neuron to the acetylcholine pulses; under these intermediate doses of sustained somatostatin application, the cell showed more potent and somewhat longer lasting effects of acetylcholine induced firing. Interestingly, this effect of somatostatin has a more rapid onset and offset than the "direct" depressant effects of somatostatin. Furthermore, there was no such synergistic interaction between somatostatin and response of neurons to L-glutamate, a transmitter with classical excitatory membrane actions. In fact, somatostatin frequently depressed glutamate responses as well as basal firing.

At still higher doses of somatostatin, a combination of the lower dose interactions could be seen depending in general on how much somatostatin this test cell had previously had. Such cells could show enhancement of acetylcholine responses promptly, with more delayed mixed effects, in which both basal firing and acetylcholine responses were depressed. Depending upon the degree to which other transmitter substances present in the multibarrel pipet were allowed to leak out, and depending upon the test history of the neuron under investigation, the responses could appear to be chaotic. By restricting carefully the number of possible interactions through careful monitoring of leakage retaining, and balancing currents (see Bloom, 1974), the interesting effects have emerged: somatostatin, even though directly inhibitory, seems capable of selectively enhancing responses to excitatory actions of applied acetylcholine but not glutamate. Understanding the cellular mechanisms responsible for these selective interactions will require substantial additional evidence. However, unless such forms of interaction are acknowledged and considered, the effects of somatostatin alone could be viewed as controversial or "inconsistent" when in fact they may reflect an important form of regulation of responsiveness of common target cells within the CNS and endocrine systems. Also important will be the interactions between somatostatin and the other potentially released products of its common prohormone (see Bakhit *et al.*, 1984 for references).

IV. Pioneering Strategies of Transmitter Discovery

The history of transmitter discovery can be viewed as having had a "classical" period and a "modern" period. Both periods produced important information about neuronal organization. The "classical" period began with the molecules acetylcholine, adrenaline, and noradrenaline discovered by Dale, Loewi, Elliott, von Euler, and the other early students of the autonomic nervous system. This period lasted until the beginning of in depth studies of transmitter systems in the central nervous system. In this latter period, dopamine, serotonin, γ-aminobutyrate, and other small molecules were added to the list from which histochemists sought to map the brain. Although there may be more such small molecules to be discovered one might surmise that we are at a transition phase. Since the early 1980s, modern biological and chemical methods have been used advantageously to expand the list of transmitter discoveries already made.

As we look back upon the growing list of established and presumed transmitters (see Iversen, 1983 for a recent listing), those molecules emerging in the classical period can attribute their discovery to one of two strategies, depending on whether the factor was discovered before, or after, the biological actions for which it is now recognized. From the "Factor First–Function Later" strategy came all those substances that bear mainly chemical names: acetylcholine, γ-aminobutyrate, dopamine, glutamate, aspartate, glycine, or taurine (von Euler, 1975; Roberts and Kuriyama, 1968; Cooper *et al.,* 1982 for more detailed references). They were given these chemical names because it was primarily their chemical structure for which they were characterized long before any possible biological functions were known or even surmised.

In the "Assay First–Factor Later" strategy, the primary question was what substance did one group of cells use to control the activity of another group of cells. These interactions provided a functional assay that became the starting point for a purification–isolation process. This was the classical approach of Starling and the early gastrointestinal regulatory peptides, and for the "sympathin" era of Cannon and colleagues. All of the regulatory molecules resulting from this approach carry functional names rather than chemical names: gastrin, cholecystokinin, heparin, adrenaline, prostaglandin, insulin and glucagon, substance P, angiotensin, oxytocin, vasopressin, histamine, and serotonin.

This methodology reached its zenith with the efforts of Guillemin, Schally, McCann, and others who pushed their colleagues to detect the hypophysiotrophic factors conceived by Geoffery Harris in the mid-1940s and early 1950s (Guillemin, 1978). These teams developed powerful methods for extracting, purifying, and isolating these peptide "factors," determining their amino acid composition, sequences, and posttranslational modifications. To prove that what they had isolated was in fact the source of the function, the molecule was synthetically replicated and shown to give all the biological and biochemical properties of the natural starting material.

Given that all of these methods had to be invented, it was perhaps no wonder that the starting sources had to be enormous quantities of freshly dissected cattle brains. From this effort came the "Assay-First," functional names for thyrotropin releasing hormone, somatostatin, gonadotropin releasing hormone, and prolactin. Most recently, the last two of the originally postulated hypophysiotrophic factors predicted, corticotropin-releasing factor (Vale *et al.*, 1981) and growth hormone-releasing factor (Guillemin *et al.*, 1982; Spiess *et al.*, 1983) have been identified. This neoclassical approach proved its value repeatedly as others used the methods to isolate factors based on rather unpredictable assays: the loss of blood pressure which lead to neurotensin (McDonald *et al.*, 1983), the opiate-like substances detected by *in vitro* assays that lead to the endorphins (cf. Snyder, 1984 for references), and the gut or vascular effects that lead to vasoactive intestinal polypeptide and gastric inhibitory peptide (Carlquist *et al.*, 1982; Mutt, 1976). Others will no doubt still be sought in this way (Benoit *et al.*, 1982). The success of the "Assay-First" strategy may also be gauged by the degree to which it is still being exploited, such as the recent discoveries of the cardiac natriopeptides, that may be anticipated to have CNS equivalents.

The discovery strategy based upon purification of factors in a functional assay (a secretogogue, or a smooth muscle contractant or relaxant) works well when the assay is sensitive and specific. However, factors discovered in this way are often found to have many actions unanticipated from the assay system on which the isolation process was based. Thus aside from the original presumed function evaluated in that assay, both Factor-First Factors and Assay-First Factors eventually have to be subjected to rigorous evaluation for sites and mechanisms of action. Put more simply, the rules for discovering a factor may be seen to have very little ultimate weight in how widespread or powerfully the factor functions.

V. Two Modern Strategies of Transmitter Discovery

Two series of developments over the past half decade have had impressive effects on the emerging list of recognized transmitters. Mutt and colleagues (Mutt, 1976; Tatemoto and Mutt, 1980, 1981) observed the frequent occurrence of C-terminally amidated peptides that functioned as chemical messengers, and adopted a strategy to search for other molecules with this common structure. From extracts of gut and brain they found a whole series of biologically active, C-terminally amidated molecules. Some appear to be members of the glucagon–VIP family (Tatemoto, 1982a,b; Tatemoto et al., 1982, 1983) and others to be members of the pancreatic polypeptide family (Tatemoto, 1982). The latter, termed NPY (a neuropeptide with a tyrosine, single letter amino acid symbol, "Y," at each end) is reckoned to be the most prominent known peptide in human cortex (Adrian et al., 1983).

The second new approach is based on a more general biological principle, that all proteins are synthesized under the direction of a specific messenger RNA (mRNA) which is encoded in the genome. With the very rapid emergence of recombinant DNA technologies, restriction endonucleases, and nucleotide sequencing, which make this field both powerful and rapidly progressive, a new opportunity for novel chemical messenger discovery became available. Thus, determination of the complete sequence of the prohormone for "opiocortin" (Nakanishi et al., 1979) directly revealed an unanticipated biologically relevant peptide, homologous in sequence to α and β MSH. The existence of the deduced γ MSH was later verified in part chemically and cytochemically (Shibasaki et al., 1982; Bloom et al., 1980).

Subsequently, the recombinant DNA approach has been employed to obtain the prohormone structural sequences for almost every one of the previously identified neuropeptides: all of the major branches of the endorphin family (Nakanishi et al., 1979; Noda et al., 1982; Gubler et al., 1982; Kakidani et al., 1982): somatostatin (Goodman et al., 1982); VIP (Itoh et al., 1983), oxytocin and vasopressin (Ruppert et al., 1984; Schmale and Richter, 1984), angiotensin (Nawa et al., 1983a), bradykinin (Okhuba et al., 1983), corticotropin-releasing factor (Furutani et al., 1983), growth hormone-releasing factor (Gubler et al., 1983; Mayo et al., 1983), substance P (Nawa et al., 1983b), and cholecystokinin (Deschenes et al., 1984). Potentially new, previously unsuspected added variants have suggested that these mRNA sequences could also lead to a new form of VIP (Itoh et al., 1983), of the aplysia egg laying hormones (Scheller et al., 1982) and of substance P (Nawa et al., 1983b). Moreover, pursuit of the prohormone for calcitonin led Rosenfeld and Evans and their collaborators to the recognition that the gene for procalcitonin could also give rise to a "calcitonin-gene related peptide" (Rosenfeld et al., 1983; also see Evans, this volume), which in fact was found in particular segments of the rat CNS and later found to possess biological activity.

Along the way, mRNAs for tyrosine hydroxylase and dopamine-β-hydroxylase have been cloned but not yet sequenced (Lamouroux et al.,

1982). Moreover, other important structural neuronal peptides and the nicotinic cholinergic receptor have also had their structure solved by this recombinant DNA approach, but space prevents further scrutiny of these findings here. More pertinent to endocrine and neuronal pharmacology is the finding that the diabetes insipidus of the Brattleboro rat is in fact due to a single nucleotide deletion in the gene for its prohormone (Schmale and Richter, 1984). This defect apparently prevents complete processing of the vasopressin preprohormone by the rough endoplasmic reticulum. Thus, the defect essentially stops synthesis of this secretory material. The fact that the same neurons also then synthesize less of the one other neuropeptide they are known to make, dynorphin (Schmale and Richter, 1984), but not of other proteins needed for structural elaboration, suggests that there may well be far greater specialization of protein synthesis regulation in neurons than was suspected. This suggests numerous possible pathophysiologic avenues for central endocrine diseases that may involve neuropeptide systems.

VI. Another Possible General Strategy for Molecular Discovery

All of these successful exploitations of molecular genetic principles indicate that better analysis of brain mRNAs might disclose the existence of further possible biologically important hormones (see Bloom, 1982a,b). In addition, such an analysis might not only yield neurotransmitters but might also yield information important to the complete characterization of the properties of neurons and their cell assemblies.

We have used molecular cloning methods to purify randomly chosen copies (cDNAs) of rat brain messengers RNAs (mRNAs). Poly(A)$^+$ RNA was purified from the brains of adult rats, copied into double-stranded cDNA, and inserted into the plasmid pBR322 for cloning in *E. coli*. Clones bearing cDNA inserts that were at least 500 base pairs in length were nick translated and evaluated for their patterns of hybridization to mRNAs isolated from brain, liver, and kidney. Those clones that hybridize to brain mRNAs, but not to mRNAs extracted from other organs, we define as being brain specific. The complete strategy has been reported (Sutcliffe *et al.*, 1983).

This categorization has been extremely productive since basic quantitative characterizations had not previously been available. For example, from the sizes of the mRNAs in brain, their relative abundances and the total complexity of the brain mRNA population, it may be calculated that the rat's brain expresses about 30,000 mRNAs, of which most are "brain-specific" (Milner and Sutcliffe, 1983). The brain-specific mRNAs tend to be larger and more rare than the mRNAs found in other major organ systems, suggesting that genetic messages in brain may encode more complex translation products. In addition, this phase of our research quickly yielded a wholly unanticipated finding an identifier or "ID" gene sequence that is necessary, but not sufficient for the expression of brain-specific genetic messages (see Sutcliffe and Milner, 1984; Sutcliffe *et al.,* 1984 for further details).

Currently, we are using the "northern" blotting strategy, a sensitive and rapid way of screening the very large number of brain-derived cDNAs produced from cloning whole brain mRNA (Milner and Sutcliffe, 1983; Sutcliffe *et al.,* 1983). This and other strategies allow us to select clones that are full length cDNA copies of specific mRNAs. Large amounts of insert are prepared and the nucleotide sequence determined. Those mRNA sequences with long open reading frames are translated from the nucleotide code to deduce the amino acid sequences of the brain-specific proteins. When sequences are obtained, they are compared by computer searches of nucleotide and peptide sequence databases so that we can invest our efforts in novel brain-specific molecules.

VII. 1B236: A Brain Specific Protein Found in a Subset of Neurons

One of the first brain-specific mRNAs that we sequenced was p1B236 (Fig. 1). The strategy used to extend our characterization of 1B236 was to examine the deduced peptide sequence, to seek out regions that might provide clues to the function of the protein. In 1B236 we found that there were 3 peptides (termed by us P5, P6, and P7) clustered at the C-terminus, enclosed by pairs of basic dipeptides. These peptides were synthesized, and the synthetic peptides used to raise polyclonal and monoclonal antisera. The antisera have now been used for immunocytochemistry, for "western" blot analysis of immunoreactive material extractable from the brain, and for radioimmunoassays of peptidic extracts partially purified by high-pressure liquid chromatography.

In immunocytochemical mapping, antisera to each of three nonoverlapping peptides gave virtually superimposable maps of intense immunoreactivity within a few specific neuronal systems, being most intense in the olfactory, limbic, somatosensory, and extrapyramidal motor systems (Bloom *et al.,* 1984). The possibility of molecular processing is still being actively pursued but current evidence suggests that the 1B236 propeptide is processed to smaller forms that share immunoreactivity with our small synthetic peptides (Malfroy *et al.,* 1984). If these synthetic fragments are in fact natural processing products of the 1B236 peptide, our preliminary evidence favors them having biological activity on the cellular and behav-

```
                    LysSerTyrGlyGlnAspAsnArgThrValGluLeuSerValMetTyrAlaProTrpLysProThrValAsnGlyThrValValAlaValGlyGluThrValSe
CTGCA(G)12AGAAGTCCTATGGCCAGGACAACCGCACGTGGAGCTGAGCGTCATGTATGCACCTGGAAGCCCACAGTGAATGGGACAGGGGGGAGACAGTCTC

rIleLeuCysSerThrAsnSerAsnProAspProIleLeuThrIlePheLysGlnIleLeuAlaThrValIleTyrGluSerGlnLeuGluLeuProAlaValThrP
CATCCTGTTCCACACAGAGCAACCCGGACCCTATTCTCACCATTCTCAAGGAGAAGCAGATCCTGGCCACGGTCATCTATGAGAGTCAGCTGGAACTCCCTGCAGTGACGC

roGluLeuAspGlyCysLeuTyrTrpCysValAlaGluAsnGlnTyrGlyArgAlaThrAlaPheAsnLeuSerValGluPheAlaProIleLeuLeuGluSerHisCysAlaAla
CCGAGGACGATGGGAGCTGTAGCTGAGAACCAGTATGGCAGAGCCACCGCCTTCAACCTGTCTGTGGAGTTTGCTCCCATAATCCTTCTGGAATCGCACTGTCAGCG

AlaArgAspThrValGlnCysLeuCysValValLysSerAsnProProSerValAlaAlaPheGluLeuProSerArgAsnValAlaThrValAsnGluThrArgGluPheValTyrSe
GCCAGAGACACCGTGCAGTGCCTGTGTGTGGTAAAATCCAACCCGCCTTCCGTGGCCTTTGAGCTGCCTTGAGCAAGTGACTGTGAACGACACAGAGGGAGTTTGTACTC
                                                                    P4

rGluArgSerGlyLeuLeuLeuThrSerIleLeuLeuThrArgGluGlnThrAlaGlyThrAlaProProAspGlnAlaProValIleCysThrSerArgAsnLeuTyrGlyThrGlnSerLeuGluLeuProP
AGAGCGCAGCGGCCTTCCTGCTCACCAGCATCCTCACGCNCTCCGGGGTCAGCCCAGCCCCACCCCGCGTCATTGTACCTCCAGGAACCTCTACGGCACCCAGAGCCTCGAGCTGCCTT
                                           P5

heGluGlnAlaAlaHisArgLeuMetTrpAlaLysIleGlyProValGlyAlaValValAlaAlaPheAlaIleLeuLeuAlaIleValCysTyrIleThrGlnThrArgArgLysLysAsnVal
TCCAGGGAGCACCGACTGATGTGGGCCAAAATCGGCCCTGTGGGTGCTGTGGTGGCTGCTTTGCCATCCTGATTGCCATCGTCTGCTACATCACCCAGACAAGAAGAAAAAGAACGTC
                          P6

ThrGlnSerProSerPheSerAlaGluValAspAsnProHisValGluLeuTyrSerProProGluPheAlaIleSerGluAlaProAsnLysThrSerGluGlyLysArgLeuGlySerGluArgAr
ACAGAGAGCCCCAGCTTCTCAGCGGGAGACACCCTCATGTCTGTACAGCCCGAATTCTGGAGCACCTGATAAGTATGAGGTAGAAGCGCCTGGGGTCCGAGAGGAG
                                                                                        P7

gLeuLeuLeuGlyLeuArgGluProProGluProGluLeuAspAspProTrpLeuAspLeuSerTyrTyrSerHisSerAspLeuGly
GCTGCTGGGCCTTAGGGGGAACCCCCAGAACTGGACCTGAGTTATTCCCACTCAGACCTGGGAAACGACCCACCCAAGGACAGCTACACCCTGACAGAGAGGAGCTGGCTACGGCAG

LeuIleAspArgIleLeu***
AAATCCGAGTCAAGTGAGGAAGCTGGGGGCTGGGCCTGTGGGGGTGGGGTCAGGAAGCT

CGGGAAGGGGGCGGGGCAGGAAAACAGTGAGGTCTTTAGGGGCCCGGCCTCCCCTCTTCTCTGCCAACATCCTGCACCTATGTTACAGCTCCCTCTCCCCTCCTTTTA

ACCTCAGCTGTTGAGAGGGGTGTCTCTGTCGTCCATGTTATTTATTGTTATCCTGGTCTCTGTGCCCCTTACCCGCCCCAGGACCTGTACAAAAGGACATGAAATAAATGTCCTAAT

GACAAGTGCCAGTCTAGACCCATCCTTTGGAGGAAAGGGGCATATTAGTAATACTTTTCTGTTGCTGTAACAAAATACTGGACAAAAACAC(A)-100(C)n
```

FIG. 1. Nucleotide sequence of the pIB236 cDNA insert, showing the open reading frame 318 amino acids long, and the positions of the synthetic peptides (P4, 5, 6, and 7) used for immunization of rabbits, and the preparation of antisera for immunocytochemistry.

ioral levels (S. J. Henriksen, personal communication; G. F. Koob, personal communication).

The immunoreactivity was especially dense in olfactory bulb, specific preoptic, and diencephalic nuclei, and also in the neostriatum, limbic, and neocortical regions. Neuropil staining was also prominent within selected thalamic and cranial nerve nuclei, as well as in cerebellum and spinal cord. Maps constructed from the optimally reactive antisera for each of the three C-terminal fragments of 1B236 gave virtually identical patterns with some minor exceptions (Bloom *et al.*, 1984).

Neuropil staining typically exhibited four major forms: (1) a fine varicose fiber, with positive immunoreactivity in both varicosities and intervaricose regions, (2) isolated punctate elements interpreted as immunoreactive fibers surrounding the perimeter of unreactive neurons or neurites, (3) thick straight immunoreactive processes travelling within myelinated tracts, and (4) broad, generally long, densely immunoreactive neurites within regions shown to have immunoreactive perikarya in colchicine-treated preparations. The first two forms are interpreted as preterminal and terminal axons, the third as fibers of passage, and the fourth as probable dendrites. The following descriptions summarize the major patterns of immunoreactivity within regions showing prominent staining in both neuropil components (normal rats) and perikarya (colchicine-treated rats) in two selected sets of neurons: the olfactory bulb-peduncle (Fig. 2), and the neocortex (Fig. 3), as examples of the data derived from this detailed analysis. Immunoreactivity is also striking in specific zones of hippocampus (Fig. 4) and cerebellum (Fig. 5), as well as in many other specific regions of the rat brain (Fig. 6). Some specific examples of these patterns of immunoreactivity provide additional insight into the potential opportunities of our approach.

A. OLFACTORY BULB AND PEDUNCLE

Intense immunoreactivity was seen within the perimeters of the glomeruli, where immunoreactive periglomerular neurons (Fig. 2) were observed in colchicine-pretreated rats. The external plexiform layer and mitral cell layer showed no immunoreactivity, while extensive fiber staining was observed surrounding the unreactive granule cells in the internal

---

FIG. 2. Immunoperoxidase localization of the peptide P6, a fragment of the brain specific protein 1B236, identified by indirect immunocytochemistry in the rat olfactory bulb. In this low power survey, immunoreactivity is visible in the periglomerular cells, in thick processes in the external plexiform layer, and in thick, terminal-like processes ending in the internal plexiform layer. The inset shows immunoreactive periglomerular neurons in sections taken from a colchicine pretreated rat. Calibration bar = 100 μM (inset = 50 μM).

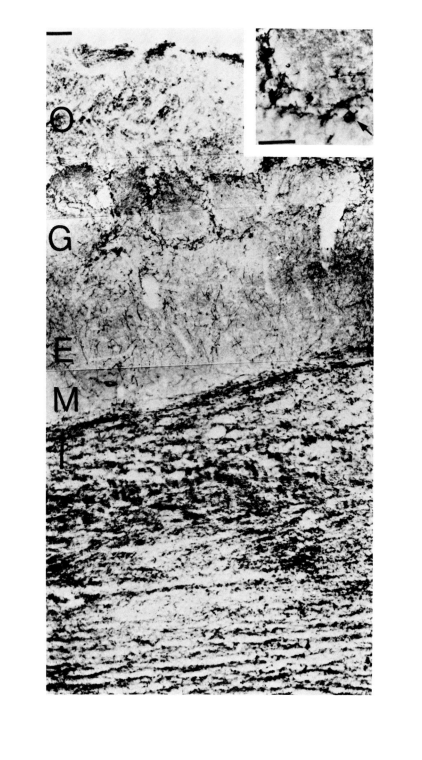

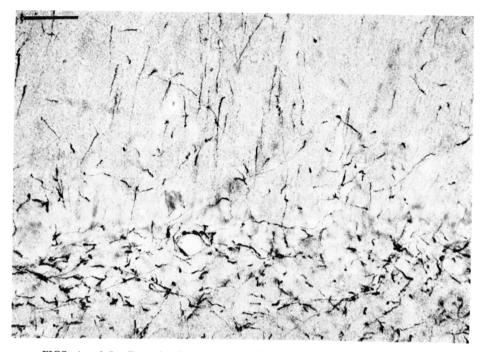

FIGS. 4 and 5. Extensive immunoreactive fibers surround the perikarya and apical dendrites of pyramidal cells in all fields of the hippocampal formation (Fig. 4) and all lobules of cerebellum (Fig. 5) and fields of the hippocampal formation (Fig. 4). In cerebellum (Fig. 5), fiber-like immunoreactive elements with thick varicose boutons are seen below and above the purkinje cells. In CA1 (Fig. 4), thick immunoreactive fibers with smaller varicosities can be seen densely packed below the pyramidal cells, with thicker but sparser fibers along the apical dendrites. Calibration bars = 25 μm for Fig. 3, 50 μm for Fig. 4.

plexiform layer. In favorable sections, isolated, small, short-axon cells could be resolved in the outer third of the internal plexiform layer. Preliminary electron microscope localization of immunoreactivity for P5 in the olfactory bulb confirmed the reactivity within dendrites and perikarya of

---

FIG. 3. Immunoreactivity within somatosensory cortex (Laminae I–IV) following exposure to antisera against P7; identical patterns were seen with antisera to P6 or P7 as well. Thick tangential processes are seen in outer lamina I, just below the pia, with relatively modest reactivity within the inner zone of this lamina. Thick radially directed processes are seen in laminae II and III, with dense, but finer, immunoreactive processes clustered around the nonimmunoreactive perikarya in laminae IV, V, and mid-VI (not shown). The contrasting bands of lighter and denser immunoreactivity are reproducible throughout this region of cortex in frontal sections. Some fiber-like staining can also be seen within the superficial layers of the subcortical white matter at bottom. Calibration bar = 50 μm.

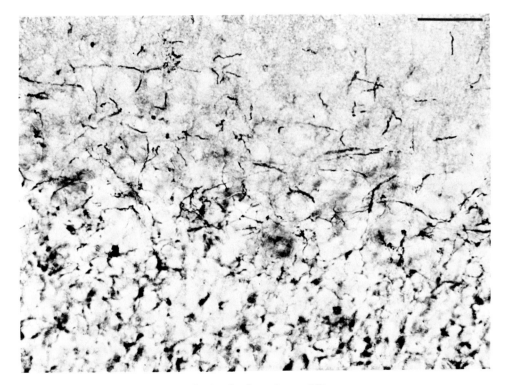

FIG. 5.   See legend on p. 353.

the periglomerular neurons, and in fine nerve terminals synapsing on
small dendritic spines within the internal plexiform layer. In immunoreactive terminals, the reaction product was associated exclusively with
the cytoplasmic face of the synaptic vesicles.

In the olfactory peduncle, extensive neuropil immunoreactivity was
observed in all nuclear fields and transition zones. Both fibers of passage
and finer processes with relatively few varicosities were observed to col-
lect at the lateral ventral pole of the peduncle, and entering the inner
surface of the lateral olfactory tract. Fiber-like staining was not seen
within the anterior commissure. In colchicine-pretreated rats, large and
medium sized multipolar neurons were also seen in all nuclear fields of the
peduncle, as well as within and around the nucleus of the anterior commissure and the nucleus of the lateral olfactory tract. Such neurons constitute up to 25% of the total neuronal population visualized in these
fields by general cytoplasmic counterstaining.

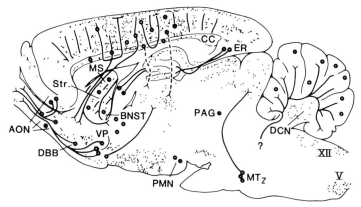

FIG. 6. Schematic Overview of neuropil and perikaryonal immunoreactivity patterns: An extensive, but virtually identical, pattern of immunoreactive fibers can be visualized throughout the normal rat CNS with antisera raised against P5, P6, or P7. The immunoreactivity is especially dense in olfactory bulb and peduncle, specific hypothalamic, and preoptic nuclei, the neostriatum, limbic, and neocortical regions. Neuropil staining was also prominent within selected thalamic and cranial nerve nuclei, as well as in cerebellum and spinal cord. Cell body-rich regions symbolized by circles, neuropil-rich regions by dots; presumptive fiber trajectories symbolized by solid lines, and putative pathways by dotted lines. The source of the immunoreactive fibers ending in the granule cell layer of the cerebellum is not yet known (?); the targets of the cells seen within the periaqueductal grey and the premammillary nuclei are also unspecifiable at this time. AON, Anterior olfactory nuclei; BNST, bed nucleus of the stria terminalis; CC, corpus callosum; DBB, diagonal band of Broca; DCN, deep cerebellar nuclei; ER, entorhinal cortex; MS, medial septal nucleus; Mtz, medial trapezoid nucleus; PAG, periaqueductal grey; PMN, premamillary nucleus; Str, striatum; V, spinal trigeminal nucleus; VP, ventral pallidal area; XII, hypoglossal nucleus.

B. CEREBRAL CORTEX

In cerebral cortex, neuropil immunoreactivity for P5, P6, and P7 showed virtually identical region-specific patterns when compared over the major cortical regions. Based upon published topographic and cytological criteria for rat cortical regions it was possible to correlate 1B236 immunoreactivity with presumptive functionally defined regions of rat cerebral cortex. Somatosensory cortex was the predominant region of cortical immunoreactivity; posterior cingulate cortex showed intermediate immunoreactivity, with motor, temporal (auditory) fields, and the occipital (visual) cortex, showing low-density immunoreactivity; anterior cingulate cortex and, in particular, the frontal medial cortex had no immunoreactivity. These regional variations were consistent from antibody to antibody and from animal to animal, whether sectioned frontally or sagitally.

Within the parietal and posterior cingulate cortex, intense radially oriented immunoreactive processes spanned the entire cortical thickness
intermingled with fine varicose fiber-like processes, and isolated punctate
structures (Fig. 3). These patterns were virtually identical for antisera
against P5, P6, or P7. All three sera showed similar laminar patterns, with
the P6 antisera showing somewhat denser overall immunoreactivity.
Thick tangential processes were seen in outer lamina I, just below the pia,
with relative modest reactivity within the inner zone of this lamina. The
thick radially directed processes were seen most clearly in deep laminae
II and III, with dense, but finer, immunoreactive processes clustered
around the perikarya in laminae IV, V, and mid-VI. Three contrasting
bands of lighter immunoreactivity in deep layer I and superficial layer II
and in the deeper portions of V and VI were reproducible throughout the
somatosensory regions of cortex in frontal sections. Some fiber-like immunoreactive processes with distinct varicosities could also be seen
within the superficial layers of the subcortical white matter.

The large multipolar neurons were also seen within the deep white matter
of the parietal cortex and within the white matter of the anterior commissure and its nucleus. Cells were detected in layers V–VI of somatosensory cortex, as well as in the peripheral white matter just below lamina
VI. Sections taken for electron microscopic localization of P5, from mid-
lamina IV show immunoperoxidase positive nerve terminals with reactivity associated with small lucent synaptic vesicles.

Regardless of whether 1B236 represents a transmitter or some other
class of cell-specific neuronal protein whose function remains to be determined, the distribution of this marker within functional circuits of the rat
brain (see Fig. 6) deserves further consideration. The 1B236 protein is
clearly not expressed by every neuron within any of these systems, even
those that are most heavily labeled. As one traces through the circuitry of
the olfactory system, for example, it is clear that the primary olfactory
nerves, as well as the primary output cells of the bulb, the mitral cells, are
both unreactive. However, periglomerular cells, short axon cells of the
internal plexiform layer, and selected large neurons within almost all
regions directly innervated by the lateral olfactory tract, and known to
send centrifugal fibers back to the granule cells of the bulb, are all strongly
positive. Furthermore, 1B236 immunoreactive afferents to the thalamus,
to the piriform, and olfactory regions of the forebrain and whose source
locations are not yet determined are also strongly positive. Somatosensory and amygdaloid neurons with immunoreactivity for 1B236 could
account for these circuits.

The density of the immunoreactivity within elements of the somatosensory and olfactory fields, as well as the more modest representation in

segments of the auditory, extrapyramidal, and cranial motor neuron fields, suggests that 1B236 is expressed in systems which are evolutionarily old.

No specific patterns can yet be simply assembled from the immunoreactive, elements within known sequential systems. Within the olfactory and limbic structures, the immunoreactive elements alternate with nonimmunoreactive elements in the multisynaptic chains of interconnected neurons that have been well studied for these functional systems. The meaning of such an alternating pattern of expression of a specific marker is not obvious. At one level, it can be directly interpreted as reflecting only that these cells contain the same protein and hence share at least one specific chemical property which may relate these separated cell types functionally.

Possibly, expression of the 1B236 mRNA and its protein product reflect some primary epigenetic property shared by neurons in each of these systems as well as by the cells of functionally separate systems. The common cells within each functional system may have arisen from a common progenitor cell class, and during ontogenesis are further separated by cellular elements that do not express 1B236. At least for the olfactory system, the immunoreactive centrifugal connections to the bulb, and the short-axon and periglomerular cells within the bulb could be viewed as a distributed, interrupted system for the regulation of olfactory information processing. The cells of the different systems, and therefore the systems themselves, may also be considered to be closely related in the evolutionary sense, having descended from a common ancestral circuit of simpler dimensions. Such concepts are ultimately testable by developmental and phylogenetic studies. The data presently at hand favor the possibility that the 1B236 protein could function as a neurotransmitter precursor within those circuits that express it, although the evidence is far from complete.

VIII. Conclusions

If 1B236 is eventually found to meet all of the criteria of a transmitter, the catalog of other brain-specific mRNAs of this relative abundance and complexity suggests that there may be several hundred more to be found and studied. Even if 1B236 does not meet the criteria, its existence within neurons linked with specific functional systems (whose neuronal elements are far from completely characterized) suggests that our strategy may have more fundamental value. Certainly, the ability to generate synthetic fragments of an unknown gene product and to raise antisera against it offers a powerful advantage over monoclonal antibodies raised to complex mixtures of soluble or membrane-bound substances (see Levitt, 1984, for a recent example).

While we are not totally ready to set aside all of our historical precedents in transmitter research, it does seem clear that the complexity and abundance of genetic messages in the brain demand that we keep an open mind about the kinds of factors and their functions that may be found if we are not to be doomed to saying that all we know now is all there can ever be. Such a view would scarcely have been compatible with the finding that somatostatin is a ubiquitous regulatory peptide within the central and peripheral nervous systems, the diffuse gastroenteric nervous system, and other endocrine tissues, nor with the fact that its actions in brain have little or nothing to do with its actions on somatotropin secretion. Clearly the road to a molecular specification of "all" regulatory factors will require enormous effort and considerable time. We anticipate that it will not be necessary to define every as yet undiscovered regulatory molecule before we can recognize approximately how many more categories and families of such substances there may be. Similarly, it should not be necessary to test every new factor on every possible target cell before coming to a fuller understanding of how many categories of response and response interactions, neurons and endocrine systems may use, and how many modes of interaction may exist for their functional control mechanisms. The interactions observed thus far with peptides and amines arising from conventional discovery strategies begin to suggest that there may be a limited repertoire of response mechanisms that may be elicitable by many different substances (see Bloom, 1984 for fuller discussion). As we and others continue to try to define these response mechanisms, important lessons will undoubtedly be learned for the advancement of endocrine and neuron science through the molecular characterization of more substances.

ACKNOWLEDGMENTS

We thank Nancy Callahan for diligent manuscript preparation, and other colleagues involved in related studies on which these present summaries depended. Supported by grants from the NIH (GM 32355, NS 20728) and the McNeil Laboratories.

REFERENCES

Adrian, T. E., Allen, J. M., Bloom, S. R., Ghatei, M. A., Rossor, M. N., Roberts, G. W., Grow, T. J., Tatemoto, K., and Polak, J. M. (1983). *Nature* (*London*) **306**, 584.
Benoit, R., Ling, N., Alford, B., and Guillemin, R. (1982). *Biochem. Biophys. Res. Commun.* **107**, 944.
Bloom, F. E. (1982a). *In* "Advances in Pharmacology and Therapeutics II" (H. Yoshida,

Y. Hagihara, and S. Ebashi, eds.), Vol. 2, "Neurotransmitters Receptors," p. 189. Pergamon Press, Oxford.

Bloom, F. E. (1982b). *In* "Molecular Genetic Neuroscience: Prospect from Retrospect" (F. O. Schmitt, S. Bird, and F. Bloom, eds.). Raven, New York.

Bloom, F. E. (1984). *Am. J. Physiol.* **246**, C184.

Bloom, F. E., Battenberg, E. L. F., Shibasaki, T., Benoit, R., Ling, N., and Guillemin, R. (1980). *Reg. Peptides* **1**, 205.

Carlquist, M., Jornvall, H., Tatemoto, K., and Mutt, V. (1982). *Gastroenterology* **83**, 245.

Catterall, W. A. (1984). *Science* **223**, 653.

Cooper, J. R., Bloom, F. E., and Roth, R. H. (1982). "The Biochemical Basis of Neuropharmacology," 4th Ed., p. 249. Oxford University Press, New York.

Deschenes, R. J., Lorenz, L. J., Haun, R. S., Roos, B. A., Collier, K. J., and Dixon, J. E. (1984). *Proc. Natl. Acad. Sci. U.S.A.* **81**, 726.

Dodd, J., and Kelly, J. S. (1978). *Nature (London)* **273**, 674.

Etgen, A. M., and Browning, E. T. (1983). *J. Neurosci.* **3**, 2487.

Ferron, A., Siggins, G. R., and Bloom, F. E. (1984). *Soc. Neurosci. Abstr.* **10**, 535.

Furutani, Y., Morimoto, Y., Shibahara, S., Noda, M., Takahashi, H., Hirose, T., Asai, M., Inayama, S., Hayashida, H., Miyata, T., and Numa, S. (1983). *Nature (London)* **301**, 537.

Goodman, R. H., Jacobs, J. W., Dee, P. C., and Habener, J. F. (1982). *J. Biol. Chem.* **257**, 1156.

Gubler, U., Seeburg, P., Hoffman, B. J., Gage, L. P., and Udenfriend, S. (1982). *Nature (London)* **295**, 206.

Gubler, U., Monahan, J. J., Lomedico, P. T., Bhatt, R. S., Collier, K. J., Hoffman, B. J., Bohlen, P., Esch, F., Ling, N., Zeytin, F., Brazeau, P., Poonian, M. S., and Gage, L. P. (1983). *Proc. Natl. Acad. Sci. U.S.A.* **80**, 4311.

Guillemin, R. (1978). *Science* **202**, 390.

Guillemin, R., Brazeau, P., Bohlen, P., Esch, F., Ling, N., and Wehrenberg, W. B. (1982). *Science* **218**, 585.

Gundersen, C. B., Miledi, R., and Parker, I. (1984). *Nature (London)* **308**, 421.

Itoh, N., Obata, K., Yanaihara, N., and Okamoto, H. (1983). *Nature (London)* **304**, 547.

Iversen, L. L. (1983). *Trends Neurosci.* **9**, 293.

Kakidani, H., Furutani, Y., Takahashi, H., Noda, M., Morimoto, Y., Hirose, T., Asai, M., Inayama, S., Nakanishi, S., and Numa, S. (1982). *Nature (London)* **298**, 245.

Klein, D. C., Sugden, D., and Weller, J. L. (1983). *Proc. Natl. Acad. Sci. U.S.A.* **80**, 599.

Krieger, D. (1983). *Science* **222**, 975.

Lamouroux, A., Faucon-Biguet, N., Samolyk, D., Privat, A., Salomon, J. C., Pujol, J. F., and Mallet, J. (1982). *Proc. Natl. Acad. Sci. U.S.A.* **79**, 3881.

Levitt, P. (1984). *Science* **223**, 299.

Luben, R. A., Brazeau, P., Bohlen, P., and Guillemin, R. (1982). *Science* **218**, 887.

Magistretti, P. J., and Schorderet, M. (1984). *Nature (London)* **308**, 280.

Malfroy, B., Bakhit, C., Milner, R. J., and Bloom, F. E. (1984). *Soc. Neurosci. Abstr.* **10**, 595.

Mancillas, J. R., Siggins, G. R., and Bloom, F. E. (1984). *Soc. Neurosci. Abstr.* **10**, 968.

Mayo, K. E., Vale, W., Rivier, J., Rosenfeld, M. G., and Evans, R. M. (1983). *Nature (London)* **306**, 86.

McDonald, T. J., Jornvall, H., Tatemoto, K., and Mutt, V. (1983). *FEBS Lett.* **156**, 349.

Milner, R. J., and Sutcliffe, J. G. (1983). *Nucleic Acids Res.* **11**, 5497.

Milner, R. J., Bloom, F. E., Lai, C., Lerner, R. A., and Sutcliffe, J. G. (1984). *Proc. Natl. Acad. Sci. U.S.A.* **81**, 713.

Morgan, N. G., Charest, R., Blackmore, P. F., and Exton, J. H. (1984). *Proc. Natl. Acad. Sci. U.S.A.* **81,** 4208.

Morrison, J. H., and Magistretti, P. J. (1983). *Trends Neurosci.* **6,** 146.

Morrison, J. H., Benoit, R., Magistretti, P. J., Ling, N., and Bloom, F. E. (1982). *Neurosci. Lett.* **34,** 137.

Morrison, J. H., Benoit, R., Magistretti, P. J., and Bloom, F. E. (1983). *Brain Res.* **262,** 344.

Morrison, J. H., Magistretti, P. J., Benoit, R., and Bloom, F. E. (1984). *Brain Res.* **292,** 269.

Mutt, V. (1976). *Clin. Endocrinol.* **5,** 175S.

Nakanishi, S., Inoue, A., Kita, T., Nakamura, M., Chang, A. C. Y., Cohen, S. N., and Numa, S. (1979). *Nature (London)* **278,** 423.

Nawa, H., Kitamura, N., Hirose, T., Asai, M., Inayama, S., and Nakanishi, S. (1983a). *Proc. Natl. Acad. Sci. U.S.A.* **80,** 90.

Nawa, H., Hirose, T., Takashima, H., Inayama, S., and Nakanishi, S. (1983b). *Nature (London)* **306,** 32.

Noda, M., Furutani, Y., Takahashi, H., Toyosato, M., Hirose, T., Inayama, S., Nakanishi, S., and Numa, S. (1982). *Nature (London)* **295,** 202.

Ohkubo, H., Kageyama, R., Ujihara, M., Hirose, T., Inayama, S., and Nakanishi, S. (1983). *Proc. Natl. Acad. Sci. U.S.A.* **80,** 2196.

Olpe, H.-R., Balcar, V. J., Bittiger, H., Rink, H., and Sieber, P. (1980). *Eur. J. Pharmacol.* **63,** 127.

Phillis, J. N., and Kirkpatrick, J. R. (1978). *Can. J. Physiol. Pharmacol.* **58,** 612.

Pittman, Q. J., and Siggins, G. R. (1981). *Brain Res.* **221,** 402.

Roberts, E., and Kuriyama, K. (1968). *Brain Res.* **8,** 1.

Rosenfeld, M. G., Mermod, J.-J., Amara, S. G., Swanson, L. W., Sawchenko, P. E., Rivier, J., Vale, W., and Evans, R. M. (1983). *Nature (London)* **304,** 129.

Ross, M. E., Park, D. H., Teitelman, G., Pickel, V. M., Reis, D. J., and Joh, T. H. (1983). *Neuroscience* **10,** 907.

Rossor, M. N., Roberts, G. W., Crow, T. J., Tatemoto, K., and Polak, J. M. (1983). *Nature (London)* **306,** 584.

Ruppert, S., Scherer, G., and Schutz, G. (1984). *Nature (London)* **308,** 554.

Scheller, R. H., Jackson, J. F., McAlliste, L. B., Schwartz, J. H., Kandel, E. R., and Axel, R. (1982). *Cell* **28,** 707.

Schmale, H., and Richter, D. (1984). *Nature (London)* **308,** 705.

Shibasaki, T., Ling, N., Guillemin, R., Silver, M., and Bloom, F. (1981). *Reg. Peptides* **2,** 43.

Siggins, G. R., and French, E. D. (1984). *Soc. Neurosci. Abstr.* **10,** 810.

Siggins, G. R., and Gruol, D. L. (1984). *In* "Handbook of Physiology, Volume on Intrinsic Regulatory Systems of the Brain" (F. E. Bloom, ed.). American Physiological Society, Bethesda, Maryland, in press.

Snyder, S. H. (1984). *Science* **224,** 22.

Spiess, J., Rivier, J., and Vale, W. (1983). *Nature (London)* **303,** 532.

Sutcliffe, J. G., and Milner, R. J. (1984). *Trends Biochem. Sci.* **9,** 95.

Sutcliffe, J. G., Milner, R. J., Shinnick, T. M., and Bloom, F. E. (1983a). *Cell* **33,** 671.

Sutcliffe, J. G., Milner, R. J., and Bloom, F. E. (1983b). *Cold Spring Harbor Symp.* **48,** 477.

Sutcliffe, J. G., Milner, R. J., Gottesfeld, J. M., and Lerner, R. A. (1984). *Nature (London)* **308,** 237.

Tatemoto, K. (1982a). *Proc. Natl. Acad. Sci. U.S.A.* **79,** 2514.

Tatemoto, K. (1982b). *Proc. Natl. Acad. Sci. U.S.A.* **79,** 5485.

Tatemoto, K., and Mutt, V. (1980). *Nature (London)* **285,** 417.

Tatemoto, K., and Mutt, V. (1981). *Proc. Natl. Acad. Sci. U.S.A.* **78,** 6603.

Tatemoto, K., Carlquist, M., and Mutt, V. (1982). *Nature (London)* **296**, 659.
Tatemoto, K., Carlquist, M., McDonald, T. J., and Mutt, V. (1983). *FEBS Lett.* **153**, 248.
Vale, W., Spiess, J., Rivier, C., and Rivier, J. (1981). *Science* **213**, 1394.
von Euler, U. (1975). *In* "The Neurosciences: Paths of Discovery" (F. G. Worden, J. G. Swazey, and G. Adelman, eds.), p. 181. MIT Press, Cambridge.

DISCUSSION

D. Krieger: Thank you for some of the generalizations that you have been able to draw on the interactions of various systems. I think that the more the field has developed and the more models that we have with regard to precursor molecules and the interactions of peptides contained therein we can begin to delineate many of these generalizations as you did in the case of somatostatin. I'm beginning to wonder after your presentation of the effects of somatostatin 28 and somatostatin 14 whether the reason for a number of peptides within a given precursor molecule is (1) to provide the opportunity of a given peptide to modulate the effects of another; similar to peptides in proopiomelamacortin, where β-endorphin and α-MSH have opposing effects on behavior, hormone secretion, or electrical activity; or (2) to strengthen the effect of a given peptide as in the TRH precursor where there are multiple copies of a given sequence and this may be the beginning of the understanding of why so many things are packaged together, and coreleased and modulate the activity of each other. I think Dr. Bloom's excellent discussion is now opened for questions from the floor.

B. F. Rice: A number of years ago Dr. Guillemin introduced a concept at this meeting in terms of the neurons secreting half a dozen different polypeptides or small peptides. I gather from your presentation that your notion is that a single neuron still secretes a single peptide. Is that correct?

F. Bloom: I think it is almost impossible to say that. I tried to indicate several kinds of coexisting transmitters that have been identified, but it is clear from the study of the magnocellular neurons that some of those magnocellular neurons, under no obvious perturbation, have within them coexisting multiple peptides. There may be combinations of dynorphin and vasopressin combinations of CRF with several other peptides in the system; whether they are released or not is really the question, and it really is almost beyond the technology at the moment to be able to speak of nerve terminals coexisting. Tomas Hökfelt, in the median eminence, has been able to show that because many of the carbocellular neurons do have such large amounts—it can be shown from serial section analysis, from macroregional analysis of the median eminence that they appear to be not just overlapping, but directly within the same neuron. At the level of electron microscopy there still is considerable room for improvement in our ability to resolve these materials, but even if one could verify that the same synaptic vesicles showed immunoreactivity for a peptide, the critical feature is whether or not it is released.

I left out a series of about a dozen slides from our work on the dynorphin family in the hippocampus, but briefly, within the prodynorphin molecule, there are at least three contending agonist peptides, that is the original Goldstein dynorphin, of 17 amino acid peptide, another one called dynorphin B or rimorphin and its close relative sometimes called rimorphin. If you divide them up, they all occur within the same nerve pathway from the dentate granule cells to the mossy fibers that synapse on the terminal cells. If you do immunohistochemistry, they all occur in the same nerve fibers; if you do release studies, they all are released; if you do electrophysiological studies, they all produce qualitatively similar actions on the post-synapse targets which can be discriminated from the encephalin input to different neurons in that system. Under that condition we have no choice but to say that classic dynorphin B, and the α-neoendorphin β-neoendorphine triad are all potentially releasable simultaneously when the dentate granule cells that make prodynorphin are activated. But they also contain CCK and what we can't document is whether the same ones that contain CCK are the same or different than those that contain dynorphin.

From our molecular genetic studies, which I didn't go into at all here, we have recognized a brain-specific peptide which I suppose adds a third dimension of peptide content to the mossy fibers; it is yet another major player in dentate granule mossy fiber synaptic input. So I would think that we're nowhere near the limit of peptides that can be recognized. Until we have a semicomplete catalogue of all the ones that are recognizable, it is really impossible to say how many a given neuron can secrete. There are some people who are so impressed with the coexistence that has been demonstrated that they are willing to bet that it is highly likely that all neurons will transmit more than one synaptic messenger. The VIP bipolar neurons have recently been shown to be among the class of cortical cholinergic neurons, so wherever I said VIP a while ago in terms of bipolar neurons, in terms of local domain regulatory functions you can add acetylcholine/VIP, but there are other acetylcholine neurons that don't contain VIP. What their other peptide might be is among that list to be discovered.

H. A. Bern: If endocrine cells such as the corticotrophs or pars intermedia cells can release more than one hormonal factor by cleavage of a POMC prohormone, the principle ought also to be applicable to neurons. The nearest thing that I know to this derives from work done in Ian Cooke's laboratory in Hawaii, where it appears that several hormonal factors from the crustacean eyestalk may arise from a neurosecretory prohormone. This X-organ–sinus gland neurosecretory system is a possible example of what could go on in peptidergic neurons of the nervous system generally.

F. Bloom: I think it is important to distinguish between two major kinds of coexistences; one kind of coexistence that we've talked about a lot is exemplified by the POMC relationship or the somatostatin relationship in which one messenger RNA codes for one prohormone that can be cleaved into different products. It is quite another thing to speak of two simultaneously existing transmitter agonists that come from different messenger RNAs, that presumably have different modes of transmitter regulation; that is the one that I think is, right now, the most open-ended.

S. M. McCann: I would just like to comment on two aspects: (1) If you are having more than one peptide released from a given neuron, and if they have opposite actions, it is a little hard to explain how this could serve any function. In this case, of course, you have the stimulatory action apparently of the somatostatin 28 1-12 and the inhibitory action of the somatostatin 14. Therefore, I think it is very important to know if we really have evidence that this smaller peptide is actually released, and I think the criterion of release by high potassium may be too easy a criterion. It is such a strong stimulus that it might well release practically anything. Therefore, I would like to ask a question. Have you used other criteria of release such as stimulating the tissue by electrical stimulation and determining if you can get release. The other statement which disturbed me was that you criticized the hypothesis that substances might enter the brain from the CSF as epitomized by injecting peptides into the ventricular system.

F. Bloom: Which I include myself.

S. M. McCann: I think that the ventricular route is a superb way of delivering compounds to the brain, but I don't agree that it is pharmacology, because I think it's mimicking what happens physiologically. Namely, that the peptide in the brain does not have to cross the blood–brain barrier, it is simply released from the neuron in the brain. Alternatively, the peptides circulating, such as CCK, can reach the brain through the various circumventricular organs. My own view would be that actually the peptides can operate both ways, either by stimulating afferents in the periphery or via the direct action on the brain, either delivered through the circumventricular system or by the neuronal systems in the brain itself. I would like you to comment on that point.

F. Bloom: I agree wholeheartedly with your unwillingness to accept 50 mM potassium as being indicative of release mechanism although that is the first release criteria one looks for biochemically. The problem we have with peptide systems is that for most of the systems, such as the somatostatin 28 cells, the cell bodies are not located so that we know how to activate them selectively and we don't know of any specific synaptic input that we could use to activate them selectively, and so far we don't have an antagonist that one could say is a selective antagonist of that end of the molecules so that we could look for endogenous release that will allow us to say that; so it is a very difficult bridge that we are trying to build in that kind of a situation. I think the breakthrough there will probably come from the magnocellular neuron system where they are both clustered together where you can stimulate them, and in some cases there are good antagonist peptides that are coming along, and that obviously has to be done in order to show at the cellular basis that some of these response mechanisms are physiology and not pharmacology. I agree with you, but I think that it is at least worth bearing in mind that somatostatin 28 or somatostatin 28, 1–12 may have actions that are different than somatostatin 14.

Whether they are totally opposing actions or just qualitatively different is something that we don't yet know and one does not know, for example, whether they are released in equimolar amounts per impulse, or whether as Hökfelt and Lundberg have shown for the peripheral presympathetic system they are frequency dependent in the way in which they are released: One of them coming out at one frequency of activation and the other one joining it when a certain frequency of activation has been reached. We don't really know what the primary transmitter might be in somatostatin-containing neurons. There is some evidence to suggest, based on comparison of maps of glutamic acid decarboxylase, that many of the cortical somatostatin-containing systems are also positive; and so, one would have a somatostatin 14 cell, with perhaps GABA acting as a classical inhibitory transmitter and these other ends of the somatostatin molecule coming in at higher frequencies to keep that cell from being permanently locked into a totally paralyzed inhibited status. I think this is a good example of what we begin to recognize that we don't know, rather than saying that we know. As to whether the cerebrospinal fluid is an avenue of access or a sewer, I think that one can't really be dogmatic about it at the moment. My remarks were directed at the fact that many people in the early days of characterization of a new peptide find it revealing to inject it into the spinal fluid until something happens; that is sort of the equivalent of what we do in neurobiology when we find a new place connected with someplace else; we put a stimulating electrode on, and turn up the current until something happens. Now that is very useful in deciding that something may happen, but it is not, in my mind, very useful in understanding what the role of the neurons that contain that peptide or transmitter might be in everyday ordinary behavior. My hair bristles when I hear people refer to a peptide as a memory peptide, or as a pain peptide, because it occurs in many synaptic connections that have as far as we know nothing to do with pain or with memory. Until we better understand the cellular mechanisms of remembering and until we better understand the cellular mechanisms of pain responding, I think we'll say ouch when we see something introduced into spinal fluid.

S. M. McCann: We're all in agreement actually. I don't think that peptides enter via the ventricular route very often physiologically, but the point is that it is just a route by which you can deliver it which can give you leads for further study to determine the precise mechanism.

D. T. Krieger: I think with regard to normal physiology that the point that you make is very good, but I think the whole question of classically considering the nervous system as working in a very specific manner via specific "wiring," then postulating physiological mechanisms effected by having this sort of CSF soup spread over the whole CNS area in contact with CSF is not the way we visualize the nervous system working. Do you consider that putting antibodies to specific peptides in the cerebrospinal fluid as an approach to delineating peptide function as being physiological or pharmacological?

F. Bloom: To me putting antibodies in the spinal fluid is putting in a specific sponge for something that should have been there in the first place. Using antibodies as ways of direct interstitial manipulation might be the closest we can come to antagonizing those for which the antagonist chemistry lags behind the peptide chemistry.

H. A. Levey: How general is this hyperpolarizing action of somatostatin? Does it apply to any tissue or just excitable tissues? If you have that information, could a change in membrane conductance in, for example, the pancreatic β cell be related in any way to the effect of somatostatin in inhibiting insulin release.

F. Bloom: There are in fact studies of direct membrane effects of somatostatin on pancreatic β cells; I don't happen to have that data available, but I'd be glad to look up the references and send them to you. In the central nervous system, the body of data that I am most familiar with, there are opposing reports of what somatostatin does to membrane potentials under apparently identical conditions. The first report came from Dodd and Kelly at Cambridge and showed somatostatin to be excitatory, but all the subsequent studies except one have shown it to have this inhibitory effect.

H. A. Levey: So somatostatin can have this generalized hyperpolarizing effect on resting membrane potentials when it is delivered via the circulatory system (or the ECF in the case of pancreatic somatostatin), as well as by direct iontophoretic application to the outer surface of the membrane.

F. Bloom: Certainly in terms of acting on the membrane potential of endocrine cells, I would say yes.

E. Knobil: I'm reminded of the difference between physiology and pharmacology: "pharmacology is what he does, physiology is what I do." I wonder if you could comment on the homology between the electrical activity of secretory cells, like the β cell of the pancreas and what occurs in the central nervous system. I ask this question because in your classification of the functional types of chemical messages, type 4 showed a pattern which was extremely reminiscent of what happens in the β cell, namely, a sudden rise in spike frequency, an overshoot returning to a plateau of activity, and then rapid return to baseline. I wonder if you could also give us your thoughts regarding this time course of electrical activity.

F. Bloom: It is not something that we tried to put together but it sort of emerged as we try to understand the various kinds of cell systems in which this response occurs. The classic pattern of secretory activity ascribed up to mammals for the magnocellular type neuron is one of burst firing when it is in its secretory mode. The cells in the central nervous system on which we have observed this kind of calcium-activated potassium conductance action are cells that can typically be induced to fire in burst modes, and what is typical of all those cells is that they will go for long periods of time firing in a single spike mode, and then suddenly, sometimes totally unpredictably, switch to burst cell mode firing. When they are in that cell mode, fire manipulation of this after hyperpolarization induced by the calcium-activation potassium conductance could in fact allow that cell to stay in its burst mode secretion firing pattern longer.

There are people who believe that if you found the right conditions, you might be able to put every large neuron in a burst mode firing pattern, and whether that mode of action, that mode of response to peptides or other monoamines would be restricted to burst firing cells is difficult to say because it is only when it is in the burst firing mode that the calcium-activated potassium conductance is apparent enough to be seen; so that is about all I can say on that issue; but I think it is one that we might want to pay attention to. When you do current voltage relationships in such a cell, those spontaneously active cells that can exhibit the burst firing mode show a particular kind of peculiar potential called the negative slope conductance potential; and that is often producible by making the cyclic AMP content of the cell go up. So one could imagine a convergence of signals that would allow the cell to switch modes and then in the new mode to be metabolically regulated by its other inputs in a way that when it is not in that mode of firing those other signals would be ignored.

R. Levine: I was intrigued by your very positive statement that peptides coming to the brain from endocrine glands via the blood probably do not play any significant role in modifying neurological function. I am thinking of one of my favorite peptides in this regard, namely, insulin, and the long story of the ups and downs, whether or not there is an action on the neurons. I am perfectly satisfied with the fact that over 90% of neurons do not seem to have insulin receptors on their surface. But from Barry Posner's work and that of others, it would seem that some neurons in strategic places may be equipped with insulin receptors. These could very well be influenced by the hormone and thus have a more general effect. Also, aren't there well documented effects of thyroxine on neuronal growth and function?

F. Bloom: I think insulin is a very good example and one that by sweeping positive generalization needs to have holes that burst in it for the moment. There certainly is documentation that in certain of the circumventricular organ systems with circulating insulin levels that are within the physiological range, there is a positive uptake; it is not quite clear how that uptake is communicated to any place, but that is an almost testable question and there certainly are feeding experiments in that range of experiments that inject something and see what happens.

There are examples, even in the primate literature, that one can alter stable patterns of eating with infusions of cerebrospinal fluid delivered insulin; that is complicated of course by the fact that there are some people who believe that insulin-like molecules may be made within the central nervous system and could be activated internally be cell signals. The issue of thyroxin is not one that many people are working on, but based on this I would say it probably falls more into the small molecule nonpeptide variety, and it is certainly clear that the thyroid state regulates early brain development and can speed up the maximum scenario that can be produced there; that is all I can say about it at the moment. The steroid responsiveness has been well documented in a great variety.

D. Krieger: Thyroxine and steroids may act by affecting neurotransmitter metabolism and turnover via receptor-mediated effects rather than by direct hormonal effects on membrane characteristics.

F. Bloom: Yes, it is hard for me to conceive of it affecting neurotransmitter metabolism without their being a receptor someplace in the system.

D. Krieger: There certainly are steroid receptors in the central nervous system—that is unquestionable. But those receptors are affecting a specific steroid action on a neuronal product, namely the neurotransmitter.

F. Bloom: Yes, it is certainly clear from the work of Walter Stumpf and colleagues that classes of neurotransmitters seem to bind gonadal steroids at very sensitive levels. What is complicating that is whether there may not also be some steroids produced directly in the central nervous system and Etienne Beaulieu has documented that dehydroepiandrosterone seems to be able to be produced directly in the central nervous system, uninfluenced by periphery, so that all forms of endocrine regulations that are important for the body have been coopted by the brain for its own local environments.

K. Ryan: I was going to pursue the same question about the possibility of diversity of steroid effects in the brain. There have been studies in the past that suggest that firing rates are changed so rapidly that one cannot imagine traditional steroid mechanisms of action causing it. I wonder if you would reflect on this and I should say that other people have been intrigued by Etienne Baulieu's concept of *de novo* synthesis of dehydroepiandrosterone in the brain but I don't think there is any evidence that that is possible. We and others have tried to confirm the actual biosynthesis of these steroids in the brain and have so far failed.

F. Bloom: Right. With regard to the first point using the kind of technology I showed here, direct iontophoretic application, it is clear that there are steroid responsive cells in several regions of the brain. The question then would be whether you can change the blood level fast enough to induce the same kind of concentration gradient with an iontophoretic pipet when it is released locally. Until one defines that parameter specifically it will be hard to emulate that with an iontophoretic pipet where the change in environmental concentration might go from picomolar to micromolar in a matter of a few seconds; but the response under those conditions is quite dramatic and reproducible.

I can only say that using Dr. Beaulieu's assistant and Dr. Beaulieu's assay, we have been able to confirm what he reported and we have also been able to show that in animals that are gonadectomized and hypophysectomized for long periods of time, steroid content does not diminish, but it has been peculiar that no matter how much hot squaline or other cholesterol precursors you put in it, it is very hard to demonstrate where it comes from; but what is striking is that if you give an animal modest doses of ethanol, the decline of dehydroepiandrosterone in the brain parallels the loss of righting reflex and the sleep time of the response to ethanol and in experiments that I have not seen but I understand have been obtained with Paul Brazeau, if you put a female rat in heat in a cage with a male rat, you will affect the concentration of dehydroepiandrosterone; in the male rat it will triple in a matter of about 24 hours. So it does seem to be something that is regulatable in the brain by both drugs and behavior; where it comes from is still a mystery to be worked out.

P. Wise: I was interested in your findings on the changing morphology of somatostatin-containing neurons relative to Alzheimer's disease. I wonder whether or not you have been able to correlate changes in the intensity of staining or changes in the morphology of the neurons with either the intensity or duration of the disease? Have you looked at the morphology of other neurons containing other peptides or neurotransmitters to know whether or not the dendritic tangles are generalized to many different kinds of neurons or whether only somatostatin-containing neurons are related to the etiology of the disease?

F. Bloom: It is accepted by neuropathologists that in general plaques and tangle density reflect the intensity of the disease, not necessarily its duration, and in rapidly progressing Alzheimer's disease, particularly Alzheimer's disease that occurs before the age of 60, there is a very good correlation between the loss of somatostatin and the rapidity of the progress of the disorder. If in any individual case we look for early and late plaques and there are neuropathological criteria by which one can make the assumption that this one came before that one, although nobody really knows what the pathological progression is. Those in which there is a little bit of amyloid have a lot more somatostatin; those in which there is a lot of amyloid have the somatostatin apparently segregated to a kind of swollen dendritic element that is proximal to where the amyloid deposit is located; but we have a very good correlation between plaques revealed either by Congo red staining, showed in these photographs, which is a brilliant fluorescent dye that reacts with amyloid; there is a very high correlation between elements that have amyloid deposit and elements that have somatostatin immunoreactivity. The data from Tim Crow and Julia Polak, where they were devoting their attention primarily to tangles, indicate that about 50% of the neurons with tangles were somatostatin positive. The VIP system has a peculiar feature, the epibiochemical content is unaffected in Alzheimer's whether of short or long duration, but we have not yet been able to visualize in the human brain the VIP neurons. Antibodies that work on the urogenital system, for human VIP do not work in the central nervous system for reasons we do not understand.

D. Krieger: Continuing with your observations on Alzheimer's disease, would you amplify your statement that you did not think the somatostatin findings had any connection with the cholinergic hypothesis of Alzheimer's disease.

F. Bloom: The cholinergic hypothesis as it is sometimes stated suggests that degeneration in the nucleus basalis leads to downstream effects in the cortex and that functional cognition might be restored if you could only in a Parkinsonian dopamine fashion give enough lecithin to get the acetylcholine levels back up. Our feeling is that somatostatin neurons intrinsic to the cortex are involved in very early pathologic changes in that cortex and that two systems of cells that project from outside the cortex into the cortex, namely the nucleus basalis and the locus coeruleus and in at least one report the raphe nuclei are also affected by the disease process.

Our belief is that something intrinsic to the cortex is the primary event in Alzheimer's disease and that secondarily systems projecting to those dying cells undergo disturbance; it has been shown by the Oxford group at least, that if you make a comparable lesion in the cortex by killing cortical neurons with neurotoxins that secondary to that nucleus basalis will undergo atrophy; so it is entirely possible that the cholinergic changes may not be the primary event but a secondary event and trying to rebolster that depends on whether you believe the acetylcholine-responsive cells are still there.

K. Sterling: I wanted to say just a word about uptake of thyroxine and triiodothyronine in the brain. Studies have been carried out by Mary Dratman showing specific brain localization, and the neurons can apparently convert T_4 to T_3, much more so in the hypothyroid state; that in the neurons the T_3 is localized in synaptosomes, whatever that implies.

F. Bloom: Yes I agree with you, Dr. Dratman's work is, often not considered.

Hypothalamic Pulse Generators

Dennis W. Lincoln, Hamish M. Fraser, Gerald A. Lincoln,
Graeme B. Martin, and Alan S. McNeilly

MRC Reproductive Biology Unit, Edinburgh, Scotland

I. Introduction

Aspects of our research on the neural control of the pituitary gland have been presented at previous meetings in the Laurentian Series (Cross *et al.*, 1975; Lincoln and Short, 1980) and related contributions have been presented by others (Knobil, 1980; Karsch *et al.*, 1984). In this review we shall, therefore, focus on one phenomenon that has been highlighted by these previous papers, namely pulsatile hormone secretion, and attempt to analyze the mechanisms underlying the neural organization of this phenomenon in the context of oxytocin and luteinizing hormone releasing hormone (LHRH) secretion. Five concepts will be advanced and discussed as summarized below.

1. Oxytocin and LHRH are both released from the hypothalamus in pulses superimposed upon a continuous or intermittent low level of secretion. These two modes of secretion could produce separate actions, or one might govern the response to the other. Pulses of oxytocin promote the contraction of the myoepithelial cells of the mammary gland, while a continuous low level of oxytocin secretion appears to be involved in fluid homeostasis. The continuous secretion of LHRH or the secretion of minipulses of LHRH, on the other hand, could prime the pituitary gland to respond more effectively to larger pulses of LHRH that may be superimposed.

2. The "synchronous" generation of action potentials at a very fast rate (30 spike/second) within a population of peptidergic neurones, perhaps lasting only a few seconds, provides the neural substrate for the release of a hormone pulse. These high frequencies of spike activity are associated with a 100- to 1000-fold increase in the amount of hormone released per spike from the nerve terminal compared with amount of hormone released at those rates of spike generation associated with background activity (0–5 spike/second).

3. The control of interpulse interval is determined by events within

369

the brain, though the interval generator per se may not reside within the neurons that secrete oxytocin or LHRH.

4. Amplitude modulation of pulsatile secretion could relate to different levels of electrical activation within the brain and/or to differences in the responsiveness of the target tissues that transduce the pulsatile signal. There is a third possibility: amplitude modulation could result from changes in stimulus–secretion coupling within the secretory nerve terminals of the median eminence and posterior pituitary, both sites being outside the blood–brain barrier and therefore accessible to the influence of large-molecular-weight hormones in the peripheral circulation.

5. Opioid peptides inhibit the secretion of both oxytocin and LHRH. This involves an inhibition of stimulus–secretion coupling within the nerve terminals, and possibly an inhibition of synaptically mediated events that impinge upon the cell bodies of the peptidergic neurons within the hypothalamus. Prolonged exposure to opiates leads to tolerance (loss of effect) and dependence (excitation on withdrawal) and these processes could govern the set point in feedback control mechanisms, including the negative feedback response to gonadal steroids.

Studies of oxytocin biosynthesis and secretion have for several decades been at the forefront of developments in neuroendocrinology. For example, oxytocin was one of the first hormones to be associated with a peptide precursor (van Dyke et al., 1942), the first peptide hormone (with vasopressin) to be sequenced and synthesized (du Vigneaud, 1956), among the first hormones to be shown to be released in an episodic pattern (Fox and Knaggs, 1969; McNeilly, 1972), the first hormone for which there were well defined electrophysiological correlates of secretion (Brooks et al., 1966; Lincoln and Wakerley, 1971, 1974, 1975), and one of the first hormones for which the genome was sequenced (Land et al., 1983; Ivell and Richter, 1984)—almost a landmark for each decade. The reason why such progress has been possible can be appreciated when one examines the anatomy of the hypothalamic–pituitary axis. Oxytocin-producing neurons are confined very largely to the paraventricular and supraoptic nuclei of the hypothalamus and, from the magnocellular portions of the nuclei, most project to the posterior pituitary. Some oxytocin-producing neurons are found elsewhere in the brain, notably in the parvicellular portions of the paraventricular nuclei, and these project their axons to many other regions, including the brain stem and spinal cord (Buijs, 1978). Vasopressin-producing neurons are found in the magnocellular nuclei in almost equal numbers. There is some regional localization of oxytocin and vasopressin-producing neurons, but this is relatively insignificant compared with the extensive intermingling of the two cell types (Swaab et al., 1975). This raises an important question: how are the two cell types organized to function independently of each other? The magnocellular nuclei of the hypothalamus and the posterior pituitary gland are all relatively accessible and this has facilitated enormously the study of hormone biosynthesis, precursor processing and the storage of the derived products (Pickering, 1978; Morris *et al.*, 1978), and spike generation, transmission, and stimulus–secretion coupling (Poulain and Wakerley, 1982). All that is required to complete this model system is an acute and selective physiological stimulus to evoke secretion and an on-line assay to measure the output of the secreted products. For the oxytocin system we are fortunate in having both. The suckling of the young provides a selective stimulus for the release of oxytocin (Bisset *et al.*, 1970; Wakerley *et al.*, 1973), and the measurement of intramammary pressure provides a second-by-second index of secretion (Harris *et al.*, 1969).

LHRH-producing neurons are not organized into such a discrete neural system and are as a consequence much more difficult to investigate. Neurons staining immunohistochemically for LHRH are found more abundantly in the medial preoptic area of the rat brain, with smaller numbers in the accessory olfactory bulbs, anterior hippocampus, and septal areas (Bennett-Clarke and Joseph, 1982; Witkin *et al.*, 1982; Terasawa and Davis, 1983). Few, if any, LHRH-containing cell bodies are found in the mediobasal hypothalamus (Silverman *et al.*, 1982). The axons of LHRH neurons project to many parts of the brain, which accords with the view that LHRH may be involved in functions other than those associated with the regulation of LH and FSH from the anterior pituitary gland. A most conspicuous convergence of LHRH-containing axons is observed in the median eminence and in the organum-vasculosum of the lamina terminalis. Those fibers converging on the median eminence have their origins in the medial preoptic area, the paraventricular region, and the arcuate nucleus (in primates) (Witkin *et al.*, 1982; Silverman *et al.*, 1982). It is plausible that the various LHRH systems innervating the median eminence could function separately in the regulation of LHRH secretion into the pituitary portal blood vessels (Polkowska *et al.*, 1980) (Fig. 1).

Much useful though indirect knowledge of LHRH secretion had been deduced from the sequential measurement of LH levels in the peripheral plasma under differing physiological and experimental circumstances (Lincoln and Short, 1980; Karsch *et al.*, 1984; Martin, 1984; Crowley, 1985), and from changes in LH secretion following the administration of LHRH (and analogs) or the removal of endogenous LHRH by passive and active immunization (Clarke *et al.*, 1978; Lincoln and Fraser, 1979; Fraser and McNeilly, 1983). Fortunately from the experimental point of view, LH is released within seconds of LHRH reaching the gonadotrophs and the half-life of LH is substantially shorter than the LH pulse interval under most physiological conditions. FSH is also released in response to

OXYTOCIN   LHRH

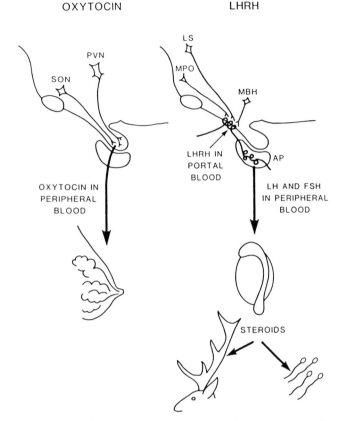

FIG. 1.   A diagrammatic illustration comparing the release and action of oxytocin and
luteinizing hormone releasing hormone (LHRH). The oxytocin-producing neurons are located mainly in the supraoptic (SON) and paraventricular nuclei (PVN) and project to the
posterior pituitary gland, from where oxytocin is released from the axon terminals to enter
the peripheral circulation. The LHRH-producing neurons that project to the median eminence and terminate on the pituitary protal blood vessels are widely scattered throughout
the hypothalamus and adjacent structures, including the mediobasal hypothalamus (MBH)
(in primates), the medial preoptic area (MPO), and the lateral septum (LS).

LHRH, but the profile of FSH in peripheral plasma is of little value in
deducing the pattern of LHRH secretion. FSH secretion is slow and
sustained in relation to LH secretion, and the half-life is much greater.

   Studies of the oxytocin and LHRH systems are very dependent therefore on the measurement of second- or third-order physiological functions, i.e., intramammary pressure and circulating levels of LH. The relationship between the neural signals and the responses they evoke is far

from linear and is without question modulated by many factors, ranging from mammary engorgement for oxytocin to positive and negative steroid feedback for LHRH. We have to continue to address these complications, but our understanding of them is such that we have been able to compile a substantial body of knowledge concerning the electrophysiological determinants of oxytocin secretion on the one hand, and of the endocrine modulation of LHRH secretion on the other. In the following discussion we shall attempt, in part, to apply our knowledge of the electrical events determining oxytocin secretion to the study of LHRH secretion and its regulation, and vice versa.

II. Patterns of Oxytocin and LHRH Secretion

The nonopeptide oxytocin and the decapeptide LHRH are both synthetized via large precursors of 112 amino acids (Land *et al.*, 1983) and 92 amino acids (Seeburg and Adelman, 1984), respectively. Within the magnocellular projection to the posterior pituitary, the neurons appear to produce either oxytocin or vasopressin, but that does not exclude them from producing other regulatory factors. Oxytocin neurons appear to produce met-enkephalin (Martin *et al.*, 1983d) while vasopressin cells produce dynorphin (Watson *et al.*, 1982; Whitnall *et al.*, 1983) and corticotropin releasing factor (CRF-41) (Dreyfuss *et al.*, 1984). As far as one can judge, oxytocin and LHRH are synthetized exclusively within the hypothalamic perikarya, and the precursor peptide is cleaved by enzymes during axonal transport to free the active hormone for secretion.

This process of biosynthesis, transport, and posttranslational processing has a number of implications. The axonal transport of oxytocin containing granules is about 1–3 mm/hour in the rat, or about 50 times faster than the rate of axoplasmic flow (Jones and Pickering, 1972). This accelerated transport of the granules is still relatively slow when related to processes of secretion which are measured in milliseconds. Any problem this might cause is circumvented by the storage of very substantial amounts of oxytocin and LHRH in the nerve terminals of the posterior pituitary and median eminence. The posterior pituitary gland of the rat for example contains about 1400 ng oxytocin or about 1000 times the content of a secreted pulse of oxytocin (Jones and Pickering, 1969; Lincoln, 1974a). By contrast, the hypothalamus of the sheep contains only 20–80 ng LHRH (Wheaton, 1979; Caraty *et al.*, 1980), but this is still a relatively large storage pool because it appears from the data of Clarke and Cummins (1982) that an individual pulse contains only 100–200 pg. These differences in the size of the storage pools and the amounts of hormone released reflect on the fact that LHRH acts via the portal blood vessels, whereas oxytocin travels to the mammary gland via the peripheral circulation. Measurable changes in the level of stored hormone could result from unusually large secretory events, as might occur during the preovulatory LH surge (Sherwood *et al.*, 1980; Ching, 1982), but even then the levels of stored hormone are unlikely to be rate limiting (Crowder and Nett, 1984). Alternatively, a change in the storage pool could result from a long-term imbalance between synthesis and secretion, as may occur following ovariectomy or in relation to seasonal breeding (Fig. 2) (Wheaton, 1979).

Cleavage of the precursor hormone occurs after it has been packaged into granules, with the exception of the removal of the signal peptide, and thus, almost by definition, other components of the precursor have to be released in parallel to the active hormone in a 1:1 ratio. Under different regulatory conditions cleavage could occur at different sites, and this could give rise to a range of secreted products with different biological properties and different half-lives, as appears to be the case with the processing of proopiomelanocortin (Guillemin *et al.*, 1977). There is no strong evidence for the differential processing of the oxytocin precursor, and no functions are known for the other parts of the precursor (including the neurophysins) that represent more than 90% of the parent molecule. It is too early to comment on the posttranscriptional processing of the LHRH precursor. An additional degree of complexity is introduced by the possibility that oxytocin and LHRH neurons may also release other regulatory peptides, and the problem is magnified by the possibility that these regulatory factors may control the release or action of the major hormone in question. Oxytocinergic neurons contain met-enkephalin (Martin *et al.*, 1983d) but, as will be discussed later, opioid peptides control oxytocin release (Haldar and Sawyer, 1978; Clarke *et al.*, 1979; Haldar *et al.*, 1982). These co-released products could be interactive at a number of sites. They could feedback to regulate the terminals from which they have been released ("ultra-ultra short-loop" feedback). Noradrenergic neurons are known for example to have adrenergic receptors on their terminals. A second possibility is that they act via the neuroglial elements that surround the secretory terminals. The pituicytes of the posterior pituitary gland retain their opioid receptors after transection of the pituitary stalk (Lightman *et al.*, 1983) and it has been suggested that opioid peptides could regulate the enclosure of the oxytocin terminals by the pituicytes and thereby regulate secretion (Tweedle and Hatton, 1982; van Leeuwen and De Vries, 1983). The third possibility is that the interaction occurs at the site of hormone action. Thus, for example, the response of gonadotrophs in the anterior pituitary gland to LHRH appears to be

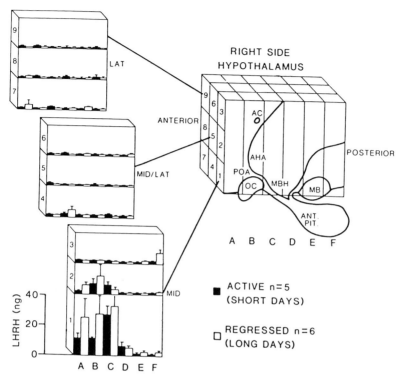

FIG. 2. Regional distribution of immunoreactive LHRH in the hypothalamus of adult Soay rams following exposure to 11–12 weeks of either short days (8L:16D which induced fully active testes) or long days (16L:8D which induced fully regressed testes). The rams were killed with an overdose of barbiturates (10 ml euthatal), the brains removed within 10 minutes of death, and a central block of brain tissue including the hypothalamus frozen on dry ice. The right side of the hypothalamus and adjacent areas were manually cut into 54 blocks using surface morphology of the brain to provide consistent landmarks as shown in the diagram. Each block was weighed (mean weight/block 44.5 ± 1.7 mg) homogenized in 1 ml of 0.1 N HCl, and neutralized before the content of LHRH was measured by radioimmunoassay using an antibody directed toward the C terminus of LHRH. Most of the LHRH activity was located in the medial basal hypothalamus (MBH) and preoptic area (POA). There was no significant difference in the content between the two groups of rams although the sexually regressed animals tended to have more LHRH. Since these animals secrete less LHRH as judged by the frequency of episodic LH pulses (Lincoln and Short, 1980), hypothalamic content does not reflect release. AC, Anterior commissure; OC, optic chiasma; POA, preoptic area; AHA, anterior hypothalamic area; MBH, medial basal hypothalamus; MB, mammillary body. Unpublished data from G. A. Lincoln and H. M. Fraser.

modulated by substance P, presumably released from the hypothalamus (Kerdelhué *et al.*, 1983).

The possibilities raised by the differential processing of precursors and/ or the corelease of other regulatory peptides are quite enormous, but for the moment many of these issues cannot be adequately addressed in the context of the physiological regulation of oxytocin and LHRH secretion due to the paucity of the information.

A. OXYTOCIN SECRETION

The lactating rat provides the clearest illustration of the pulsatile secretion of oxytocin (Fig. 3) (Lincoln *et al.*, 1973). The rat suckles her young for 15–18 hours each day in episodes of 15–60 minutes duration, and during each nursing period transient milk ejections are observed at intervals of 2–10 minutes. Curiously, these milk ejections only occur

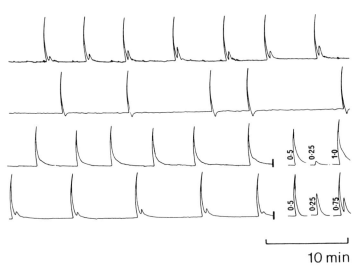

10 min

FIG. 3.   Recordings of intramammary pressure from four lactating rats during anesthesia induced with 7.5 mg/kg im xylazine and 5 mg/kg im diazepam. The main galactophore of one mammary gland was cannulated. Eight to ten hungry pups were then applied to the uncannulated nipples and left there *throughout* the duration of these recordings. Abrupt increases in intramammary pressure were observed at intervals of 4–10 minutes, each increase in pressure representing a single milk ejection. Each response peaked at about 10 mm Hg pressure. The lower two recordings were also calibrated against bolus iv injections of oxytocin in milliunits (1 mU = approximately 2 ng oxytocin). Note, milk ejections recurred at relatively regular intervals despite the continuous attachment of the pups to the nipples.

when the mother is in a state of slow-wave sleep (Lincoln *et al.*, 1980), and the phenomenon is arrested by *any* stimulus that causes arousal (wakefulness). Suckling-induced milk ejections can also be observed in the anesthetized rat, providing the anesthetic drugs evoke a slow-wave electroencephalographic pattern and do not contain opiates (Clarke *et al.*, 1979). When examined under the more controlled conditions provided by anesthesia, each milk ejection is seen to involve an abrupt but transient rise in intramammary pressure of about 15 seconds duration (Fig. 3), and in response to the ejection of milk from the alveoli into the main galacto-phore the pups suck with increased vigor. There is no obvious relation-ship between the general sucking of the pups and the intermittent pattern of milk ejection that results (Wakerley and Drewett, 1975), but if the pups are removed from the nipples the intermittent increases in intramammary pressure no longer occur. Two other features are very obvious. The first milk ejection following the application of the pups to the nipples does not occur immediately and may in anesthetized animals be delayed for 5–30 minutes or longer. Conversely the interval between one milk ejection and the next is remarkably regular once milk ejection has commenced. The afferent stimulus provided by the pups appears to be continuous and sustained, to judge from observations of behavior (Wakerley and Drew-ett, 1975) and measurements of the electrical activity of mammary nerves (Findlay, 1966) and the spinal neurons onto which they project (Poulain and Wakerley, 1984), whereas the efferent response of the sys-tem in terms of oxytocin secretion appears to be intermittent or pulsatile.

The individual milk ejection expressed by the rat during lactation is readily simulated by the administration of a bolus (iv) injection of 1–2 ng oxytocin and by the electrical stimulation of the posterior pituitary at 40–60 Hz for 2–4 seconds (see Figs. 12 and 15). The abrupt contraction of the myoepithelial cells of the mammary gland represents a "first pass" phe-nomenon, i.e., a response to a *sudden* rise in oxytocin concentration. The contractile response of the mammary gland is reduced or totally absent if the injection of the 2 ng dose of oxytocin is spread over 10 seconds or more. Low levels of continuous oxytocin infusion produce no visible rise in intramammary pressure, though they may augment the response to superimposed pulses (see Fig. 15). Higher levels of infusion tend to evoke wave-like contractions that are not synchronized between adjacent mam-mary glands, and under these conditions the gland may cease to respond to superimposed physiological pulses of oxytocin. No one has success-fully measured the plasma levels of oxytocin in the rat in relation to the very transient period of oxytocin secretion observed during suckling. The pulse of oxytocin to which the mammary gland responds is of such short duration that it would require the collection of blood samples at intervals of 5 seconds for several minutes for its detection. This is not practical given the sensitivity of current oxytocin assays and that hemorrhage itself releases oxytocin (Poulain *et al.*, 1977).

Very marked differences are observed between species in the pattern of nursing and in the kinetics of the mammary response to oxytocin, and these differences have generated a number of misconceptions concerning the underlying pattern of oxytocin secretion. Sustained increases in intramammary pressure or wave-like episodes of contractility are observed during nursing in women (Cobo *et al.*, 1967), but these do *not* necessarily reflect sustained or parallel changes in oxytocin secretion. These wave-like contractions could represent the spread of electrical activity through the myometrial syncytium or they could represent changes in the access of oxytocin to the myoepithelial cells brought about by changes in blood flow. Wave-like or sustained contractions can be induced in the lactating mammary glands of species as diverse as women (Cobo *et al.*, 1967), wallabies (Lincoln and Renfree, 1981), and seals (Lincoln *et al.*, 1983) by bolus injection of oxytocin at suitably spaced intervals. Infrequent blood sampling (3 minute intervals) in women during nursing suggests that the plasma levels of oxytocin are continuously elevated, though the variation in the levels observed is very marked (Weitzman *et al.*, 1980). More frequent sampling (1 minute intervals) provides a rather different profile and suggests that a number of episodes of secretion may occur during each nursing period (McNeilly *et al.*, 1983). The domestic pig is the only species in which detailed measurements of oxytocin have been related to discrete changes in intramammary pressure (Ellendorff *et al.*, 1982). An abrupt rise in the plasma level of oxytocin, but not lysine vasopressin, is observed for 30–60 seconds and commences immediately before the rise in intramammary pressure that signals milk ejection. From these observations it was concluded that each milk ejection in the pig resulted from the "spurt-like" release of about 50 ng oxytocin. Pigs do not have to sleep in order to eject milk (Poulain *et al.*, 1981), and that may be the case for most species other than rodents. The kinetics of the mammary contraction have evolved even further in some marsupial species such that they can now regulate two asynchronous lactations independently of each other. In the agile wallaby, for example, the mammary gland in early lactation and supporting the pouch young is extremely sensitive to oxytocin, and contracts in a wave-like manner with pressure peaks at 4 minute intervals to continuous low-level infusions of oxytocin. The much larger mammary gland formed following the previous pregnancy is an order of magnitude less sensitive to oxytocin, but is fully capable of responding to a large pulse of oxytocin such as might be released by the occasional nursing of the juvenile still running at foot (Lincoln and Renfree, 1981). Thus low levels of oxytocin secretion could promote milk ejection only in the mammary gland to which the new born is continuously attached while larger pulses of oxytocin would promote milk ejection in both glands.

There is little information regarding the release of oxytocin in the rat under other physiological conditions and nothing is known of oxytocin release in the male. Dehydration, hemorrhage, and the administration of hyperosmotic stimuli all release oxytocin under experimental circumstances (Jones and Pickering, 1969; Poulain et al., 1977; Brimble et al., 1978; Wakerley et al., 1978; Poulain and Wakerley, 1982). Oxytocin release in response to these experimental stimuli appears to be continuous rather than pulsatile (see Fig. 14), and the plasma levels of oxytocin are observed to increase. Although these results could relate more to pharmacology than physiology, they do suggest the possibility of two quite distinct modes of secretion, pulsatile secretion stimulating the mammary contraction and continuous secretion regulating fluid homoeostasis.

B. LHRH SECRETION

A pulsatile pattern of LH secretion has now been observed in a wide range of species. Pulses are very prominent in ewes, rams, and castrates (Figs. 4 and 5), and the interpulse interval varies considerably according to the time of the year and/or the stage of the reproductive cycle. In rams, it is typically shorter in the breeding than the nonbreeding season (~120 minutes versus ~1440 minutes) (Lincoln et al., 1977b, 1982; Lincoln and Short, 1980), and in ewes it is shorter during the follicular than the luteal phase of the estrous cycle (~70 minutes versus ~220 minutes) (Baird et al., 1976; Hauger et al., 1977; Baird, 1978). For the most part, the interpulse interval is substantially shorter than the half-life of LH (about 30 minutes) (Geschwind and Dewey, 1968), and that permits the individual pulses to be resolved with some clarity providing samples are taken at intervals no greater than about 10–15 minutes. An inverse relationship tends to be observed between pulse frequency and pulse amplitude (Goodman et al., 1982; Martin et al., 1983a), although there are exceptions to this rule, such as the changes at the onset of the preovulatory LH surge (Martin, 1984). Castration and ovariectomy in both the breeding and nonbreeding seasons lead to a profound increase in LH pulse frequency, with pulses recurring at regular intervals of 30–60 minutes. The time course of this response to gonadectomy is longer during the nonbreeding season compared to the breeding season (Lincoln and Short, 1980; Montgomery et al., 1985). Collectively, these extensive observations of LH secretion indicate that the pulse generator driving LH secretion expresses itself continuously in both sexes, with gonadal regulation being primarily inhibitory in nature.

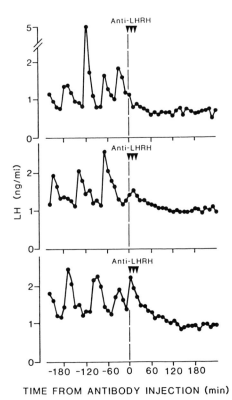

FIG. 4.   Effect of an iv injection of an ovine antiserum to LHRH on plasma LH concentrations during the follicular phase of the oestrous cycle in the ewe. The LHRH antiserum injections were made ın 3 equal aliquots (arrows). Note, the effect of administration of the antiserum at different times in relation to the endogenous LH pulses. From Fraser and McNeilly (1983).

There is evidence indicating that the LH pulse generator can be driven at a faster rate than that observed in the castrate. Ovariectomized ewes which have been kept in isolation display an increase in LH pulse frequency within minutes of exposure to a ram, though the effect is more obvious when the LH pulse frequency has been suppressed by an estrogen implant (Fig. 5) (Martin *et al.*, 1983b,c). Similarly, very frequent sampling during the LH surge indicates that it is composed of many LH pulses at intervals shorter than those observed in the castrate. These intervals, of perhaps 10 minutes, are substantially shorter than the half-life of LH, and as a consequence the basal level of LH rises dramatically (Thomas, Martin and Oldham, unpublished observations).

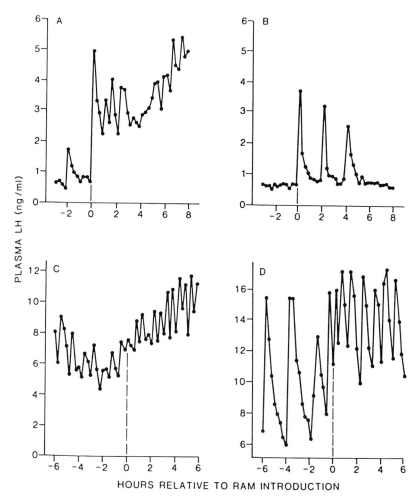

FIG. 5. Increase of LH pulse frequency by the "ram effect." During the anestrous season, the frequency of LH pulses increases within 10 minutes in Merino ewes following the introduction of rams. Profiles A and B were observed in entire ewes during the experiments described by Martin *et al.* (1983b). Profile C was observed in a long-term ovariectomized ewe in the absence of exogenous steroid and profile D was observed in an ovariectomized ewe bearing a subcutaneous implant which released approximately 2 µg estradiol per day. These experiments were described by Martin *et al.* (1983b). Between them, the four profiles show that the responses are variable, not completely dependent upon steroids, and that the ultimate frequency achieved can exceed that observed in ovariectomized ewes.

There is now convincing evidence that each LH pulse is driven by an LHRH pulse. The pituitary gland of sheep can be driven to release pulses of LH by pulsatile administration of LHRH during the nonbreeding season (Lincoln, 1979) and following hypothalamic–pituitary disconnection (Clarke *et al.*, 1984), using doses of about 250 ng iv at intervals of 2 hours. Conversely, the removal of endogenous LHRH by neutralization with an antiserum eliminates the endogenous pulsatile secretion of LH, and the effect is sufficiently acute to block an LH pulse in mid-stream (Fig. 4) (Fraser and McNeilly, 1983; Ellis *et al.*, 1983). In ewes immunized against native LHRH, pulsed injections of a synthetic LHRH analog, that does not cross-react with the antibody, will evoke LH pulses (Caraty *et al.*, 1984). Very recently, irrefutable evidence regarding the dependency of LH release upon LHRH secretion has been provided by studies in which LHRH has been measured in the pituitary portal blood of conscious sheep at frequent sampling intervals (Fig. 6) (Clarke and Cummins, 1982; Levine *et al.*, 1982). All the major LH secretory episodes are immediately preceded by a transitory increase in the concentration of LHRH in the pituitary portal blood. The duration of these LHRH pulses is still difficult to assess—most are shorter than the sampling period of 5–10 minutes.

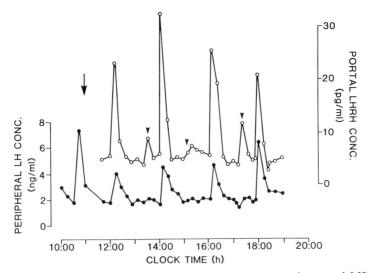

FIG. 6. Simultaneous measurements of LH in jugular venous plasma and LHRH in pituitary portal blood of an ovariectomized Corriedale ewe. Data adapted from Clarke and Cummins (1982). The animal was heparinized and a proportion of the pituitary portal vessels were cut (denoted by the arrow). Approximately 1.5 ml samples of blood were then taken at intervals of 5–15 minutes. Each LH pulse was directly associated with a major episode of LHRH secretion. There were a number of minor increases in LHRH (arrowheads) that were not associated with LH secretion.

The continuous exposure of the pituitary gland to supraphysiological levels of LHRH or its agonists leads to "down-regulation," and the gradual loss of responsiveness to LHRH (Amundson and Wheaton, 1979; Nett *et al.*, 1981). Conversely, the exposure of the pituitary gland to low levels or small pulses of LHRH has the effect of stimulating the production of more LHRH receptors and further LH biosynthesis (Clayton, 1982), and effectively primes the pituitary gland to respond more effectively to any subsequent LHRH pulse that may follow at an appropriate time (Fink *et al.*, 1976; Pickering and Fink, 1979). What appears to have been overlooked is the possibility that low levels of LHRH secretion, either in the form of "mini-LHRH" pulses or continuous secretion, may also serve a priming function. Mini-LHRH pulses have been observed in the pituitary portal blood of sheep (Clarke and Cummins, 1982). These could be artifacts due to apparent changes in pituitary portal blood flow, but equally they could have a physiological function. The latter possibility has been well illustrated in ewes following hypothalamic–pituitary disconnection. These ewes do not pulse LH spontaneously, but do so in response to bolus injections of 250 ng LHRH given every 2 hours (Clarke *et al.*, 1984). Low levels of LHRH given by infusion or in the form of mini-LHRH pulses causes no measurable increase in LH secretion but considerably augment the response to superimposed pulses of 250 ng LHRH. Similarly, continuous low levels of LHRH infusion (125 or 250 ng/hour) into anestrous ewes for 48 hours evoked an increase in LH secretion and ovulation followed (McLeod *et al.*, 1983). Thus down-regulation may be avoided *in vivo*, even during continous exposure to LHRH, provided the concentrations are low. Indeed such low levels of secretion may augment the response to superimposed pulses.

In summary, both oxytocin and LHRH appear to be released in two modes, pulses superimposed on a basal level of secretion. The mechanisms controlling the two pulse generators appear to differ in one important aspect. The oxytocin pulse generator only functions when driven by an appropriate afferent stumulus, namely the sucking of the young. The LHRH pulse generator, on the other hand, runs continuously in both sexes, and is primarily controlled through inhibition by gonadal steroids.

III. Electrophysiological Determinants of Secretion

Very exacting criteria have to be fulfilled in order to establish the electrophysiological determinants for the secretion of a hypothalamic hormone. Methods have to be developed to permit the selective identification of the neurons releasing the hormone and, preferably, these need to be based on electrophysiological criteria that permit identification during the course of the experiment. Second, procedures have to be developed that permit the physiological activation of these identified neurons, and ways found to measure their secretions on a second-by-second scale. Only in the context of the magnocellular projection to the posterior pituitary gland have we come anywhere near to fulfilling all these criteria. The introduction of the technique of antidromic activation for the electrophysiological identification of neurosecretory neurons was the first step in this direction (Kandel, 1964; Dyball, 1971). Electrical stimulation of the posterior pituitary gland releases oxytocin (Harris *et al.*, 1969) and vasopressin (Harris, 1947), and the result can be monitored from recordings of intramammary pressure. At the same time, each stimulus pulse causes an antidromic potential to pass back along the axon to its perikaryon located in the magnocellular nuclei. Thus neurons which display action potentials that are time-locked to posterior pituitary stimulation, which follow on a 1-to-1 basis to high frequency stimulation, and which exhibit collision between orthodromic and antidromic potentials can reasonably be assumed to project to the posterior pituitary gland. Such neurons are probably oxytocinergic or vasopressinergic since few other cell types project to the posterior pituitary. Even then, the final breakthrough in these studies came with the fortuitous discovery that rats milk eject as a response to suckling when fully anesthetized (Lincoln *et al.*, 1973). It would have been close to impossible to apply antidromic identification and record intramammary pressure during milk ejection in the conscious unrestrained rat, given that stress blocks milk ejection (Cross, 1953).

A. ELECTROPHYSIOLOGICAL DETERMINANTS OF PULSATILE SECRETION

Two highly distinctive patterns of electrical activity were observed in studies on antidromically identified neurons in lactating rats, namely "explosive activation" and "phasic activation" (Wakerley and Lincoln, 1971; Lincoln and Wakerley, 1971). Approximately half of the magnocellular neurons in the supraoptic and paraventricular nuclei displayed an explosive acceleration in spike activity some 9–12 seconds before each milk ejection. The firing rate of these putative oxytocinergic neurons increased from 0 to 5 spikes to 30 to 80 spikes/second for 2–4 seconds (Fig. 7) (Wakerley and Lincoln, 1973; Lincoln and Wakerley, 1974, 1975). Thereafter, there was usually a hiatus in the recorded activity lasting for 10–40 seconds. A similar latency to milk ejection of 9–12 seconds was observed following electrical stimulation of the posterior pituitary gland; this represents the time it takes for the oxytocin to be released, to circulate, and to stimulate the contraction of the myoepithelial elements of the

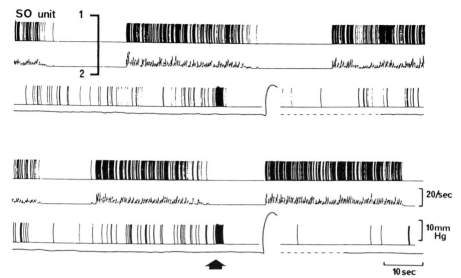

FIG. 7. Polygraph recordings of the spike activity of two antidromically identified neurons in the supraoptic nucleus of an anesthetized lactating rat. The recordings were made simultaneously and the activities of the two cells were separated using a level discriminator. Each deflection represents a single action potential (spike). The upper trace of the pair (1) displays the "phasic" activity of a putative vasopressinergic neuron and immediately below this is an integrated function of its activity calibrated in spikes/second. The lower trace (2) illustrates the activity of an oxytocinergic neuron, and displays an explosive burst of activity (arrowed) about 12 seconds before the rise in intramammary pressure at milk ejection. The intramammary pressure trace did not return promptly to base line due to blockage, and that part of the trace has been excluded. The two periods of recording that are shown were separated by about 30 minutes. Note: (1) the lack of cross-talk between the activities of the two neurons, and (2) the background firing of the oxytocinergic neuron both before and after the explosive activation associated with the milk ejection. Adapted from Lincoln and Wakerley (1974).

mammary gland. Similar recordings to these have now been obtained in a number of other laboratories (Akaishi *et al.*, 1980; Moos and Richard, 1983) and also in the unanesthetized lactating rat (Summerlee and Lincoln, 1981).

Although these early recordings of putative oxytocinergic neurons were obtained one at a time, the existence of a fixed latency between neural activation and milk ejection showed that neural activation was essentially synchronized within the population of oxytocinergic neurons (Fig. 8). This has recently been confirmed by the simultaneous recording of single oxytocinergic neurons in separate magnocellular nuclei (P. Richard, personal communication). We can be quite confident therefore that each oxytocin pulse is fashioned from an explosive high-frequency burst of spike activity synchronized between many neurons.

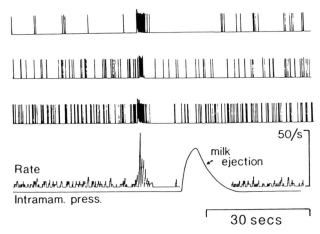

FIG. 8. Recordings of three oxytocinergic neurons from anesthetized lactating rats during milk ejection evoked by the sucking of a litter of pups. Each deflection on these recordings corresponds to a single action potential (spike). The three neurons were recorded separately, but the traces have been aligned relative to the rise in intramammary pressure at milk ejection. The mammary pressure trace and the rate meter integration of spike activity were recorded in association with the lower of the three neurons whose activity is illustrated. This neuron was situated in the paraventricular nucleus; the other two were in the supraoptic nuclei. Data adapted from Poulain and Wakerley (1982).

The remainder of the magnocellular neurons, i.e., those that were antidromically identified from stimulation of the posterior pituitary gland and which failed to display any change in activity at milk ejection, frequently displayed a "phasic pattern" of spike activity with periods of sustained activity of 5–15 spikes/second of 10–40 seconds duration alternating with similar periods of total silence (Fig. 7) (Wakerley and Lincoln, 1971; Dreifuss et al., 1976; Poulain and Wakerley, 1982). These are the putative vasopressinergic neurons of the brain and they are possibly directly osmosensitive (Mason, 1980). They display two additional features of note in the context of the present review. Phasic neurons do not normally fire in synchrony, and thus the total electrical activity entering the posterior pituitary from these cells represents the sum of their activity at any point in time. The total activity is therefore increased if the relative period of firing to silence is increased or if the rate of firing during the "on" phase is elevated. In effect, continuous vasopressin secretion is fashioned from an intermittent, asynchronous pattern of neural activity. The second point of note is the apparent lack of cross-talk between adjacent oxytocin and vasopressin cells. Occasionally, phasic cells have been observed to display explosive bursts of activity immediately before milk ejection, but the majority show no change in spike activity during the period of oxytocin secretion (Fig. 7). This is quite amazing when one considers that the two cell types are extensively intermingled. Clearly, the genome concerned with hormone biosynthesis is tightly coupled to that regulating electrical activation.

Such precise electrophysiological correlates are not available for the secretion of LHRH, largely because the LHRH neurons are few in number, widely scattered, and project to many areas of the brain. There is, however, a very extensive innervation of LHRH terminals in the median eminence, and a number of attempts have been made to monitor the electrical activity of these axons and terminals using large implanted electrodes. These multiunit recordings represent the sum of the spike activity in the neural tissue adjacent to the electrode tip, so it is not possible to estimate from such recordings the rate of spike activity within single neurons, axons, or nerve endings, or to separate one neural system from another. Surprisingly, however, some very notable correlations have been observed with regard to the pattern of LH secretion. Thiéry and Pelletier (1981) observed a statistical correlation between multiunit activity in the retrochiasmatic region and the level of LH in the peripheral plasma of ovariectomized ewes. Kawakami et al. (1982) examined ovariectomized rats and recorded striking increases in multiunit activity in the mediobasal hypothalamus which lasted for about 5 minutes and were usually followed by an increase in the plasma level of LH within 2–9 minutes (Fig. 9). No changes in activity were recorded from the medial-preoptic area, presumably because the LHRH neurons in this area are too diffusely scattered. Even more convincing are recent recordings of multiunit activity in the arcuate region of the ovariectomized rhesus monkey (Wilson et al., 1984). In this study, a large and very abrupt increase in electrical activity was associated with the onset of each LH pulse (Fig. 10). This intense period of neural activity lasted for about 5 minutes and was then followed, in many recordings but not all, by a period of sustained activity of lower intensity. These last two studies with multiunit recording are both notable for the magnitude and clarity of the electrical changes observed. The recordings indicate a high degree of synchronization between the neural elements involved, an a priori condition for pulsatile secretion. The magnitude of the response on the other hand seems to totally dominate all other neural events in the area. This is somewhat surprising when one considers that these same areas control the release of many other regulatory factors, e.g., somatostatin, substance P. Of course, changes related to the release of factors other than LHRH would not be observed if these other factors were released continuously or in synchrony with LHRH, or if their release involved only minimal changes in brain activity relative to that associated with LHRH.

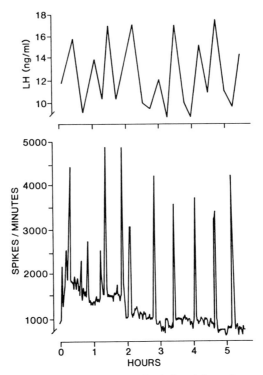

FIG. 9.   Recordings of multiunit activity (spikes/minute) from the arcuate region of the hypothalamus and levels of LH in the peripheral blood of an ovariectomized rat. Data adapted from Kawakami *et al.* (1982). The animal was maintained under anesthesia throughout this recording by the continuous infusion of thiopental. Note, abrupt increased in multiunit activity of 1–5 minutes duration normally preceded a rise in the circulating level of LH.

B.   SYNCHRONIZATION BETWEEN NEUROENDOCRINE CELLS

The synchronization observed during the activation of the oxytocinergic neurons in the rat indicates the existence of a very effective system for linking the activity of the cells in both paraventricular and supraoptic nuclei. This could be brought about by the existence of a common afferent input from a pacemaker located elsewhere in the brain. Alternatively, one could envisage a simple trigger-like input that was propagated via local circuit interneurons within and between the magnocellular nuclei. Two-thirds of the synapses terminating on each of these neurons arise within, or in the immediate vicinity of, these nuclei and

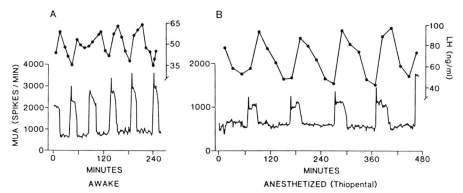

FIG. 10. Recordings of multiunit activity in the mediobasal hypothalamus and LH levels in the peripheral circulation of an ovariectomized rhesus monkey, when awake (A) and when placed under thiopental anesthesia (B). Data adapted from Wilson *et al.* (1984). In the awake animals increases in multiunit activity of 11 minutes duration were associated with increases in circulating LH, and recurred at intervals of 47 minutes. During anesthesia, these increases in multiunit activation lasted 30 minutes, a 3-fold increase, and recurred at intervals of almost 150 minutes.

could represent the interconnections that determine synchronous activation (Léranth *et al.*, 1975). The neurons within the magnocellular nuclei are separated by extensive neuroglial cell processes, but these can undergo a remarkable reorganization that appears to parallel periods of increased secretion. In late pregnancy and lactation, the magnocellular neurons enlarge and the neuroglial processes retract from between the neurons (Hatton and Tweedle, 1982; Hatton *et al.*, 1984). As a consequence, there is a very substantial increase in the area of apposition between adjacent oxytocin neurons (Fig. 11), and a marked increase in the incidence of situations where one presynaptic element contacts two neurons at one and the same time (Theodosis *et al.*, 1981). These observations indicate a high degree of neuronal plasticity, and thus oxytocin cells may only be linked to fire in synchrony under specific circumstances. There is some evidence for the existence of excitatory interconnections, via synapses or other forms of junction. Leng (1981) subjected putative oxytocin cells in the rat to constant antidromic collision by stimulating the posterior pituitary gland coincident with the occurrence of each orthodromic spike. The recorded cells were not therefore antidromically invaded but some displayed brief increases in activity, due presumably to the transmission of excitatory information from adjacent neurons that were invaded. It is even plausible that these connections might use oxytocin as a local transmitter to generate a form of positive feedback. Oxyto-

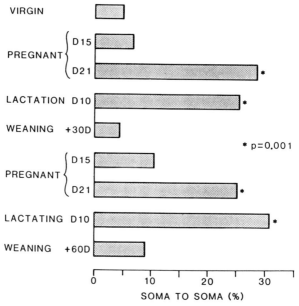

FIG. 11. Structural plasticity in the supraoptic nucleus of rats. A bar graph illustrating the proportion of soma to soma apposition, as measured by electron microscopy, and the changes observed during late pregnancy (D21) and lactation (D10) brought about by the withdrawal of the neuroglial processes that otherwise separate the neurons. The level of significance is related to the virgin group. Note the dramatic reversal of these anatomical changes during the weaning period. Data redrawn from Theodosis and Poulain (1984).

cin applied iontophoretically to paraventricular neurons has been reported to increase their spike activity (Moss *et al.*, 1972). This was largely ignored because oxytocin does not cross the blood–brain barrier to any significant extent (Mens *et al.*, 1983) and peripherally administered oxytocin does not modify the suckling-induced release of oxytocin (Lincoln, 1974b). However, oxytocin could be released within the brain, and possibly within the vicinity of the magnocellular nuclei (Kiss *et al.*, 1983). This possibility is strongly supported by the recent studies of Freund-Mercier and Richard (1984) in which they observed an increase in the spike activity of putative oxytocin neurons following the injection of 10 pg oxytocin into the third ventricle of the rat brain, and an increase in the magnitude of the explosive bursts of spike activity that precipitate pulsatile oxytocin release. The intraventricular injection of an oxytocin antagonist [d(CH$_2$)$_5$ OVT; Bankowski *et al.*, 1980] blocked this facilitation and inhibited suckling-induced milk ejections. Thus oxytocin acting at a central level may form an essential component of the mechanism that triggers the pulsatile secretion of the hormone from the posterior pituitary gland.

Virtually nothing is known of the mechanisms that link the LHRH neurons so that they can function in synchrony. These neurons are thought to have extensive dendritic fields that extend over large areas of the hypothalamus, and these could be connected by reciprocal synapses (Marshall and Goldsmith, 1980). Alternatively, the LHRH neurons could be driven to function in unison via a discrete afferent projection system, such as the ventral noradrenergic tract. Another possibility is that the LHRH terminals are interconnected at the level of the median eminence or these terminals could be directly regulated by an afferent pathway. The role of opioid peptides in modulating release from these LHRH terminals is discussed in a later section.

C. FREQUENCY FACILITATION AND STIMULUS–SECRETION COUPLING

The high rate of spike activity associated with the pulsatile release of oxytocin at milk ejection in rats (20–80 spikes/second) has the effect of augmenting the amount of oxytocin released *per spike* by a factor of 100- to 1000-fold, compared with the amount of hormone released by background rates of firing (less than 5 spikes/second) (Lincoln, 1974a). The nature of this frequency-dependent facilitation is not fully understood, but it could relate to the dynamics of the calcium flux associated with the exocytosis of the oxytocin-containing granules. Harris and his colleagues (1969) reported in detail on the parameters of electrical stimulation for oxytocin release and noted that there is a threshold of about 20 Hz in the frequency of stimulation of axons entering the posterior pituitary below which no measurable release of oxytocin occurred. A comparable study has been conducted in which different rates and periods of stimulation were applied to the posterior pituitary gland of the lactating rat. The amplitudes of the mammary contractions that resulted were then divided by the number of stimulus pulses applied to give an index of efficiency (Fig. 12) (Lincoln *et al.*, 1977a; Dreifuss *et al.*, 1981). The optimal stimulation parameters for the induction of milk ejection were in the range of 1.3 seconds at 67 Hz and 3 seconds at 40 Hz, with frequencies of stimulation below 20 Hz releasing insufficient oxytocin to produce a mammary contraction. These parameters of electrical stimulation are very similar to the frequencies and duration of accelerated spike activity observed in recordings of oxytocinergic neurons immediately before milk ejection.

A similar frequency dependence has been observed for the stimulation of LHRH release. *In vivo*, electrical stimulation of the mediobasal hypothalamus of the proestrous rat, anesthetized with sodium pentobarbitone during the critical period, at 10 Hz and above reliably induces ovulation

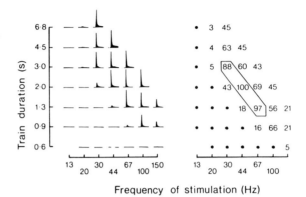

Frequency of stimulation (Hz)

FIG. 12. Induction of milk ejection in the rat by electrical stimulation of the posterior pituitary gland. The rat was anesthetized and the pituitary stalk was exposed from a ventral route. Stimulation, in the form of 1 msec square waves, was then applied to the stalk via two silver electrodes, and recordings made of intramammary pressure from a cannulated galactophore. Both stimulus frequency and train duration were varied; the resulting increases in intramammary pressure are plotted on the left. The amplitude of these responses was then divided by the number of pulses applied to the stalk to give an index of efficiency, scaled from 0 to 100. The most efficient parameters of stimulation in this experiment were 3.0 seconds at 30 Hz and 1.3 second at 67 Hz (outlined).

(Dyer and Mayes, 1978). Similar observations have now been made involving electrical stimulation of the mediobasal hypothalamus *in vitro*. Indeed, higher rates of stimulation released progressively more LHRH per stimulus pulse, providing the duration was limited to 4 minutes. Thus at 10 Hz each stimulus pulse released 20×10^{-15} LHRH, whereas at 100 Hz this had increased to 45×10^{-15} g LHRH (Dyer *et al.*, 1980). Frequency facilitation was less obvious when the period of stimulation was increased. Release at all frequencies of stimulation was blocked in calcium-free media, though release still occurred when action potential conduction was blocked by tetrodotoxin (Fig. 13). By these criteria, therefore, high rates of spike generation would appear to be most *efficient* in terms of the amount of LHRH released per spike.

D. BACKGROUND SPIKE ACTIVITY AND BASAL HORMONE SECRETION

Most oxytocinergic neurons display a continuous background of spike activity in the absence of the suckling pups, usually in the range of 0–5 spikes/second. If continued day and night, this activity would generate 10–100 times the amount of spike activity associated with the explosive

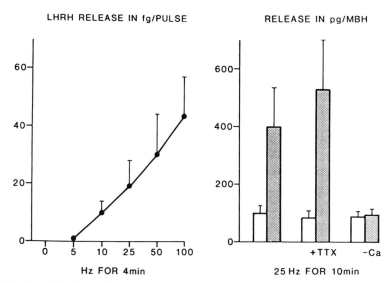

FIG. 13.   Induction of LHRH release by electrical stimulation of the mediobasal hypothalamus, *in vitro*. On the left is shown the effect of stimulating at different frequencies over
a 4-minute period, and illustrates that high frequencies of 50 and 100 Hz were most efficient
at releasing LHRH in terms of the amount of hormone released per stimulus pulse. The 10
Hz frequency was as effective as 100 Hz when 10 minutes of stimulation was applied.
Stimulation at 5 Hz for 4 or 10 minutes failed to release a measurable amount of LHRH. On
the right is depicted the total amount of LHRH released in a 10 minute period before (open
bars) and after stimulation (hatched bars), and the effects of adding tetrodotoxin (1 μg/ml)
and of removing calcium from the medium. Data adapted from Dyer *et al.* (1980).

bursts of activity recorded from suckling rats, based on a rat milk ejecting
100 times each day. While such background activity may not be very
efficient at releasing hormone, the scale on which it occurs is such that it
cannot be ignored. It could potentially account for the production of a
basal blood level of hormone and produce a daily turnover of oxytocin
within the posterior pituitary gland in the absence of any obvious stimulus
for secretion. A small change in the mean basal firing rate from 2 to 4
spikes per second (not a very remarkable change when one considers the
variability in the firing rate between neurons) could profoundly affect the
total electrical activity generated per day and thus influence basal secretion. Differences of this order have been observed during the estrous
cycle of the rat (Negoro *et al.*, 1973) and this could account for the large
change that has been observed in the content of oxytocin in the posterior
pituitary gland during the estrous cycle (Heller, 1959). That the basal
firing rate determines the basal level of hormone secretion is given further

blood pressure

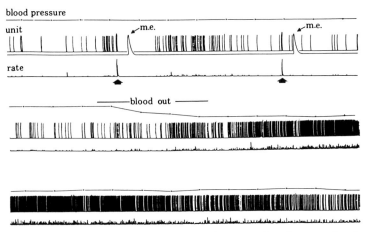

FIG. 14. A recording of the electrical activity of an oxytocinergic neuron in a lactating rat to illustrate two different patterns of response. The three traces in each section represent from above, blood pressure with a superimposed 1 minute marker, the unit recording where each deflection corresponds to an action potential (spike), and below that an integrated plot of the rate of spike activity. The three sections of recording are continuous. In response to the sucking of the young the neuron displayed an explosive burst of activity (arrowed in the upper trace) immediately before milk ejection (m.e.). Five milliliters of blood was then withdrawn, and in response to this hemorrhage the neuron displayed a sustained increase in spike activity. The rate of discharge returned to the pretreatment level when the blood was returned 33 minutes later (data not shown). Adapted from Poulain *et al.* (1977).

credence by the observation that various manipulations that cause a sustained increase in firing rate produce an elevation in the plasma level of oxytocin (Figs. 14 and 23) (Poulain *et al.*, 1977; Bicknell *et al.*, 1984). Indeed, one could propose that because neurons normally display a tonic level of spike activity there has to be a basal level of hormone secretion.

There is no similar electrophysiological evidence for LHRH neurons but, by analogy, it is possible that the background firing rate of LHRH-producing neurons would produce a basal level of secretion. This level of secretion could be well below the level of detection in pituitary portal blood using current assays.

IV. Modulation of Pulse Frequency and Amplitude

A. LOCALIZATION AND CONTROL OF THE INTERVAL GENERATOR

One of the most striking features of milk ejection in rats is the regularity of the interval between one milk ejection and the next (Fig. 3), and the lack of any precise association with the sucking activities of the young (Wakerley and Drewett, 1975). For example, increasing the number of pups attached to the nipples from 8 to 12 does not increase the frequency of milk ejection. Such observations suggest that the interval between one oxytocin pulse and the next is largely controlled by central factors, and this interval could well be determined by the time it takes for the system to recover from a state of refractoriness that follows each milk ejection. The possibility of the interpulse interval being generated by a refractory element is difficult to evaluate but is supported by various lines of circumstantial evidence. The enormous vigor with which the pups suck at milk ejection does not lead to any changes in the electrical activity of the magnocellular neurons (Figs. 7 and 8), yet unquestionably this increase in sucking activity must cause a profound increase in the sensory information entering the spinal cord via the mammary nerves (Poulain and Wakerley, 1984). Of course, reactivation of the magnocellular neurons as a consequence of milk ejection must not occur, otherwise one oxytocin pulse might follow another at an interval of 15–25 seconds and that would quickly lead to desensitization of the mammary gland. The normal interpulse interval of 3–5 minutes is perfectly set to maximize the contractile potential of the mammary gland. Further evidence for the existence of a refractory component is observed when one anesthetized rat is suckled by about six pups. Under these conditions, milk ejections will cease if a single pup is removed, but if the pup is returned within 2 minutes of the previous milk ejection the sequence of milk ejections will continue as programmed. If the pup is not returned until somewhat later (e.g., 6–10 minutes) then a milk ejection may be triggered coincident with the reattachment of the pup. This suggests that the refractory period from the last milk ejection has now passed, but the afferent input is below the threshold for activation until the pup is returned (Lincoln and Wakerley, 1975).

So where is the interval generator that displays this timing function? It does not appear to be a property of the magnocellular neurons whose explosive activation leads to the secretion of an oxytocin pulse. Neither the bolus injection of oxytocin (Lincoln, 1974b) nor the release of an endogenous oxytocin pulse by electrical stimulation of the posterior pituitary gland (Wakerley and Deverson, 1975) is capable of resetting the endogenous pattern of milk ejections evoked by the sucking of the young (Fig. 15). Both experimental procedures introduce additional milk ejections to which the young suck with vigor, and the latter also results in the antidromic invasion of the magnocellular nuclei. Despite these effects, the next endogenously regulated milk ejection occurs at the expected time. Furthermore, one can evoke milk ejection in the rat at intervals of 1 minute or less by electrical stimulation of the magnocellular nuclei, and

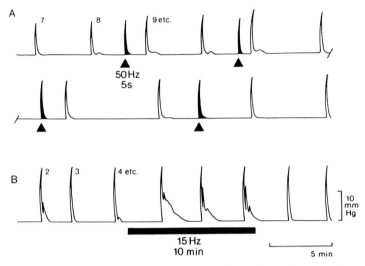

FIG. 15. Recordings of intramammary pressure from a lactating rat to illustrate the failure of milk ejection evoked by electrical stimulation of the posterior pituitary gland to modify the timing of the milk ejection sequence evoked by the sucking of the pups. The rats were anesthetized with urethane (1.1 g/kg ip), the main galactophore of one mammary gland was cannulated, an electrode was inserted in the posterior pituitary gland from a dorsal approach, and then 10 hungry pups were applied to the nipples. (A) The sequence of milk ejections numbered from the start of the nursing period. Additional milk ejections were introduced by electrical stimulation (50 Hz for 5 seconds) of the posterior pituitary gland (arrowed); these failed to reset the established sequence evoked by the sucking of the pups. The recording in (B) is from another rat and demonstrates that continued stimulation at 15 Hz was equally ineffective. Stimulation at 15 Hz probably increased the circulating levels of oxytocin, and that could account for the augmented contractions observed during stimulation. Data adapted from Wakerley and Deversen (1975).

similar results have been obtained by stimulation of the anterolateral columns of the spinal cord (Poulain and Dyer, 1984). Such electrical stimulation is possibly acting centrally to the period generator or, alternatively, these procedures may simply override the timing mechanism or, in the case of spinal cord stimulation, activate a separate projection system to the magnocellular neurons to that used by the suckling stimulus. The optimal parameters of stimulation of the spinal cord are 10 Hz for 30 seconds, a slower rate and a longer duration than is optimal when stimulating the magnocellular system directly. Two lines of evidence suggest that the midbrain might be involved in the control of pulse interval. Lesions of the ventral tegmentum of the midbrain, which could interfere with the 5-HT projection from the raphe nuclei, disrupt the regular pattern of milk ejection and from time to time result in "double" milk ejections separated by an interval of 15–30 seconds (Juss and Wakerley, 1981). Similar doublets have now been observed following the administration of 5-HT antagonists to lactating rats (Moos and Richard, 1983). Interestingly, these double milk ejections are associated with two appropriately placed episodes of high-frequency spike activity. The 5-HT antagonists are not therefore simply dissociating the magnocellular nuclei from each other.

The secretion of LH, and presumably LHRH, is also extremely regular in the castrate. In this case, however, one is dealing with a free-running rhythm, and a considerable amount of evidence, largely based on the use of lesions and knife cuts, indicates that the period generator might be contained within the hypothalamus, even within the mediobasal hypothalamus (Blake and Sawyer, 1974; Krey et al., 1975; Thiéry et al., 1978; Jackson et al., 1978). Even so, the mechanism that governs the interval between one LH pulse and the next need not be contained within those neurons that release the LHRH pulse. In sheep, at least, the frequency of LH pulsing is very powerfully reduced by gonadal steroids (Fig. 16) (review: Martin, 1984). Thus, in the intact animal, one is in effect dealing with a rhythm which is under continuous inhibitory control, where the delay leading up to the next LH pulse is governed both acutely and chronically by the quality of the gonadal response to the previous LH pulse or pulses. This introduces an irregularity into the pattern of LH secretion which becomes quite evident over long sampling periods (36 hours or more).

The feedback sensitivity to gonadal steroids varies markedly during lactation and according to the time of year in seasonal breeding species. In sheep, only minimal amounts of steroid are required to almost totally suppress LH secretion during anoestrus, while in the breeding season the feedback response is less effective (Figs. 17 and 18) (Legan and Karsch, 1979; Goodman et al., 1982; Martin et al, 1983a; Lincoln, 1984). These changes in feedback sensitivity and their effects on LH pulsatility are mediated by the daily duration of melatonin secretion from the pineal gland. Melatonin is secreted during the hours of darkness, thus under short days there is a longer period of melatonin secretion than under long days (Bittman et al., 1983). Melatonin implants can be used to override the daily pattern prescribed by day length and elicit what is in effect a short day response (Lincoln and Ebling, 1985). The mechanisms by which the melatonin signal transcribes day length were extensively reviewed by Karsch et al. (1984) and will not be discussed further. There remain, however, a number of totally unresolved issues. How does melatonin suppress the negative feedback effects of gonadal steroids? Why do changes in the pattern of melatonin secretion take weeks to influence

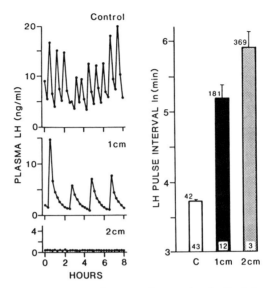

FIG. 16.   Reduction of LH pulse frequency by negative feedback in ewes. During the anestrous season, plasma LH profiles were observed in 3 groups of 4 long-term ovariectomized Romanov ewes. The ewes were either left untreated (controls, C) or implanted subcutaneously with 1 or 2 cm lengths of silastic tubing which release an estimated 2.3 or 4.7 μg estradiol per day. The ewes were implanted 6 days prior to sampling. The mean interpulse interval was determined and transformed logarithmically (base e) before group data were plotted as histograms. The figures at the top and base of each bar are the back-transformed mean interval, and the total pulses observed per group, respectively. The profiles on the left are examples from each of the groups. Regression of dose against ln (min) shows them to be linearly related ($r^2 = 0.83$, $p < 0.01$). Source: Martin, Montgomery, and Thiery, 1984, unpublished.

reproduction? We have no answers to these questions; indeed, we have no solid evidence regarding the site of melatonin action within the brain. Interestingly, Goodman and Meyer (1984) have recently published evidence to indicate that seasonal anestrus may involve active inhibition within the brain in that they observed LH pulse frequency to increase markedly during pentobarbital anesthesia in intact anestrous ewes. The opposite effects were observed during the breeding season and in castrates. Such observations suggest that it would be worth examining the effects of various *selective* neurotransmitter antagonists during anestrus. Opioid peptides were considered as possible inhibitors of reproductive function during anestrus but the administration of the opioid antagonist, naloxone, is without effect at this time (Ebling *et al.*, 1984).

The inhibition of reproductive cyclicity during lactation also appears to involve an increase in the negative feedback response to gonadal steroids

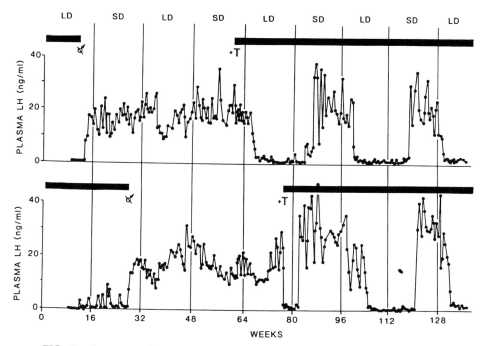

FIG. 17. Long-term changes in the blood plasma concentration of LH in two adult Soay rams sampled 1–2 times weekly during exposure to alternating 16-week periods of long days (16L:8D, LD) and short days (8L:16D, SD) for 140 weeks. The animals were castrated either during long days (above) or short days (below) and later implanted with silastic enveloped containing testosterone (T). Note, the photoperiodic modulation of LH secretion is only clearly evident in the castrates following the replacement therapy with testosterone. Data from Lincoln (1984) (and additional results).

(Baird *et al.,* 1979). This probably involves a reduction in LH pulse frequency; certainly, very marked increases in pulse frequency are observed in the sow within hours of weaning (Haresign *et al.,* 1983). The pattern of breastfeeding throughout the day appears to be a most important factor in the maintenance of this inhibition (McNeilly *et al.,* 1981), as was the duration of melatonin secretion discussed above, although nothing is known of how these effects are transcribed.

B. AMPLITUDE MODULATION AND OPIOID INHIBITION

Amplitude modulation could be achieved at three distinct levels: (1) by changing the level of neural activation that determines pulsatile secretion; (2) by priming or down-regulating the target gland or tissue; and (3) by modulating stimulus–secretion coupling at the neurosecretory terminals.

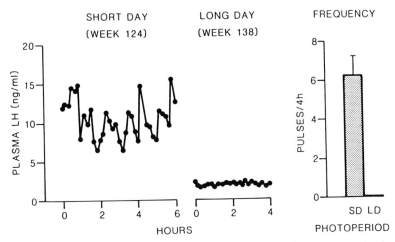

FIG. 18. Changes in the episodic pattern of LH secretion in testosterone-implanted adult Soay rams during exposure to short days (8L : 16D, SD, week 124) and long days (16L : 8D, LD, week 138) (Fig. 17). Individual values for one representative ram are illustrated, and the episodic pulses of LH are summarized for the group ($n = 4$) in the histogram. Note, LH pulses are fully suppressed by long days plus testosterone. Data from Lincoln (1984) (and additional results).

In this review, we will concentrate on the latter, because it is conceptually new and potentially important.

Attention has already been focused on the augmentation of secretion within the terminals of the posterior pituitary gland and median eminence that result from high rates of spike activity, but there is now good evidence to suggest that this facilitation can be suppressed by opioid peptides. This was stumbled upon more by accident than by design. Some of the rats being used for studies of magnocellular activity failed to release oxytocin when their posterior pituitary glands were electrically stimulated, and over the years these failures had been attributed to any one of a number of technical problems. By chance, one of these nonresponding rats was given the opioid antagonist, naloxone. To our amazement, the rat released a large amount of oxytocin on restimulation of the posterior pituitary gland (Clarke et al., 1979). This observation provided clear evidence to indicate that endogenous opioid peptides were capable of inhibiting hormone release by an action on or in the vicinity of the neurosecretory terminals. Among the more interesting follow-up studies was one by Bicknell and Leng (1982) which suggests that the effect is "terminal" specific. They stimulated the posterior pituitary gland in vitro and found that naloxone augmented the release of oxytocin but not vasopressin (Fig.

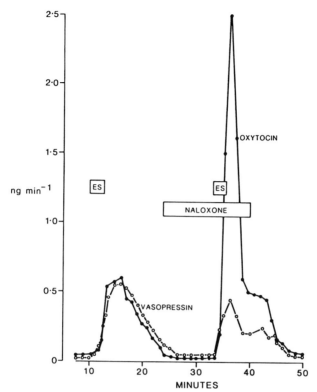

FIG. 19. Naloxone, the opiate antagonist, augments the release of oxytocin but not vasopressin following electrical stimulation of the posterior pituitary gland, *in vitro*. Electrical stimulation was applied at 13 Hz (ES) and naloxone added to the perfusion medium at 5 × $10^{-6}M$. Oxytocin and vasopressin were then assayed in the culture medium and the values expressed in ng oxytocin or vasopressin secretion/minute. Data adapted from Bicknell and Leng (1982).

19). This study also indicated the existence of an effective amount of opioid peptide to reduce secretion in the isolated gland.

The amount of LHRH released from the isolated mediobasal hypothalamus by K^+ depolarization is also substantially reduced by a range of opioid peptides, although naloxone alone had no effect (Fig. 20) (Drouva *et al.*, 1981). K^+ depolarization hardly mimics the pattern of activation one assumes mediates pulsatile LHRH secretion, but such observations are not inconsistent with the concept of opioid peptides inhibiting secretion from LHRH terminals at a site outside the blood–brain barrier.

All three families of opioid peptides are present within the hypothalamic–pituitary axis. Enkephalins and dynorphin appear to coexist within

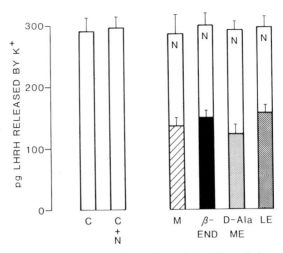

FIG. 20. Inhibition of LHRH release from the mediobasal hypothalamus by opiates and opioid peptides, *in vitro*. Slices of the mediobasal hypothalamus of male rats were maintained *in vitro*, and the levels of LHRH measured following a 6-minute pulse of K+ (56 mM). Morphine (M at 10^{-6} M), β-endorphin (β-END at 10^{-7} M). D-Ala-metenkephalin amide (D-Ala Me at 10^{-7} M) and leuenkephalin (LE at 10^{-7} M) all suppressed the release of LHRH evoked by potassium stimulation. Naloxone at 10^{-7} M (N) reversed this inhibition but it did not evoke additional secretion over and above the control in the absence of the opiates. Data adapted from Drouva *et al.* (1981).

the magnocellular neurons, and are prime candidates for some form of autoregulation of secretion (Watson *et al.*, 1982; Martin *et al.*, 1983d; Whitnall *et al.*, 1983). However, the most abundant opioid peptide is β-endorphin. Neurons producing β-endorphin are almost unique in having cell bodies in the arcuate nucleus of the hypothalamus, and in sending axons out to many other parts of the brain, including the magnocellular nuclei (Bloom *et al.*, 1978; Finley *et al.*, 1981). β-Endorphin is also released into the pituitary portal vessels in substantial amounts, especially in the presence of high levels of steroid feedback (Wehrenberg *et al.*, 1982; Wardlaw *et al.*, 1982). And to complete the story, β-endorphin from the anterior pituitary could reach the posterior pituitary gland and possibly the median eminence, though most of the β-endorphin so far detected in pituitary portal blood appears to be of hypothalamic origin.

Our early thoughts on the function of opioid peptides within the neuroendocrine axis revolved around their role in inhibiting secretion under conditions of stress and trauma. This may be true in the acute situation, but slowly a more subtle role appears to be emerging in which opioid peptides mediate the negative feedback effects of gonadal steroids on LH

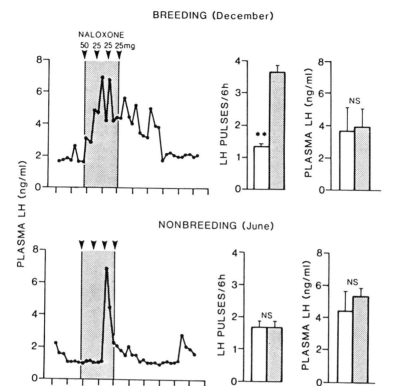

FIG. 21. Changes in the episodic pattern of LH secretion in adult Soay rams during the late breeding season (December) and nonbreeding season (June) following the iv injection of the opiate antagonist, naloxone. On these two occasions, blood samples were collected at 20 minute intervals for 12 hours on 2 consecutive days; day 1 was the control period with no treatment; on day 2 the rams received naloxone (4 hourly iv injections, total dose 125 mg). The LH data for day 2 from one representative ram is illustrated and the summary of the episodic pulses for the group ($n = 3$) is shown in the histograms (C, control day; N, naloxone treatment day). Naloxone treatment resulted in a significant increase in the frequency of LH pulses only in the breeding season. There was no change in the amplitude of the pulses. Data from Ebling *et al.* (1984).

secretion. Opiate agonists and β-endorphin inhibit the secretion of LH in acute studies (Sylvester *et al.,* 1982), and the effect is eliminated in rats by gonadectomy (Bhanot and Wilkinson, 1984). Second, very high levels of β-endorphin are observed in the pituitary portal blood during the late follicular and luteal phases of the reproductive cycle of the rhesus and pig-tailed monkeys (Wehrenberg *et al.,* 1982). These high levels are reduced to unmeasurable values following ovariectomy and are restored by the replacement of gonadal steroids to luteal phase levels (Wardlaw *et al.*, 1982). Third, the opiate antagonist naloxone is only effective at increasing LH secretion under conditions of pronounced negative steroid feedback, such as during the luteal phase of the menstrual cycle (Ropert *et al.*, 1981) and during the breeding season in sheep (Fig. 21) (Ebling *et al.*, 1984). Finally, naloxone abolishes the negative feedback actions of ovarian hormones administered to ovariectomized rats (Sylvester *et al.*, 1982). Collectively, these observations suggest that endogenous opioid peptides mediate the negative feedback actions of gonadal steroids, at least under conditions of high steroid feedback. What is the site of action? Is it at the level of the pituitary gland, the median eminence, or above? The first possibility can be firmly eliminated because opiates do not influence the response of pituitary gonadotrophs to exogenous LHRH (Ferin *et al.*, 1982). One cannot resolve the remaining issue on current evidence: opioid peptides could express their effects either centrally or at the level of the median eminence. If the opiates affect exclusively pulse frequency this

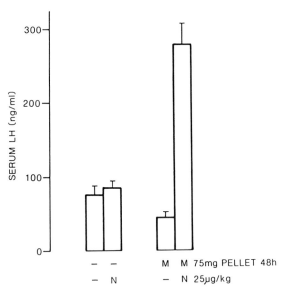

FIG. 22. Enhanced release of LH to naloxone after chronic morphine treatment. Male rats were implanted with a morphine-containing pellet (75 mg) and 48 hours later were given naloxone (0.025 mg/kg) to promote opiate withdrawal. Thirty minutes later the rats were decapitated and LH measured in trunk blood. Morphine (M) slightly reduced the level of LH, but a massive increase in the level of LH was observed following naloxone (N). No increase in LH was observed following naloxone administration to control rats. Data from Cicero *et al.* (1983).

would argue for a central site of action. Alternatively, if opiates modulate the amplitude of secretion at the level of the median eminence, as we have suggested, then they could in effect turn mini-LHRH pulses (see Clarke and Cummins, 1982) into LHRH pulses large enough to drive the pituitary gland and vice versa, and the effect would express itself as an apparent change in LH pulse frequency.

The story does not end here. Opiates are inhibitory in the short term, but with chronic treatment this gives way to tolerance and dependence, a concept familiar to pharmacologists concerned with drug addiction but novel when applied in the context of neuroendocrinology. Morphine, for example, if given to male rats in the form of an implant for 48 hours only marginally reduces the circulating levels of LH (Cicero *et al.*, 1983). If the opiate-treated rats are then given naloxone the LH levels immediately

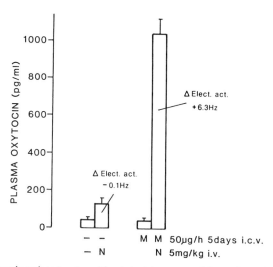

FIG. 23.   Chronic opiate treatment leads to tolerance and dependence in terms of oxytocin secretion. Morphine was infused into the lateral cerebral ventricle (i.c.v.) of female rats by osmotic minipumps in doses up to 50 μg/hour for 5 days. The plasma levels of oxytocin in these morphine-treated rats were no different to controls after 5 days. Within 5 minutes of naloxone treatment (5 mg/kg iv), however, the levels of oxytocin increased enormously in the morphine-treated rats, from 44 to 1072 pg/ml. The control rats also responded to naloxone but the effect was less marked. Putative oxytocinergic neurons were recorded and their response analysed in relation to opiate withdrawal induced by naloxone. No changes in electrical activity were observed in response to naloxone in the control group (−0.1 spikes/second) suggesting that the increase in oxytocin secretion was an effect on the oxytocin terminals. A substantial increase in spike activity of 6.3 spikes/second was observed following naloxone administration to the morphine-treated rats. Such a change in spike activity is indicative of a central effect, in addition perhaps to effects on the terminals. Data from Bicknell *et al.* (1984).

increase 5-fold, whereas control rats display no response to naloxone (Fig. 22). An almost identical phenomenon has also been observed in the context of oxytocin secretion. Morphine initially inhibits oxytocin release and milk ejection in suckled rats (Haldar *et al.,* 1982) but after 5 days of continuous infusion of morphine into the cerebral ventricles milk ejections are once again expressed at regular intervals (Russell, 1984). However, the administration of naloxone to these morphine-tolerant rats results in a massive release of oxytocin (Fig. 23). Associated with this outpouring of oxytocin is a large and sustained increase in the spike activity of putative oxytocinergic neurons (Bicknell *et al.,* 1984; Russell *et al.,* 1984). Together these observations on both LH and oxytocin secretion following chronic morphine treatment highlight new possibilities for opioid regulation of neuroendocrine events. Loss of responsiveness to the opiate represents tolerance, but the opiate is still having an effect because its withdrawal results in a massive increase in secretion (or excitability). When applied to the action of endogenous opioid peptides, these principles could serve to establish the set-point of sensitivity to feedback by gonadal steroids—our subject perhaps for a future Laurentian presentation.

V. Why Release Pulses Anyway?

The secretion of a pulse can almost be equated to a digital signal within the context of the nervous system. A pulse is generated by an explosive increase in the spike activity of a group of neurons, which are probably linked synaptically, where synchrony and duration of activation are events that are probably controlled via local circuit interconnections. Such an "all-or-none" style of signal allows the use of quite simple control systems. All one needs is a "go" signal to be produced by the period generator, which once triggered allows the pulse to be duly expressed by the final peptidergic pathway. The high rates of spike activity associated with pulsatile secretion are also very efficient in that they summate to augment secretion at the terminals. The oxytocin pulse, for example, is secreted without any substantial increase in overall spike activity, because the 2–4 second burst is followed by 10–30 seconds of total silence. Effectively, all the activity for this 30-second period has simply been compressed in a concertina fashion into a 2- to 4-second period, yet in so doing the amount of hormone released per spike has been increased 100- to 1000-fold.

Information theory dictates that it is more efficient to transmit information in digital than in analog form, and for electronic circuitry it is far easier and certainly far more reliable to transmit information in the form of discrete events than as a continuously graded signal. At the level of the pituitary gland or at any other target, a pulse provides a signal that is effectively clear of any background noise that may be present. Furthermore, by limiting the reoccurrence of the pulses relative to the response kinetics of the target tissue, one can maximize responsiveness and/or utilize minimal amounts of hormone to bring about the required response. The only efficient way to promote a mammary gland of a rat to contract, for example, is to subject it to small discrete pulses of oxytocin at intervals of 3 minutes or more. Larger injections, given over more protracted periods of time and/or at intervals shorter than 3 minutes, will lead to varying degrees of contractility, but the efficiency of the system in terms of the quality of the response relative to the amount of hormone used will be greatly reduced.

It would, on the other hand, be wrong to regard pulses of hormone as solely digital events. Pulse amplitude is potentially important, particularly where the endocrine signals are transduced, for example from LHRH to LH within the pituitary gland and from LH to testosterone in the testis. Furthermore, our digital signals (the pulses) are superimposed on an analog signal represented by basal secretion. Low levels of secretion are almost unavoidable given the continuous firing of most neurons. These two modes of secretion could allow one hormone to be used for two unrelated functions, such as milk ejection and fluid homoeostasis. Alternatively, low levels of secretion may prepare and prime a tissue such as the anterior pituitary gland to respond more effectively to superimposed pulses.

In effect, therefore, the neuroendocrine axis has evolved to use both digital and analog signals. Not only does this maximize on the transfer of information, but it is exceedingly simple in terms of organization, and extremely efficient in that it minimizes the mass of hormone secreted and maximizes the response this produces—important lessons, perhaps, for those now attempting to evolve the fifth generation of computers.

REFERENCES

Akaishi, T., Negoro, H., and Kobayasi, S. (1980). *Brain Res.* **188,** 499.

Amundson, B. C., and Wheaton, J. E. (1979). *Biol. Reprod.* **20,** 633.

Baird, D. T. (1978). *Biol. Reprod.* **18,** 359.

Baird, D. T., Swanston, I., and Scaramuzzi, R. J. (1976). *Endocrinology* **98,** 1490.

Baird, D. T., McNeilly, A. S., Sawers, R. S., and Sharpe, R. M. (1979). *J. Clin. Endocrinol. Metab.* **49,** 500.

Bankowski, K., Manning, M., Seto, J., Haldar, J., and Sawyer, W. H. (1980). *Int. J. Peptide Protein Res.* **16,** 382.

Bennett-Clarke, C., and Joseph, S. A. (1982). *Cell Tissue Res.* **221,** 493.

408 DENNIS W. LINCOLN ET AL.

Bhanot, R., and Wilkinson, M. (1984). *J. Endocrinol.* **102**, 133.

Bicknell, R. J., and Leng, G. (1982). *Nature (London)* **298**, 161.

Bicknell, R. J., Leng, G., Lincoln, D. W., and Russell, J. A. (1984). *J. Physiol (London)* **357**, 97P.

Bisset, G. W., Clark, B. J., and Haldar, J. (1970). *J. Physiol. (London)* **206**, 711.

Bittman, E. L., Dempsey, R. J., and Karsch, F. J. (1983). *Endocrinology* **113**, 2276.

Blake, C. A., and Sawyer, C. H. (1974). *Endocrinology* **94**, 730.

Bloom, F. E., Rossier, J., Battenburg, E. L. F., Bayon, A., French, E., Henriksen, S. J., Siggens, G. R., Segal, D., Browne, R., Ling, N., and Guillemin, R. (1978). *Adv. Biochem. Psychopharmacol.* **18**, 89.

Brimble, M. J., Dyball, R. E. J., and Forsling, M. L. (1978). *J. Physiol. (London)* **278**, 69.

Brooks, C. McC., Ishikawa, T., Koizumi, K., and Lu, H-H. (1966). *J. Physiol. (London)* **182**, 217.

Buijs, R. M. (1978). *Cell Tissue Res.* **192**, 423.

Caraty, A., de Reviers, M., Pelletier, J., and Dubois, M. P. (1980). *Reprod. Nutr. Dev.* **20**, 1489.

Caraty, A., Martin, G. B., and Montgomery, G. W. (1984). *Reprod. Nutr. Dev.* **24**, 439.

Ching, M. (1982). *Neuroendocrinology* **34**, 279.

Cicero, T. J., Owens, D. P., Schmoeker, P. F., and Meyer, E. R. (1983). *J. Pharmacol. Exp. Ther.* **225**, 35.

Clarke, G., Wood, P., Merrick, L., and Lincoln, D. W. (1979). *Nature (London)* **282**, 746.

Clarke, I. J., and Cummins, J. T. (1982). *Endocrinology* **111**, 1737.

Clarke, I. J., Fraser, H. M., and McNeilly, A. S. (1978). *J. Endocrinol.* **78**, 39.

Clarke, I. J., Cummins, J. T., Findlay, J. K., Burman, K. J., and Doughton, B. W. (1984). *Neuroendocrinology* **39**, 214.

Clayton, R. N. (1982). *Endocrinology* **111**, 152.

Cobo, E., de Bernal, M. M., Gaitan, E., and Quintero, C. A. (1967). *Am. J. Obstet. Gynecol.* **97**, 519.

Cross, B. A. (1953). *J. Endocrinol.* **9**, 7.

Cross, B. A., Dyball, R. E. J., Dyer, R. G., Jones, C. W., Lincoln, D. W., Morris, J. F., and Pickering, B. T. (1975). *Recent Prog. Horm. Res.* **31**, 243.

Crowder, M. E., and Nett, T. M. (1984). *Endocrinology* **114**, 234.

Crowley, W. F. (1985). *Recent Prog. Horm. Res.* **41**, in press.

Dreyfuss, F., Burlet, A., Tonon, M. C., and Vaudry, H. (1984). *Neuroendocrinology* **39**, 284.

Dreifuss, J. J., Tribollet, E., Baertschi, A. J., and Lincoln, D. W. (1976). *Neurosci. Lett.* **3**, 281.

Dreifuss, J. J., Tribollet, E., and Muhlethaler, M. (1981). *Biol. Reprod.* **24**, 51.

Drouva, S. V., Epelbaum, J., Tapia-Arancibia, L., Laplante, E., and Kordon, C. (1981). *Neuroendocrinology* **32**, 163.

Du Vigneaud, V. (1956). *Harvey Lect. Ser.* p. 1.

Dyball, R. E. J. (1971). *J. Physiol. (London)* **214**, 245.

Dyer, R. G., and Mayes, I. C. (1978). *Exp. Brain Res.* **33**, 383.

Dyer, R. G., Mansfield, S., and Yates, J. O. (1980). *Exp. Brain Res.* **39**, 453.

Ebling, F. J. P., Lincoln, G. A., Anderson, N., Cunningham, R. A., and Downey, L. (1984). *Annu. Conf. Soc. Study Fertil., U.K.* Abstr. 34.

Ellendorff, F., Forsling, M. L., and Poulain, D. A. (1982). *J. Physiol. (London)* **333**, 577.

Ellis, G. B., Desjardins, C., and Fraser, H. M. (1983). *Neuroendocrinology* **37**, 177.

Ferin, M., Wehrenberg, W. B., Lam, N. Y., Alston, E. J., and Vande Wiele, R. L. (1982). *Endocrinology* **111**, 1652.

Findlay, A. L. R. (1966). *Nature (London)* **211**, 1183.

Fink, G., Chiappa, S. A., and Aiyer, M. S. (1976). *Endocrinology* **69**, 359.

Finley, J. C. W., Lindstrom, P., and Petrusz, P. (1981). *Neuroendocrinology* **33**, 28.

Fox, C. A., and Knaggs, G. S. (1969). *J. Endocrinol.* **45**, 145.

Fraser, H. M., and McNeilly, A. S. (1983). *J. Reprod. Fertil.* **69**, 569.

Freund-Mercier, M. J., and Richard, P. L. (1984). *J. Physiol. (London)* **352**, 447.

Geschwind, I. I., and Dewey, R. (1968). *Proc. Soc. Exp. Biol. Med.* **129**, 451.

Goodman, R. L., and Meyer, S. L. (1984). *Biol. Reprod.* **30**, 374.

Goodman, R. L., Bittman, E. L., Foster, D. L., and Karsch, F. J. (1982). *Biol. Reprod.* **27**, 580.

Guillemin, R., Vargo, T., Rossier, J., Minick, S., Ling, N., Rivier, C., Vale, W., and Bloom, F. (1977). *Science* **197**, 1367.

Haldar, J., and Sawyer, W. H. (1978). *Proc. Soc. Exp. Biol. Med.* **157**, 476.

Haldar, J., Hoffman, D. L., and Zimmerman, E. A. (1982). *Peptides* **3**, 663.

Haresign, W., Foxcroft, G. R., and Lamming, G. E. (1983). *J. Reprod. Fertil.* **69**, 383.

Harris, G. W. (1947). *Philos. Trans. R. Soc. London Ser. B* **232**, 385.

Harris, G. W., Manabe, Y., and Ruf, K. B. (1969). *J. Physiol. (London)* **203**, 67.

Hatton, G. I., and Tweedle, C. D. (1982). *Brain Res. Bull.* **8**, 197.

Hatton, G. I., Parlmutter, L. S., Salm, A. K., and Tweedle, C. D. (1984). *Peptides (Suppl.)* **5**, 121.

Hauger, R. L., Karsch, F. J., and Foster, D. L. (1977). *Endocrinology* **101**, 807.

Heller, H. (1959). *Recent Prog. Endocrinol. Reprod.* p. 365.

Ivell, R., and Richter, D. (1984). *Proc. Natl. Acad. Sci. U.S.A.* **81**, 2006.

Jackson, G. L., Kuehl, D., McDowell, K., and Zateski, A. (1978). *Biol. Reprod.* **18**, 808.

Jones, C. W., and Pickering, B. T. (1969). *J. Physiol. (London)* **203**, 449.

Jones, C. W., and Pickering, B. T. (1972). *J. Physiol. (London)* **227**, 553.

Juss, T. S., and Wakerley, J. B. (1981). *J. Endocrinol.* **91**, 233.

Kandal, E. R. (1964). *J. Gen. Physiol.* **47**, 691.

Karsch, F. J., Bittman, E. L., Foster, D. L., Goodman, R. L., Legan, S. J., and Robinson, J. E. (1984). *Recent Prog. Horm. Res.* **40**, 185.

Kawakami, M., Uemura, T., and Hayashi, R. (1982). *Neuroendocrinology* **35**, 63.

Kerdelhué, B., Lenoir, V., Pasqualini, C., Elabed, A. M., and Millar, R. (1983). *In* "Multi-hormonal Regulations in Neuroendocrine Cells" (A. Tixiervidal and P. Richard, eds.), p. 221. INSERM, Paris.

Kiss, J. Z., Palkovitz, M., Zaborsky, L., Tribollet, E., Szabo, D., and Makara, G. B. (1983). *Brain Res.* **265**, 11.

Knobil, E. (1980). *Recent Prog. Horm. Res.* **36**, 53.

Krey, L. C., Butler, W. R., and Knobil, E. (1975). *Endocrinology* **96**, 1073.

Land, H., Grez, M., Ruppert, S., Schmale, H., Rehbein, M., Richter, D., and Schutz, G. (1983). *Nature (London)* **302**, 342.

Legan, S. J., and Karsch, T. J. (1979). *Biol. Reprod.* **20**, 74.

Leng, G. (1981). *Exp. Brain Res.* **41**, 135.

Léranth, C., Zaborsky, L., Marton, J., and Palkovits, M. (1975). *Exp. Brain Res.* **22**, 509.

Levine, J. E., Pau, K. Y. F., Ramirez, V. D., and Jackson, G. L. (1982). *Endocrinology* **111**, 1449.

Lightman, S. L., Ninkovic, M., and Hunt, S. P. (1983). *Prog. Brain. Res.* **60**, 353.

Lincoln, D. W. (1974a). *In* "Neurosecretion—the Final Neuroendocrine Pathway" (F. Knowles and L. Vollrath, eds.), p. 192. Springer-Verlag, Berlin and New York.

Lincoln, D. W. (1974b). *J. Endocrinol.* **60**, 193.
Lincoln, D. W., and Renfree, M. B. (1981). *J. Reprod. Fertil.* **63**, 193.
Lincoln, D. W., and Wakerley, J. B. (1971). *J. Physiol.* (*London*) **222**, 23P.
Lincoln, D. W., and Wakerley, J. B. (1974). *J. Physiol.* (*London*) **242**, 533.
Lincoln, D. W., and Wakerley, J. B. (1975). *J. Physiol.* (*London*) **250**, 443.
Lincoln, D. W., Hill, A., and Wakerley, J. B. (1973). *J. Endocrinol.* **57**, 459.
Lincoln, D. W., Clarke, G., Mason, C. A., and Dreifuss, J. J. (1977a). *In* "Neurohypophysis" (A. M. Moses and L. Share, eds.), p. 101. Karger, Basel.
Lincoln, D. W., Hentzen, K., Hin, T., van der Schoot, P., Clarke, G., and Summerlee, A. J. S. (1980). *Exp. Brain Res.* **38**, 151.
Lincoln, D. W., Boyd, I. L., Pedersen, P., Kovaks, K., and Marwood, J. (1983). *Proc. Congr. Physiol. Sci. 29th, Sydney* Abstr. 136.03.
Lincoln, G. A. (1979). *J. Endocrinol.* **83**, 251.
Lincoln, G. A. (1984). *J. Endocrinol.,* in press.
Lincoln, G. A., and Ebling, F. J. P. (1985). *J. Reprod. Fertil.* **73**, 241.
Lincoln, G. A., and Fraser, H. M. (1979). *Biol. Reprod.* **21**, 1239.
Lincoln, G. A., and Short, R. V. (1980). *Recent Prog. Horm. Res.* **36**, 1.
Lincoln, G. A., Peet, M. J., and Cunningham, R. A. (1977b). *J. Endocrinol.* **72**, 337.
Lincoln, G. A., Almeida, O. F. X., Klandorf, H., and Cunningham, R. A. (1982). *J. Endocrinol.* **92**, 237.
McLeod, B. J., Haresign, W., and Lamming, G. E. (1983). *J. Reprod. Fertil.* **68**, 489.
McNeilly, A. S. (1972). *J. Endocrinol.* **52**, 177.
McNeilly, A. S., Howie, P. W., and Houston, M. J. (1981). *In* "Research Frontiers in Fertility Regulation" (G. I. Zatuchni, M. M. Lubbok, and J. J. Sciarra, eds.), p. 102. Harper, New York.
McNeilly, A. S., Robinson, I. C. A. F., Houston, M. J., and Howie, P. W. (1983). *Br. Med. J.* **286**, 257.
Marshall, P. E., and Goldsmith, P. C. (1980). *Brain Res.* **193**, 353.
Martin, G. B. (1984). *Biol. Rev.* **59**, 1.
Martin, G. B., Scaramuzzi, R. J., and Henstridge, J. D. (1983a). *J. Endocrinol.* **96**, 181.
Martin, G. B., Scaramuzzi, R. J., and Lindsay, D. R. (1983b). *J. Reprod. Fertil.* **67**, 47.
Martin, G. B., Scaramuzzi, R. J., Oldham, C. M., and Lindsay, D. R. (1983c). *Aust. J. Biol. Sci.* **36**, 369.
Martin, R., Geis, R., Holl, R., Schafer, M., and Voigt, K. H. (1983d). *Neuroscience* **8**, 213.
Mason, W. T. (1980). *Nature* (*London*) **287**, 154.
Mens, W. B. J., Witter, A., Van Wimersma Greidanus, Tj. B. (1983). *Brain Res.* **262**, 143.
Montgomery, G. W., Martin, G. B., and Pelletier, J. (1985). *J. Reprod. Fertil.* **73**, 173.
Moos, F., and Richard, P. (1983). *Neuroendocrinology* **36**, 300.
Morris, J. F., Nordmann, J. J., and Dyball, R. E. J. (1978). *Int. Rev. Exp. Pathol.* **18**, 1.
Moss, R. L., Dyball, R. E. J., and Cross, B. A. (1972). *Exp. Neurol.* **34**, 95.
Negoro, H., Visessuwan, S., and Holland, R. C. (1973). *J. Endocrinol.* **59**, 545.
Nett, T. M., Crowder, M. E., Moss, G. E., and Duello, T. M. (1981). *Biol. Reprod.* **24**, 1145.
Pickering, A. J. M. C., and Fink, G. (1979). *J. Endocrinol.* **81**, 223.
Pickering, B. T. (1978). *Essays Biochem.* **14**, 45.
Polkowska, J., Dubois, M.-P., and Domanski, E. (1980). *Cell Tissue Res.* **208**, 327.
Poulain, D. A., and Dyer, R. G. (1984). *Exp. Brain Res.* **55**, 313.
Poulain, D. A., and Wakerley, J. B. (1982). *Neuroscience* **7**, 773.
Poulain, D. A., and Wakerley, J. B. (1984). *J. Physiol.* (*London*) **350**, 72P.
Poulain, D. A., Wakerley, J. B., and Dyball, R. E. J. (1977). *Proc. R. Soc. London Ser. B* **196**, 367.
Poulain, D. A., Rodriguez, F., and Ellendorff, F. (1981). *Exp. Brain, Res.* **43**, 107.

Ropert, J. F., Quigley, M. E., and Yen, S. S. C. (1981). *J. Clin. Endocrinol. Metab.* **52,** 583.

Russell, J. A. (1984). *J. Physiol. (London),* in press.

Russell, J. A., Leng, G., Bicknell, R. J., and Lincoln, D. W. (1984). *J. Steroid Biochem.* **20,** 1503.

Seeburg, P. H., and Adelman, J. P. (1984). *Nature (London)* **311,** 666.

Sherwood, N. M., Chiappa, S. A., Sarkar, D. K., and Fink, G. (1980). *Endocrinology* **107,** 1410.

Silverman, A. J., Antunes, J. L., Abrams, G. M., Nilaver, G., Thau, R., Robinson, J. A., Ferin, M., and Krey, L. C. (1982). *J. Comp. Neurol.* **211,** 309.

Summerlee, A. J. S., and Lincoln, D. W. (1981). *J. Endocrinol.* **90,** 255.

Swaab, D. F., Nijveldt, F., and Pool, C. W. (1975). *J. Endocrinol.* **67,** 461.

Sylvester, P. W., van Vugt, D. A., Aylsworth, C. A., Hanson, E. A., and Meites, J. (1982). *Neuroendocrinology* **34,** 269.

Terasawa, E., and Davis, G. A. (1983). *Endocrinol. Jpn.* **30,** 405.

Theodosis, D. T., Poulain, D. A., and Vincent, J. D. (1981). *Neuroscience* **6,** 919.

Theodosis, D. T., and Poulain, D. A. (1984). *Cell Tissue Res.* **235,** 217.

Thiéry, J. C., and Pelletier, J. (1981). *Neuroendocrinology* **32,** 217.

Thiéry, J. C., Pelletier, J., and Signoret, J. P. (1978). *Ann. Biol. Anim. Biochem. Biophys.* **18,** 1413.

Tweedle, C. D., and Hatton, G. I. (1982). *Brain Res. Bull.* **8,** 205.

Van Dyke, H. B., Chow, B. F., Greep, R. O., and Rothen, A. (1942). *J. Pharmacol. Exp. Ther.* **74,** 190.

Van Leeuwen, F. W., and De Vries, G. J. (1983). *Prog. Brain Res.* **60,** 343.

Wakerley, J. B., and Deverson, B. M. (1975). *J. Endocrinol.* **66,** 439.

Wakerley, J. B., and Drewett, R. F. (1975). *Physiol. Behav.* **15,** 277.

Wakerley, J. B., and Lincoln, D. W. (1971). *Brain Res.* **25,** 192.

Wakerley, J. B., and Lincoln, D. W. (1973). *J. Endocrinol.* **57,** 477.

Wakerley, J. B., Dyball, R. E. J., and Lincoln, D. W. (1973). *J. Endocrinol.* **57,** 557.

Wakerley, J. B., Poulain, D. A., and Brown, D. (1978). *Brain Res.* **148,** 425.

Wardlaw, S. L., Wehrenberg, W. B., Ferin, M., Antunes, J. L., and Frantz, A. G. (1982). *J. Clin. Endocrinol. Metab.* **55,** 877.

Watson, S. J., Akil, H., Fischli, W., Goldstein, A., Zimmerman, E. A., Nilaver, G., and van Wimersma Greidanus, Tj. B. (1982). *Science* **216,** 85.

Wehrenberg, W. B., Wardlaw, S. L., Frantz, A. G., and Ferin, M. (1982). *Endocrinology* **111,** 879.

Weitzman, R. E., Leake, R. D., Rubin, R. T., and Fisher, D. A. (1980). *J. Clin. Endocrinol. Metab.* **51,** 836.

Wheaton, J. E. (1979). *Endocrinology* **104,** 839.

Whitnall, M. H., Gainer, H., Cox, B. M., and Molineaux, C. J. (1983). *Science* **222,** 1137.

Wilson, R. C., Kesner, J. S., Kaufman, J.-M., Uemura, T., Akema, T., and Knobil, E. (1984). *Neuroendocrinology* **39,** 256.

Witkin, J. W., Paden, C. M., and Silverman, A.-J. (1982). *Neuroendocrinology* **35,** 429.

DISCUSSION

E. Knobil: I would just like to say a word about the localization of the pulse generated in the rhesus monkey. As Dr. Lincoln mentioned, we have come to the conclusion from our studies done over the past 10 years or so, that this activity is localized within the medial basal hypothalamus and probably within the region of the arcuate nucleus. This is based on fairly straightforward experiments in which we have totally differentiated the medial basal hypothalamus using the Halasz knife technique and found that this had no influence whatsoever on the pulsatile release of LH. Furthermore, lesions within these islets had no effect on pulsatile LH secretion unless they obliterated the arcuate nucleus. LH secretion was uninterrupted if these lesions spared a significant amount of arcuate tissue. When we started looking for the electrophysiological correlates of this pulsatile mode of LH secretion we are mindful of the fact that each pulse of gonadotropin released by the pituitary was initiated by a pulse of LHRH coming down the pituitary portal vessels, and such a large bolus of LHRH must represent the integrated activity of a large number of LHRH neurons. And we reasoned that this integrated activity should be measurable in electrical terms if secretory activity was preceded by or accompanied by electrical activity, and it was for this reason that we chose to record multiple unit activity rather than single unit activity from the arcuate nucleus. We expected fairly minor changes in electrical activity at best, we didn't expect any spectacular responses; we were counting on the peroidicity and predictable frequency of LH pulsatile discharges. We hoped that we could associate change in electrical activity with these endocrine events, and were prepared to apply complex statistical techniques to differentiate that anticipated electrical activity from that associated with other hypothalamic activities. We were absolutely stunned when we finally succeeded after some 5 years of attempting to record the electrical physiological concomitants of pulsatile LH release by what we saw. It very much resembled the pattern described by Dennis Lincoln and his colleagues for the oxytocin pulse-generator with a sudden burst, a very dramatic increase and equally dramatic cessation of activity.

In a slow motion rendition of the data that Dr. Lincoln was kind enough to show (the electrical activity is expressed in events per minute, and is plotted in 1 minute bins; LH concentrations in the peripheral plasma are given) a dramatic increase from about 800 spikes per minute to 3300 was observed and this was followed within 2 minutes by an increase in the plasma level of LH. What is very curious is that after this initial overshoot in electrical activity there is a plateau phase in many instances but not always which lasts depending on the circumstances for as long as 20 minutes, and then a very rapid falling off.

Concerning the effect of the administration of phenoxybenzamine, an α-adrenergic blocking drug, a single intervenous injection of this compound at a not stupendous dose causes a complete arrest of pulsatile electrical activity and a concomitant decline in LH levels in the plasma. After a long period of quiescence there is recovery from the action of the drug and a pulse, a volley of electrical activity, is immediately followed by a large pulse of LH, as reflected in the concentrations in the plasma. We attribute the large size of this discharge to an enlargement of the releasable pool during the long interval when no LH pulses were released, and to continued biosynthesis.

In the response to an anti-dopaminergic compound, I'm more interested in the resumption of activity and the association between electrical activity and pulsatile release of LH into the circulation. The character of the electrical activity does not change very much in the face of very dramatic change in the amplitude of the LH pulse.

Also shown is the response to a more specific α_1-adrenergic blocker; α_2 blockers were seemingly without effect. Dr. Lincoln mentioned our recent studies dealing with a short-loop feedback modulation of the pulse generator. Would increasing LH concentrations in peripheral plasma have any effect on the pulse generator activity? To this end, we administered a large dose of long-acting GnRH agonist which elevated plasma LH concentration dramatically. This essentially eliminated the pulsatile nature of the LH in the circulation without any effect whatsoever on the pulse generator. The big question which confronts us now, which has already been alluded to by Dr. Lincoln, is what synchronizes the activity of the cells in the medial basal hypothalamus? What establishes the periodicity of the system? What tells them all to turn on at the same time? What determines the duration of the activity of all of these cells, and what tells them all to turn off at the same time? We really won't be able to understand the operation of the system until we can come to grips with these very fundamental questions.

D. Krieger: One of the fascinating observations you presented was the varying degree of apposition of the SON (supraoptic neurons) in different states of hormonal stimulation; you suggested that this was due to effects on glial structures between those cells; is there any evidence for steroid hormone receptors on these glial cells?

D. Lincoln: I cannot answer your question. I am not aware of any studies that indicate that there are steroid receptors on the neuroglial cells in the magnocellular nuclei, but I would not be at all surprised if they were steroid sensitive. One can observe changes in neuronal elements in culture which have a very short time course indeed. Glial elements are very dynamic in their movement and in their interposition between cells.

V. Ramirez: We are studying the specific question that both Dr. Lincoln and Dr. Knobil have referred to. What we have done using *in vitro* hypothalamic preparations from male rats is to examine if we can synchronize the activity of the LHRH pulse generator *in vitro*. This was a very serendipitous finding. In immature male rats if you stimulate the preparation continuously with forskoline, that is a specific adenylate cyclase activator but not tissue specific or neuron specific, we were able to synchronize the activity. The mean levels indicate that the activity before forskoline was flat but immediately after forskoline there was an increase in the release of LHRH and curiously enough when you pool the individual values they still show a period of approximately 30 to 40 minutes. Interestingly, in the adult rat we didn't see that phenomena, which suggests to me that perhaps we are dealing with inhibitory and stimulatory neurons by just chance. In the immature prepubertal rat we were stimulating mainly stimulatory neurons and not activating inhibitory inputs to the LHRH pulse generator. Certainly we are just beginning to examine this problem of what the mechanisms are by which pulse generators can be activated at a biochemical level. I would like to address a question to Dr. Dennis Lincoln though I have several questions that I would like to ask you and I have a lot of arguments really triggered from your very challenging presentation. Let me just mention that your calculation of 250 pg per pulse probably has an error of possible 10-fold magnitude. I think this is a minor question and a minor problem but I would like to mention also that that type of calculation is very attractive but I believe we are perhaps trying to do more than our current methodology allows us to do. This type of calculation also depends on what animal we are using. So that will be one type of argument that I would like to raise. Another point on which I don't agree with you is the use of the words tolerance and withdrawal. I think that I would be more careful in using these words. In my own perception of the problem I believe that endorphin plays a very important inhibitory role in the control of the LHRH pulse generator but there is nobody that really has demonstrated that yet in a convincing manner. There is much beautiful indirect evidence and very possibly progesterone may play an important role. To try to conclude that when we use naloxone and get a response it is probably because the animal was tolerant—I think it's too much.

D. Lincoln: May I answer your second point first. I was using the words tolerance and withdrawal to try and draw your attention to the fact that we are dealing with a situation which is very different to that of down-regulation or desensitization. We have rats under chronic opiate treatment, but one observed no reduction in LH or oxytocin secretion. The animals have adapted to the opiate, become tolerant to it, but it is still expressing a very powerful action. This one sees when one withdraws the opiate; LH and oxytocin levels increase dramatically. I agree with you in that it is tricky to extrapolate those observations into a physiological context. I sense, however, that in some reproductive conditions there are high levels of β-endorphin playing onto the system, and one observes this in those situations where there is a lot of steroid feedback. Very prominent effects of opiate withdrawal, as expressed through the use of naloxone, are seen under these circumstances. This phenomenon differs from the desensitization that one observes at the level of the pituitary gland. As regards to your other point, I would rather let my colleagues answer that. We went through quite a lot of calculations to try and estimate what we thought was the size of a pulse coming down the portal vessels of the sheep. I accept that these calculations are subject to many errors. What we were trying to do was to build up in our mind a measure of how large that pulse is, relative to what we think is stored in the brain. Certainly, on the oxytocin side, we have a massive store of hormone—700 times as much oxytocin is stored in the pituitary compared with content of a pulse. In the early days, people went in for measuring the depletion of oxytocin during suckling. Such an approach to the study of the problem has very little meaning when you realize how much is stored there, and how much you release. A pulse of oxytocin is, in this situation, a very small part of the readily releasable pool. Now the question is, does the same relationship hold good for the LHRH system or can you run into a situation where you are releasing so many pulses, that you're actually getting depletion. I think that the ovarectomized animal may be releasing so much LHRH that the readily releasable pools are reduced.

V. Ramirez: I agree with you perfectly on that. The amount released is a very small percentage of the total amount present in the hypothalamus. In our studies it is no more than 5–10% of the total amount of stored hormone.

D. Lincoln: So do you think I have overestimated or underestimated the content of a pulse in the ewe?

V. Ramirez: I think you have overestimated the amount.

S. Cohen: Do you have any idea how the oxytocin concentration in the blood of a rat compares with that of a pregnant woman?

D. Lincoln: Well, nobody has so far managed to measure the blood levels of oxytocin in a rat with regard to the bolus of secretion that the mammary gland responds to. We can estimate what the peak levels would be, because we know we can simulate the rise in intermammary pressure with a 2 ng injection and you can, on the basis of that, calculate what the peak levels might be—70 to 100 pg/ml—which would be in keeping with what you see in some situations in the human field in the context of labor, or in the context of milk ejection in women.

S. Cohen: Second, I have a question about the dosage of estradiol. We did some experiments using human myometrium and most of the literature available uses doses of 5 to 30 μg of estradiol/ml of perfusion fluid and this dose suppressed myometrial contraction. Since we had assayed the estradiol content in human myometrium and found it to be in the range of 5 ng/mg we use that and we found that the lower dosages increases them, so that obviously the large doses are pharmacological and are not physiological. Now what dosage did you use?

D. Lincoln: I don't understand to which studies you are referring to.

S. Cohen: When you ovarectomized animals.

D. Lincoln: These are the studies of Negoro et al. (*J. Endocrinol.* **59,** 545, 1973). I think you are referring to where we were talking about the background electrical activity of oxytocin cells during the estrous cycle and then after ovariectomy with hormone replacement therapy. They administered 5 μg of estradiol benzoate per rat, sc.

J. Weisz: I would like to introduce a concept for which Dr. Long at the Hershey Medical

Center has recently obtained some evidence and it relates to the question of the role of opioid peptides that may be coreleased with oxytocin and vasopressin in the posterior pituitary and it refers to what you said about Dr. Cross' talk that the purpose might be when to modulate the differential release of the two hormones, that is to prevent the release or attentuate the release of oxytocin when vasopressin release is required. The rationale for the idea was stimulated by work carried out in your laboratory by ideas postulated by you and by Dr. Barry Cross. The idea being that if you start off from an evolutionary standpoint, with a single vasotocin and then you want to become discriminating and have different physiological stimuli to release one or another preferentially, do you rewire the whole circuitry or do you then call in some modulator, such as peptide which will prevent the release of oxytocin when vasopressin becomes more important, and vice versa. I just want to stress this is not my work, not my idea, this is Dr. Long's.

D. Lincoln: I don't think I can answer your question or elaborate on the point to any extent. I think something we have all come to realize is that all the stimuli that we deal with for the release of vasopressin also releases oxytocin in significant amounts. We have a very selective stimulus in the form of suckling for oxytocin release. We do not have a selective stimulus for the release of vasopressin, when we dehydrate the animal. when we hemorrhage the animal, when we subject the animal to hypertonic sodium chloride injections into the gut or the brain, in fact we release more oxytocin than we do vasopressin. I know of no situation where we can get, in the rat at least, selective release of vasopressin in the absence of oxytocin, and certainly we activate both cell types but we activate the oxytocin cells not in a pulsatile mode but in the sustained mode that I showed you in one of my slides.

J. Weisz: That is why the word being used is not selective but differential—that is under certain conditions when you introduce a peptide blocker or a blocking agent you get a further augmentation of what you might call the inappropriate, that we haven't reached the evolutionary stage when we are really selective but just somewhat differential in our release potential.

D. Lincoln: Yes.

C. S. Nicoll: You stated that the rats will not release oxytocin unless they are sleeping. Does the suckling stimulus put them into the sleeping state? Do women show changes in the EEG patterns during nursing?

D. Lincoln: Suckling is a soporific stimulus; it sends the rat to sleep. We have only been able to analyze this effectively in animals which have already been anesthesized. The EEG of a rat under urethane anesthesia alternates spontaneously between slow-wave sleep and arousal; we saw this back in the 1960s. When the pups are placed on the nipples of the rat, for the next hour continuous slow-wave EEG activity will be observed. In other words, the suckling stimulus is sleep-inducing. When this period of continuous slow-wave sleep ceases and the EEG begins to oscillate once again, then milk ejections are confined to periods of slow-wave activity. If you sustain a period of EEG arousal by any pharmacological means or you subject the animal to any stress, you will block milk ejection. You can do 101 things to a rat and block the pulsatile release of oxytocin, simply because you cause EEG arousal. It's virtually impossible to answer that same question in the unanesthetized unrestrained rat because she will go to the nest and will suckle her pups, and will in the process go to sleep. You cannot dissociate the stimulus that the pups are providing from the maternal desire to feed her young. Do women show EEG changes during breast feeding? Women do in fact tend to fall asleep when they are breast feeding, but whether that is a response to the sucking stimulus or a response to the entire environment scene, I can't say. But certainly, if they were to fall asleep then you would see electroencephalographic changes.

C. S. Nicoll: You also showed data indicating that the extent of communication among magnocellular neurons in the superoptic nucleus is increased in the lactating rat and in late pregnancy. Are these morphological changes correlated with changes in the magnitude of oxytocin responses that can be elicited by nipple stimulation or electrical stimulation of these neurons?

D. Lincoln: We have been unable as yet to tie this together. Jonathan Wakerley, who is working in Bristol, has been attempting to look at pulsatile oxytocin release in the rat outside the normal period of lactation that we have been dealing with in this presentation. He presented data at a meeting of the Anatomical Society in July indicating that he could get milk ejection by about day 15 of pregnancy in the rat. There is enough milk in the mammary glands on day 15 to record mammary pressure; he can put babies on the nipple and get those animals to milk eject. Clearly it is possible to drive the oxytocin pulse generator even in the last stages of pregnancy, at a time when there are morphological changes. But we're a long way, let me say, from being able to relate morphological changes to any electrophysiological communication that may be occurring.

C. S. Nicoll: Do you have any thoughts on why the posterior pituitary contains such an seemingly enormous surplus store of oxytocin?

D. Lincoln: Not at all really. I've often wondered this, and I've often wondered whether it indicates that one needs a massive release of oxytocin at other times in life without lactation. It is plausible that one might need a very massive release of posterior pituitary hormones, for example, in relation to severe hemorrhage. Certainly, you can get a very massive release of oxytocin in response to hemorrhage-like conditions. Whether the oxytocin, as well as the vasopressin, has some physiological significance under those circumstances is not known. You may need a massive release of oxytocin at some stages during labor, in some species, at least; releases of oxytocin which could exceed the level of release that I've been talking about here in the context of lactation. There are many species which are dependent on oxytocin for parturition, the rabbit, for example.

B. F. Rice: Over the years I've been impressed by Dr. Knobil's efforts to convince us that there is such a thing as a pelvic clock; am I to understand that Dr. Lincoln and Dr. Knobil both now agree that there is no such thing as a pelvic clock?

D. Lincoln: May I answer first. The LHRH pulse generator is capable certainly of functioning independent of the feedback of gonadal steroids, but gonadal steroids feedback do affect the generator and the response of the pituitary gland to LHRH. In sheep, there is a modulation of pulse frequency during a reproduction cycle, and if you're going to change pulse frequency then you're changing the frequency at which the LHRH pulse generator operates within the brain. We recognize that you can drive a reproductive cycle by the simple expedience of giving regular pulses which do not change in frequency. This does not necessarily simulate a physiological situation, especially in species where one observes prominent changes in pulse frequency during the cycle. They suggest a dynamic interplay between the brain and the ovary and the dynamics of that feedback control govern cycle length. The inhibition of the LHRH pulse generator is well illustrated by the increase in LH pulse frequency after ovariectomy.

E. Knobil: I think everyone would agree that the primary stimulus to the initiation of the preovulatory gonadotropin surge, the central event in the ovarian cycle, is occasioned by a rise in estrogen so that the controller, if you like to think of the ovary as being the site of a pelvic clock, is still the primary controller, or initiator, or whatever modifier you want to use, of the preovulatory gonadotropin surge. Gonadotropin secretion, what we used to think of as tonic gonadotropin secretion, is not a continuous event, but a pulsatile event and that is

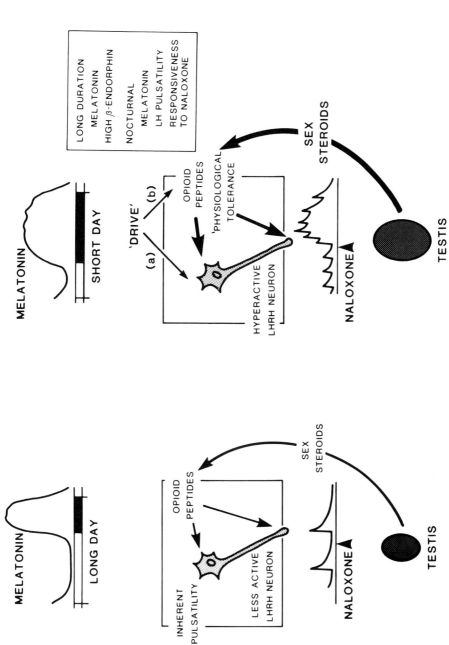

FIG. A. The two reproductive states: nonbreeding (left) and breeding (right).

driven by a hypothalamic clock if you will, or a cerebral clock if you want to become more global, which has a periodicity of once every 20–90 minutes depending on the species or the circumstance. The pelvic clock has a periodicity of once every 28 days, if you take the higher primates. These two views are not at all incompatible. I think there are some major species differences, whether we like them or not, in the mechanism whereby estrogen elicits the preovulatory gonadotropin surge. In the rat, I think there is much agreement that the estrogen acts in the hypothalamus, and I think the evidence is pretty compelling that it is the anterior hypothalamus, and there causes the initiation of an LHRH surge which then comes down the pituitary portal vessel and tells the pituitary to dump a preovulatory gonadotropin surge. In the sheep a number of beautiful studies have been performed which clearly indicate that the preovulatory gonadotropin surge is the consequence of an increase in the frequency of these pulses, but the increase in the frequency of the pulses is occasioned by the rising tide of estrogen produced in the ovary. In the higher primates, in the rhesus monkey, there is no evidence that there is any change in frequency associated with the initiation of the surge. There the estrogen seems to act directly at the level of the anterior lobe of the pituitary gland, under the influence of a permissive action of the cerebral clock, and there it causes the release of a surge. Recent evidence in the human seems to suggest that there is in some women a very slight, or a small increase, small compared to what happens in the ewe, a very small increase in frequency, but whether that is involved in the initiation of the preovulatory gonadotropin surge isn't really known. Suffice it to say that one does not require a change in frequency in either women or female monkeys to initiate the surge. So I think the species differences have to be kept clearly in mind.

D. W. Lincoln: What we desperately need is very detailed information on the LHRH profile in the portal vessels during the estrogen-induced surge, and until we get that information we are going to continue arguing between ourselves.

D. T. Krieger: I was wondering if either of you wanted to interrelate the pelvic clock to the central clock with effect of estrogens on endorphin concentrations in the central nervous system which undergo marked variation during the course of the estrous cycle.

D. Lincoln: I think we would just be speculating to do so.

G. Lincoln: The negative feedback control of LH and FSH by gonadal steroids involves inhibitory actions at the level of the hypothalamus controlling the release of LHRH. Naloxone is a powerful blocker of that inhibition implying that steroids mediate their feedback effects through endogenous opiates. Soay rams were studied at two times of the year.

Figure A shows the two reproductive states. The nonbreeding season long-day state is shown on the left where the testes are "switched off;" there is a low LHRH pulsatility as judged by the LH secretion and no response to naloxone in the face of low gonadal steroid feedback. On the right is depicted the breeding season states as occurs under short days. There is high endogenous LHRH activity, as judged by the LH secretion, large testes secreting large amounts of sex steroids, and naloxone induces a rapid increase in LH pulsatility implying the existence of endogenous opiate inhibition. Now we also know that both centrally and peripherally there are high levels of β-endorphin in these animals; they are in other words in an opiate dominated state. How then do the LHRH neurons fire at high pulse frequencies in the presence of high opiate levels, which might normally act to inhibit the system? What we have suggested is that a state of physiological tolerance develops in the breeding season. Thus neurons can fire at an inappropriate activity in the face of the opiate which at one time would have caused their total inhibition. Thus chronic exposure to a physiological level of opiate will result in a change in the basic firing activity of neurons.

If we wish to drive this system from the breeding season to the nonbreeding season first of all we must get an increase in LHRH pulsatility which drives up the circulating levels of steroids. This can be achieved by exposure to short days or long duration daily melatonin.

The steroids will then feedback to activate the opiate system which will induce the onset of the physiological tolerance phenomena, such that the negative feedback system will no longer be as effective because it operates through opiates. The system will gradually move into a new state of activity; we are changing the gonadostat in other words. The animal is now fully sexually active, producing a large number of LH pulses, a large amount of steroid, a large opiate inhibition, but now this opiate inhibition is not able to fully block the endogenous LHRH activity as it has done previously. So we believe that here is a possible explanation for the gonadostat in terms of physiological tolerance to opiates.

RECENT PROGRESS IN HORMONE RESEARCH, VOL. 41

Progesterone Action on the LHRH and the Nigrostriatal Dopamine Neuronal Systems: *In Vitro* and *in Vivo* Studies

V. D. RAMIREZ, K. KIM, AND D. DLUZEN

Department of Physiology and Biophysics, University of Illinois, Urbana, Illinois

I. Introduction

One of the scientific preoccupations of the 1960s was how the hypothalamus controls the pituitary gland, in particular, the release of LH. From those earlier studies, the first generation of hypothalamic neuropeptides was discovered, the breakthrough in the field of neuroendocrinology that still has considerable impact in our present research (Guillemin, 1978; Schally, 1978). The late Gregory Pinkus wrote in 1947: "it is hoped that the publication of critical evaluations and work in progress will be valuable not only as a record of knowledge and accomplishment, but as incitement to research." It is in that spirit that I will summarize our scientific preoccupations of the 1980s: how hormones affect central nervous system function.

II. The Problem

Since the pioneer studies of Sawyer and Everett (1959), it is known that the effect of progesterone (P_4) on neuroendocrine reproductive functions can be characterized by a two-phase process, initially an activational phase followed several hours later by an inhibitory phase. This biphasic, stimulatory–inhibitory effect of P_4 will be the focus of this article. Our work has mainly centered in the initial stimulatory phase though clear examples of the inhibitory phenomenon have been also revealed in the course of our studies.

The generality of the action of P_4 on CNS functions can be illustrated by the many neural substrates that can be affected by this steroid as partially summarized in Table I. The most salient scientific efforts have been channeled to the clarification of the effect of P_4 on the hypothalamic–pituitary–ovarian axis in a great number of species (for reviews see Rothchild, 1965; Feder and Marrone, 1977; Kalra and Kalra, 1983; Karsch *et al.*, 1984). Comparatively little is known of the effect of P_4 in other neural systems

421

TABLE I

Examples of Phenomena Associated with Involvement of P_4 in CNS Activity

CNS function	Reference
1. Anesthesia	Selye (1941); Gordon *et al.* (1956)
2. Appetite	Gilbert and Gillman (1956)
3. Running activity	Brobeck *et al.* (1947); Marrone *et al.* (1975)
4. Thermogenicity	Rothchild and Barnes (1952)
5. Ovulation	Everett and Sawyer (1949)
6. Sexual Reproductivity	Beach (1947); Feder and Marrone (1977); Pfaff and McEwen (1983)
7. Parental behavior	Lehrman (1964); Rosenblatt *et al.* (1979)
8. Premenstrual syndrome	Kessel and Coppen (1963)

and certainly they are in need of fundamental research if one is going to construct an universal explanatory hypothesis of the mechanism of P_4 action. The variety of neural substrates affected by P_4 indicate that probably more than one and at least two different but probable complementary mechanisms might best explain the ambivalent effect of P_4 on CNS functions: stimulation and inhibition. Herein, we are only concerned with the effect of P_4 on the functions of the nigrostriatal dopamine (NS-DA) and the luteinizing hormone releasing hormone (LHRH) neuronal systems.

First, we will discuss some descriptive, but what we believe novel data on the action of P_4 on the NS-DA system of rats (Fig. 1A). This system is a typical closed neuronal circuit (Carlsson and Lindqvist, 1963) involving cell bodies clustered in the zona compacta of the substantia nigra with long dopamine axons terminating in the corpus striatum (CS). Intrastriatal interneurons, particularly of the acetylcholine type (Moore and Wuerthele, 1979), are intermediate cells between dopamine input to the CS and positive feedback output to the dendritic terminals of the dopamine neurons in the zona reticulata of the substantia nigra. This extrahypothalamic target site of hormone action (Ramirez, 1983) can be considered as an internodal neuronal relay station where signals from dopaminergic terminals are channeled to a series of neuronal structures of the telencephalon, limbic system (through amygdala and ventral extension of the striatum, the nucleus accumbens, and olfactory tubercle), and mesencephalon, assuring a coordinated and precise neuronal mechanism for the functional coupling of the neuroendocrine system and somatomotor responses in adaptive behavior.

Second we will discuss in depth the action of P_4 on the LHRH neuronal system (Fig. 1B), a system which includes two anatomically distinct clus-

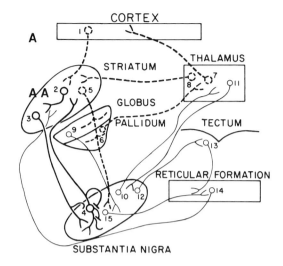

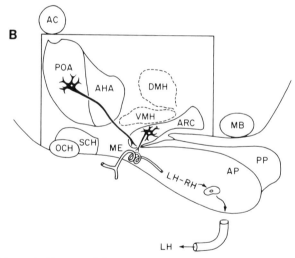

FIG. 1. Schematic diagram of the two neuronal systems in which the role of P_4 was investigated. (A) The nigrostriatal-dopamine (NS-DA) system is a complex closed loop neuronal circuit (neurons 2, 3, and 4) in which dopaminergic cell bodies in the substantia nigra send long axons which terminate in the corpus striatum. Other established neuronal connections are also indicated in numbers. (B) The preoptic-anterior hypothalamic-mediobasal hypothalamic (POA-AHA-MBH) unit (enclosed within square) is a classic neuroendocrine open loop neuronal circut in which nerve cell bodies primarily located in the POA project axons which terminate in the median eminence. A small number of immunoreactive LHRH cell bodies in the arcuate nucleus (ARC) have also been demonstrated.

ters of cell bodies—one in the preoptic-septum area and the other in the mediobasal hypothalamus. This classic neuroendocrine circuit is, in essence, an open-loop system whose major output at the level of the median eminence, the 10 amino acid decapeptide LHRH, controls the release of LH and thereby reproductive functions.

Following such description we will formulate an explanatory hypothesis of our current views of the effect of P_4 on these two unrelated neuronal target sites of P_4 action. The article as a whole attempts to highlight new approaches to examine the effect of hormones on CNS function.

III. The Strategies

Two strategies will serve this purpose: an *in vitro* that takes advantage of a superfusion chamber to measure the magnitude and temporal characteristics of the neurosecretory release (Gallardo and Ramirez, 1977) and an *in vivo* that uses a push-pull cannula device to estimate the *in vivo* output of neuroactive substances (Levine and Ramirez, 1980).

The first strategy examines *in vitro* the function of isolated fragments of hypothalamic and corpus striatal tissue, in an effort to reduce the variables involved in their functions and to control more precisely the input–output relationship of these two isolated systems. As related to the LHRH system, a number of experimental validations from our laboratory (Hartter and Ramirez, 1980; Kim and Ramirez, 1982; Gallardo and Ramirez, 1977) and others (Drouva *et al.,* 1981; Rasmussen and Yen, 1983; Miyake *et al.,* 1982) attest to the functional viability of LHRH neurons superfused *in vitro*. For instance, isolated median eminence fragments from ovariectomized 30-day-old rats primed with estrogen for 2 days and infused repetitively with 30 mM K$^+$, responded with reliable, rapid and short-lived neurosecretory LHRH outputs as shown in Fig. 2. Such responses can be observed for at least 5 hours of *in vitro* superfusion, however the magnitude of the responses tend to decline by the end of the experiment. This potassium-evoked LHRH release *in vitro* is calcium and temperature dependent (Hartter and Ramirez, 1980; Ramirez *et al.,* 1980b). More pertinent to this article is the work of Drouva *et al.* (1983) who have shown that K$^+$-evoked LHRH release can be altered by previous exposure of the animal to P_4. The steroid initially facilitates the potassium-evoked LHRH release within the first 4 hours after a high dose of P_4 (25 mg/rat) whereas 24 hours after its systemic injection the response to potassium was clearly reduced. In addition to these functional validations superfused hypothalamic fragments show at the electron microscopic level a well preserved cytoarchitectonical organization of the median eminence neuropile. Moreover, in K$^+$-stimulated hypothalamic

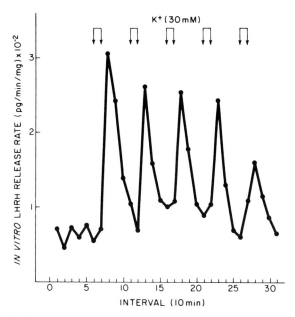

FIG. 2. Typical example of *in vitro* K⁺-stimulated release of LHRH from isolated median eminence fragments from ovariectomized-estrogen primed immature female rats. Following a 1-hour basal release period, 30 m*M* K⁺ was infused *in vitro* for 10 minutes every 40 minutes. Repetitive K⁺ pulses rapidly and reliably evoked a 5- to 6-fold increase in LHRH release, a response which diminished only toward the end of the 5 hour superfusion.

fragments, clear changes in median eminence nerve terminals, characterized by large diameters containing low quantities of microvesicles and granular vesicles were observed. These K⁺-evoked ultrastructural changes can be blocked in the absence of calcium (Zamora and Ramirez, 1983). As related to the NS-DA system, the spontaneous endogenous dopamine release from superfused isolated fragments of the CS showed marked changes following potassium stimulation, a calcium-dependent response (Becker *et al.*, 1984) and after amphetamine (AMPH) stimulation, a calcium-independent response (Ramirez, 1983). An example of the latter is presented in Fig. 3. Of relevance for the purpose of the present article is our report that the *in vitro* AMPH-evoked dopamine release can be modified by the hormonal condition of the animal. Specifically, it is reduced following ovariectomy, restored following steroid treatment (Ramirez, 1983) and changes during the rat estrous cycle (Becker and Ramirez, 1981).

The second strategy estimates the output of these two neuronal systems *in vivo*. To this end, we introduced in the field of neuroendocrinology in

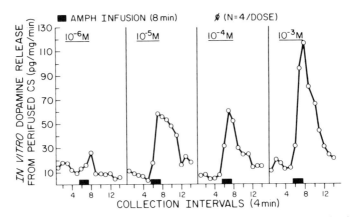

FIG. 3. Dose–response relationships of *in vitro* amphetamine (AMPH)-stimulated dopamine release from corpus striatum tissue fragments of ovariectomized female rats. Following a 20-minute basal dopamine release collection period, AMPH (10^{-6} to 10^{-3} M) was
infused for an 8-minute period. Under these conditions, AMPH at 10^{-5} M reliably produced
a 5- to 6-fold increase in dopamine release.

1980, thanks to the effort of Dr. Jon Levine (at that time a graduate
student in our laboratory), the push-pull cannulae technique of Gaddum
(1960) to estimate the output of LHRH from the MBH of conscious,
unrestrained rats. Lately, we have extended the use of the push-pull
perfusion (PPP) technique to our studies of the NS-DA system (Chen *et
al.*, 1984). Such a device can be stereotaxically implanted into precise
areas of the brain of various animal models to estimate LHRH output or
changes in dopamine neurotransmission (Ramirez, 1984). An example of
the latter is presented in Fig. 4. In this case, perfusate samples collected
at 20-minute intervals from the pull-line of the push-pull cannulae with its
tip in the caudate nucleus (CN) of a male rat were immediately injected
into the port of a high-pressure liquid chromatography coupled to electrochemical detector (HPLC-EC) system which allowed us to record simultaneously five different neurochemicals. Continuous PPP of the rostral
caudal portion of the CN in this conscious, unrestrained male rat who
went through the normal gamut of rat behavior during the experimental
session (sleeping, resting, drinking, eating, grooming, etc.) revealed
marked changes in the two main metabolites of dopamine neurotransmission, 2,4-dihydroxyphenylacetic acid (DOPAC), and homovanillic acid
(HVA). Surprisingly, however, no changes in DA output were recorded
during the 24-hour period of the experiment.

With the help of these two tools, while remaining cognizant of their
advantages and disadvantages (Ramirez, 1984), let us now examine first

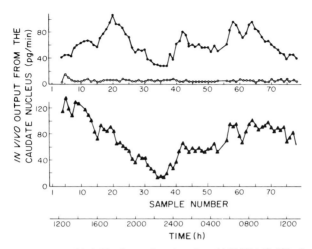

FIG. 4. *In vivo* output of 2,4-dihydroxyphenylacetic acid (DOPAC) (●), dopamine (DA) (○), and homovanillic acid (HVA) (▲) as determined from an unrestrained male rat during a continuous 24-hour push-pull perfusion (PPP) session. The push-pull cannula was located at the rostral-caudal portion of the caudate nucleus and neurochemicals from each 20-minute perfusate sample were immediately analyzed with an HPLC-EC system. Although DOPAC and HVA levels showed marked fluctuations, DA levels remained fairly stable throughout this 24-hour period.

the role of P_4 in the activity of the NS-DA neuronal system and second, the role of this steroid in the activity of the LHRH neuronal system.

IV.   Progesterone and the NS-DA Neuronal System

It has become apparent that hormones in an as yet unresolved manner influence the activity of the NS-DA system (Ramirez, 1983). Previously, we published that ovariectomy but not orchidectomy attenuated the DA response of striatal fragments superfused *in vitro* to a large pulse of amphetamine. Moreover, the responsiveness of the *in vitro* striatal fragments to AMPH was dependent on the stage of the estrous cycle of the rat (Becker and Ramirez, 1981). Progesterone administered to ovariectomized estradiol benzoate (OVX + Eb) treated animals reinstated the response of the striatal fragments to the highest level obtained in diestrus-1 (Ramirez, 1983). Further, we have recently found that in a similar OVX + Eb rat preparation, P_4 exerted a strong bimodal effect on the *in vitro* DA activity of superfused striatal fragments (Dluzen and Ramirez, 1984). Initially, the steroid stimulated the spontaneous DA release, facilitated amphetamine-evoked dopamine release, and increased dopamine

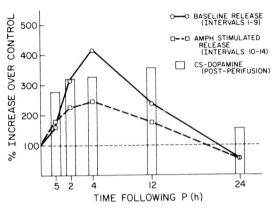

FIG. 5. *In vitro* basal and AMPH-stimulated DA release and postsuperfusion DA concentrations from corpus striatum (CS) fragments of ovariectomized estrogen-treated rats administered progesterone (P_4, 1.25 mg/rat) *in vivo* at 0.5, 2, 4, 12, and 24 hours prior to sacrifice and superfusion. Results are expressed as the percentage increase over controls—a pooled group of ovariectomized females receiving various combinations of hormone and vehicle injections (oil + oil, EB + oil, oil + P_4). Maximal basal and amphetamine stimulated dopamine release occurs at 4 hours following P_4 administration, while at 24 hours post-P_4, release rates are actively inhibited as evidenced by levels of 50% of that of controls. (Modified from Dluzen and Ramirez, 1984.)

concentration in the tissue, followed by an active inhibitory phase 24 hours later (Fig. 5). Because of these robust bidirectional changes induced by P_4 in the NS-DA system, we wondered if this effect of P_4 would occur directly at the level of the dopaminergic terminals in the CS. Using a similar experimental model, we were able to demonstrate that P_4 can indeed directly alter the *in vitro* output of DA from CS-DA terminals as shown in Fig. 6. However, to our surprise, only the pulsatile mode of direct infusion of P_4 in the CS in low concentrations (2 ng/ml) was effective in activating basal dopamine release and markedly augmenting the response of the CS tissue to 10^{-5} *M* amphetamine stimulation, as compared to control preparations run in parallel superfusions. Intriguingly, a constant infusion of the steroid using an identical concentration and for a time equivalent to that corresponding to the four pulses of P_4 produced a notable reduction in the response of the tissue to amphetamine. These two *in vitro* modes of P_4 infusions not only altered AMPH-evoked DA release, but they also produced distinct changes in postsuperfusion tissue DA concentrations (see legend to Fig. 6). A significant 60% increase in dopamine concentration in the CS was observed in superfusion units receiving the pulsatile mode of P_4 infusion in contrast to a 40% reduction

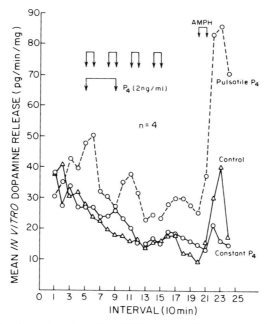

FIG. 6. *In vitro* dopamine release from CS fragments of ovariectomized rats treated with 5 μg estradiol benzoate subcutaneously for 4 days. On the fifth day animals were decapitated at 0900–1000 hours (0500–1900 hour photoperiod) and the CS removed and placed in superfusion chambers. Following a 40-minute basal collection period, CS fragments received either four pulsatile (10 minutes on–20 minutes off) or one continuous (40 minute) P_4 infusion (2 ng/ml). All preparations received a 10 minute infusion of 10^{-5} M AMPH at the end of the superfusion. Pulsatile P_4 administration markedly augmented both basal and AMPH-stimulated DA release while a continuous P_4 infusion apparently inhibited the AMPH-stimulated response as compared to control superfusions. In addition, pulsatile P_4 increased (1.2 ± 0.3) while continuous P_4 decreased (0.4 ± 0.03) CS-DA concentrations (ng/mg) as compared to controls (0.7 ± 0.1).

in those experimental units receiving the constant infusion when these values are compared to control superfusions.

V. Summary and Conclusions

From this series of studies, it can be postulated with confidence that P_4 might play a physiological role in the control of DA neurotransmission in the NS-DA system. The *in vivo* bidirectional action of the steroid stimulation and inhibition, on the spontaneous *in vitro* dopamine release, AMPH-evoked DA release and DA tissue concentration, is intriguing and puzzling. However, this bimodal action of P_4 is well established in other neuroendocrine phenomena such as sexual activation (Feder and Marrone, 1977) and LH release (Drouva *et al.*, 1983) though no clear explanations have been offered as yet. Feder and Marrone (1977) speculated that the inhibitory action of P_4 on lordosis behavior may involve DA neurotransmission since implants of P_4 in the midbrain left for 8 hours at the point of origin of dopamine cells inhibited the lordosis response to a systemic injection of P_4 in OVX + E_2 primed guinea pigs (Morin and Feder, 1974). Interestingly, similar implants of P_4 but acting for a short time period (2 hours) stimulated lordosis in rats instead of inhibiting this behavior (Ross *et al.*, 1971).

From our studies, it appears that P_4 can, in part at least, exert this sequence of effects, facilitation–inhibition, at the level of the CS, and that the response of the tissue is stimulus dependent. Low doses of P_4 administered in a pulsatile mode were stimulatory. In contrast, continuous infusion of P_4 using an equivalent total dose to that of the pulsatile mode drastically reduced the AMPH-evoked DA release and significantly decreased tissue DA concentration without, however, affecting the spontaneous endogenous release of the neurotransmitter. We wish to propose that P_4 exerts its stimulatory effect by a direct action on the DA nerve terminals in the CS and its inhibitory effect indirectly through activation of inhibitory neurons suppressing the AMPH-evoked DA release. The likely candidates for the inhibitory neurons are the enkephalin neurons, localized in the CS (Khachaturian *et al.*, 1983) and which are known to inhibit K^+-evoked DA release from similar *in vitro* preparations (Broderick *et al.*, 1983). Other inhibitory neurotransmitters like GABA cannot be discarded (McGeer and McGeer, 1976). Further studies are needed to prove or deny such testable hypotheses.

VI. Progesterone and the LHRH Neuronal System

Abundant literature has previously established that P_4 can (1) advance as well as block ovulation in the rat and rabbit, (2) advance and amplify the discharge of LH in proestrous, and (3) stimulate the release of LH in a variety of experimental conditions and experimental animal models. All of them requiring some level of estrogen priming. In addition, in all conditions tested, P_4 will inhibit the discharge of LH following initial stimulation, and considerable data indicate that P_4 can activate the central noradrenergic and/or adrenergic systems. These transmitters may be the main mediators involved in the discharge of LH (for review see Barraclough and Wise, 1982; Ramirez *et al.*, 1984a; Kalra and Kalra, 1983). it is now well accepted that LHRH is the final stimulatory chemotransmitter controlling LH release, though an inhibitory putative substance of hypothalamic origin has also been postulated and may be of importance in the final regulation of LH output (Kalra, 1976; Ramirez, 1978; Wildt *et al.*, 1981; Barraclough *et al.*, 1984).

Since the pioneer work of Everett and Sawyer, it is well established that P_4 in rodents and rabbits has a biphasic effect on LH release, stimulation followed 24 hours later by inhibition. However, the stimulatory effect of P_4 on LH release has not been shown in seasonal breeders like the sheep (Karsch *et al.*, 1984). The stimulatory effect of P_4 on LH release has also been questioned in primates with menstrual cycles (Knobil, 1980) though there are also strong data supporting the sequence facilitation–inhibition of P_4 (Helmond *et al.*, 1981; Yeoman and Teresawa, 1985). At any rate, the inhibitory effect of P_4 on LH release seems to be a rather universal phenomenon since it occurs across several species.

In the studies previous to our work, the effect of P_4 on LH release was assumed to occur through activation of the LHRH neural apparatus, but never proved because of the lack of adequate procedures to measure LHRH release. In 1980, we published in *Science* (Ramirez *et al.*, 1980a) that P_4 administered subcutaneously to ovariectomized 30-day-old rats primed 2 days earlier with estrogen increased the spontaneous release rate of LHRH from hypothalamic fragments superfused *in vitro*. In that paper, we also reported that 2 days after ovariectomy, the hypothalami from these 30-day-old rats secreted significantly less LHRH *in vitro* than those from intact animals. Replacement therapy with estrogen by silastic capsules, though inducing a clear rise in blood LH levels in the afternoon of the photoperiod, as compared with low levels of LH in the morning did not change *in vitro* LHRH release (see Table II). In this immature rat

TABLE II

Relationship between Photoperiod, Steroid Hormones, and LHRH-LH in Ovariectomized Immature 30-Day-Old Rats[a]

Photoperiod[b] (0500–1900)		Condition (30-day-old-rat)	Mean LHRH output (pg/10 min)	Blood LH (ng/ml)
Light $\xrightarrow{}$	(−) AM	OVX + E_2	4	17
$\dashrightarrow$	PM	OVX + E_2	3	894
Light $\xrightarrow{}$	(−) AM	OVX + E_2 + P_4	14	84
$\dashrightarrow$	PM	OVX + E_2 + P_4	13	3554

[a] From Ramirez *et al.* (1980a).

[b] It is assumed that in the morning of the photoperiod inhibitory inputs [→ (−)] keep in check either the LHRH pulse generator and/or the gonadotrops. In the afternoon those light-dependent inhibitory inputs (---→) cease. For details see text.

model (OVX + E_2), P_4 as indicated above, was highly effective in increasing LHRH release from hypothalami removed from OVX + E_2 animals receiving the steroid 6 hours previous to decapitation, either in the morning or in the afternoon of the photophase. Significant, but slight increases in blood LH levels were noticed in the morning which were, however, markedly elevated in the afternoon, reaching proestrous levels.

These data clearly suggested that P_4 was somehow involved in the activation of the LHRH neuronal apparatus and presumably it is responsible for the P_4-evoked LH release in rodents. Since then, we have pursued this finding step-by-step in an effort to clarify the role of P_4 on LHRH release, using this *in vitro* preparation as a model to investigate the effect of steroids on hypothalamic peptidergic neurons. An account of such findings which gave origin to the formulation of an explanatory hypothesis of the possible nongenomic role of P_4 in dealing with the activation of the LHRH neural apparatus is described below.

Shortly after we published the effect of systemic P_4 on *in vitro* LHRH release, we demonstrated using the push-pull perfusion technique that, indeed, P_4 could stimulate the release of LHRH *in vivo* since in ovariectomized + E_2 adult rats bearing a PPC in the MBH, an increase in LHRH output was detected approximately 5–6 hours after a subcutaneous injection of P_4 at 1000 hours on the morning of the period (Levine and Ramirez, 1980). Lately, we showed that *in vitro* P_4 can exert a direct action on hypothalamic units (including the preoptic area, anterior hypothalamus, and medial basal hypothalamic region) derived from ovariectomized + E_2 primed 30-day-old rats. Interestingly, the effect of P_4 on the LHRH neural apparatus was stimulus dependent since only a pulsatile but not a constant mode of P_4 infusion was effective in stimulating *in vitro* release of LHRH with a latency of approximately 60 minutes. Moreover, the stimulatory effect of P_4 on LHRH release lasted for about 1 hour. Subsequently, LHRH levels returned to basal release in spite of continuous pulsing of the preparation with P_4 (Kim and Ramirez, 1982). Profiting from one of the advantages of the PPC procedure that allows one to infuse substances locally into the site of perfusion, we determined the effect of P_4 infused directly into the MBH of OVX + E_2 rats (Fig. 7). Three different conditions were studied: (1) animals who were perfused only with control medium, (2) animals, who after a 3-hour control period, received P_4 continuously for a 4-hour period, and (3) animals who received 8 pulses of P_4 (10 minutes on–20 minutes off), using the same concentration of steroid as in group II (10 ng/ml). It is evident that only in the last group was P_4 effective in modifying the activity of the LHRH pulse generator with first noticeable activation after the third pulse of P_4. A summary of these data are shown in Table III. It is only the group that received P_4 in

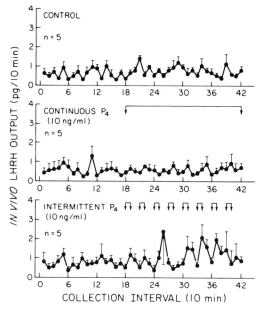

FIG. 7. *In vivo* LHRH output (mean ± SE) as determined in PPP samples collected at 10 minute intervals from OVX + E_2 adult female rats. Following a 3-hour basal collection period, female rats were divided into three treatment conditions (n = 5/condition): (1) control—perfused with control medium; (2) continuous-P_4 (10 ng/ml)—perfused continuously with P_4 for 4 hours; and (3) intermittent-P_4 (10 ng/ml)—perfused intermittently (10 minutes on–20 minutes off) with P_4 for 4 hours. Only the intermittent P_4 infusion was effective in significantly increasing mean LHRH output and amplitude during the infusion period (Kim, 1984).

an intermittent mode that showed significantly higher mean LHRH output, mostly due to LHRH pulses of larger amplitude without significant changes in frequency. In the constant P_4 infusion group, the activity of the LHRH pulse generator diminished, although not significantly. The stimulatory effectiveness of P_4 on the LHRH neural apparatus depends on estrogen priming (Kim and Ramirez, 1985), since P_4 was ineffective in ovariectomized rats treated with oil, but clearly augmented *in vitro* LHRH release in a dose-dependent manner when similar hypothalamic units derived from immature ovariectomized rats were treated with either low (30 pg/ml), medium (60 pg/ml), or high doses (120 pg/ml) of estradiol administered in silastic capsules (Fig. 8). This estrogen-priming effect has also been reported independently by Miyake *et al.* (1982) and Drouva *et al.* (1983). It appears that estrogen pretreatment somehow creates the necessary biochemical condition in hypothalamic neurons that is an absolute prerequisite for P_4-evoked LHRH release *in vitro*.

TABLE III

In Vivo LHRH Output in the OVX + E₂ Rat Model

Condition[a]	Number of experiment	Output (pg/10 min)	Amplitude (pg)	Period (minutes)
1. Control infusion	5	0.76 ± 0.06	1.04 ± 0.07	52 ± 9
2. Intermittent P₄ infusion	5	1.12 ± 0.23	1.99 ± 0.53	42 ± 5
3. Continuous P₄ Infusion	5	0.59 ± 0.07	1.02 ± 0.16	63 ± 19

[a] *In vivo* activity of the LHRH pulse generator of ovariectomized estrogen primed female rats under three push-pull perfusion conditions: (1) Control infusion, (2) intermittent (10 minutes on–20 minutes off) progesterone (P₄) infusion, and (3) continuous (4 hour) P₄ infusion. Following a 3-hour control period, P₄ (10 ng/ml) was locally infused either intermittently or continuously into the medial basal hypothalamus while control preparations were continuously perfused with medium in the absence of P₄. The mean output and amplitude of *in vivo* LHRH of female rats receiving intermittent P₄ infusions were significantly increased during the 4-hour P₄ infusion period compared to that of the control and the continuous P₄ infusion condition. There was also a trend, albeit not significant, for a decrease pulse period in the intermittent P₄ infused group.

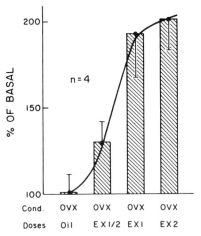

FIG. 8. Percentage increase of P₄-evoked LHRH release *in vitro* (10 ng/ml) (mean ± SE) as a function of estrogen priming dose. Immature (28 day) female rats were overiectomized and implanted with silastic capsules (Ramirez *et al.*, 1980) containing oil (OVX-Oil), 117.5 μg estradiol (OVX-E₂ × 1/2), 235 μg estradiol (OVX-E₂ × 1), and 2 capsules with 235 μg estradiol (OVX-E₂ × 2). After 2 days of estrogen priming hypothalamic units from these rats were superfused and the percentage increase of *in vitro* LHRH release was calculated during the intermittent (10 minutes on–20 minutes off) P₄ infusion period. All doses of estrogen resulted in a significant increase in P₄-stimulated LHRH release as compared to oil controls with the magnitude of the P₄-stimulated LHRH release increasing as a function of increasing blood estrogen levels (Kim and Ramirez, 1985).

Since we observed that P_4-evoked LHRH release *in vitro* from hypothalamic units was different from that of isolated median eminences derived from OVX + E_2 30-day-old rats (Kim and Ramirez, 1985) we decided to test the effect of P_4 infused either intermittently or continuously in median eminence preparations containing mainly nerve endings. Figure 9A and B illustrate such findings. First, when progesterone was infused intermittently to isolated median eminences, each pulse of the steroid elicited within the first 20–30 minutes a rapid response with a remarkable synchrony among the different experiments as proved by the periodic oscillations of the mean responses. This type of response resembles the potassium-evoked LHRH release from similar preparations which, however, were elicited within the first 10–20 minutes after pulsing with potassium (please compare Fig. 2 with Fig. 9A). Curiously, when P_4 was administered continuously to similar median eminence preparations, the tissue also responded with an increase in LHRH release. This stimulus mode

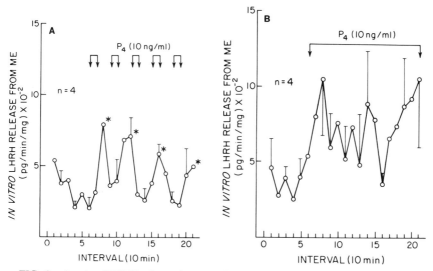

FIG. 9.   *In vitro* LHRH release (mean ± SE) from median eminence fragments from ovariectomized estrogen-primed immature female rats. Following a 60-minute basal collection period progesterone (P_4, 10 ng/ml) was infused either in an intermittent (10 minutes on–20 minutes off, A) or continuous (B) mode for the remainder of the 2.5 hour superfusion. Both modes of infusion resulted in increased LHRH release, although these increases were qualitatively different. Synchronized pulses of LHRH were observed following intermittent P_4 while an erratic general increase in LHRH followed constant P_4. The response of these median eminence preparations to a continuous P_4 infusion is in marked contrast to that of the entire hypothalamic unit in which continuous P_4 was ineffective in augmenting LHRH release (Kim and Ramirez, 1982).

was ineffective when the median eminence was attached to the rest of the hypothalamus. The responses to constant-P_4 infusion consisted of erratic pulses of LHRH, although the mean output of the peptide was clearly increased over its previous control values (Fig. 9B). Recently, Drouva and Kordon (1985) have found similar effects of continuous or pulsatile P_4 on hypothalamic slices from OVX + E_2 primed adult rats. The latency to the response was approximately 30 minutes and lasted for about 30 minutes after which the high level of LHRH release declined abruptly in spite of continuous P_4 infusion. These results undeniably support an effect of P_4 on nerve terminals of the median eminence and confirm previous results of P_4 on LHRH release from incubated rat hypothalamic synaptosomes (Bennett et al., 1975). The physiological relevance of this effect of progesterone on nerve terminals isolated from the rest of the hypothalamus is not clear at the present time. At any rate this effect of P_4 is likely mediated through a nongenomic gating mechanism, probably by altering membrane permeability to Ca^{2+} either directly on LHRH nerve terminals or indirectly through activation of other nerve terminals. It is intriguing that when the median eminence is attached to the rest of the hypothalamus, P_4 is effective in stimulating in vitro LHRH release only when infused with an intermittent mode, but not when it is infused continuously. Perhaps hypothalamic fragments with more normal neuronal interconnections represent a more physiological preparation as opposed to slices. In the former preparations the stimulus-characteristic of P_4 can now be discriminated by functionally active neurons. One could hypothesize that a continuous P_4 infusion as opposed to an intermittent mode stimulates endogenous opioid neurons whose cell bodies are located in the arcuate nucleus and known to inhibit the release of LHRH under certain specific hormonal conditions (Ferin et al., 1984). In the absence of such normal connections, for example, in the isolated median eminence, or in hypothalamic slices the direct "ionophoretic" effect of P_4 on the LHRH nerve terminals would be unopposed and thereby LHRH release would ensue. Further studies are required to prove or disprove such an hypothesis.

The specificity of the effect of P_4 on LHRH release is partially summarized in Table IV. From the beginning of our experiments, we learned that cholesterol, a common precursor of steroid biosynthesis and a component of plasma membranes, administered in a pulsatile manner was ineffective in releasing in vitro LHRH release (Kim and Ramirez, 1982). Although 5α-DHP and 20α-OHP are effective, the releasing activity is only one-third to one-fourth that of progesterone at comparable concentrations, respectively. Interestingly, estrogen, although crucial as a "priming" factor for P_4-evoked LHRH release was itself ineffective in activating the LHRH neural apparatus either in vivo (see Table II) or in vitro (Drouva

TABLE IV
LHRH Releasing Activity in Vitro[a]

Steroid	Activity (% stimulation)	Reference
(1)	P₄ (100)	Kim and Ramirez (1982)
(2)	Chol(0)	Kim and Ramirez (1982)
(3)	20α-OH-P₄ (~30)	Rasmussen and Yen (1983)
(4)	5α-DH-P₄ (~25)	Kim and Ramirez (1985)
(5)	E₂(0)	Drouva *et al.* (1985)

[a] Structural relationship of various steroid molecules which have been examined for their *in vitro* ability to release LHRH. Maximal releasing activity was obtained with progesterone (100%). The LHRH releasing activity of the two metabolites of P_4, 20α- and 5α-DH-P_4 was only one-third and one-fourth of the activity of P_4, respectively. Neither cholesterol, the common precursor of steroid biosynthesis, nor estrogen evoked any release of LHRH suggesting that P_4-evoked LHRH release is structurally specific.

and Kordon, 1985). It is well established that estrogen can elicit repetitive LH surges in OVX rats (Legan *et al.*, 1975) or induce ovulation in intact rats (Everett, 1969). The stimulatory action of estrogen might be due to a direct effect on the pituitary cells (Goodman and Knobil, 1981) although an action on the LHRH neural apparatus cannot be excluded. Recently, Leadem and Kalra (1984) showed that 10 or 30 μg of Eb administered to

ovariectomized rats induced 2 days later changes in *in vitro* LHRH release from superfused hypothalami. These changes in LHRH release
were, however, observed only in the late afternoon, which may be the
result of adrenal P_4 and not of estrogen by itself. Further work is necessary to clarify the role of estrogen as a trigger of LHRH release, although
its role as a permissive agent in the CNS for the ovulatory LH surge in a
photo-dependent species like the rat is undeniable. Moreover, additional
work is required to clarify the role of 5α-DHP and 20α-OHP on the LHRH
neuronal apparatus since it is known that there is 5α-reductase activity in
the hypothalamus and the highest concentrations of this enzyme are detected in the median eminence (Karavolas, personal communication).

Up to this point, the effect of progesterone on LHRH release *in vitro*
has been demonstrated in hypothalamic tissue derived from ovariectomized estrogen-primed rats. Because of the artificial condition of this rat

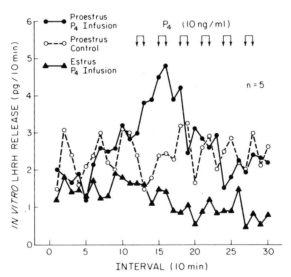

FIG. 10. Mean *in vitro* LHRH release from hypothalamic units from proestrous and
estrous female rats. Following a 2-hour basal collection period hypothalamic units of proestrous and estrous female rats were infused intermittently (10 minutes on–20 minutes off)
with P_4 (10 ng/ml) while an additional group of hypothalami from proestrous females was
infused intermittently with the vehicle. Only from hypothalamic units from proestrous female rats infused with P_4 was there a significant increase in LHRH release, which was
limited to the first hour of P_4 infusion. In contrast, the *in vitro* LHRH release of hypothalamic units from estrous females decreased during P_4 infusion. Interestingly, the spontaneous *in vitro* LHRH release during the 2-hour basal collection period of proestrous female
rats was characterized by high-frequency high-amplitude pulses and was markedly different
from the low-frequency low-amplitude pulses obtained from estrous females (see Fig. 11).

model, it was of importance to test the P_4-evoked LHRH release effect on hypothalamic tissue derived from rats in different phases of the estrous cycle. A summary of these results is shown in Fig. 10. The response of hypothalamic units derived from proestrous and estrous rats to pulsatile P_4 was compared to that of proestrous animals receiving only the vehicle. It is evident that P_4 was stimulatory only in hypothalamic units derived from proestrous rats. Further, it was effective only during a narrow window of the total time of superfusion in spite of the continuous pulsing of P_4, indicating that the *in vitro* LHRH neural apparatus is responsive to this stimulus for a rather short time period, approximately 1 hour. The effectiveness of P_4 on these hypothalamic neurons was lost in neurons derived from estrous or diestrus-1 or 2 animals (data not shown). These results argue in favor of the physiological specificity of the action of P_4 and suggest that the rise in endogenous blood levels of estrogen known to occur during the rat estrous cycle (Barraclough *et al.*, 1984) from low levels in diestrous-1 (15 pg/ml) to highest in proestrous morning (30–40 pg/ml) may be crucial to prime the hypothalamus to the stimulatory, short-lived effect of P_4 on the LHRH neural apparatus. An interesting bonus

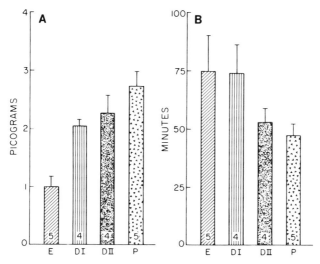

FIG. 11. Pulse amplitude (pg/10 min) (A) and interpulse interval (minutes) (B) of basal *in vitro* LHRH release (mean ± SE) from hypothalamic fragments of female rats as a function of the estrous cycle. This summary depicts that marked changes in the activity of the LHRH pulse generator occur throughout the estrous cycle as illustrated by changes in pulse amplitude and pulse frequency of *in vitro* LHRH release. Maximal activity, that is greatest amplitude and highest frequency is obtained at proestrus while minimal activity is obtained at estrus.

from these studies was that when we analyzed the data corresponding to the 2-hour basal release period, we found that the spontaneous *in vitro* activity of the LHRH pulse generator changed markedly during the rat estrous cycle as summarized in Fig. 11. A clear trend in LHRH pulse amplitude and LHRH pulse frequency was evident during the rat estrous cycle. At estrous, 24 hours after the natural LH surge and exposure of the hypothalamus–pituitary axis to high blood levels of P_4 the LHRH pulse generator *in vitro* appears inhibited as reflected by LHRH pulses of low amplitude and low frequency. At the other extreme of the cycle, during proestrus, the operation of the LHRH pulse generator is at its maximum, with pulses of largest amplitude and highest frequency. Interestingly, this is exactly what occurs *in vivo,* when the activity of the LHRH pulse generator and blood LH level are measured in conscious, freely moving animals during the rat estrous cycle. Minimal activity was detected in estrous and maximal activity in the afternoon of proestrus (Levine and Ramirez, 1982; Gallo, 1981).

VII. Summary and Conclusions

From the foregoing discussion, it is evident that P_4 can stimulate the release of LHRH only from hypothalamic preparations primed with estrogen, either naturally as demonstrated in proestrus or artificially, in ovariectomized + E_2 implanted rats. This effect of the steroid can be revealed when administered systemically with an apparent latency of about 5–6 hours or with shorter latencies (approximately 60 minutes) when infused locally into the hypothalamus in the afternoon or infused directly into hypothalamic fragments superfused *in vitro.*

Though P_4, in contrast to estrogen, exerts very robust effects on the LHRH neural apparatus leading to increases in LHRH release from hypothalami derived from animals sacrificed 6 hours after its systemic injection, either in the morning or in the afternoon of the photoperiod, blood LH levels rose to proestrus levels only in the afternoon (see Table II). Therefore, the afternoon elevation in blood LH levels is related largely to time of the day and not primarily to the hour of P_4 injection as shown by Everett and Sawyer (1949). These diurnal changes in the LH levels apparently unrelated to *in vitro* LHRH release strongly suggest that other factor(s) besides LHRH may control the timing of the ovulatory surge of LH in photo-dependent species like the rat. Perhaps inhibitory influences dominate over stimulatory during the morning of the photoperiod thus keeping in check the function of the LHRH pulse generator and/or inhibiting the pituitary gonadotropins to LHRH. Such light-dependent inhibitory impulses then gradually or abruptly cease in the afternoon allowing the expression of the stimulatory effect of P_4 and/or estrogen on the LHRH-LH axis, both steroids acting most probably at the level of the hypothalamus and the pituitary. Therefore, the concept of Sawyer and Everett (1959) of a daily neurogenic impulse which will be activated only in the afternoon during the critical period of the rat estrous cycle may very well be instead a daily cessation of a photo-dependent inhibitory signal. The nature of this putative inhibitory signal requires experimental demonstration.

The stimulatory effect of P_4 on the LHRH neural apparatus appears structurally specific since it requires both the side chain and the normal configuration of the A-ring of the C-21 progesterone molecule for full expression of LHRH releasing activity and the main effect of the P_4 appears to be in the amplitude of the LHRH pulses but not in the frequency of the LHRH discharges. Interestingly, the highest LHRH pulse amplitude and pulse frequency were detected in proestrus and the lowest detected in estrus which is remarkably similar to the operation of the LHRH pulse generator *in vivo* during the rat estrous cycle (Levine and Ramirez, 1982).

The action of the steroid can be elicited at both nerve endings in the median eminence as well as in the whole hypothalamic unit, although a very fundamental difference in the response to P_4 is observed from these two tissue preparations. In the former, the nerve endings isolated from the rest of their normal connections with the hypothalamus responded to either constant or pulsatile P_4 infusion with a short latency and without apparent refractoriness. In the whole hypothalamic unit, the P_4 stimulus needs to be pulsatile to be effective since a continuous infusion of the hormone does not elicit a response. Therefore, a specific-stimulus characteristic may be required to trigger the initial stimulatory phase of P_4 on the LHRH neural apparatus. A small increase in blood P_4, probably pulsatile in nature and acting for a short duration as it occurs in the afternoon of proestrous in the rat (Kalra and Kalra, 1983), might be perceived by hypothalamic neurons as an effective stimulatory signal. Conversely high levels of progesterone lasting for hours can be perceived by hypothalamic neurons as effective inhibitory signals.

VIII. Mechanisms of Progesterone Action on the LHRH Neural Apparatus: A Hypothesis

In light of these results, we wondered what might be the mechanism or mechanisms by which progesterone under specific physiological conditions can so clearly activate the LHRH neuronal system in the rat. Initially, we thought to pursue the progesterone receptor route since this was an obvious cause–effect relationship to investigate. Our attempts were disappointingly unsuccessful. Progesterone receptor (PR) in the cytoplasmic fraction of the hypothalamus of immature rat can be shown and, most importantly, they can be induced in the MBH of 30-day-old ovariectomized rats after 2 days of estrogen treatment (Fig. 12), confirming previous data on this subject (Attardi, 1981; Attardi and Palumbo, 1981). The receptors, however, decayed very rapidly during *in vitro* superfusion of hypothalamic tissue as shown in Fig. 13. Notice that the presence of the PR in the cytoplasmic fraction of hypothalamic units superfused *in vitro* decayed with a half-life of 6 minutes at 37°C and of about 60 minutes at 30°C. This effect of temperature on the cytosolic PR is related only to changes in number of sites available to the ligand, since their K_ds were approximately 10^{-10} M and they did not differ in the three temperatures tested (Fig. 14). Moreover, no PR in the nucleus or in other membrane compartments of a superfused hypothalami were detected under these conditions (Jasper and Ramirez, unpublished). Since the effects of P_4-stimulated LHRH release were obtained after any trace of cytosolic or

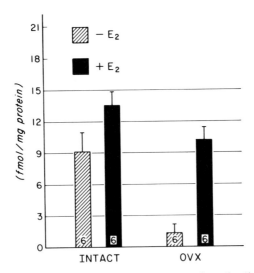

FIG. 12. Hypothalamic progesterone receptor concentrations (fmol/mg protein, mean ± SE) in the cytosolic fraction (PRc) of intact and ovariectomized 30-day-old female rats as a function of estrogen treatment. Immature female rats were either ovariectomized or subjected to sham surgery at 28 days of age. Half the subjects in each of the two groups received silastic capsules containing 235 μg/ml estradiol while the remaining half received capsules containing oil. In both intact and ovariectomized 30-day-old female rats estrogen induced PRc. This effect was particularly effective in the ovariectomized estrogen-primed female rat where it restored PRc values to those of intact rats (Jasper and Ramirez, unpublished).

nuclear PR were detectable in these preparations, we sought other avenues of research to investigate the mechanism of P_4 action on LHRH release from hypothalamic units superfused *in vitro*.

Abundant literature in the rat and other species indicate that P_4 may activate the LHRH–LH axis through changes in both norepinephrine (NE)–epinephrine (EPI) metabolism in the hypothalamus which secondarily may then trigger the release of LHRH during the ovulatory phase (for reviews see Barraclough and Wise, 1983; Kalra and Kalra, 1983; Ramirez *et al.*, 1984a). In view of these findings, we formulated a working hypothesis based on the work of several laboratories. Given the experimental premise that P_4 action on the regulation of the ovulatory surge of LH and on sexual behavior happens through a related but independent two-phase process, namely, stimulation and inhibition, and based on the assumption that the inhibitory phase is not necessarily an obligatory consequence of the stimulatory phase, we postulated that the action of the steroid on these two processes is probably mediated through different mechanisms and/or requires different types of stimuli (Fig. 15).

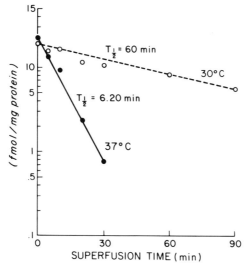

FIG. 13. Progesterone receptor concentrations (fmol/mg protein) in the cytosolic fraction (PRc) of hypothalami superfused *in vitro* as a function of time and temperature. Hypothalamic units were obtained from ovariectomized estrogen-treated immature female rats and PRc were determined at various times during a 37°C or 30°C *in vitro* superfusion. PRc concentrations rapidly declined throughout *in vitro* superfusion, a phenomenon which is temperature dependent as evidenced by half-life values of 60 and 6.2 minutes under 30 and 37°C superfusion, respectively (Jasper and Ramirez, unpublished).

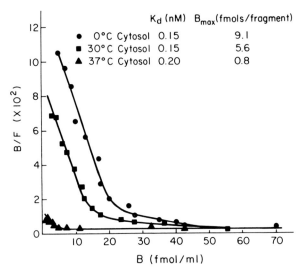

FIG. 14.   Binding curves for cytosolic progesterone receptors (PRc) obtained from hypothalamic units of ovariectomized-estrogen primed immature female rats following *in vitro*
superfusion under various temperatures. Following a 30 minute superfusion under 0, 30, or
37°C, hypothalamic units were prepared for cytosolic PRc determinations. Since very similar apparent K_ds of approximately 10^{-10} M were obtained regardless of superfusion temperature, it appears that the degradation of PRc with increasing temperatures is primarily due to
changes in the number of binding sites available to the ligand (Jasper and Ramirez, unpublished).

Initially P_4 through a nongenomic mechanism probably involving a
plasma membrane site, releases NE which then activates an LHRH neuron through a cascade of events including the release of prostaglandin E_2
(PGE_2), cyclic adenosine monophosphate (cAMP), and release of LHRH,
in this particular case the biological response under consideration. On the
basis of several experimental data demonstrating (1) that PR in the rat
hypothalamus preoptic area (HPOA) but not in other brain regions increases following estrogen treatment and is highly correlated with the
action of P_4 to facilitate estrogen-induced female sexual behavior
(McEwen *et al.*, 1982; Feder, 1984), (2) that antiestrogen inhibits PR
formation (Roy *et al.*, 1979; Wade and Blaustein, 1978), and (3) that the
effect of *in vivo* P_4 to facilitate and then inhibit gonadotropin release in
estrogen-primed ovariectomized rats may be related to an estrogen induction of PR in the hypothalamus and pituitary (Attardi and Palumbo, 1981),
it is not unreasonable to propose that the late phase of P_4 on the function
of the LHRH pulse generator may require activation of PR. These receptors probably are, however, not in LHRH neurons as recently shown for

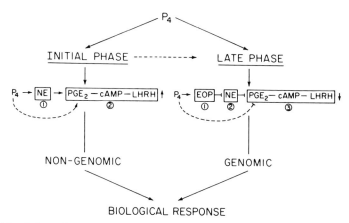

FIG. 15. Schematic diagram outlining proposed events involved in the biphasic (stimulatory and inhibitory) effects of progesterone (P_4) upon LHRH release. During the initial (activational) phase, P_4, most likely through a nongenomic mechanism, acts upon a NE neuron (1) which then through NE release activates a cAMP generating mechanism in an LHRH neuron (2) leading ultimately to LHRH release. During the late (inhibitory) phase, P_4 may act through an endogenous opiod neuron (3) or other inhibitory neuron to inhibit this series of events through a genomic mechanism involving PR receptors. Alternatively, P_4 may have a more direct effect upon the LHRH neuron to exert these stimulatory and inhibitory effects as indicated by the dashed lines. See text for details.

the chicken brain (Sterling *et al.*, 1984), but in different neurons. An appealing candidate could be the β-endorphin neurons whose cell bodies are clustered in the arcuate region of the MBH, an area rich in progesterone receptors (MacLusky and McEwen, 1980). There are strong evidences supporting the notion that β-endorphins may play a pivotal role in the inhibitory control of LH release, presumably through inhibition of LHRH release and that P_4 may be one of the activators of the β-endorphin neurons. Interestingly enough, estrogen priming is required for this effect (for a recent view on this topic, see Ferin *et al.*, 1984). It has been proposed that β-endorphin neurons inhibit NE neurotransmission and thereby control LHRH release (Kalra and Kalra, 1983). The possible role of dopamine (Barraclough *et al.*, 1984) and/or other neurotransmitters like GABA (McCann, 1982) on the inhibitory effect of P_4 on LH release should also be considered.

In the remaining section of this article, evidence from our laboratory supporting a nongenomic hypothesis of the stimulatory action of P_4 on the LHRH neural apparatus will be discussed. First, the work of Ojeda *et al.* (1979, 1982) has shown that NE can activate the release of LHRH *in vitro* from median eminence terminals through an α-mediated receptor mechanism, which probably involves PGE$_2$ stimulation. This effect of NE on LHRH release *in vitro* has recently been confirmed *in vivo,* as reported independently in two recent abstracts at the last meeting of the Society for the Study of Reproduction (Ramirez *et al.,* 1984b; Pau and Spies, 1984). Figure 16 illustrates our results which clearly show that NE at relatively low concentrations and delivered through the push-side of the PPC sitting on the tuberal region of the hypothalamus of a freely moving female rabbit was a powerful stimulator of the LHRH pulse generator as indicated by the two marked increases in LHRH output following NE stimulation. In this particular experiment, at necropsy 48 hours afterward both ovaries showed ruptured follicles and presence of corpora lutea. Since NE is known to stimulate indiscriminately both α- and β-adrenoceptors which may have opposite effects in the control of LH release (Dotti and Taleisnik, 1984; Leung *et al.,* 1982), it was necessary to discriminate between these opposite actions of NE. Therefore, we examined the effect of the α_2-receptor agonist, clonidine and that of the β-receptor agonist, isoproterenol, on LHRH release *in vitro* from hypothalamic units derived from OVX + E$_2$ primed immature rats (Ramirez *et al.,* 1984a). In this

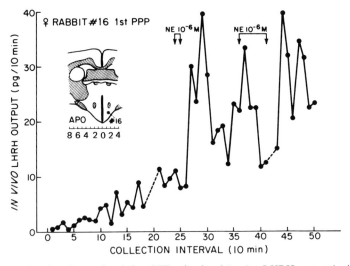

FIG. 16.   Basal and norepinephrine (NE) stimulated *in vivo* LHRH output (pg/10 minutes) from an intact female rabbit as determined with push-pull perfusion. Following a 4-hour period of basal collection (from 1140 to 1540 hours), 10^{-6} M NE was infused for a 10-minute period followed 2 hours later by a 50 minute NE infusion. This preliminary data demonstrate that NE at relatively low concentrations can markedly increase *in vivo* LHRH release. Interestingly, the ovaries of this particular animal showed ruptured follicles and presence of corpora lutea when examined at necropsy 48 hours after the experiment. Inset indicates location of push-pull cannula in this animal. (From Ramirez *et al.,* 1984b.)

preparation, pulses of clonidine in micromolar concentrations were capable of activating the LHRH neural apparatus in a rather similar manner to that evoked by pulses of P_4. On the contrary, isoproterenol was ineffective or slightly inhibitory. Since clonidine may have also α_1-receptor activity, particularly at high doses (Cavero and Roach, 1980) we decided to test a more specific α_1-receptor agonist, methoxamine, in a similar *in vitro* preparation. In this case, MBH fragments derived from regular cycling proestrous rats were used. This drug was clearly effective in stimulating the release of LHRH from these fragments because each time the preparation was pulsed with 10^{-5} *M* methoxamine for a 20-minute period, the basal release rate of LHRH increased significantly (Fig. 17). Hence, it seemed that the α_2-agonist, clonidine and the α_1-agonist, methoxamine can clearly stimulate LHRH release from hypothalamic fragments derived from ovariectomized estrogen primed immature rats and from proestrous adult rats respectively. These *in vitro* data agree well with the stimulatory effect of α_1 agonists and clonidine on LH release *in vivo* (Estes *et al.*, 1982; Drouva *et al.*, 1982) indicating that these effects are probably mediated through changes in LHRH release. Since we have

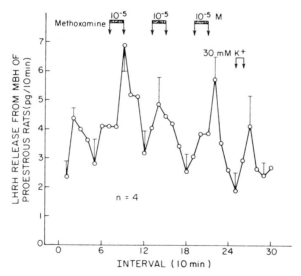

FIG. 17. *In vitro* LHRH release from hypothalamic fragments from proestrous rats in response to intermittent (20 minutes on–40 minutes off) 10^{-5} *M* methoxamine. Animals were decapitated at 1500 hours and following a 1-hour basal collection period, preparations received 3 pulses of methoxamine followed by an infusion of 30 m*M* K$^+$. Each infusion of this specific α_1-adrenoceptor agonist resulted in marked increases in LHRH release followed by a rapid return to basal levels. These responses are similar to that obtained with a 30 m*M* K$^+$ infusion. Mean ± SE of 4 superfusions (Gitzen and Ramirez, unpublished).

previously shown that continuous P_4 was ineffective in evoking LHRH release from hypothalamic units derived from OVX + E_2 primed immature rats (Kim and Ramirez, 1982) we decided to test the effect of this α_1-agonist (methoxamine) on the responsiveness of the LHRH neural apparatus under continuous P_4 infusion (Fig. 18). In spite of continuous infusion of P_4 a clear significant response in LHRH release to each methoxamine pulse was observed proving that the refractoriness of the tissue to continuous P_4 infusion occurs at a neuronal level not involving the α_1-receptor-LHRH release coupling mechanism. However, recently we found that methoxamine-evoked LHRH release did not require estrogen priming since the drug was equally effective in increasing LHRH release *in vitro* from hypothalami derived from either ovariectomized or ovariectomized estrogen-treated adult rats (Gitzen and Ramirez, unpublished). These results suggest that the absolute requirement of estrogen for the P_4-evoked LHRH release must reside in neurons other than those

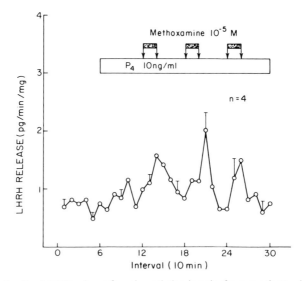

FIG. 18. *In vitro* LHRH release from hypothalamic units from ovariectomized estrogen-primed immature rats in response to pulses of methoxamine during a continuous progesterone (P_4) infusion. Actual LHRH values were multiplied by 100. Following a 60-minute basal collection period, P_4 (10 ng/ml) was infused continuously for the remainder of the superfusion period. During the continuous P_4 infusions, 3 intermittent (20 minutes on–40 minutes off) 10^{-5} M methoxamine pulses, beginning at 1 hour after initiation of continuous P_4 infusion, were included. Although the continuous P_4 did not alter LHRH release rate as has been previously shown (Kim and Ramirez, 1982) each methoxamine infusion resulted in a marked increase of *in vitro* LHRH release suggesting that a desensitization of α_1-receptors cannot account for the absence of stimulated LHRH release during a continuous P_4 infusion.

involved in the coupling of the α_1-receptor to LHRH release. In other words, estrogen-priming effects may be crucial for the coupling of the P_4 putative membrane receptor to NE release in either NE cell bodies or in NE terminals, but not in LHRH neurons. The fact that in the artificial condition of ovariectomy, the α_1 agonist methoxamine can stimulate LHRH release and in a similar preparation P_4 is ineffective strongly suggests that the primary site of action of the stimulatory effect of P_4 involves a neuron other than LHRH, most likely a site in a noradrenergic neuron. Interestingly, estrogen receptors have been found in catecholamine-containing neurons (Stumpf and Sar, 1981), but not in LHRH neurons (Pfaff, 1983).

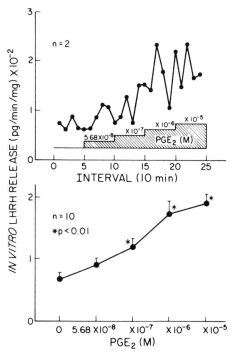

FIG. 19. Mean *in vitro* LHRH release from rat hypothalamic units in response to increasing doses (5.68×10^{-8} to 5.68×10^{-5} M) of prostaglandin E_2 (PGE_2). Following a 50-minute control period of spontaneous *in vitro* LHRH release hypothalamic units were infused for 50 minute intervals with increasing doses of PGE_2. The upper panel represents the actual mean release rate profiles of two preparations in response to this infusion mode while the bottom panel summarizes these data with each point representing the mean $\pm$ SE of LHRH release averaged over the 50-minute infusion period at each of the 5 doses (including the 0 dose) for both preparations. As depicted in this summary, PGE_2 infusions increased LHRH release in a dose-dependent manner with statistically significant increases in LHRH obtained with doses of 5.68×10^{-7} M or greater (Kim, 1984).

Abundant data in the literature strongly indicate prostaglandins, particularly PGE_2, in the control of LH release (Harms et al., 1973) possibly through changes in LHRH metabolism (Ojeda et al., 1982; Eskay et al., 1975). Early experiments from our laboratory showed that prostaglandin E_2 was an effective stimulator of LHRH release from superfused male rat hypothalami even in absence of extracellular Ca^{2+} (Ramirez and Kordon, 1977; Gallardo and Ramirez, 1977). Therefore, we decided to reexamine in depth the effect of this putative, intracellular lipid component on LHRH release from hypothalamic preparations derived from ovariectomized estrogen primed immature rats. As expected, PGE_2 was a very effective stimulator of LHRH release as shown in Fig. 19. Interestingly, cumulative doses of PGE_2 from 10^{-8} to 10^{-5} M were able to stimulate the LHRH release mechanism in a dose-dependent relationship without

TABLE V

Effect of PGE_2 on AC Activity of MBH Membrane Preparations[a]

PGE$_2$ (M)	Condition	
	OVX	OVX + E
	(cAMP production, pmol/min/mg protein)	
0	188 ± 24	224 ± 20
5.68 × 10⁻⁹	221 ± 32	254 ± 31
5.68 × 10⁻⁸	231 ± 29	279 ± 22
5.68 × 10⁻⁷	261 ± 35	302 ± 28
5.68 × 10⁻⁶	276 ± 34	341 ± 35

[a] Mean ± SE of cyclic AMP production from medial basal hypothalami (MBH) membrane preparations of ovariectomized (OVX) and ovariectomized-estrogen primed (OVX + E_2) immature female rats as a function of prostaglandin E_2 (PGE_2) dose. The MBH membrane preparations were preincubated with four doses (5.68×10^{-9} to 5.68×10^{-6} M) of PGE_2 for 30 minutes prior to initiation of the enzymatic reaction. Both membrane preparations (derived from OVX and OVX + E_2 immature rats) responded in a dose-dependent manner to increasing doses of PGE_2, however only with the 5.68×10^{-6} M dose were increases statistically significant compared to controls. Interestingly, for basal levels as well as for each dose of PGE_2 tested, cAMP production was augmented in MBH preparations of rats receiving estrogen.

evidence of desensitization of the response for at least the 200 minute duration of the experiment. Since PGE_2 is known to increase cAMP levels in CNS tissues (Dismukes and Daly, 1975; Partington *et al.*, 1980) we tested the effect of this polyunsaturated fatty acid on adenylate cyclase (AC) activity of MBH membranes derived from ovariectomized as well as from ovariectomized estrogen-primed immature rats (Table V). The data show that *in vitro* AC activity can be stimulated by PGE_2 in both preparations in a dose–response related manner. Notice that, however, estrogen by itself administered for 2 days was capable to augment the basal activity of the AC of such membrane preparations, a finding that agrees well with previous work showing an increase in hypothalamic cyclic AMP following estrogen stimulation (Gunaga and Menon, 1973; Weissman and Skolnick, 1975). Lastly, 5.68×10^{-6} M PGE_2 administered in pulses clearly augmented cAMP efflux from hypothalamic units superfused *in vitro* (Fig. 20). Therefore, at least two criteria of cyclic AMP involvement in PGE_2-evoked LHRH release have been fulfilled: the polyunsaturated fatty acid

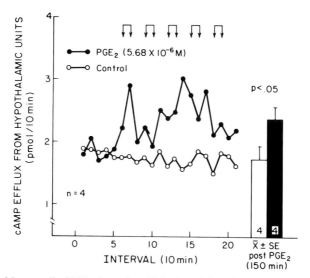

FIG. 20.   Mean cyclic AMP release (pmol/10 minutes) from hypothalamic units following intermittent infusion of prostaglandin E_2 (PGE_2). Following a 1-hour basal release period, intermittent pulses of PGE_2 (10 minutes on–20 minutes off) were infused or control medium was continued throughout the remainder of the superfusion. The basal *in vitro* cyclic AMP released from hypothalamic units was significantly stimulated following intermittent PGE_2 pulses. A summary of this increase is presented in the bar graph in which mean release during the 150-minute infusion period of PGE_2 is compared with that of the control superfusion.

is (1) capable of activating AC and (2) releases cyclic AMP from hypothalamic fragments superfused *in vitro*.

If cyclic AMP is involved in the *in vitro* release mechanism of LHRH from hypothalamic units derived from ovariectomized estrogen primed rat we need to prove that this nucleotide is, indeed, capable of activating such mechanism. This is well illustrated in Fig. 21 in which dibutyryl cyclic AMP in relatively low doses (10^{-7} M) and administered in pulses was highly effective in eliciting release of LHRH each time the pulses were applied to rat median eminence preparations. In addition, forskolin, a specific AC activator, was effective in releasing LHRH from similar hypothalamic preparations. This effect was blocked in the absence of

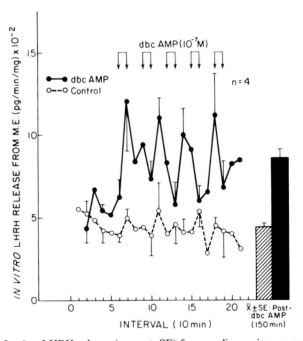

FIG. 21. *In vitro* LHRH release (mean ± SE) from median eminence preparations in response to intermittent infusions of 10^{-7} M dibutyryl cAMP or 10^{-7} M butyrate. Following a 1-hour control period of spontaneous *in vitro* LHRH release median eminence preparations were intermittently infused (10 minutes on–20 minutes off) with either dibutyryl cAMP or butyrate for a 2.5-hour period. Intermittent infusions of dibutyryl cAMP resulted in rapid and reliable increases in LHRH while identical infusions of butyrate failed to change the LHRH release rate profile from that observed during the control period of spontaneous *in vitro* LHRH release. The mean release of LHRH from perparations infused with dibutyryl cAMP was significantly greater than that of preparations infused with butyrate during the 2.5-hour infusion period as summarized in the bar graph (Kim, 1984).

CA^{2+} (Fig. 22). Then, it seems clear from these data and previous work from our laboratory (Hartter and Ramirez, 1985) that the intracellular second messenger cAMP is somehow involved in the mechanism of LHRH release.

Therefore, we wish to know if P_4 would be acting through the sequence norepinephrine-prostaglandin E_2-cyclic AMP and finally LHRH release. Numerous investigators have shown that P_4 can increase hypothalamic NE neurotransmission in rats and other species (Barraclough et al., 1984) and that this increase in NE impulse flow seems to be a crucial component in the activation of the spontaneous or induced ovulatory LH surge. Dr. Barraclough and colleagues presented last year to this Meeting an extensive and excellent review of his view on this topic. In a preliminary study, using the push-pull cannulae (PPC) coupled to HPLC-EC to measure catecholamines (CA) and an RIA to measure LHRH output simultaneously in the same animal, we have evidence supporting such a notion as it is illustrated in Fig. 23. In two ovariectomized rats, primed with estrogen and injected with P_4 at 1000 hours in the morning and with push-pull cannulae tips resting in the anterior portion of the hypothalamus we ob-

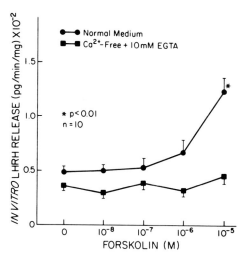

FIG. 22. Changes in *in vitro* LHRH release following various doses of forskolin (10^{-8} to 10^{-5} M) in normal and Ca^{2+}-free + 10 mM EGTA medium. Values shown are mean ± SE. Following a basal release period (0) increasing doses of forskolin were infused for 50 minute time intervals, using a similar paradigm as in Fig. 19. Forskolin significantly increased *in vitro* LHRH release of hypothalamic units superfused with normal medium with maximal effectiveness obtained at a concentration of 10^{-5} M. Forskolin was ineffective and basal release was significantly reduced when superfusions were conducted with CA^{2+}-free plus EGTA medium (Kim, 1984).

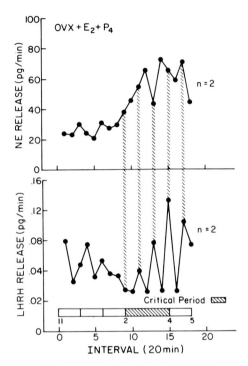

FIG. 23. Mean *in vivo* NE (upper panel) and *in vivo* LHRH (lower panel) release rate as determined from the same push-pull perfusate samples of the two ovariectomized estrogen primed rats (bearing a silastic capsule containing E_2 for 2 days) and receiving a subcutaneous P_4 injection at 1000 hours. Female rats were implanted with push-pull cannulae in the anterior portion of the hypothalamus and perfusate samples were analyzed for NE using HPLC-EC (20 μl) and LHRH (200 μl) using RIA. From these preliminary data, it can be seen that NE increases precede the increase of LHRH release at the initiation of the critical period.

served a 3-fold increase in NE release beginning approximately at the initiation of the critical period which was correlated with the expected rise in LHRH release rate. As far as we know, this is the first *in vivo* demonstration in the OVX + E_2 + P_4 rat model that increases in NE output occur during the critical period of conscious, unrestrained rats. Current work in our laboratory using this approach is undergoing to clarify the role of estrogen and possible circadian changes in CA release from the hypothalamus of conscious, freely moving rats.

Then, it appears that P_4 most likely activates NE transmission which then stimulates LHRH release through changes in hypothalamic adenylate cyclase activity. If this is correct, we should be able to demonstrate

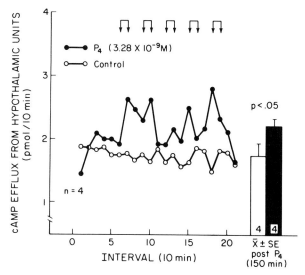

FIG. 24. Mean cyclic AMP release (pmol/10 minutes) from hypothalamic units following intermittent infusions of progesterone (P_4). Following a 1-hour basal release period, intermittent pulses of P_4 (10 minutes on–20 minutes off) were infused or control medium was continued throughout the remainder of the superfusion. The basal *in vitro* cAMP release from hypothalamic units was significantly stimulated by intermittent P_4 pulses. A summary of the increase is presented in the bar graphs in which mean release during the 150-minute infusion period of P_4 is compared with that of the control superfusion.

that *in vitro* P_4 can increase cyclic AMP efflux from hypothalamic units derived from ovariectomized + E_2 primed immature rats. Such a case is shown in Fig. 24. Pulsatile P_4 was capable of increasing cyclic AMP efflux from hypothalamic units receiving the steroid as compared with that of controls infused with the vehicle only. Hence, based on our current data and data available from several laboratories (Barraclough and Wise, 1982; Kalra and Kalra, 1983) it is safe to assume that P_4 activates the LHRH pulse generator indirectly through increase in hypothalamic NE and/or EPI impulse flow (Adler *et al.*, 1983) which subsequently leads to activation of LHRH release through an α_1-receptor mediated mechanism. In pursuing this line of thought, we found that *in vitro* NE significantly activated the AC enzyme complex of MBH membrane derived from OVX + E_2 primed immature rats (Fig. 25). Intriguingly, in the case of membranes derived from OVX + oil-treated animals, the catecholamine was slightly, but not significantly effective on the AC. Moreover, the α_1-receptor agonist methoxamine also activated the AC enzyme complex of MBH membranes derived from OVX + E_2 rats. This *in vitro* effect was com-

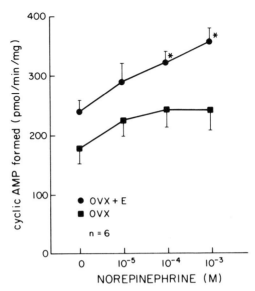

FIG. 25. Cyclic AMP produced by MBH membrane preparations derived from ovariectomized or ovariectomized + E_2 immature female rats as a function of increasing doses of norepinephrine (10^{-5} to 10^{-3} M). Only in preparations derived from OVX + E_2 rats was there a significant dose–response effect with doses of 10^{-4} and 10^{-3} M significantly greater than preparations without norepinephrine (0). Interestingly, basal adenylate cyclase activity of OVX + E_2 rats was significantly greater than that of OVX female rats. Values are mean ± SE (Kim, 1984).

pletely blocked by the cyclooxgenase inhibitor of prostaglandin E_2 synthesis, indomethacin (Fig. 26). In addition, this inhibitor was also capable of blocking the P_4-evoked LHRH release from similar hypothalamic preparations, while controls infused only with the steroid responded in the usual manner (Fig. 27).

These data and previous demonstrations by Ojeda et al., (1979, 1982) of the role of NE and PGE_2 on LHRH release and the fact that indomethacin can block NE-evoked LHRH release from median eminence incubated in vitro lent credance to the idea that PGE_2 metabolism or perhaps phosphatydylinositol metabolism (Nishizuka et al., 1984), a phospholipid known to contain arachidonic acid at position 2, a precursor of PGE_2, might be a crucial step in the activation of the AC enzyme complex by NE. Interestingly, Partington et al. (1980) demonstrated that the accummulation of cyclic AMP elicited by NE or α-adrenergic receptor agonists was virtually abolished by treatment of incubated hypothalamic slices with indomethacin. They suggested that prostaglandin E_2 activity may be required as

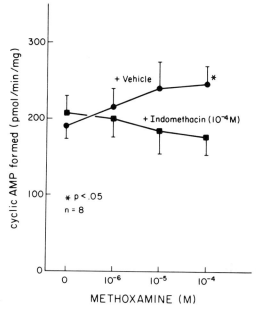

FIG. 26. Cyclic AMP formed (pmol/min/mg of protein, mean ± SE) from medial basal hypothalamic (MBH) membrane preparations derived from ovariectomized estrogen-primed immature rats in the presence or absence of indomethacin and as a function of methoxamine dose. MBH membrane preparations were incubated with either 10^{-4} M indomethacin or the vehicle and cyclic AMP formation following increasing doses of methoxamine (10^{-6} to 10^{-4} M) was determined. Although both preparations initially started at similar levels in the absence of methoxamine (0), indomethacin clearly blocked the dose-dependent increase in cyclic AMP formation as compared to those receiving the vehicle. In this latter group, a significant increase was obtained with 10^{-4} M methoxamine. Interestingly, similar results were obtained using membrane preparations derived from OVX rats.

an intermediary for the NE-mediated increase in cyclic AMP formation in hypothalamic slices.

IX. Summary and Conclusions

The hypothesis put forward in this section purposely reduced the complexity of the LHRH neural apparatus to a simplistic but operationally useful set of two neurons: a NE neuron and an LHRH neuron. Though the LHRH neural apparatus is presumably under the influence of various stimulatory and inhibitory signals, as summarized to this audience by Barraclough and colleagues in 1984, rigorous direct proof of such presumptions is still lacking. It is apparent, however, from our ongoing discussion

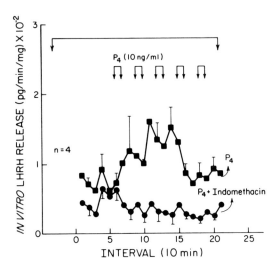

FIG. 27. *In vitro* LHRH release (mean ± SE) from hypothalamic units receiving intermittent infusions of P_4 (10 minutes on–20 minutes off) and superfused with either normal medium or medium containing 100 μM indomethacin. Following a 1-hour control period of basal release, pulses of P_4 (10 ng/ml) were applied for a 2.5-hour period. Indomethacin was effective in completely blocking the *in vitro* P_4-stimulated LHRH release obtained from control hypothalamic units superfused only with normal medium (Kim, 1984).

that P_4 can activate NE neurons and that this neurotransmitter appears to be the final signal to trigger LHRH release. Interestingly, in the conscious rat, a pulsatile mode of NE administration is required to release LH (Gallo, 1982). Similarly, P_4-evoked LHRH release in the conscious, unrestrained rat requires a pulsatile administration of P_4. The effective NE pulsatile signal is probably perceived by an α_1-adrenoceptor, likely localized in a LHRH neuron (Hoffman *et al.*, 1982; McNeill and Sladek, 1978), and coupled to an AC enzyme complex through PGE_2 or coupled to the so called phosphatydylinositol response (Berridge, 1984). The resulting intracellular increase in cAMP and/or intracellular Ca^{2+} triggers the release of LHRH through a calcium-dependent exocytosis mechanism. We have presented evidence in this paper and previously published (Hartter and Ramirez, 1985) that cyclic AMP and forskolin, a specific stimulant of AC activity, are very effective in releasing LHRH from immature male hypothalami or from hypothalami of ovariectomized + E_2 implanted immature rats. In this cascade of neural events initiated by P_4 and leading to LHRH release, there are several salient features that should be underlined.

First, the fact that the α_1-agonist methoxamine, but not P_4, is capable of releasing LHRH from hypothalami derived from ovariectomized rats leads us to believe that P_4 does not act directly on LHRH neurons, but most likely indirectly through NE activation. In support of this idea is the relevant demonstration that methoxamine still releases LHRH in spite of continuous P_4 infusion to hypothalami *in vitro* a condition in which P_4 is ineffective in releasing LHRH or it is slightly inhibitory. Estrogen, an absolute requirement for P_4-evoked LHRH release, may very well function in a permissive capacity for P_4 action at the level of NE neurons.

Second, it seems that a functional PGE_2 metabolism is necessary for either P_4 or NE-evoked LHRH release. In addition, this polyunsaturated fatty acid is also required for the *in vitro* activation of AC of rat MBH membranes by either NE or methoxamine. Intriguingly, NE was only slightly effective in activating AC of MBH membranes derived from ovariectomized rats, but highly effective in membranes derived from ovariectomized + E_2 rats. The α_1 agonist methoxamine was equally effective in both cases which indicates a substantial difference between these two *in vitro* AC activators. It may be that NE-stimulated AC requires a β-receptor mechanism which is E_2 dependent and probably inhibitory in nature for LHRH release (Leung *et al.*, 1982; Ramirez *et al.*, 1984a) whereas the methoxamine-sensitive AC requires an α-receptor coupling mechanism which is E_2 independent and stimulatory in nature for LHRH release.

Third, it is known that estrogen can activate norepinephrine efflux (Paul et al., 1979), prostaglandin synthesis (Ojeda and Campbell, 1982), and prostaglandin release (Ojeda *et al.*, 1982; Cardinali *et al.*, 1982) from rat hypothalami. Moreover, the *in vitro* E increases in hypothalamic cyclic AMP concentrations result from increases in α- and β-receptor-mediated NE transmission (Weissman *et al.*, 1975) and that changes in cyclic AMP levels during the rat estrous cycle are also dependent on α- and β-receptor mediated NE transmission (Zubin and Taleisnik, 1983). Hence, estrogen appears to be required to "set the rat LHRH neural apparatus" for a high level of responsiveness to the stimulatory action of P_4.

Fourth, as we discussed the stimulatory action of P_4 on the LHRH neural apparatus is mediated through increases in NE impulse flow in the hypothalamus. Therefore, the question regarding the mechanism of action of P_4 on the LHRH neural apparatus needs to be rephrased by saying: what is the mechanism by which P_4 activates the release of NE? We are currently working on this premise and the assumption that P_4 binds to putative plasma membrane receptors in NE terminals of the hypothalamus which either by the cAMP generating system and/or through the hydrolyse of membrane phosphoinositides increases intracellular calcium and thereby triggers NE release.

Precedent for an action of P_4 on AC activity of membranes from oocytes of *Xenopus laevis* is well documented, though in this case, P_4 inhibits forskolin-stimulated adenylate cyclase activity (Baulieu, 1983; Sadler and Maller, 1981). P_4 also induces a rapid increase in intracellular calcium of *Xenopus laevis* oocytes (Wasserman *et al.*, 1980) and recently a P_4 receptor has been characterized by photoaffinity labeling in the plasma membrane of *Xenopus laevis* oocytes using R5020 (Blondeau and Baulieu, 1984; Sadler and Maller, 1982). We have shown that P_4 is capable of increasing cyclic AMP efflux from *in vitro* hypothalamic tissue and preliminary results indicate that P_4 can activate an AC enzyme complex from MBH membrane preparations and that there appears to exist also putative plasma membrane receptors for P_4 with low affinity (K_d approximately 10^{-7} M) in the female rat hypothalami. Previously Towel and Sze (1983) reported similar binding properties of $[^3H]P_4$ to brain membranes. Overall, these data suggest that P_4 may act at the surface membrane level of NE neurons to activate NE release. Future experiments will be required to prove or deny such a challenging problem.

X. Overview

In this article, we have presented evidence supporting the thesis that P_4 under specific physiological (rat estrous cycle) or experimental conditions (ovariectomized + E_2 rat model) can have a biphasic action on the functional activity of the LHRH and the NS-DA neuronal systems (Fig. 28). Initially, the stimulatory activity of the steroid in these two systems depends on the presence of either one or all of these three P_4-stimulus characteristics: (1) low doses, (2) short duration (minutes), and (3) pulsatile mode. Under these stimulus conditions, putative plasma membrane receptors coupled to an AC enzyme complex are activated (solid arrows) leading secondarily to increases in intracellular cyclic AMP and release of a specific neurosecretory chemical. Alternatively, or in addition, the steroid may bind to putative membrane receptors (broken arrows) which through as yet an unidentified mechanism perhaps involving the PI response, leads to increases in intracellular calcium that then trigger the release of a specific neurosecretory chemical.

Though we have not studied in depth, as yet, the late phase of P_4 action on these neuronal systems, data from several laboratories including ours, as described earlier, indicate that in conditions of P_4-stimulus such as (1) high doses, (2) long duration (hours), and (3) constant exposure, both the LHRH and the NS-DA neuronal systems are actively inhibited. A case in point, is inhibition of the LHRH-LH axis observed in estrus in the rat or in the luteal phase in humans and nonhuman primates, as well as in other

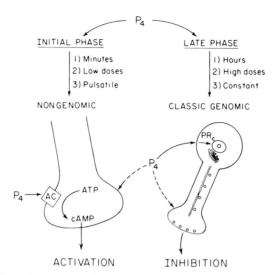

FIG. 28. Schematic summary of proposed mechanisms and stimulus-dependent characteristics of P_4 by which this steroid molecule produces its biphasic effects upon the NS-DA or LHRH neuronal systems. During the initial (activational) phase, limited exposure, low doses and/or pulsatile administration of P_4 results in the activation of a neuron. Most likely, this activation is through a plasma membrane nongenomic mediated mechanism of action which involves a cAMP generating system ultimately leading to exocytosis of specific neuroactive substances. Alternatively, steroid binding to putative plasma membrane receptors triggers hydrolysis of membrane phospholipids resulting in increased intracellular calcium which can then trigger the release of neurosecretory products (left dashed arrow). During the late (inhibitory) phase, prolonged exposure, high doses, and/or constant administration of P_4 result in inhibition of a neuron. While this inhibition may involve a classic genomic mechanism of action through progesterone receptors, it is also possible that a nongenomic inhibitory effect may be exerted directly at the nerve terminal (right dashed arrow).

species. We wish to propose that this inhibitory action of P_4 involves cytoplasmic progesterone receptors which via a change of gene expression at the transcription level triggers the biosynthesis of neurosecretory chemicals with inhibitory biological activity.

It is, therefore, tempting to generalize that P_4-stimulus characteristics of low doses, short duration, and/or pulsatile mode result in activation; conversely, P_4-stimulus characteristics of high doses, long duration, or continuous action result in inhibition. Appropriate membrane and cytoplasmic receptor mechanisms may be crucial to discriminate among the specific stimulus characteristic of P_4 and, accordingly, regulate stimulatory or inhibitory P_4-dependent CNS responses.

ACKNOWLEDGMENTS

The authors are grateful to several colleagues and students for their contribution to this work. Particularly to Dr. Jon Levine, responsible for establishing the PPC in our laboratory and Mr. J. C. Chen and G. D. Chang for their generous time to help in the use of the HPLC-EC and AC assay systems, respectively. Special thanks go to Dr. D. Hartter and Dr. T. Jasper for their contributions. Lastly to N. Ramirez and Kathy Roberts for their expert technical and secretarial assistance, respectively. This work was possible in part by support from a grant of NIH-HD-14625-05, and NSF-PCM 81-6276 to VDR.

REFERENCES

Adler, B. S., Johnson, M. D., Lynch, C. O., and Crowley, W. R. (1983). *Endocrinology* **113**, 1431–1438.
Attardi, B. (1981). *Endocrinology* **108**, 1487–1496.
Attardi, B., and Palumbo, L. A. (1981). *Endocrinology* **109**, 1365–1374.
Barraclough, C. A., and Wise, P. M. (1982). *Endocr. Rev.* **3**, 91–119.
Barraclough, C. A., Wise, P. M., and Selmanoff, M. K. (1984). *Recent Prog. Horm. Res.* **40**, 487–521.
Baulieu, E. E. (1983). *Exp. Clin. Endocrinol.* **81**, 1–16.
Beach, F. A. (1947). *Physiol. Rev.* **27**, 240–307.
Becker, J., and Ramirez, V. D. (1981). *Brain Res.* **204**, 361–372.
Becker, J. B., Castaneda, E., Robinson, T. E., and Beer, M. E. (1984). *J. Neurosci. Methods* **11**, 19–28.
Bennett, G. W., Edwardson, J. A., Holland, D., Jeffcoate, S. L., and White, N. (1975). *Nature (London)* **257**, 323–325.
Berridge, M. J. (1984). *Biochem. J.* **220**, 345–360.
Blondeau, J. P., and Baulieu, E. E. (1984). *Biochem. J.* **219**, 785–792.
Brobeck, J. R. (1947). *Endocrinology* **40**, 65–72.
Broderick, P. A., Blaha, C. D., and Lane, R. F. (1983). *Brain Res.* **269**, 378–381.
Cardinali, D. P., Pardal, J. F., Gimeno, M. F., and Gimeno, A. L. (1982). *J. Neural Transm.* **53**, 39–47.
Carlsson, A., and Lindqvist, M. (1963). *Acta Pharmacol. Toxicol.* **20**, 140–144.
Cavero, I., and Roach, A. G. (1980). *Life Sci.* **27**, 1525–1540.
Chen, J. C., Rhee, K. K., Beaudry, D. M., and Ramirez, V. D. (1984). *Neuroendocrinology* **38**, 362–370.
Dismukes, K., and Daly, J. W. (1975). *Life Sci.* **17**, 199–210.
Dluzen, D. E., and Ramirez, V. D. (1984). *Neuroendocrinology* **39**, 149–155.
Dotti, C., and Taleisnik, S. (1984). *Neuroendocrinology* **38**, 6–11.
Drouva, S. V., Laplante, E., and Kordon, C. (1985). *Neuroendocrinology*, in press.
Drouva, S. V., Epelbaum, J., Hery, M., Tapia-Arancibia, L., LaPlante, E., and Kordon, C. (1981). *Neuroendocrinology* **32**, 155–162.
Drouva, S. V., LaPlante, E., and Kordon, C. (1982). *Eur. J. Pharmacol.* **81**, 341–344.
Drouva, S. V., LaPlante, E., and Kordon, C. (1983). *Neuroendocrinology* **37**, 336–341.
Eskay, R. L., Wurberg, J., Mical, R. S., and Porter, J. C. (1975). *Endocrinology* **97**, 816–824.
Estes, K. S., Simpkins, J. W., and Kalra, S. P. (1982). *Neuroendocrinology* **35**, 56–62.
Everett, J. W. (1969). *Annu. Rev. Physiol.* **31**, 383–416.
Everett, J. W., and Sawyer, C. H. (1949). *Endocrinology* **45**, 581–595.
Feder, H. H. (1984). *Annu. Rev. Physiol.* **35**, 165–200.

Feder, H. H., and Marrone, B. L. (1977). *Ann. N.Y. Acad. Sci.* **286**, 331–354.

Ferin, M., VanVugt, D., and Wardlaw, S. (1984). *Recent Prog. Horm. Res.* **40**, 441–480.

Freeman, M. E., Dupke, K. C., and Croteau, C. M. (1976). *Endocrinology* **99**, 223–229.

Gaddum, J. H. (1960). *J. Physiol. (London)* **155**, 1–2P.

Gallardo, E., and Ramirez, V. D. (1977). *Proc. Soc. Exp. Biol. Med.* **155**, 79–84.

Gallo, R. V. (1981). *Biol. Reprod.* **24**, 771–777.

Gallo, R. V. (1982). *Neuroendocrinology* **35**, 380–387.

Gilbert, C., and Gillman, J. (1956). *S. Afr. J. Med. Sci.* **21**, 75–79.

Goodman, R. L., and Knobil, E. (1981). *Neuroendocrinology* **32**, 57–63.

Gordon, G. S., Guadagni, N., Ricchi, J., and Adams, J. E. (1956). *J. Interm. Coll. Surg.* **25**, 9–15.

Guillemin, R. (1978). *Science* **202**, 390–402.

Gunaga, K. P., and Menon, K. M. J. (1973). *Biochem. Biophys. Res. Commun.* **54**, 440–448.

Harms, P. G., Ojeda, S. R., and McCann, S. M. (1973). *Science* **181**, 760–761.

Hartter, D. E., and Ramirez, V. D. (1980). *Endocrinology* **107**, 375–382.

Hartter, D., and Ramirez, V. D. (1985). *Neuroendocrinology*, in press.

Helmond, F. A., Simons, P. A., and Heim, P. R. (1981). *Endocrinology* **108**, 1837–1842.

Hoffman, G. E., Wray, S., and Goldstein, M. (1982). *Brain Res. Bull.* **9**, 417–430.

Kalra, S. P. (1976). *Brain Res.* **114**, 541–544.

Kalra, S. P., and Kalra, P. S. (1983). *Endocr. Rev.* **4**, 311–351.

Karsch, F. J., Bittman, E. L., Foster, D. L., Goodman, R. L., Legan, S. J., and Robinson, J. E. (1984). *Recent Prog. Horm. Res.* **40**, 185–225.

Kessel, N., and Coppen, A. (1963). *Lancet* **2**, 61–64.

Khachaturian, H., Lewis, M. E., and Watson, S. J. (1983). *J. Comp. Neurol.* **220**, 310–320.

Kim, K. (1984). Dissertation thesis, Dep. of Physiology and Biophysics, University of Illinois, Urbana.

Kim, K., and Ramirez, V. D. (1982). *Endocrinology* **111**, 750–757.

Kim, K., and Ramirez, V. D. (1985). *Endocrinology* **116**, 252–258.

Knobil, E. (1980). *Recent Prog. Horm. Res.* **36**, 53–88.

Leadem, C. A., and Kalra, S. P. (1984). *Endocrinology* **114**, 51–56.

Legan, S., Coon, G. A., and Karsch, F. (1975). *Endocrinology* **96**, 50–56.

Lehrman, D. S. (1964). *Sci. Am.* **211**, 48–54.

Leung, P. C. K., Whitmoyer, D. I., Garland, K. E., and Sawyer, C. H. (1982). *Proc. Soc. Exp. Biol. Med.* **169**, 161–164.

Levine, J. E. and Ramirez, V. D. (1980). *Endocrinology* **107**, 1782–1790.

Levine, J. E., and Ramirez, V. D. (1982). *Endocrinology* **111**, 1439–1448.

McCann, S. M. (1982). *In* "Neuroendocrine Perspectives" (E. E. Muller and R. M. MacLead, eds.), pp. 1–22. Elsevier, Amsterdam.

McEwen, B. S., Biegon, A., Davis, P. G., Krey, L. C., Luine, V. N., McGinnis, M. Y., Paden, C. M., Parsons, B., and Rainbow, T. C. (1982). *Recent Prog. Horm. Res.* **38**, 41–92.

McGeer, P. L., and McGeer, E. G. (1976). *In* "GABA in Nervous System Function" (E. Robert, ed.), pp. 487–496. Raven, New York.

MacLusky, N. J., and McEwen, B. S. (1980). *Endocrinology* **106**, 192–202.

McNeil, T. H., and Sladek, J. R. (1978). *Science* **200**, 72–74.

Marrone, B. L., Roy, E. J., and Wade, G. N. (1975). *Horm. Behav.* **6**, 231–236.

Miyake, A., Tasaka, K., Kawamura, Y., Sakumoto, T., and Aono, T. (1982). *Acta Endocrinol.* **101**, 321–324.

Moore, K. E., and Wuerthele, S. M. (1979). *Prog. Neurobiol.* **13**, 325–359.

Morin, L. P., and Feder, H. H. (1974). *Brain Res.* **70**, 71–80.

464   V. D. RAMIREZ ET AL.

Nishizuka, Y., Takai, Y., Kishimoto, A., Kikkawa, U., and Kaibuchi, K. (1984). *Recent Prog. Horm. Res.* **40**, 301–341.
Ojeda, S. R., and Campbell, W. B. (1982). *Endocrinology* **111**, 1031–1037.
Ojeda, S. R., Negro-Vilar, A., and McCann, S. M. (1979). *Endocrinology* **104**, 617–624.
Ojeda, S. R., Negro-Vilar, A., and McCann, S. M. (1982). *Endocrinology* **110**, 409–412.
Partington, C. R., Edward, M. W., and Daly, J. W. (1980). *Proc. Natl. Acad. Sci. U.S.A.* **77**, 3024–3028.
Pau, K. Y. F., and Spies, H. G. (1984). *Soc. Study Reprod. Abstr.* No. 1, 31.
Paul, S. M., Axelrod, J., Saavedra, J. M., and Skolnick, P. (1979). *Brain Res.* **178**, 499–505.
Pfaff, D. W. (1983). *Recent Prog. Horm. Res.* **39**, 127–175.
Pfaff, D. W., and McEwen, B. S. (1983). *Science* **219**, 808–814.
Ramirez, V. D. (1978). *Annu. Meet. Endocrine Soc., 60th Abstr.* No. 752, 453.
Ramirez, V. D. (1983). *In* "The Anterior Pituitary" (A. S. Bhatnagar, ed.), pp. 97–105. Raven, New York.
Ramirez, V. D. (1985). *In* "In vivo Perfusion and Release of Neuroactive Substances in the Central Nervous System. Methods, Findings and Perspectives" (A. Bayon and R. Drucker-Collin, eds.) pp. 249–270. Raven, New York.
Ramirez, V. D., and Kordon, C. (1977). *In* "Cell Biology of Hypothalamic Neurosecretion" (J. D. Vincent and C. Kordon, eds.), pp. 579–598. CNRS, Paris.
Ramirez, V. D., Dluzen, D., and Lin, D. (1980a). *Science* **208**, 1037–1039.
Ramirez, V. D., Gallardo, E., and Hartter, D. (1980b). *J. Endocrinol. Invest.* **3**, 29–37.
Ramirez, V. D., Feder, H. H., and Sawyer, C. H. (1984a). *In* "Frontiers in Neuroendocrinology" (L. Martini and W. F. Ganong, eds.), Vol. 8, pp. 27–84. Raven, New York.
Ramirez, V. D., Ramirez, A. D., and Slamet, W. (1984b). *Soc. Study Reprod. Abst.* No. 180, 120.
Rasmussen, D. D., and Yen, S. S. C. (1983). *Life Sci.* **32**, 1523–1530.
Rosenblatt, J. S., Siegel, H. I., and Mayer, A. D. (1979). *Adv. Study Behav.* **10**, 225–311.
Ross, J., Claybough, C., Clemens, L. G., and Gorski, R. A. (1971). *Endocrinology* **89**, 32–38.
Rothchild, I. (1965). *Vitam. Horm.* **23**, 209–327.
Rothchild, I., and Barnes, A. C. (1952). *Endocrinology* **50**, 485–496.
Roy, E. J., MacLusky, N. J., and McEwen, B. S. (1979). *Endocrinology* **104**, 1333–1336.
Sadler, S. E., and Maller, J. L. (1981). *J. Biol. Chem.* **256**, 6368–6373.
Sadler, S. E., and Maller, J. L. (1982). *J. Biol. Chem.* **257**, 355–361.
Sawyer, C. H., and Everett, J. W. (1959). *Endocrinology* **65**, 644–651.
Schally, A. V. (1978). *Science* **202**, 18–28.
Selye, H. (1941). *J. Pharmacol. Exp. Ther.* **73**, 644–651.
Sterling, R. J., Gasc, J. M., Sharp, P. J., Tuohimaa, P., and Balieu, E. E. (1984). *J. Endocrinol.* **102**, R5–R7.
Stumpf, W. E., and Sar, M. (1981). *In* "Steroid Hormone Regulation of the Brain" (K. Fuxe, J. A. Gustafsson, and L. Watterberg, eds.), pp. 41–50. Pergamon, Oxford.
Towel, A. C., and Sze, P. W. (1983). *J. Steroid Biochem.* **18**, 135–143.
Wade, G. N., and Blaustein, J. D. (1978). *Endocrinology* **102**, 245–251.
Wasserman, W. J., Pinto, L. H., O'Conner, C. M., and Smith, L. D. (1980). *Proc. Natl. Acad. Sci. U.S.A.* **77**, 1534–1536.
Weissman, B. A., and Skolnick, P. (1975). *Neuroendocrinology* **18**, 27–34.
Weissman, B. A., Daly, J. W., and Skolnick, P. (1975). *Endocrinology* **97**, 1559–1566.
Wildt, L., Hutchison, J., Marshall, G., Pohl, C., and Knobil, E. (1981). *Endocrinology* **109**, 1293–1294.
Yeoman, R. R., and Teresawa, E. (1984). *Endocrinology* **115**, 2445–2452.

Zamora, A. J., and Ramirez, V. D. (1983). *Neuroscience* **10**, 463–473.
Zubin, P., and Taleisnik, S. (1983). *Brain Res.* **271**, 273–277.

DISCUSSION

W. W. Leavitt: I have a question about the specificity of progesterone action particularly with your *in vitro* system. Without the progesterone receptors, the classic site of steroid action, one thinks immediately about the possibility of progesterone metabolism. You showed that the 5α-dihydroprogesterone and the 20α-hydroxyprogesterone were less active than progesterone. As I recall in the rat the major metabolite of progesterone metabolism is pregnanolone; have you had occasion to test pregnanolone in your system?

V. Ramirez: I think your question is very important; we haven't yet tested pregnanolone. It is in our agenda to test several products. However, in the hypothalamus, in collaboration with Dr. Karavolas we have used an inhibitor of progesterone metabolism available to him by a commercial source. That is an analog of 5α-dihydroprogesterone. As far as I can tell using this inhibitor in our preparation together with progesterone the magnitude of response is unchanged.

W. W. Leavitt: The latency of the responses comparing the subcutaneous with the direct application versus the *in vitro* response is suggestive of metabolism and perhaps peripherally. If the liver were involved, one might expect to find 5β-progestin metabolites. Have you tested any of these?

V. Ramirez: No, we haven't tested those (see Note Added in Proof).

M. S. Smith: My question has to do with the frequency of the progesterone pulses that you are administering *in vitro*. How faithfully do the LHRH pulses follow the progesterone pulse frequency; that is if you alter the frequency of your pulsatile progesterone administration, do you also alter the frequency of the LHRH pulses secreted *in vitro*?

V. Ramirez: That is a very excellent question and we have tried different frequencies. The one that was optimal for our studies is the one we presented, that of 10 minutes on and 20 minutes off; however, it is possible to elicit a response using only one single pulse and also it is possible to induce responses using an interval of approximately 50 minutes to 1 hour; so the minimum frequency or that minimum interval that we have used is 20 minutes, and then after that we have gone into the constant infusion, that doesn't evoke a response in the complete unit.

M. S. Smith: What evidence do you have that the hypothalamus would be seeing progesterone in any kind of a pulsatile fashion? During the rat estrous cycle basal LH pulses seem to occur at a fairly constant frequency of about one pulse per 50 or 60 minutes. If the pulse frequency has any relationship as to how the ovary is perceiving that stimulation, what would you imagine the hypothalamus might be seeing in terms of the frequency of progesterone pulses? How do you envision that occurring?

V. Ramirez: That's another very critical question that we are in the process of studying. I thought that certainly very soon it will be published in the literature the pulsatile frequencies of progesterone in the rat. It has been demonstrated very clearly in monkeys, in humans, and cows; there is also an old paper on hamsters in which the frequency of progesterone was approximately 2 hours. But in the rat it has not been done. Unless I am wrong we don't really know if the ovary of the rat secretes progesterone in a pulsatile mode in proestrous. We are in the process of doing that experiment and measuring both LH and progestin in the blood; however, I feel very confident that this effect of progesterone probably reveals a physiological event because though we found this phenomenon first in an *in vitro* preparation we were later able to demonstrate, as I showed, that when we infused the steroid directly in the hypothalamus of conscious animals, the pulsatile mode was the one that worked and the constant infusion mode did not. So that seems to me an indication that probably this is a real phenomenon and not an artifact.

M. S. Smith: I am sure you are aware that Dr. Claude Kordon has been conducting similar *in vitro* studies and has been successful in showing sustained LHRH release in response to constant stimulation with progesterone. He has administered progesterone for 30 minutes continuously and has been able to show sustained LHRH release. Could you provide some insight into what the differences might be between your tissue preparation and the preparation he is using?

V. Ramirez: This is really a puzzling question. I happen to be the referee of Claude Kordon's paper in which he and Dr. Drouva showed very convincingly that when they infused progesterone continuously in their *in vitro* hypothalamic preparation they got a very rapid discharge of LHRH, within 30 minutes. That finding really puzzles me, but the data were robust, very specific, and it was unquestionable; therefore, we went and examined what happened in median eminence fragments. Since some of you are not familiar with the technical aspects let me say that Dr. Drouva slices the hypothalamus in very thin slices, probably disrupting all the normal connections; so I thought maybe what she has is just nerve terminals, and a very good preparation to test this effect of progesterone would be the median eminence, and as I show you here when we use the median eminence we also get an effect with constant progesterone infusion. Now that indicates to me that perhaps progesterone has a very peculiar effect at nerve ending; that is not necessarily an artefact but perhaps under normal conditions progesterone not only has that effect on nerve terminals but it may have other effects on other portions of the neuron that can finally modulate the final output from the nerve terminals.

M. S. Smith: The similarity in your data is that you both showed these delayed LHRH responses on progesterone. He also did not see any increase in LHRH in the first 30 or 40 minutes after progesterone stimulation.

N. Ben-Jonathan: My question relates to the first portion of your talk and the last summary slide. I wonder why you selected to study a relationship between progesterone and the dopaminergic system of the corpus striatum? In other words, what is your biological end-point? Is there any indication at all that the regulation of reproductive hormone secretion is accomplished by the corpus striatal dopaminergic system? Why didn't you look at the relationship between progesterone and the tuberoinfundibular dopaminergic system?

V. Ramirez: The reason is that perhaps I like to be different and since a lot of people are working in the tuberoinfundibular DA system, I ask whether the nigrostiatal dopamine system, that has very specific connections, may also respond to hormones. At that time I read a paper by Dr. Crowley and colleagues in which they have clearly shown that during the rat estrous cycle there are marked changes in the content of dopamine in the corpus striatum; that gave me the physiological basis to pursue this question further, and as far as I know and from many other people working in this area, the corpus striatum now has to be considered a target of the steroid hormones, and not only of the steroid hormone but possible also of protein hormones from the pituitary gland.

N. Ben-Jonathan: Could there by any connection between this system and sexual behavior which is not necessarily related to the regulation of prolaction and LH release?

V. Ramirez: I think this is a very important question also, because Dr. Harvey Feder some years ago postulated that perhaps progesterone could act on the cell bodies of the nigrostriatal dopamine system to inhibit sexual behavior, because when he implanted progesterone in the mesencephalon he observed 24 hours after he left the implants in that area an inhibition of sexual behavior as measured by lordosis reflex. Interestingly enough, if the implants of progesterone are left in that area estrous behavior measured by the lordosis reflex appeared within the first hours, so this clearly demonstrates the sequence of progesterone effect on sexual behavior, facilitation first and then inhibition 24 hours later.

K. Sterling: This was a spectacular presentation, especially to me since I know nothing about it. To invoke several simple minded questions. I take it the rats or rabbits don't bother the cannula they adapt to, do they?

V. Ramirez: As far as I can tell we observe our animals very carefully; we are very concerned about the humane aspect of these kind of experiments, but in terms of physiological measurements and behavioral observations, we have not observed any abnormality that we can detect. The animals seem to be tranquil, and I guess I would say this for my own benefit, happy undergoing brain superfusion.

R. Sterling: It would seem as if this push-pull cannula could probably be adapted to many other studies in the central nervous system. The second question was already anticipated by Susan Smith, and I wonder why in the primate cycle, I have never heard of any evidence of pulsatile progesterone. I've just heard of progesterone being low in the follicular and high in the luteal phase; could there be something missed or could it be that the progesterone is acting at the nerve terminals. What is your speculation at this stage, with regard to the clock in primates; is it pelvic or is it the brain that has the clock of the pulse generator.

V. Ramirez: I guess Dr. Ei Teresawa will have some interesting data to present that are very relevant to your questions.

K. Sterling: At the end of the first third of the talk you were using CS a few times. Does that stand for corpus striatum?

V. Ramirez: Yes.

K. Sterling: I have a general question about all this in terms of the substantia nigra and corpus striatum which constitute a large area of the brain involved in the Parkinsonian syndrome of all etiologies with the alternating tremor-at-rest, essentially reversed by providing DOPA to human subjects, as we have known for quite a while. I am just wondering if you can give me any further thought on how it is working; how just giving DOPA that becomes dopamine somehow suppresses these troublesome alternating tremors?

V. Ramirez: We have not studied that kind of issue yet, but certainly as you mentioned the push-pull cannula procedure will be a very valuable tool for the individual interested in this kind of a specific question. The only thing that I can mention to you is that by using this procedure we were not able to observe changes in spontaneous dopamine release and that has been confirmed by others. What we see is changes in the metabolite of dopamine transmission; now that makes sense to me because dopamine is released into the synaptic cleft, probably is taken up very rapidly by the terminals, inactivated inside the terminal, and then one can see changes in the metabolities; that is exactly what I showed you in one of the slides.

N. Schwartz: I would like to ask something about estrogen per se. I was rather surprised recently by an experimental finding of Dr. Charlesworth in my lab. She was able to get vigorous and very fast (within 1 hour) suppression of serum LH following an injection of estrogen in rats 4 weeks after ovariectomy. Within an hour we had a 40 to 60% suppression which we do not see in the presence of pretreatment with a GnRH suppression. When you give estrogen how rapidly can you change LHRH secretion?

V. Ramirez: That is a very important question, but I would like to rephrase it. When we start with an ovariectomized animal, I would like to emphasize that we start with an abnormal condition, so whatever we see by injecting estrogen into that experimental rat model probably indicates that estrogen is bringing the system back to normality and that can be, if that interpretation is correct, a key element to understand what perhaps appear paradoxical effects of estrogen. When we inject estrogen into our ovariectomized female rat bearing a push-pull cannula what we observe is exactly the opposite of what one would expect. First the activity of the LHRH pulse generator in ovariectomized animals is very depressed; when we give estrogen the activity increases instead of decreasing. So here we have a paradox, estrogen inhibited the high level of LH in blood, but on the contrary is activating the LHRH pulse generator; we don't have any explanation yet to that phenomenon, but it seems to me that all that is happening is that the animal now is becoming a diestrous animal for say something. In other words it is becoming a more normal condition.

N. Schwartz: Does it distress you that within 1 hour we see a 60% suppression of serum LH and you see an increase in LHRH via the push-pull cannula?

V. Ramirez: It distresses me, but I think that the problem with estrogen is that in that condition it is acting directly into the pituitary not at the level of the hypothalamus to act as a negative feedback signal.

N. Schwartz: However, estrogen does not do that in the presence of an antagonist to LHRH.

V. Ramirez: I would like you to remember that in order to maintain the function of the pituitary gland, as it was beautifully demonstrated by Dr. Knobil, you have to have that constant pulse generator functioning. Now by using the anti-LHRH antiserum, it is possible that under those conditions the pituitary gland is not functioning as it should be and that could be one reason to explain this apparent paradox.

S. M. McCann: I would like to interject a note here. Actually this point that Dr. Schwartz brought up bothered me also and I might say that back in 1962 we showed that intravenous estrogen would suppress LH release within a matter of minutes and we confirmed that in the early 1970s by RIA. We further showed at that time that you could get the effect by intraventricular estrogen which inhibited LH release in the face of normal responsiveness to LHRH which suggests just the opposite to what Dr. Ramirez has found with the push-pull cannula, namely that the estrogen was turning off the LHRH at the same time; we have also found that when given systemically estradiol could block the response to LHRH very quickly. Therefore, we felt that there were dual actions very acutely of estrogen to suppress both at the hypothalamic and pituitary levels. This does not fit with the push-pull cannula, namely that in the ovariectomized animals, the pulses get more infrequent and smaller in the chronic ovariectomized animals in the face of massive increase in LH release. This also does not fit with the results even of portal blood collections from ovariectomized sheep. So this is a real paradox and it comes from both sides, namely the removal of estrogen one would expect to enhance the pulsations of LHRH release in the cannula and administration of estrogen would be expected to suppress them and yet you get absolutely the reverse; I don't understand it, do you?

V. Ramirez: The problem with the rat and I guess one of the reasons we have moved to the sheep and also currently to the rabbit is because in the rat the release rate of LHRH is very low in amplitude; by moving to a larger animal we may be able to have larger pulses of LHRH release; then we will be able to detect changes in the down direction. The problem is that when we ovariectomized a rat or orchidectomized a male rat, the activity of the LHRH pulse generator is so low that we practically can't detect levels of LHRH release. So we don't really know what is happening and my suggestion is that maybe we have a high frequency and that frequency perhaps with low amplitude is the one that is keeping the pituitary functioning. Now in the sheep this was a clear demonstration, because there we were able to correlate that every pulse of LH corresponds with an LHRH pulse. So the rat is perhaps not a good model to study this issue because of what I am saying and in order to resolve the question we are now using the rabbit.

S. M. McCann: I have another suggestion. One other possibility would be that since the push-pull cannula is monitoring activity in that particular location, perhaps your push-pull cannula is not monitoring the activity at the portal capillaries, but monitoring activity concerned with something other than LH release from terminals which may be projecting somewhere else. How about that? And the activity of those terminals might be opposite in sign from the activity of the terminals projecting directly to portal vessels.

V. Ramirez: It certainly is a possibility, but we do not have evidence in favor of that.

M. Selmanoff: I have a question related to Dr. Ben-Jonathan's. You have shown elegant results of progesterone action on dopamine release in the striatum. Have you studied progesterone action on their hypothalamic, mesolimbic, or tuberoinfundibular terminal projection fields to see how generalizable this kind of steroid effect is on other dopaminergic neurons?

V. Ramirez: It is a very good question. We examined this not by directly injecting progesterone in the hypothalamus as we did in the corpus striatum; we injected systemically progesterone and then we removed the medial basal hypothalamus and investigated what happened with the release of dopamine under this condition. To our surprise we did not see anything. In the same experimental condition we were seeing this remarkable change in corpus striatum activity following systemic injection of progesterone.

E. Knobil: I was wondering if you could refresh my memory and perhaps that of others in the audience regarding the role of progesterone in the initiation of the preovulatory gonadotropin surge, within the physiologic context of the rat estrous cycle?

V. Ramirez: I guess, certainly Dr. Barraclough could do a better job than I, but there is no question that progesterone rises before the initiation of the surge of LH approximately between 13 and 14 hours in the afternoon of proestrus. I would like to emphasize this point because I think this is a very important problem. I am working with a hypothesis which is certainly not novel, because this has been known for many years; but many of us have forgotten that progesterone in small increments and acting for a short time can be stimulatory and it seems to me that it is exactly what it does in the rat and it may also do that in the monkey and in women. However, the main role of progesterone, if one can divide the effect of hormones in secondary and primary roles, I would think in the rat is controlling in this manner the estrous cycle as it was clearly shown before by Dr. Freeman. So then high doses of progesterone now and maintained for a continuous long time will trigger inhibitory mechanisms. We are trying to understand how this happens and my hypothesis is that perhaps the stimulatory phenomenon of progesterone is mediated by putative plasma membrane receptors; I would like to mention that we are working on that and we have recently shown that there are putative membrane receptors for R5020 in the hypothalamus of the female rat but not in the hypothalamus of the male rat. The K_d of this putative plasma membrane receptor is approximately $10^{-8}\,M$ which indicates that it is of low affinity; but that is correct with the idea that this effect of progesterone should be a rapid effect and the hormone has to be dissociated from the receptor also in a rapid manner.

J. Meites: I want to congratulate you on a very fine and detailed study. I am puzzled by your title, "Progesterone Action on LHRH and Dopamine Neurons." The part that puzzles me is the dopamine. Now you have emphasized and have shown, unless I am mistaken, that the action on LHRH is not via dopamine but via norepinephrine, and dopamine in fact does not appear to participate in LHRH function. Of course this bring up the question that you and Dr. McCann were involved with very early, namely the claim that dopamine is the major stimulator of LHRH and LH release. So this seems to contradict your earlier views, since now you are stating very definitely, it seems to me, that norepinephrine is the catecholamine involved in stimulating LHRH release. How do you resolve this question?

S. M. McCann: Let me tackle that one first. It takes half an hour to discuss in detail the role of dopamine; however, as shown by ourselves and by Kordon's group, dopamine stimulates LHRH release in the median eminence in *in vitro* preparations and I wondered why Dr. Ramirez didn't test it; he showed that there was release of dopamine in the striatal system with progesterone since its metabolite increased, and yet he failed to test it in his system. Do you care to comment on that?

V. Ramirez: We have tried dopamine but unsuccessfully since our results are negative. No effect at all. I'm not sure why we are not getting the stimulatory results under our *in vitro* conditions. Now that certainly adds more confusion than clarification, so we have not pursued that avenue of research.

E. Terasawa: Progesterone causes a similar stimulatory effect on LHRH and LH releases in primates as reported in rodents. There are two reasons that we have been interested in investigating progesterone effects in the female rhesus monkey. First, we have hypothesized that a small, but significant increase in progesterone during the preovulatory LH surge in this species may have physiological significance, and second, because the stimulatory effect of estrogen on the hypothalamus appears to be masked by the response induced by its pituitary action, estrogen is not an effective tool for neuroendocrinological studies. To test the progesterone effect, we initially used intact females (*J. Clin. Endocrinol. Metab.* **51**, 1245, 1980), but in recent years we have been using ovariectomized females that are implanted with a small silastic capsule containing estradiol-17β to maintain LH levels mimicking the follicular phase. Progesterone injection 24 to 30 hours after estradiol benzoate consistently induces a LH surge with an initial rise at 3 hours, a peak latency of 6 to 9 hours, and a duration of 18 hours (*J. Endocrinol.* **92**, 327, 1982; *Biol. Reprod.*, in press).

I would like to call your attention to the fact that this time-course of the progesterone-induced LH surge in rhesus monkeys is very similar to that observed in rodents. Hypothalamic sites of the progesterone effect were evidenced by several experiments: (1) the progesterone-induced LH surge was blocked by pentobarbital anesthesia (*J. Endocrinol.* **92**, 327, 1982), (2) complete deafferentation did not block the progesterone-induced LH surge (*Endocrinology* **112** *Suppl:* 156, 1983), (3) lesions of the medial basal hypothalamus or stalk sections with teflon barriers blocked the progesterone-induced LH surge in monkeys receiving pulsatile LHRH infusion (Abstracts of the 7th International Congress of Endocrinology, July 1–10, 1984, Quebec, Canada, No. 2071), and (4) progesterone stimulates LHRH release from the median eminence. Median eminence perfusates from unanesthetized rhesus monkeys were collected by push-pull cannula methods which were specifically adapted for repeated insertion using a hydraulic microdrive.

In Fig. A the effect of progesterone on circulating LH (sampled every 3 hours) and on LHRH release (sampled every 10 minutes) in an animal is shown. Data obtained in 5 animals indicated that the first large release of LHRH occurred at approximately 2.5 to 3 hours after progesterone coinciding with the initial rise of LH. Between 3 to 9 hours after progesterone, a second and often a third large episode of LHRH release reoccurred in intervals of 2 to 3 hours. During this period not only was the interpulse interval of LHRH shortened, but also the overall pulse amplitude of LHRH release increased. The changes in LHRH release reached a maximum between 3 and 6 hours after progesterone and returned to control levels by 9–12 hours after progesterone, again coinciding with increased levels and subsequently declining levels of circulating LH. Three animals which received an oil injection as controls showed neither an LH surge nor LHRH changes. These results suggest the possibility that the increase in progesterone arising from the preovulatory follicle may give a signal to the hypothalamus to stimulate the release of LHRH, thereby setting the timing of the LH surge, which coincides with the full maturation of the Graafian follicles and effectively results in ovulation.

V. Ramirez: I am very happy that you have been able to find the same thing in monkeys.

P. Wise: Dr. Ramirez I was impressed with your beautiful data showing a correlation between norepinephrine activity during the critical period and LHRH activity during that

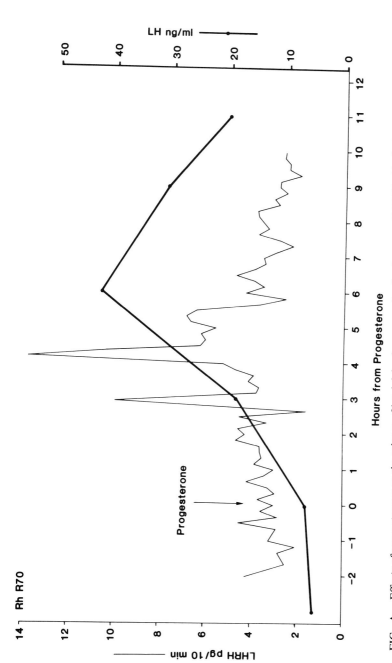

FIG. A. Effects of progesterone on the release of luteinizing hormone releasing hormone (LHRH, thin line) and LH (thick line) in an ovariectomized and estrogen-primed rhesus monkey (Rh R70). Estrogen (30 μg) was injected 24 hours before progesterone. Progesterone (2.5 mg) was injected at time 0. LHRH release from the median eminence was obtained by means of push-pull perfusion every 10 minutes. Circulating LH was measured in serum sampled every 3 hours (unpublished).

same period of time. There have been some recent reports showing that some monoamines show a diurnal rhythm with increased activity during the afternoon. I wonder whether you have looked to see whether the norepinephrine activity increases or remains constant and does not increase on days when you do not observe an LHRH release to be more certain that there is a causal relationship between the increase in noradrenegic activity and the increase in LHRH?

V. Ramirez: That is a very important question because the push-pull cannula is now allowing us to examine *in vivo* what is happening in an unrestrained conscious animal and I would like to mention that certainly it looked as if in the afternoon, in rodents and also in rabbits, there is a tremendous increase in noradrenergic activity. So I am not yet prepared to indicate to you that what we saw in the proestrous rat is just a unique phenomenon for that proestrous animal. It is very possible that there is an increase in activity in the afternoon in other faces of the estrous cycle, but we have not studied that yet.

S. Cohen: I haven't kept up with this field very much, but from my last information, LHRH could also be FSHRH. If that is true, then perhaps that could explain the apparent mix up in feedback mechanisms reported here.

V. Ramirez: Certainly LHRH can release FSH under very specific conditions but not always. The problem of just one single factor controlling the two pituitary hormones is still debatable and has not been resolved yet. I don't think there is any definite word on that. Our studies so far have been focused only at looking for a correlation between LHRH and LH release and not FSH. So I cannot answer your question.

S. McCann: I might say, that we still believe that FSHRF exists; however, we are in a minority, at least for the moment, until we can provide the structure.

NOTE ADDED IN PROOF. Recently we have tested the effect of the 5-β metabolite of P_4, pregnanolone, on *in vitro* LHRH release from rat hypothalami derived from OVX $\times$ E_2 adult animals. Interestingly, pulsatile pregnanolone (10 min on, 20 min off) was highly effective at very low concentrations (0.01 ng/ml). In contrast, continuous infusion of this metabolite using a similar concentration was ineffective.

The Physiology of Gonadotropin-Releasing Hormone (GnRH) Secretion in Men and Women

WILLIAM F. CROWLEY, JR., MARCO FILICORI, DANIEL I. SPRATT. AND NANETTE F. SANTORO

The Reproductive Endocrine Unit at the Vincent Research Laboratories of the Massachusetts General Hospital, Harvard Medical School, Boston, Massachusetts

I. Introduction

The study of the normal physiology of GnRH secretion in the human is complicated by two features unique to neuroendocrine systems in which hypothalamic neuronal messages interface with the classical endocrine pathways. These difficulties stem from (1) the intermittent mode of secretion of a series of evanescent releasing factors and (2) the closed portal blood supply which they traverse. Consequently the approaches employed to study the central nervous system control of reproduction may be applicable to many neuroendocrine models and establish precedents for subsequent investigations into the secretion of other releasing factors.

The nature of the portal blood supply, which links the central nervous system to the anterior pituitary, gives rise to the practical problem that the vast majority of all GnRH secreted from the hypothalamus never leaves this limited anatomic space. In addition to the low circulating levels of GnRH in the periphery which result from this sharply circumscribed anatomy, another aspect which further confounds attempts to obtain a direct assessment of GnRH secretion is its rapid half-life of 2–4 minutes (1–3). Consequently, these two features impart a special degree of complexity to the study of GnRH. Moreover, as the vast majority of neuroendocrine systems share these anatomic limitations and secrete short-lived peptides in a pulsatile manner, a series of inferential approaches must be taken to examine the physiology of hypothalamic secretion in the human.

II. Previous Approaches

The first approach which was employed to obtain an indirect assessment of GnRH secretion was the use of frequent sampling of peripheral

473

blood to evaluate the episodic secretion of gonadotropins. Since each burst of gonadotropin release presumably follows an antecedent bolus of GnRH secretion, gonadotropin pulses can be examined for their frequency of occurrence, a reflection of the frequency of GnRH release which generates these pulses. Consequently the term "hypothalamic pulse generator" has been employed to describe this frequency function of GnRH-secreting neurons in the hypothalamus (4). In addition, the amplitude of each gonadotropin pulse can also be measured to provide an indirect assessment of the combination of the quantity of GnRH released as well as the modulation of each GnRH bolus at the level of the pituitary gland by the feedback effects of gonadal secretions. Thus, the amplitude of gonadotropin pulses is a more complex function to interpret than their frequency.

The second major approach employed to study the secretion of GnRH has been the use of various defects of GnRH release in the form of hypogonadotropic disorders. These GnRH-deficient states have been extraordinarily helpful in shaping our understanding of the mechanism of GnRH secretion and in guiding the construction of replacement regimens of exogenous GnRH which restore reproductive competency. For example, GnRH deficient models have been used to determine the absolute requirement for a pulsatile mode of delivery of GnRH for restoration of physiologic secretion of gonadotropins in castrate or prepubertal Rhesus monkeys (5–7). Similar experiments in the human have employed this knowledge to induce puberty and ovulation in GnRH-deficient subjects (8–10).

III. Limitations of Existing Approaches

While a considerable body of our present understanding of the physiology of GnRH has been derived from either of these two approaches, several critical assumptions underlie their general utility. Failure to recognize these assumptions and to interpret data conservatively in their light can lead to significant errors and misinterpretations of this system. The first potential difficulty arises during the "tracking" of spontaneous gonadotropin pulsations. This approach makes the tacit assumption that all major secretory episodes are fully visualized. Should some of these bursts of gonadotropin secretion escape detection, incorrect inferences regarding the frequency and/or amplitude of GnRH-induced gonadotropin secretion can ensue. Erroneous estimates of the frequency of GnRH release may then be made and give rise to apparent disagreements from one investigation to another. While many features are important in maximizing the visualization of gonadotropin pulsations (such as assay precision, method of pulse identification etc.), perhaps the most important and often-neglected variable is the intensity of blood sampling employed during these studies. An example of a potential error of this type is shown in Fig. 1 in which a patient with polycystic ovarian disease underwent peripheral

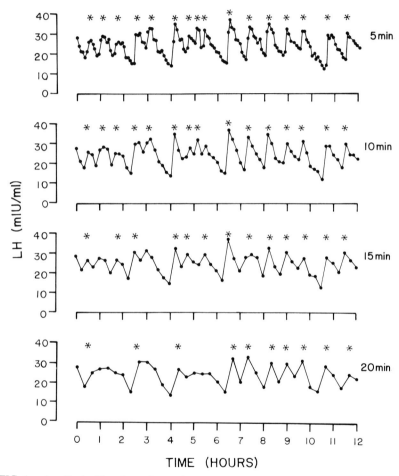

FIG. 1. A patient with polycystic ovarian disease underwent sampling of her gonadotropin levels at 5 minute intervals. Data were then progressively modified to simulate data series of 10, 15, and 20 minute intervals and sequentially reanalyzed for episodes of gonadotropin secretion. It is apparent that a 20 minute interval is inadequate for visualization of all major secretory episodes of gonadotropin release. Asterisk indicates computer identified pulses as indicated in the text.

blood sampling at 5 minute intervals to determine the frequency of her LH pulsations. The data was subsequently reanalyzed by deletion of the appropriate points to simulate series which would have been obtained if the patient had undergone sampling at 10, 15, or 20 minute intervals. As can be seen from comparing the 20 minute series, i.e., the conventional sampling frequency previously employed in such studies with that obtained during 5 minute sampling, several discrete episodes of GnRH-induced LH pulsations have escaped detection.

The practical importance of intensified sampling of gonadotropins as an estimate of GnRH secretion during a physiologic event is portrayed in Fig. 2. In this figure, the frequency of GnRH secretion in the follicular phase of the normal menstrual cycle, as previously reported by various investigators, is related to the frequency of sampling which they employed (11–16). Much of the apparent controversy over the frequency of LH pulses disappears when it is realized that this factor is more a property of the sampling frequency utilized than of the physiologic event under study. Thus it would appear optimal to obtain peripheral blood samples at 5–10 minute intervals, to visualize all major secretory episodes of GnRH, and to maximize the information obtained during such physiologic studies. However, since the phlebotomy limitations of 5 minute sampling often do not permit full 24-hour studies, we have chosen to perform the majority of our investigations at sampling frequencies of 10 minutes to obtain information on the full circadian pattern of GnRH secretion. It is recognized, however, that this selection of a 10 minute sampling interval may slightly underestimate the actual frequency of GnRH secretion in

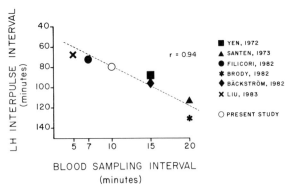

FIG. 2.   The LH interpulse interval in the early follicular phase of the cycle as obtained in a variety of studies (see text for references) are examined as a function of the sampling intervals employed. There is an excellent correlation ($r = 0.94$) between the sampling interval utilized and the LH interpulse interval obtained.

selected circumstances such as when the frequency of LH pulsations is very high (e.g., polycystic ovarian disease) or the amplitude is low (such as hypogonadotropic disorders). In these special circumstances, a 5 minute interval might well be important.

The second major assumption involved in employing the monitoring of LH pulsations as an indirect assessment of the secretion of GnRH is that only GnRH is capable of eliciting a discrete burst of gonadotropin secretion from the anterior pituitary. This assumption seems reasonable in that there is presently no evidence that another gonadotropin-releasing factor exists. All *in vitro* and *in vivo* experiments indicate the mandatory presence of GnRH for gonadotropin release. However, the converse of this assumption, namely that all GnRH pulses from the hypothalamus are translated to a discernible burst of gonadotropin secretion at the level of the anterior pituitary, may not be true. As evidence of "blocked" GnRH pulses will be presented subsequently in this review, such an assumption may well be invalid. Therefore our estimates of the amplitude and frequency of GnRH secretion in the human should always be conservative and this line of investigation would benefit from corroboration by a complimentary approach. However, the most often used secondary line of evidence regarding GnRH secretion is derived from the study of ablation and replacement models and is not without its own pitfalls. The most common difficulty encountered in using the administration of exogenous GnRH to hypogonadotropic models as the sole approach to the physiology of GnRH comes from an overinterpretation of the results. Merely because such an experiment has been successful in restoring a normal pituitary–gonadal axis does not mean that this noteworthy goal has been accomplished by physiologic means. Thus, while a simulation of all the normal events of folliculogenesis, an LH surge, and corpus luteum formation can occur with the administration of GnRH at a 2 hour frequency in Kallmann's Syndrome (9), this frequency is not that which simulates endogenous GnRH release across the normal human cycle. In a normal ovulatory cycle in the human in which all of these similar endocrine events occur, the frequency of GnRH secretion varies markedly (see below). Consequently the normal physiology of endogenous GnRH secretion achieves similar gonadal effects by means of a very different secretory program and this fact must be taken into account in the use of all ablation and replacement models in neuroendocrinology.

IV. The Combined Approach

As a result of these inherent limitations of both approaches—either passive monitoring of endogenous GnRH secretion via observation of gonadotropin pulsations or active intervention with exogenous GnRH in deficiency states—a combination of these two techniques is required to maximize physiologic information. This combination of approaches is especially appealing since each line of investigation by itself offers a unique insight into a different aspect of GnRH physiology, but at the same time suffers from a major potential limitation. Therefore, the general schema of the combined approach which our group has found most useful for the study of the physiology of GnRH in the human is outlined in Fig. 3. Input of information about the frequency and amplitude of GnRH secretion in the human can come from study of the pattern of GnRH release in normal physiologic and developmental states as long as it is recalled that this information is primarily useful for obtaining data relating to the frequency of GnRH pulsations in each of these circumstances. Considering that various compromises are made in sampling frequency and the possibility of "blocked" or nontransmitted pulses of GnRH exists, only a minimum frequency figure can be derived from such models. This under-

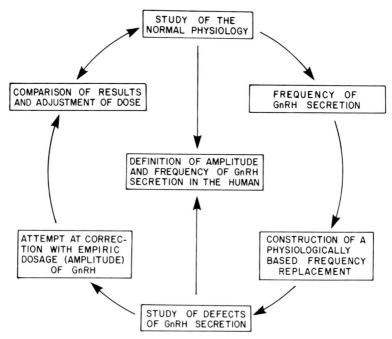

FIG. 3. The combined approach for study of the amplitude and frequency of GnRH secretion in the human.

standing may then be employed to construct a physiologically based frequency program of exogenous GnRH replacement for use in GnRH-deficient models.

Study of the spectrum of GnRH-deficient states then adds another dimension to the investigation of the neuroendocrine control of reproduction. These disorders present themselves to physicians because of a clinically noteworthy deviation from the normal population resulting in a definable reproductive disorder. Study of the aberrant pattern of GnRH secretion in these conditions is then most useful for two purposes. First, as a definable clinical disorder has resulted from this aberrant pattern, such cases assist us in defining the outer limit of normal or the overlap of normal with abnormal GnRH secretory states in a more precise fashion. The second advantage of the study of these abnormalities of GnRH secretory disorders is that they serve as a baseline evaluation of the condition under investigation prior to the institution of any GnRH replacement. As such this baseline examination, when used in a retrospective fashion, helps to define the suitability of various subsets of each GnRH-deficient state for long-term GnRH replacement. An example of this utility is seen in the contrast of the variable responsiveness of discrete subsets of the anovulatory infertility population to exogenous GnRH replacement (e.g., polycystic ovarian disease vs hypothalamic amenorrhea). In addition, it is useful to correlate the abnormality of GnRH secretion which is present with other, more readily available clinical markers in these conditions. Such steps facilitate the transfer of the evaluation of abnormal GnRH secretion from clinical research settings into the more familiar and easily available clinical parlance used to describe these conditions. An example of the utility of this approach can be seen in the correlation of abnormal gonadotropin secretion seen in subjects with hypothalamic amenorrhea with other clinical markers such as uterine withdrawal bleeding following progesterone administration, circulating estradiol levels, or clomiphene responsiveness.

Of all of these abnormalities of GnRH secretion, the ones which are most helpful but, unfortunately from an investigative perspective the rarest in occurrence, are the complete absence of any GnRH-induced gonadotropin pulsations as is seen in idiopathic hypogonadotropic hypogonadism (IHH). These subjects are of particular importance since the interpretations of their responses to exogenous GnRH replacement are not obscured by consideration of the role of any endogenous GnRH secretion. As such they are truly important experiments of nature which afford a unique opportunity for the study of the physiology of GnRH in the human.

Once a physiologically based frequency program of GnRH administration has been constructed from a normative study of the circumstance under investigation, e.g., the human menstrual cycle, and the nature of the abnormal GnRH secretory pattern has been identified, the normal GnRH program can be applied to the disorders of GnRH secretion (Fig. 3). However, a selection of a GnRH dosage must first be made. While this dosage is often empiric, there can be some logic applied in its selection. First, the levels of GnRH achieved in the peripheral circulation following injection of a given dosage can be compared to levels obtained by direct measurement of hypophyseal-portal blood in nonhuman primates (17) or, in rare circumstances, in humans during neurosurgical procedures (18). Second, the amplitude of the pituitary gonadotropin response to a given dose of GnRH can be compared to a range of randomly determined gonadotropins or gonadotropin pulse amplitudes in normal individuals (19). Third, as will be seen below, an even more exacting comparison can be made by employing a detailed analysis of the pulse characteristics of the normative data upon which the frequency program is based. Thus the amplitude, time to peak, and decay of each pulse or, preferably, a series of pooled pulses from the GnRH responses of the IHH subjects can be compared to those derived from the normal subjects. A determination can then be made as to whether or not the dosage and frequency of GnRH selected meets all of the goals of restoring a normal pituitary *and* gonadal response in the IHH subjects. Such a combined approach allows for a comparison of the endocrine "macroenvironment," such as induction of ovulation or puberty, as well as a detailed comparison of the "microenvironment" of pulse characteristics between normal and GnRH-deficient states. It is this latter point which permits the physiologic lessons to be maximized and minute adjustments to be made, allowing valuable insight into the subtleties of this system. It is on the basis of these comparisons to normal that all of our adjustments of GnRH dose and consequently gonadotropin pulse characteristics have been made. Such a comparison permits the fullest utilization of the normative data base including both amplitude and frequency of the pulsatile hormone analysis.

This combined approach, by continually forcing a comparison with normal, avoids many of the limitations of previous strategies. For example, it circumvents criticism that one is merely reestablishing a relatively macroscopic normal endocrine endpoint, such as ovulation, with a GnRH frequency which is not physiologic. Similarly, should "blocked" or nontransmitted GnRH pulses play a significant role in the normal physiology, then there would be a continued inability of the chosen program of exogenous GnRH administration to restore normal physiology. In such a case, the failure would reflect that the frequencies and amplitudes selected had not incorporated the possibility of "blocked pulses" into their construction. Yet another advantage of this perspective is that the initiation of the cycle of investigation can arise from the study of either normal or abnormal states. As such, this approach has the advantage of utility in a wide variety of circumstances and can be employed in both sexes as illustrated below. It can also be of use in the study of developing as well as mature states. Thus it should be a generally applicable schema with which to study several neuroendocrine systems in addition to many other models which are characterized by episodic hormone secretion.

The limitations of such an approach center about the ultimate accumulation of a large body of normative data. In addition, this data must be obtained at a sampling interval which is sufficiently rigorous and appropriate to the system under investigation to sustain the scrutiny of such careful and detailed comparisons. Finally, the normative data base employed should be sufficiently large to take into account the range of normal responses in the event under study. Thus the demands of such a combined approach are great; however, the yield is equally high.

V. Methods of Pulse Analysis

While a full discussion of the various methods of analysis of episodic hormone secretion is beyond the scope of this review, it seems that at present there is no general agreement as to a single optimal method of pulse analysis. What is clear is that specific assays with low intraassay variance and the use of an intensified sampling interval are at least as important in the identification of pulses as the actual program employed. As the basic problem of pulse analysis is one of recognizing a discrete, albeit small, signal against a noisy background, any factor which reduces this noise (i.e., decreased assay variance and/or lowered assay crossreactivity) or increases the sharpness of the signal (i.e., intensified sampling) is of great importance. In general, however, the majority of analysis of our data has been performed primarily with the use of the nadir-to-peak method of Santen and Bardin (12) with the added criteria that a pulse must exceed a given threshold (1–3 mIU/ml of second IRP) and have a duration of at least 2 timepoints. The latter criterion was added to most of the studies in which samples were obtained at 10 minute intervals. In addition, a second computer program, Pulsar (20), was also used to evaluate the data series. In general there was an excellent qualitative agreement between these 2 methods, although some quantitative differences between them did exist.

VI. GnRH Physiology in the Male

A. STUDIES IN HYPOGONADOTROPIC HYPOGONADISM

Our initial studies into the physiology of GnRH were undertaken in hypogonadotropic males and were prompted by their apparent clinical, biochemical, and genetic heterogeneity. While many of these subjects were initially diagnosed by Albright and his colleagues on the basis of a persistence of the prepubertal state beyond age 18 and low urinary gonadotropins, they often presented with a wide variety of findings suggesting that this condition is more heterogeneous than was originally expected (21–30). While some of the patients are anosmic and therefore carry the diagnosis of Kallmann's Syndrome, others have a normal sense of smell. Some cases are associated with a series of congenital midline defects but again this is not a consistent finding (25). By history, a subset of these patients recall the earliest stirrings of puberty with the appearance of erections and nocturnal emissions but further signs or symptoms of puberty failed to ensue or actually regressed over time. On physical examination, there is a striking degree of variability in the gonadal size of these patients with testes varying from 1 ml and cryptorchid to 10–12 ml, i.e., nearly normal. Similarly their baseline and stimulated gonadotropin levels span an equally wide range from undetectable to those in the lower ranges of normal adult males (26–28). Perhaps the most persuasive evidence of heterogeneity within this clinical syndrome is the reports of its association with at least 2 differing modes of inheritance. While the majority of cases appear to follow an autosomal dominant pattern of inheritance with evidence of a marked variability of phenotypic expression (28,29), clear-cut evidence of an autosomal recessive mode of inheritance has also been reported (30).

With these findings of clinical, biochemical, and genetic heterogeneity as a background, we sought to examine a series of men with well-characterized IHH utilizing frequent sampling of gonadotropins, testing the hypothesis than a spectrum of abnormalities of endogenous GnRH secretion may, in part, underlie the apparent heterogeneity within this disorder. Accordingly, 40 men with IHH underwent a thorough evaluation to assure the diagnosis prior to a detailed profiling of their GnRH secretory pattern. Each had failed to undergo puberty by age 18 and had a serum testosterone concentration of less than 100 ng/dl in the face of normal to low gonadotropin levels. In addition, each exhibited a normal cortisol and growth hormone response following administration of insulin (0.15 U/kg iv) and a normal TSH and prolactin response to thyrotropin stimulation

(200 μg iv). In addition, each was euthyroid and had a normal cranial tomography of the hypothalamic–pituitary area.

Following this diagnostic evaluation, each subject was then admitted to the Clinical Research Center of the Massachusetts General Hospital for a period of 12–24 hours of intensive gonadotropin sampling during which sleep was monitored visually by trained personnel. This study demonstrated that several patterns of gonadotropin secretion were evident within this population. The vast majority (75%) of these IHH men exhibited a total absence on any endogenous secretion of GnRH as attested to by their apulsatile pattern of LH release (Fig. 4). On the other hand three subjects exhibited clear-cut evidence of augmentation of gonadotropin pulsations during sleep (Fig. 4) giving them the appearance of early puber-

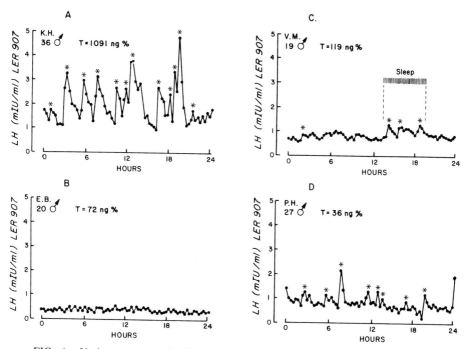

FIG. 4. Various patterns of LH secretion observed in hypogonadotropic and normal men. (A) LH secretory pattern observed in a normal adult male. (B) Apulsatile pattern of LH secretion observed in the majority of IHH males. (C) A pattern of developmental arrest in an adult male with IHH in whom LH pulsations are apparent only during sleep. (D) Reduced LH pulse amplitude pattern seen in another male with IHH. T, serum testosterone level. Reprinted by permission of "Current Topics in Endocrinology and Metabolism" (D. T. Krieger and C. W. Bardin, eds.), p. 157. Decker, New York, 1985.

tal GnRH secretion (31). Since all of these subjects had a larger testicular size and/or gave a history of early pubertal development, this pattern of GnRH secretion has been viewed as a developmental arrest. The fact that these gonadotropin pulses are not merely assay noise is proven by their replicability in two different LH radioimmunoassays with different determinants when repeated by a second technician (Fig. 5). In addition, this

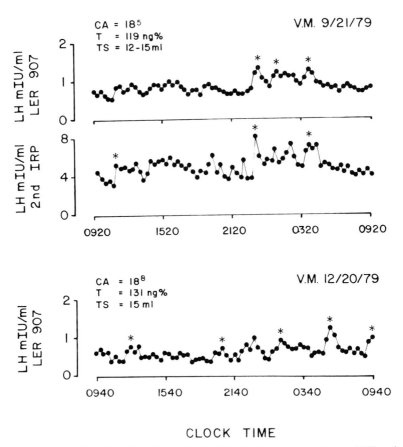

CLOCK TIME

FIG. 5. The replicability of small-amplitude LH pulsations observed in one IHH patient (VM) during repeated studies analyzed in two radioimmunoassays for LH. The upper panel portrays a radioimmunoassay which has a moderate degree of α cross-reactivity (approximately 30%) whereas the middle panel demonstrates bloods from the same admission processed in a second radioimmunoassay which has <5% cross-reactivity with α subunit. This same pattern reappeared in this patient during a second admission 3 months later (bottom panel).

pattern has proven to be a reproducible during subsequent studies in all of these subjects.

A third pattern of GnRH abnormality was seen in three siblings of a family in which four brothers had IHH, three of whom were also crypt-orchid. All three brothers sampled (the fourth was not available) exhibited LH pulses which seemed to be reduced in their amplitude (Fig. 4). This assertion of a defect in the amplitude of GnRH-induced gonadotropin release is bolstered by three lines of evidence. First, their endogenous LH pulses were of insufficient amplitude to generate secretion of testosterone from their own Leydig cells. Second, these pulses were markedly reduced from those documented in their sibling controls who were unaffected by the clinical syndrome of IHH. Third, when they underwent long-term GnRH replacement, each IHH subject subsequently normalized his pituitary–gonadal axis when the amplitude of his endogenous LH secretion was restored to the normal range by exogenous GnRH administered at a physiologic dose and frequency.

A fourth potential defect of endogenous GnRH secretion is typified by Fig. 6 which portrays two brothers who presented with severe gyneco-mastia and markedly variable serum testosterone levels (109–600 ng/dl) during outpatient evaluation. Both subjects had only 6–7 LH pulses during their 24-hour study (Fig. 6), a figure which was considerably less than our normal mean LH pulse frequency of 12.0 ± 1.1 (SE) pulses/24 hours. Perhaps more impressive was the fact that their serum testosterone levels varied markedly over the study period depending on the duration from their previous LH pulse. As this interval lengthened, serum testosterone secretion waned only to be restored to normal by subsequent LH pulses. The normal sibling control, who exhibited 11 LH pulses/24 hours demonstrated no such fluctuations in serum testosterone levels out of the normal adult male range. That their LH pulse frequency was the basis for their defect is supported by the observation that clomiphene and pulsatile GnRH administration, both of which increased the frequency of their gonadotropin pulses, also increased their serum testosterone values to consistently normal ranges. Thus it appears that these patients have a relative defect in the frequency of their GnRH secretion as the basis for at least part of their clinical defect.

The final pattern of abnormal GnRH secretion which we have identified in IHH males is demonstrated by a patient in whom both the amplitude and frequency of GnRH-induced gonadotropin pulsations appeared to be normal. However, his serum LH appeared to be biologically inactive when tested in the dispersed rat Leydig cell assay. Consequently, the defect appears to be the secretion of a biologically inactive LH molecule,

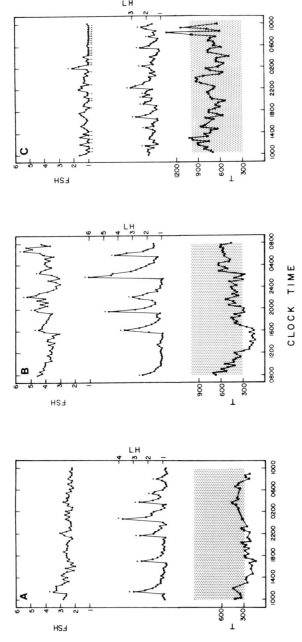

FIG. 6. This study examines the 24-hour gonadotropin and sex steroid secretory patterns of three brothers, two of whom presented with hypogonadotropic hypogonadism. The subjects in A and B exhibited severe gynecomastia and variably low serum testosterone levels. C represents their normal sibling control. The shaded area portrays the normal adult male range of serum testosterone in ng/%.

the majority of which appears to be immunologically identical to α subunit.

Thus it appears that a wide variety of abnormal patterns of GnRH secretion are present in IHH males and account for much of the above-mentioned heterogeneity of this disorder. The clinical correlation of each of these patterns is not yet totally clear but it appears that, in general, patients with the presence of endogenous pulses and/or a prior history of some pubertal symptoms exhibited testicular sizes in excess of 5 ml. Moreover, each pattern of abnormal GnRH secretion was consistent within a pedigree suggesting that these abnormalities are genetically determined. In this regard the subjects exhibiting the apulsatile pattern of GnRH secretion are the most likely to suffer from deletions of the GnRH gene. One alternative speculation is that point substitutions within the GnRH gene could be present translating to the synthesis of an inactive GnRH molecule. On the other hand, those subjects in whom endogenous GnRH secretion was present, but in an enfeebled pattern, might well represent examples of disordered modulation of GnRH secretion.

B. GnRH SECRETION IN NORMAL MALES

Having acquired some understanding of the abnormalities of GnRH secretion in hypogonadotropic males, we next turned our attention to the acquisition of a normative data base from which to derive our frequency program of exogenous GnRH administration. Accordingly, we examined 15 men aged 18–35, who exhibited a normal history of sexual development and a normal gonadal size ($\geq$15 ml) as well as a normal seminal fluid analysis ($\geq$30 $\times$ 10/cm^3, 60% motility and 2 cm^3 volume). Each underwent a 24-hour period of sampling of their gonadotropin levels at 10 minute intervals. While our normative data agree well with previous studies (12, 32–34) several differences are of interest. As can be seen by the subject shown in Fig. 7, the 10 minute sampling frequency permits a clear-cut visualization of each discrete, major secretory episode of gonadotropin release. In addition, the serum testosterone levels determined every 6 hours are maintained well within the normal adult male range. However, the normal man portrayed in Fig. 8 exhibit's some striking differences from this expected pattern of GnRH secretion in that the predominance of his LH pulses are clustered during sleeping hours. This pattern of GnRH secretion was formerly thought to occur only during puberty (31) but, as can be seen in Fig. 8, it appears to be a reproducible finding in at least some of the patients during repeated studies. In addition, we have observed a range of LH pulse frequencies in normal men

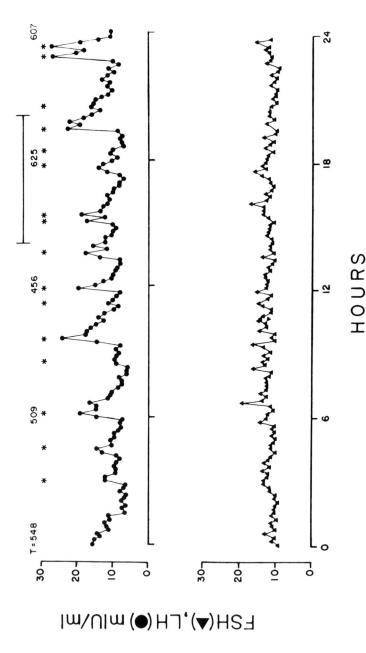

FIG. 7. Twenty-four hour LH and FSH secretory patterns obtained in a normal adult male who was sampled at 10 minute intervals. LH pulses are identified by asterisks. Serum testosterone levels were determined every 6 hours and sleep is indicated by the brackets.

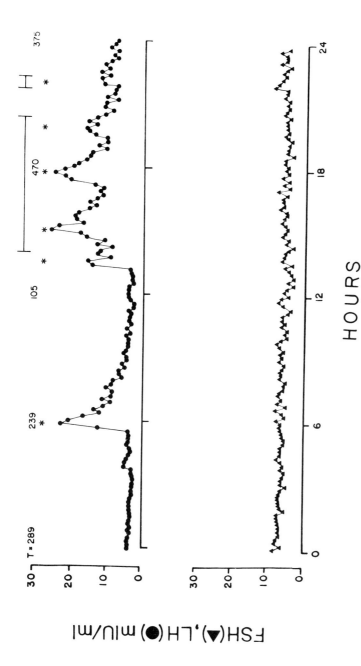

FIG. 8. Twenty-four hour LH and FSH secretory patterns obtained in a normal male as defined in the text. LH pulses are identified by asterisks. Serum testosterone levels were determined every 6 hours and sleep is indicated by the brackets. In this otherwise normal males, LH pulses occur predominantly at night.

489

varying from 7 to 17 pulses per 24 hours as well as serum testosterone levels which can fall as low as 91 ng/dl in normal men during periods of lengthened LH interpulse intervals. Consequently, this finding of marked variability in GnRH pulse frequency and serum testosterone values within the normal population has made us more conservative in our interpretations of frequency disorders since it is very likely that this circumstance (i.e., slowed LH pulse frequency) may represent the interface between normal and abnormal GnRH secretory states.

When the results of the studies of our normal male population are then examined (Table I), an excellent agreement is found with that of previous investigations with the differences between these studies often being resolvable on such technical issues as sampling frequency and method of pulse identification (12,32–34). Table I also illustrates the impact of varying the threshold criteria which the amplitude of an LH pulse must exceed to be identified as a discrete LH pulsation by the nadir-to-peak method (12). The frequency of sampling with the additional requirement of the pulse duration being at least 2 points in length (only required when a 10 minute sampling interval is employed) would appear to be of overriding importance since these various amplitude thresholds have only a slight impact upon the analysis of this data.

In summary, the study of a large group of adult males has provided normative information regarding mean levels of gonadotropin and sex steroids, the frequency of LH pulsations, and the amplitude and contour of an idealized mean pulse. These data are most useful for construction of a physiologically based frequency program of exogenous GnRH administration to GnRH-deficient models. In addition, this data base will be important for subsequent comparison and adjustment of the dosage of GnRH to be used in evaluating the pituitary responsiveness of IHH males undergoing long-term GnRH administration.

C.   GnRH REPLACEMENT IN IHH MALES

Having ascertained the frequency, amplitude, and contour of gonadotropin pulsations in normal individuals, it was next possible to infer the proper frequency of endogenous GnRH secretions in the normal adult male, i.e., every 2 hours, and initiate studies of GnRH replacement in IHH men. The apulsatile subset of IHH subjects is of particular importance since interpretation of their responses to exogenous GnRH is not obscured by consideration of the role of any endogenous hypothalamic activity. Therefore, this subset of IHH men has generally been selected

TABLE I

Pulse Characteristics in Normal Men[a]

Pulse criteria (mIU/ml)	Frequency (pulses/24 hours)	Amplitude (mIU/ml second IRP)
>1	12.6 ± 1.0	9.4 ± 0.9
>2	12.0 ± 1.1	9.7 ± 0.9
>3	10.9 ± 1.0	10.8 ± 0.8

[a] The characteristics of pulsatile LH secretion in 15 normal men sampled at 10-minute intervals. For identification a pulse was required to exceed an amplitude of 1, 2, or 3 mIU/ml and consist of at least two consecutive points.

for physiologic studies of the type outlined below. Fortunately, this group is the most common, comprising more than 75% of all IHH men.

Following baseline evaluations, these men were then placed on a regimen of 25 ng/kg of GnRH administered subcutaneously at 2 hourly intervals. This dosage of GnRH was selected on the basis of previous studies (19) in which this regimen yielded LH pulses within the range of normal males. The delivery of this medication was achieved by means of small, lightweight portable infusion pumps (Ferring Company) which have proven to be quite reliable in their timing and precision of medication delivery. The subcutaneous route of administration was chosen because of the long-term nature of the replacement program to be undertaken.

The symptoms which were induced by this regimen recapitulated those

TABLE II

Symptomatic Changes in IHH Men during Prolonged GnRH Administration[a]

↑ Libido, potency (14/14)	100%
↑ Spontaneous erections (14/14)	100%
↑ Testicular size (13/14)	93%
Appearance of an ejaculate (11/14)	79%
↑ Facial hair (9/14)	64%
↓ Voice (9/14)	64%
Appearance of mature sperm in ejaculate (7/11)	64%

[a] The appearance of symptoms of puberty in 14 hypogonadotropic men during long-term GnRH administration.

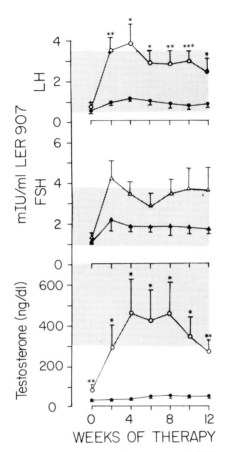

FIG. 9. Gonadotropin and gonadal steroid responses of IHH males during long-term administration of GnRH at a 2 hour frequency. The shaded areas represent the normal adult male ranges for LH, FSH, and serum testosterone levels. The open symbols indicate six subjects treated with 25 ng/kg whereas the closed symbols represent another three males treated with 10 ng/kg for the same interval. Reprinted by permission of *New Eng. J. Med.* **307,** 1239 (1982).

of a normal puberty (Table II). These responses, shown in the first 14 subjects, have been repeated in 22 consecutive IHH men treated with a similar regimen. Figure 10 demonstrates the pituitary and Leydig cell responses of the first 6 IHH subjects to be treated with this unvarying dosage of GnRH (25 ng/kg) for a 3-month period. During this time, the serum testosterone level was normalized in 5/6 subjects while the serum LH and FSH responses continued to rise above the normal adult male ranges until the fifth to the seventh week during which negative feedback

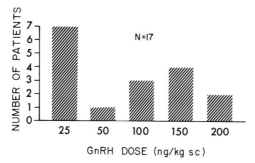

FIG. 10. GnRH doses required to normalize serum testosterone and pituitary gonadotropin secretion in 17 consecutive IHH males treated with low dose, pulsatile GnRH administration.

inhibition by sex steroids occurred. It is important to recall that these IHH subjects, while on a fixed dose and regimen of GnRH, are capable of modulating their circulating levels of gonadotropins only by changes in the amplitude of their pituitary responses. Thus Fig. 9 is really a graph of the mean amplitude of LH and FSH responses of the gonadotrophs since the hypothalamic input has been "clamped" and hence is unavailable to participate in feedback mechanisms. This particular feature is one of the most attractive experimental aspects of this model as it is now possible to isolate the pituitary portion of the hypothalamic–pituitary axis. For example, as is shown in Fig. 9, the delayed feedback effects of sex steroids upon this system are potentially more compatible with the time course of aromatization of testosterone to estradiol than with a direct androgen effect. Another interesting experimental feature of the IHH model is evident in Fig. 9. The closed circles represent three patients who received a dose of 10 ng/kg of GnRH at 2 hourly intervals for 3 months. In each case, the pulsatile release of LH was induced, mean LH and FSH levels rose into the normal adult range, yet no testosterone secretion occurred. Thus, while a physiologic frequency of GnRH secretion was applied, the threshold dose appeared to be at 25 ng/kg. Moreover, it has been possible to convert the apulsatile subset of men employed for this experiment into a group now characterized by a sole defect in the amplitude of gonadotropin secretion. It is important to point out that all three of these men subsequently normalized their pituitary–gonadal axis on higher doses of GnRH, thereby confirming that their defect was related to the amplitude of LH responses induced by their subthreshold GnRH program and not an independent defect of pituitary or Leydig cell responsiveness.

Although 25 ng/kg represents the threshold dose for activation of the

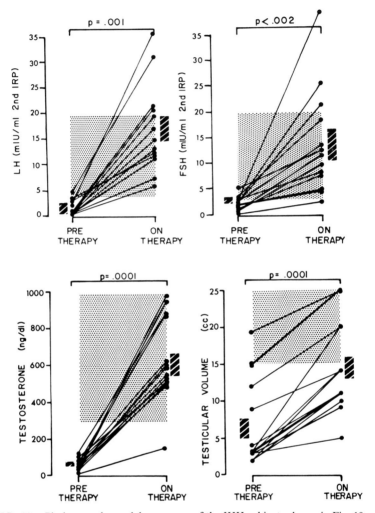

FIG. 11. Pituitary and gonadal responses of the IHH subjects shown in Fig. 10 prior to and following long-term GnRH administration. The sole subject who did not normalize his serum testosterone level developed an antibody to GnRH which appeared prior to completion of his sexual maturation. The shaded areas indicate normal ranges for adult males.

pituitary–gonadal axis in IHH men, the dosage required to achieve a final result of mid-adult levels of testosterone in these patients varies considerably and as is shown on Fig. 10, spans a range from 25 to 200 ng/kg. The differences between these doses largely arises from the variability of subcutaneous absorption of GnRH. The final pituitary and gonadal responses

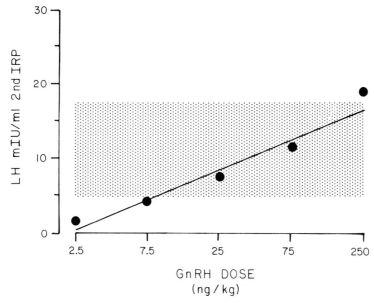

FIG. 12. The amplitude of LH secreted versus the dose of GnRH administered in an IHH subject who received GnRH doses administered in randomized order at a physiologic frequency (every 2 hours). Mean serum testosterone during this experiment was 471 ng/dl.

achieved on these doses of GnRH in IHH subjects during long-term GnRH replacement are shown in Fig. 11. The single patient portrayed in whom a normal pituitary and gonadal response was not achieved is a man who developed an antibody to GnRH prior to the achievement of full sexual maturity.

Thus it is possible to achieve full sexual maturation in IHH men in whom the pituitary–gonadal axis can be normalized over prolonged periods of time via long-term administration of exogenous GnRH. In addition to confirming the nature of the hypothalamic defect in IHH, these men afford an unusual opportunity for physiologic investigations into the adult male reproductive system in that the dosage and frequency of GnRH input can be varied experimentally. The consequences of these variations upon the ratio, quantity, and quality of pituitary gonadotropin secretion and the effects of these changes, in turn, upon gonadal function can then be examined. In addition, it should be possible to determine precisely the site of action of sex steroids in this model as only those steroids having a pituitary site of action should affect IHH men undergoing long-term GnRH replacement.

D.   PHYSIOLOGIC STUDIES IN IHH MALES

As the IHH men do not appear to achieve a sufficient degree of stability of their gonadotropin and sex steroid levels until after 3 months of administration of their threshold dosage of GnRH, we have customarily waited until this period of normalcy has transpired prior to initiating further investigations. Following this "induction phase," the IHH men undergoing long-term GnRH replacement return to our Clinical Research Center for an admission during which a "physiologic" dosage of intravenous GnRH is established by examining the dose–response relationship of GnRH vs pituitary LH secretion when GnRH is administered at a physiologic frequency (every 2 hours), utilizing a protocol of randomized GnRH administration. An example of the type of data which are obtained from such an experiment is shown in Fig. 12. With this experimental approach, the pituitary LH (and to a lesser extent FSH) response of the IHH men can be compared to the now firmly-established normative data base in relation to (1) the mean circulating level of gonadotropins achieved, (2) the mean amplitude of the LH pulse (Fig. 12), (3) the area under the LH curve, and (4) the contour of the LH pulse (including time to peak and rate of decay). Of course the latter three comparisons require extensive pooling and analysis of both the normative as well as the experimental data, but this task can be achieved through the use of computer-assisted statistical methods. A combination of several of these approaches then allows a fair degree of confidence that the particular GnRH program being employed mirrors the normal, endogenous GnRH secretion to the greatest possible extent. In addition, it permits a normalization of not only the "macroenvironment" of the restoration of normal mean levels of gonadotropins and sex steroids within the relatively wide ranges of normal; but it also assures that the "microenvironment" of episodic hormonal release is similarly normalized. This last point is particularly important in that it forces a continued comparison of both the frequency and amplitude of the normal endogenous GnRH characteristics with those of the IHH men undergoing long-term GnRH administration. Such an approach also establishes that a linear dose–response relationship exists between the dose of GnRH given and the quantity of LH and FSH secreted from the anterior pituitary (Fig. 12) when these parameters are examined at a physiologic frequency and in a physiologic steroid hormonal milieu. Such studies have thus confirmed the fact that 20–25 ng/kg of GnRH (Fig. 13), when administered by the intravenous route, replicates a normal gonadotropin pulse amplitude, area under the curve, time to peak, and rate of decay at the same time it achieves peak GnRH levels in the peripheral circulation

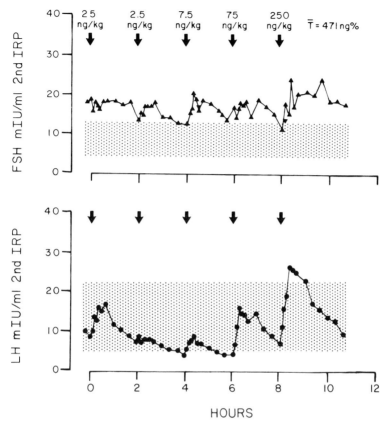

FIG. 13.   The pituitary LH responses to varying doses of GnRH administered at a 2 hour frequency. The shaded area indicates the range of amplitudes of LH secretion which follow endogenous GnRH stimulation in normal men.

of 500–1000 pg/ml. These levels are similar to those obtained by direct measurement in the hypophyseal-portal blood of primates (17).

Having established the physiologic dosage of GnRH which meets all of these criteria of normalcy, it then became possible to set this dose constant and next examine the changes which ensue when alterations of GnRH frequency are undertaken. Figure 14 illustrates an example of an IHH subject in whom this physiologic dose of GnRH was determined in the fashion outlined above. He then received the GnRH intravenously (all physiologic studies are performed with iv GnRH) at a frequency which was progressively increased from every 2 hours to every 15 minutes.

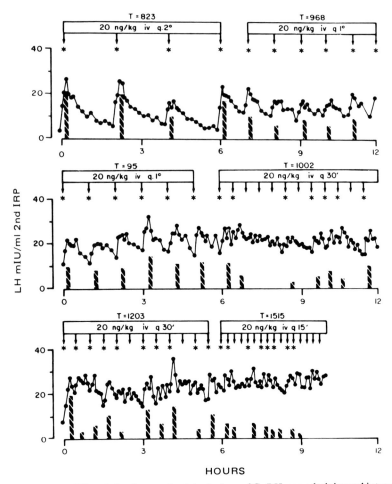

FIG. 14. An IHH male in whom a physiologic dose of GnRH was administered intravenously at an increasing frequency over 3 successive weeks. The amplitude of each LH pulse is demonstrated by the hatched bars whereas the mean circulating levels are portrayed by the circles. With increasing GnRH frequency there is a progressive decline of pituitary responsiveness.

Throughout this time the gonadal steroid levels remained within the normal adult range, the mean LH level increased, but the pituitary responsiveness to each GnRH pulse progressively declined and "blocked" or nontransmitted GnRH pulses became apparent. As the temporal progression was increased further, highly erratic pituitary responsiveness appeared and exhibited a marked waxing and waning with resulting wide fluctuations of the mean serum LH levels. While these changes were somewhat variable in the frequency of onset, similar changes occurred in all four IHH men undergoing identical increases in the frequency of their GnRH administration. These changes are quite characteristic of pituitary desensitization in its earliest stages.

Thus while examining the interaction of GnRH and the gonadotrophs at a physiologic frequency, an increase in dosage of GnRH was accompanied by a linear increase in gonadotropin output in a ratio defined by the slope of the dose–response curve. When pituitary exposure to GnRH was increased by means of increasing the frequency of GnRH administration, a decreasing amplitude of pituitary responsiveness ensued. This decreasing output of pituitary responses with increasing releasing hormone input meets the loose requirements of desensitization and indicates that in the male under these steroid hormone conditions, desensitization occurs with frequencies of GnRH stimulation under 2 hours. It is likely, however, that the conditions for the appearance of desensitization (i.e., GnRH frequency, sex, and steroid hormone milieu) may vary considerably.

VII. α Subunit Secretion in IHH Men during Long-Term GnRH Administration

The precise control of circulating free α subunit secretion is incompletely understood. Previous studies have suggested some degree of TRH control based upon the observation that circulating free α subunit levels are increased in hypothyroidism (35) and are normalized by thyroid replacement (36). In addition, the administration of pharmacologic doses of TRH causes an immediate release of free α levels (35,37,38). However, other studies suggest a role for GnRH in the control of free α secretion as free alpha levels are elevated in primary hypogonadism and are returned to normal by sex steroid replacement (36). α subunit levels also rise during pharmacologic administration of GnRH (38,39). However, no data exist regarding the control of α subunit secretion during physiologic GnRH stimulation of the pituitary. Since the IHH subjects are euthyroid men with normal TRH stimulation of the pituitary but are GnRH deficient, they are useful to examine the relative contribution of GnRH and TRH to the control of circulating free α subunit levels under physiologic circumstances. Accordingly, we have examined the levels of free α subunit in the circulation of IHH men prior to and following institution of physiologic GnRH replacement. In each of the six IHH men examined, circulating free α levels prior to the institution of GnRH replacement were at the limits of detectability in our specific α subunit assay (0.3–0.5 ng/ml) which demonstrated <4% cross-reactivity with intact LH. Following ad-

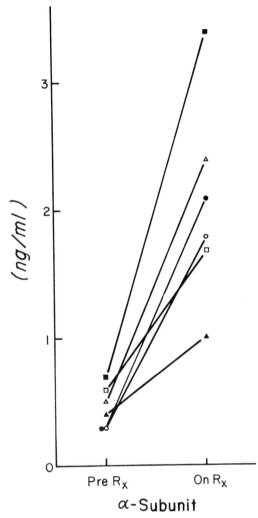

FIG. 15.   Circulating levels of free α subunit in IHH subjects before and following long-term GnRH therapy are shown. All levels prior to GnRH are at or below the assay sensitivity limits.

ministration of physiologic doses of GnRH and normalization of the pituitary–gonadal axis in these men, their α subunit levels rose well into the normal range (Fig. 15). Moreover, the pattern of free α release following GnRH replacement is pulsatile in nature. Finally, over several weeks of follow-up in these men during a period of sexual maturation which spanned a wide variety of circulating gonadotropin levels and sex steroid hormone milieus, a very tight correlation existed between circulating free α and LH levels while no such correlation was observed with FSH levels. Thus it appears that GnRH controls yet another major aspect of gonadotroph function in the secretion of circulating levels of free α subunit. While the physiologic significance of this finding is presently unclear, this facet of GnRH physiology gives us yet another parameter with which to examine GnRH–pituitary interactions. Finally, taken together these experiments suggest that within the normal physiologic range, GnRH is a major regulator of free α subunit secretion in the human male. Only the use of the GnRH deficient model undergoing long-term hypothalamic replacement has permitted this new insight into pituitary function.

VIII. GnRH Physiology in the Female

A. NORMATIVE DATA

Studies in the female were initiated with an intensive study of the neuroendocrine control of the normal menstrual cycle as we were aware of the marked differences in previous reports of the amplitude and frequency of GnRH secretion across an ovulatory cycle (11–16). To date we have examined 62 individual cycles in normal women to provide a clearer understanding of the normal patterns of GnRH secretion across the menstrual cycle. The participants were paid volunteers aged 18–40 who had regular menstrual cycles of 27–32 days in duration. None had a history of excessive exercise nor had received any hormonal medications in the 3 months preceding the study. Each had a body weight within the 15–85 percentile of normal and had a normal physical exam (40). Each was euthyroid and had a normal serum prolactin level. In the month preceding the study each subject demonstrated a biphasic basal body temperature chart and a midluteal phase serum progesterone level of ≥ 6 ng/ml. Ovulatory cycles were defined as those in which the luteal phase progesterone level exceeded 3 ng/ml. The data were subsequently analyzed in relation to the day of ovulation which was set as day 0 and defined as the day when three of the following four events occurred: (1) the LH peak, (2) the FSH peak, (3) the day of or day after the estradiol peak, and (4) the day on which the progesterone levels doubled from baseline or exceeded 0.6 ng/ml (41). In addition to the daily blood determination, each subject underwent a 20–24 hour period of 10 minute sampling at one of the six stages of the menstrual cycle–early follicular phase (days −13 to −9), midfollicular phase (days −8 to −5), late follicular phase (days −4 to 0), early luteal

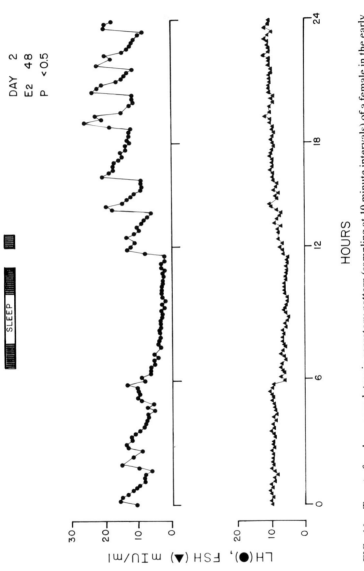

FIG. 16. Twenty-four hour gonadotropin secretory pattern (sampling at 10 minute intervals) of a female in the early follicular phase (day 2) of the menstrual cycle. Sleep is indicated by the hatched bars. Notice the near total suspension of LH secretory activity during sleep in the early follicular phase.

phase (days +1 to +4), midluteal phase (days +5 to +9), or late luteal phase (days +10 to +14).

The pattern of gonadotropin secretion characteristic of the early follicular phase of the cycle is shown by the patient portrayed in Fig. 16. Typically, patients at this stage of the cycle exhibited gonadotropin pulsations which were relatively easy to visualize because of their slow frequency of approximately 90 minutes (Table III) and moderate amplitude. However, the majority of patients studied during this phase of the cycle exhibited a striking and near-total suspension of pulsatile gonadotropin release during sleep. Even brief periods of awakening were associated with a reversal of this sleep-related absence of pulsatile gonadotropin release. By the mid-follicular phase (Fig. 17), the pattern of gonadotropin release changed markedly. The frequency of LH pulsations increased to approximately circhoral. However, the amplitude of each pulse decreased and the sleep-related suspension of pulsatility observed in the early follicular phase had disappeared. This decrease in the amplitude of gonadotropin pulsations made it difficult to identify discrete episodes of gonadotropin secretion at this one stage of the cycle and it is here that the 10 minute sampling regimen is of critical assistance in identifying pulses of such low amplitude.

By the late follicular phase, the amplitude of the LH pulses increased markedly from the midfollicular phase (Fig. 18). In fact, many of these pulses were comprised of one or two points raising the question of

TABLE III
Pulse Frequency and Amplitude in Normal Women[a]

Pulse criteria (mIU)	EF	MF	LF	EL	ML	LL
			Frequency			
1	87'	61'	67'	100'	161'	192'
2	104'	65'	72'	101'	236'	303'
3	113'	73'	83'	109'	265'	339'
			Amplitude			
1	6.2 ± 0.6	5.1 ± 1.8	10.3 ± 3.9	14.6 ± 1.6	12.2 ± 2.0	7.6 ± 1.1
2	7.0 ± 0.7	5.4 ± 1.7	10.4 ± 3.9	14.7 ± 1.7	18.5 ± 4.0	11.5 ± 1.4
3	7.5 ± 0.8	5.8 ± 1.4	10.8 ± 3.8	15.8 ± 1.7	19.8 ± 4.0	12.4 ± 1.3

[a] The characteristics of pulsatile LH secretion over the normal menstrual cycle. Pulse identification was performed as in Table I. EF, MF, LF, early, mid, and late follicular phases, respectively. EL, ML, LL, early, mid, and late luteal phases respectively. The effect of altering the various criteria is readily seen. $n = 62$.

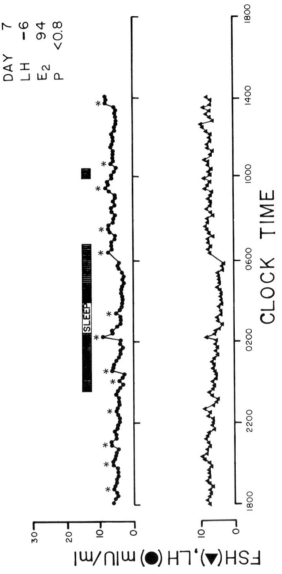

FIG. 17. Twenty-four hour LH secretory pattern (sampling at 10 minute intervals) in a normal female during the mid-follicular phase. Note the decreased amplitude of LH pulsations compared to the early follicular phase and the absence of sleep-related suspension of GnRH secretory activity.

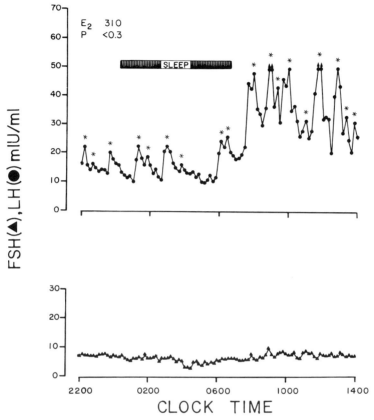

FIG. 18. The LH secretory response in a normal female studied on the day of the LH surge. Note the increase in amplitude and frequency of GnRH secretion, the absence of any day/night variation, and the discernible FSH pulsations.

whether or not a further increase in the intensity of sampling frequency at this stage of the cycle might yield an even higher estimate of LH pulse frequency. Following the formation of the corpus luteum and its secretion of progesterone, the pattern of gonadotropin secretion changes again in the early luteal phase. There was a marked slowing of the LH pulse frequency which became evident as the progesterone level became elevated (Fig. 19). The other more subtle change in the early luteal phase was the appearance of a bimodal pattern of LH secretion with large, infrequent pulses of >15 mIU/ml amplitude being interspersed with pulses of amplitudes <5 mIU/ml. Often these smaller LH pulses appeared to follow closely after the larger ones. Also, the plasma progesterone secretion

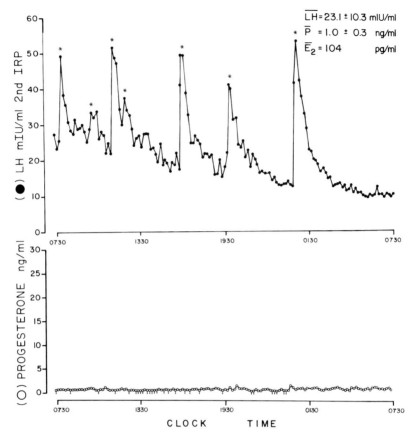

FIG. 19. LH and progesterone secretory patterns in the early luteal phase (LH surge + 1) of a normal female. Note the progressive slowing of the LH secretory pattern over 24 hours as well as the bimodal distribution of LH pulse amplitude. Serum progesterone is secreted in a tonic fashion during the early luteal phase.

appeared constant at a low level of secretion during the early luteal phase with no apparent relationship to the appearance of either the large or the small LH pulses. By the midluteal phase all of the changes in the gonadotropin secretion pattern seen in the early luteal phase became exaggerated. The LH pulse slowing (Fig. 20) became more marked, the bimodal LH pulse distribution was more apparent with the smaller LH pulses now compromising nearly 50% of all pulses, and their association with the descending shoulder of the larger LH pulses was particularly evident. The pattern of progesterone secretion in the midluteal phase was also quite different, with the appearance of pulsatile progesterone secretion (Fig.

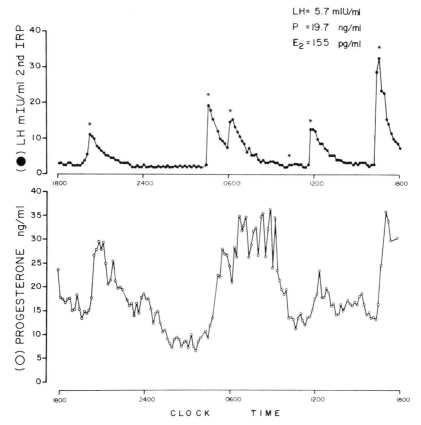

FIG. 20. LH and progesterone secretory pulses of a normal female in the mid luteal phase of the cycle (LH +8). Observe the progressive slowing of LH pulse frequency and the appearance of pulsatile progesterone secretion from the corpus luteum. Reprinted from Filicori *et al.* (43) with permission.

20), which bore a one-to-one correspondence to the LH pulses. In fact, it became apparent that the majority of the smaller LH pulses occurred at the time of the peak progesterone levels which followed the larger LH pulses. The cross-correlation of these small LH pulses with the ambient progesterone level was highly significant (Fig. 21) while this observation was not true for the larger LH pulses (43).

By the end of the luteal phase (Fig. 22), the LH pulse frequency continued to slow until there was only one or two larger LH pulses apparent during a 24-hour period. However, the pulsatile secretion of progesterone persisted into the late luteal phase albeit at a lower level. Finally, a single

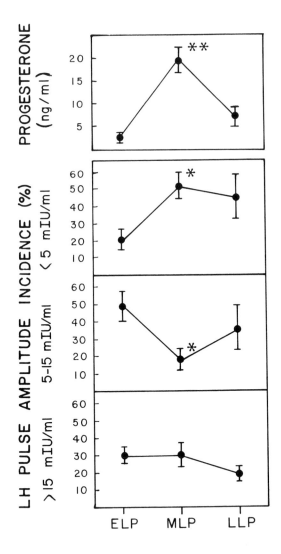

STAGE OF LUTEAL PHASE

FIG. 21. Changes in LH pulse amplitude distribution across the human luteal phase.
The changes in concentration of plasma P are shown in the upper panel. The relative
incidences of LH pulses of different amplitudes (<5 mIU/ml, 5–15 mIU/ml, >15 mIU/ml)
are shown in the lower three panels. The incidence of LH pulses of smaller amplitude (<5
mIU/ml) significantly increases from the ELP to the MLP, while at the same time the
incidence of intermediate size LH pulses (5–15 mIU/ml) decreases significantly, the parallel
with the increment in plasma P concentration. All values are expressed as mean ± SE.
*$p < 0.05$; **$p < 0.01$. Reprinted from Filicori *et al.* (43) with permission.

subject was studied during the transition from the late luteal to the early follicular phase. She demonstrated the change from the low amplitude LH pulses seen at the end of the luteal phase in the first 12 hours of her study, to the more regular, higher amplitude pattern of the early follicular phase. Also of interest was the reappearance of the sleep-associated suspension of LH pulsatility observed only in the early follicular phase of the cycle. This subject experienced the onset of her menstrual flow midway into her 24 hour study.

The progression of changes in the amplitude and frequency of GnRH-induced gonadotropin pulsations throughout the human menstrual cycle is portrayed in Fig. 23 and Table III. The amplitude of the LH pulsations initially falls from the early to the midfollicular phase only to become elevated again by the late follicular phase. The amplitude of LH pulsa-

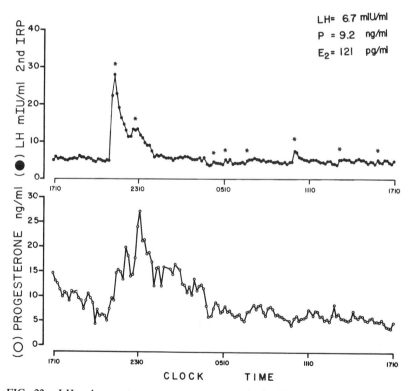

FIG. 22. LH and progesterone secretory pattern obtained in a woman in the late luteal phase of the cycle (LH + 10). Note the further slowing of the LH pulse pattern, the emergence of smaller, more frequent LH pulses, and the persistance of pulsatile progesterone secretion. Reprinted from Filicori *et al.* (43) with permission.

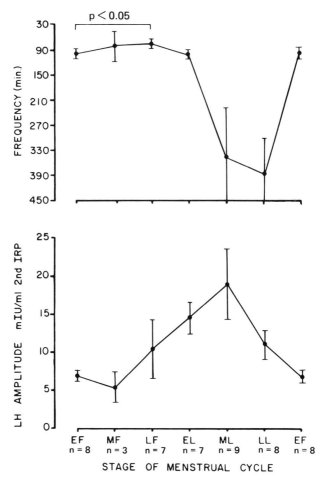

FIG. 23.   A summary of frequency and amplitude of episodic gonadotropin release over the normal menstrual cycle.

tions then becomes bimodal following ovulation, but the mean amplitude continues to rise in the early luteal phase to a peak by the midluteal phase, following which it declines to a nadir by the time of menstruation. The frequency of GnRH secretion, as determined by LH pulsations, increases significantly from the early to the late follicular phase of the cycle in parallel with the rising serum estradiol level. As progesterone secretion from the corpus luteum appears, there is a marked and progressive decrease in the LH pulse frequency which continues across the luteal phase, with the degree of slowing correlating well with the duration of exposure

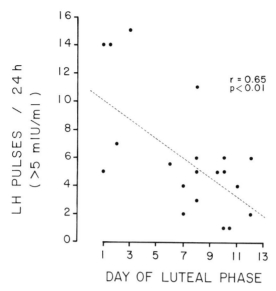

FIG. 24. Patterns of LH pulse amplitude and frequency modulation of the human luteal phase. The LH pulse frequency is negatively correlated with the day of the luteal phase when the 24-hour frequent sampling was performed.

of the hypothalamic-pituitary axis to progesterone (Fig. 24) but not with the ambient level of progesterone. On the other hand, the smaller LH pulses appear predominantly when the ambient progesterone level is high (i.e., immediately following the large LH pulses), correlate quite closely with the acute progesterone level (cf. Fig. 21), and exhibit no relationship to the duration of progesterone exposure.

Thus, estrogen appears to exert its primary effect upon the hypothalamic–pituitary axis by modulating the anterior pituitary responsiveness to GnRH through negative followed by positive feedback. However, there also appears to be a secondary effect of estrogen to increase the frequency of GnRH-induced gonadotropin pulsations. Whether this latter effect is primarily due to an increase in GnRH pulse frequency occurring at the level of the hypothalamus or a facilitated expression of GnRH pulses at the level of the anterior pituitary cannot be distinguished in the intact human. Progesterone, on the other hand, appears to mediate its primary neuroendocrine effects by slowing the frequency of LH pulses and thus appears to act upon the hypothalamic frequency of GnRH discharge. However, the appearance of the correlation of the LH pulses of smaller amplitude with the ambient level of progesterone raises the question of whether or not progesterone also has a secondary direct pituitary effect upon LH pulse amplitude.

B.   ABNORMALITIES OF GnRH SECRETION IN THE FEMALE

Having completed a detailed examination of the normal changes of frequency and amplitude in the human menstrual cycle, we next turned our attention to the study of hypogonadotropic states in the female. This group of disorders, termed hypothalamic amenorrhea by Albright and his colleagues, has proven to be a perplexing and heterogeneous group of disorders to most clinicians. The varied association of this condition with disorders of nutrition, exercise, and stress represents several clinical settings in which these conditions frequently occur. In addition, the gonadotropin levels of females with hypothalamic amenorrhea, whether determined by random sampling on a baseline evaluation (44), short-term studies employing more frequent sampling (45), or following the diagnostic administration of GnRH (44,46), have proven perplexing in their wide ranges. Similarly, the responses of these patients to diagnostic maneuvers such as progestin-induced withdrawal bleeding or clomiphene administration have proven similarly heterogeneous (44–47). Perhaps most distressing to the patients is their variable responsiveness to the therapeutic uses of clomiphene (47) and Pergonal (48).

On the assumption that these disorders represent a spectrum of GnRH deficiencies similar to that encountered in the male, we have examined 40 patients with hypogonadotropic hypogonadism. Nineteen of these patients had primary amenorrhea and thus had been previously classified as idiopathic hypogonadotropic hypogonadism (IHH). The remaining 21 patients had experienced loss of menstruation following menarche and were considered to exhibit hypothalamic amenorrhea (HA). Each patient had experienced amenorrhea for at least 6 months, had received no hormonal medications for 6 months prior to study, and gave no history of excessive exercise. On physical examination each patient had a body weight which was greater than the 15th percentile of normal, no evidence of galactorrhea or hirsutism, and a normal pelvic examination. Their laboratory evaluation revealed a normal serum prolactin, thyroid function tests, and adrenal androgens in each case. The hypogonadism of these patients was associated with low or normal serum gonadotropins in each case.

Following this baseline evaluation, the patients were admitted to our Clinical Research Center for a period of 12–24 hours of frequent blood sampling at 10–20 minute intervals. Each evaluation included a period of nocturnal sampling during which sleep was visually monitored. A spectrum of abnormal patterns of GnRH secretion similar to that observed in

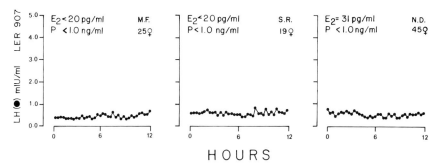

FIG. 25. Apulsatile pattern of LH secretion in women with hypogonadotrophic hypogonadism and hypothalamic amenorrhea.

IHH males was encountered. Figure 25 demonstrates a subset of female hypogonadotropic patients with an apulsatile pattern of GnRH-induced gonadotropin secretion. In each case these patients had very low estradiol levels, did not exhibit withdrawal bleeding following progestin administration, and were uniformly unresponsive to clomiphene when this agent was administered. Figure 26 portrays a second pattern which was observed, consisting of the onset or augmentation of GnRH secretion during sleep. Since this pattern was never encountered in the normal menstrual cycle patients and has previously been associated with puberty (31), this pattern was referred to as a developmental arrest. A third pattern of gonadotropin secretion was identified in which a disorder of the amplitude of LH pulsations could be discerned. These abnormalities of pulse amplitude were defined in those patients in whom both mean levels and ampli-

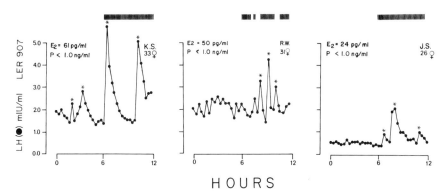

FIG. 26. A sleep-entrained pattern of LH pulse secretion in females with hypogonadotropic amenorrhea.

tude of LH pulsations GnRH fell below our previously established range of normal. Figure 27 demonstrates another group of patients in whom LH pulsations were observed at a frequency which was inappropriately slow for the early follicular phase, the stage of the cycle that these amenorrheic subjects were presumably experiencing as determined by their gonadal steroid pattern. The frequency of gonadotropin release seen in this abnormal frequency subset was quite similar to that observed in the luteal phase of normal cycling women. However, none of the amenorrheic subjects exhibited evidence of recent ovulation or corpus luteum function.

Perhaps the most interesting finding of hypogonadotropic hypogonadism in the female is the fact that these abnormalities of GnRH-induced gonadotropin secretion can change within a given patient over time. Figure 34 demonstrates a woman (KG) who was studied three times over the course of 1 year during which she suffered from persistent hypothalamic amenorrhea. The patient had not had any menstrual periods for several years prior to these studies. When she was studied on each of the three occasions, her LH secretory pattern differed markedly (Fig. 28). During the first period of study, the amplitude and frequency of her gonadotropin release appeared nearly normal, yet was presumably sufficiently aberrant to be unable to sustain folliculogenesis. In the second study 7 months later, she demonstrated a different pattern of GnRH secretion in which high, infrequent LH pulsations appearing quite similar to patients in the early luteal phase were observed. Finally, in her third study 2 months later, she had a single large LH peak reminiscent of the LH pulse pattern seen in the mid- to late-luteal phase of normal ovulatory women. However, no spontaneous ovulation or corpus luteum formation had occurred between any of these studies as demonstrated by her persistent early follicular phase levels of gonadal steroids and amenorrhea. The similarities of her patterns to those of the normal are also portrayed in Fig. 28. The LH secretory patterns of three patients selected from the normal menstrual cycle study are contrasted with the patterns of patient KG with hypothalamic amenorrhea. This figure underscores the subtlety of the abnormalities existing in patients with hypothalamic amenorrhea in that such patients are incapable of ripening a follicle and ovulating during a period of time in which their LH secretory patterns may be quite close to those encountered by normal women during an ovulatory menstrual cycle. It appears that the female gonad is intolerant of any deviations from the usual progression of amplitude and frequency changes of GnRH-induced gonadotropin secretion which must occur in the normal menstrual cycle, and amenorrhea ensues when this pattern is disordered. Such a patient also serves to demonstrate the variability which can occur both within and between patients with hypothalamic amenorrhea and thus

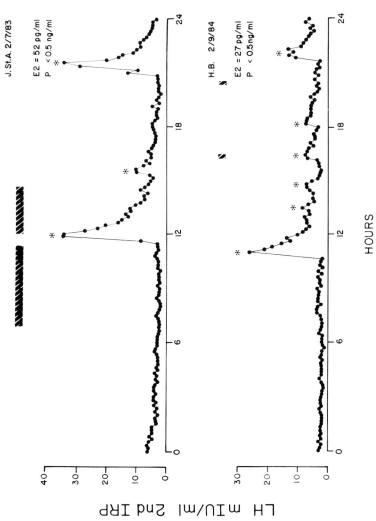

FIG. 27.   Defects in the frequency of LH secretion episodes in subjects with hypothalamic amenorrhea.

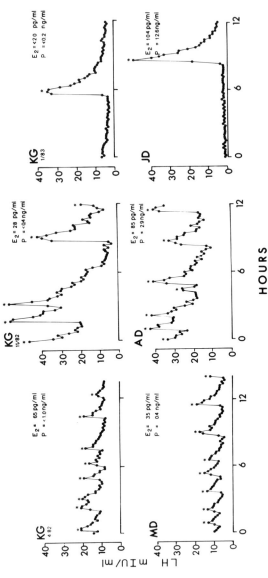

FIG. 28. Serial studies in one patient with hypothalamic amenorrhea (KG) indicating a spectrum of defeats of amplitude and frequency of GnRH secretion during three separate 12 hour pulsation studies. The lower three panels represent three women studied at various stages of a normal ovulatory menstrual cycle indicating the similarity of patterns of patients with hypothalamic amenorrhea and normals.

helps to account for some of the clinical and biochemical heterogeneity encountered in this disorder.

C. GnRH-INDUCED RESTORATION OF OVULATION IN IHH FEMALES

Having determined the spectrum of baseline abnormalities of GnRH secretion in these hypogonadotropic patients, we then attempted to induce ovulation in them employing our physiologically based frequency program (Fig. 29). This figure demonstrates the results of our normal menstrual cycle study of 62 cycles and portrays the mean values (±SE) of

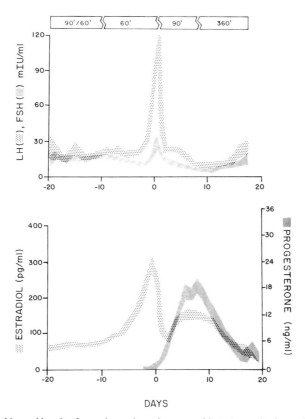

FIG. 29.   Normal levels of gonadotropin and sex steroids (±1 standard error) observed in 62 normal women studied throughout the menstrual cycle. The frequencies of GnRH secretion are indicated at the top of the panel and were employed in all attempts to induce ovulation in hypogonadotropic subjects.

gonadotropin and sex steroids. The frequency of GnRH-induced gonadotropin pulsations which we have observed across the menstrual cycle is
shown at the top of this figure and represents the frequency of exogenous
GnRH which we employed. Having chosen these frequencies of GnRH
administration, we next examined the effect of the dose of GnRH upon
the amplitude of the pituitary response and its ensuing gonadal effects.
Twenty-five nanograms per kilogram represents a dose of GnRH which
we have previously employed to induce ovulation in Kallmann's syndrome (9) and one which has proven similarly successful in IHH men (10).
A second dose of 100 ng/kg was also administered for purposes of comparison. All doses were administered intravenously.

Seventeen patients with hypothalamic amenorrhea or IHH underwent
24 cycles of GnRH replacement ($n = 11$ at 25 ng/kg; $n = 13$ at 100 ng/kg).
Overall results of these studies which indicate that only 80% of the patients responded to 25 ng/kg of GnRH. Follicles which were ripened at
this dose were invariably single follicles. However, the peak estradiol
levels achieved in the late follicular phase and the subsequent area under
the progesterone curve of the ensuing corpus luteum (cf. Fig. 30) were
statistically lower than the normals. Therefore, 25 ng/kg appears to represent a threshold dose of GnRH for treatment of the hypogonadotropic
female. On the other hand, 100 ng/kg proved uniformly successful in
inducing ovulation in GnRH deficient subjects. However, frequently two
or more follicles were documented by ultrasound at midcycle on this dose
of GnRH. This finding was reflected in the statistically higher estradiol
levels achieved in the late follicular phase when compared with those
which occurred in the normal menstrual cycle. Similarly, progesterone
elevations in the luteal phase of the 100 ng/kg cycles, as measured by the
area under the curve, were significantly higher than those encountered in
both the normal menstrual cycle and those which occurred on the 25 ng/
kg dose. The mechanisms of this exuberant response with 100 ng/kg as
compared to the threshold response with 25 ng/kg may reflect the degree
to which FSH stimulation occurs in the early follicular phase (cf. Fig. 31).
On the 25 ng/kg dose, early follicular phase FSH levels were less than
normals or 100 ng/kg cycles; the rate of FSH rise appeared slower than
the 100 ng/kg cycles; and this delay appeared to translate into more variable follicular development with a subsequently inadequate corpus luteum. The 100 ng/kg dose demonstrated a rapid rise in the serum FSH to
levels which were, although in the normal range, slightly high and greater
than those achieved by the 25 ng/kg dose.

These results indicate that slightly excessive doses of GnRH can override the normal negative feedback mechanisms of estradiol upon the pituitary since the late follicular phase FSH levels on the 100 ng/kg cycles

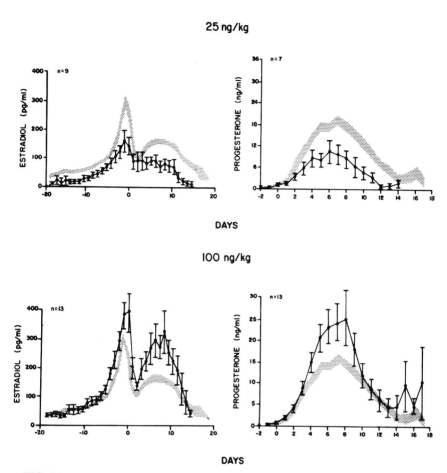

FIG. 30. Results of ovulation induction employing a physiologic frequency of GnRH administration to hypogonadotropic hypogonadal women: comparison of 25 versus 100 ng/ kg dose upon ovarian steroid secretion. Normal values are represented by shaded areas as presented in Fig. 29.

were maintained within the low normal range, which is particularly note-worthy given the higher than normal levels of circulating estradiol which occurred at this time. Moreover, this finding indicates that if the dose of GnRH is not controlled, it may well be possible to induce the ripening of multiple follicles. Recognition of this feature may be helpful in the utiliza-tion of pulsatile GnRH for *in vitro* fertilization programs. However, it should be noted that in the 100 ng/kg cycles, estradiol levels increased significantly above the normal range in the late follicular phase and a

25 ng/kg

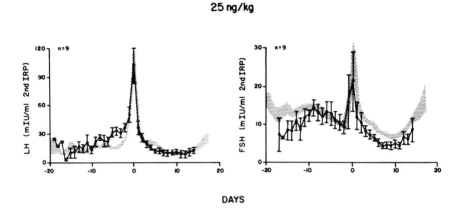

DAYS

100 ng/kg

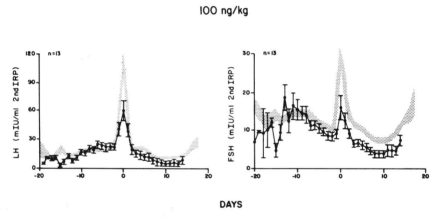

DAYS

FIG. 31. Results of ovulation induction employing a physiologic frequency of GnRH administration to hypogonadotropic hypogonadal women: comparison of 25 versus 100 ng/kg dose upon serum gonadotropin levels. Normal values are represented by shaded areas as presented in Fig. 29.

corresponding blunting of the subsequent LH surge occurred. This observation suggests that the addition of hCG may be required to rupture these multiple follicles if higher levels of estradiol are achieved with larger GnRH doses and further blunting of the LH surge. The possibility of achieving multiple gestations with GnRH certainly exists and may be slightly higher than that occurring within the normal population. In fact,

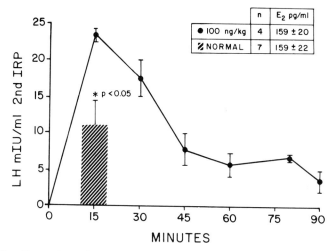

	n	E₂ pg/ml
● 100 ng/kg	4	159 ± 20
▨ NORMAL	7	159 ± 22

FIG. 32. Comparison of mean LH pulse contour (± SE) in women undergoing GnRH replacement with a 100 ng/kg dose versus the normal LH pulse amplitude determined in the late follicular phase. Subjects were matched for the level of follicular development as indicated by mean estradiol values (± 1 SE).

we have already experienced one twin pregnancy out of seven to date on the 100 ng/kg dose of GnRH.

To evaluate the possible mechanisms by which GnRH produced a relatively attenuated or augmented recapitulation of the normal menstrual cycle, we next examined the "microenvironment" of pulsatile hormone release which ensued with either the 25 or 100 ng/kg doses. Since the pattern of GnRH secretion varies from day to day across the menstrual cycle, it was much more difficult to make such comparisons in the female than it was in the male. In each circumstance, subjects were selected from the normal menstrual cycle study who were at a similar stage of their menstrual cycle as our "experimental" group as attested to by equivalent gonadal steroid levels. In the luteal phase of the cycle the control subjects and patients were matched for both estradiol and progesterone levels. The contour of the spontaneous LH pulses occurring in the normal subjects was compared to the GnRH-induced pulses of the hypogonadotropic women undergoing ovulation induction. The 100 ng/kg dose of GnRH produced LH pulses of a significantly greater amplitude than those which occurred in the normal menstrual cycle at a point of equivalent gonadal maturation (cf. Fig. 32). Thus, this comparison of the pulse dynamics of intravenous GnRH administration confirms the earlier ultrasonic and go-

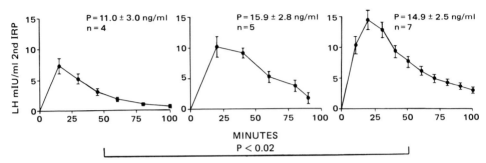

FIG. 33. Comparison of mean LH pulse contour (± SE) in women undergoing GnRH replacement with 25 ng/kg (left) and 100 ng/kg doses. The right panel indicated the mean LH pulse contour spontaneously generated by normal women at the same stage of the luteal phase of their menstrual cycles. Subjects were matched for gonadal steroid levels (mean ± 1 SE).

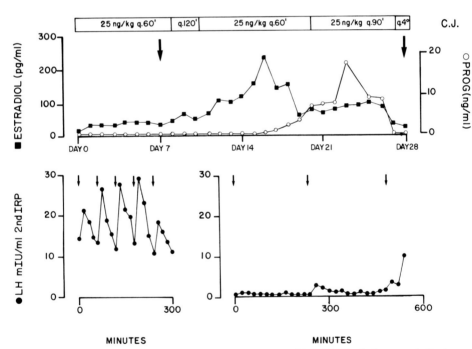

FIG. 34. Results of ovulation induction in a subject with IHH. The dark arrows indicate two 8 hour studies in which the pituitary responsiveness to a fixed dose of GnRH in the mid follicular and late luteal phases was examined. Note the decreasing pituitary responsiveness to GnRH observed in the late luteal phase. This patient exhibited an apulsatile pattern of LH release prior to induction of ovulation. The estradiol levels in the two studies are equivalent.

nadal steroid findings suggesting that 100 ng/kg represents a slightly excessive dose of GnRH than that which is normally present during the follicular phase of the cycle. Furthermore, comparison of the gonadotropin and sex steroid levels across the follicular phase of the induced cycles with the normals suggests that both negative and positive feedback of estradiol can be expressed without any changes in the quantity of GnRH administration.

When similar comparisons of the amplitude of LH pulses occurring in normals were made to those achieved with these two doses of GnRH given in the luteal phase, yet another difference became apparent (Fig. 33). Neither 25 nor 100 ng/kg of GnRH produced LH pulse amplitudes equivalent to those which occurred in the luteal phase of normal subjects. Thus it appears that a significantly greater quantity of endogenous GnRH is secreted during the luteal phase than in the follicular phase

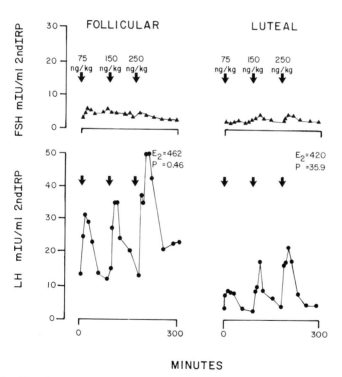

MINUTES

FIG. 35. The dose response relationship of GnRH and LH secretion observed in a hypogonadotropic woman without any evidence of endogenous pulses prior to therapy. Note the markedly attenuated dose response curve observed in the luteal phase. The serum estradiol levels in the two studies are comparable.

of the normal menstrual cycle. This finding was initially suggested by the appearance of the large amplitude, i.e., >15 mIU/ml, LH pulses observed in the normal luteal phase. Furthermore, none of our studies of GnRH administration in IHH subjects has precisely mimicked the pattern of large and small LH pulses occurring in the normal luteal phase, suggesting that we have not yet been able to reproduce the pattern of endogenous GnRH secretion which occurs at this stage of the cycle.

A direct pituitary effect of progesterone in the human is indicated by the fact that higher luteal phase doses of GnRH are required to achieve LH pulse amplitudes similar to normals. An example of this finding can be seen in Fig. 34, in which a patient's pituitary responsiveness following an identical dose of GnRH administered in the follicular and luteal phases was compared. As can be seen, the amplitude of the pituitary responses to this fixed dose of GnRH is markedly blunted in the luteal phase despite the presence of levels of estradiol equivalent to those encountered during the follicular phase. Since progesterone is the only variable, it appears to be exerting a direct pituitary effect, blunting the LH responsiveness to GnRH in the luteal phase. This observation has been confirmed by dose–response testing performed in both the early follicular and late luteal phases of the cycle of IHH patients as demonstrated in Fig. 35. In this patient, whose estradiol levels were equivalent in each circumstance, there is a marked blunting of the dose–response curve in the luteal phase of the menstrual cycle. These findings confirm the presence of a direct pituitary effect of progesterone and may in part explain the heterogeneity of pulses previously encountered in the luteal phase of the normal menstrual cycle.

IX. Summary

The study of the physiology of GnRH in the intact human requires several complimentary approaches. Comprehensive evaluation of endogenous LH secretion in normal subjects affords the opportunity to establish a minimum physiologic frequency of GnRH secretion. This, in turn, can be used to construct a physiologically based frequency program of GnRH replacement which can then be employed in subjects with defects of endogenous GnRH secretion to restore normal pituitary and gonadal relationships. These experiments of GnRH physiology provide valuable information regarding the range of changes in the amplitude and frequency of GnRH secretion which demarcate the boundary of normal from abnormal reproductive states. Comparing baseline study of these abnormal states with a replacement program of GnRH which continually avails itself of a broad normative data base provides the best approach to the study of GnRH physiology in the human. Such an approach maximizes our understanding of both normal and abnormal GnRH secretion. In addition to providing new treatments for various reproductive disorders, this physiologic perspective provides powerful insights into the neuroendocrine control of reproductive processes in the human.

ACKNOWLEDGMENTS

The authors acknowledge their gratitude to the able nursing staff of the Massachusetts General Hospital Clinical Research Center without whom such studies would have been impossible; to Steven Trigilio, Donna Beardsworth, Judith Donnelly, Jan Campbell, Birgit Keller, and A. Raechel Katzin whose technical assistance and organization were invaluable; and to Nancy Delaney-Perry and Jacquelyn Donnelly for their expert typing.

REFERENCES

1. Arimura, A., Kastin, A. J., Gonzalez-Barcena, D., Siller, J., Weaver, R. E., and Schally, A. V. (1974). *Clin. Endocrinol* **3**, 421.
2. Pimstone, B., Epstein, S., Hamilton, S. M., Le Roith, D., and Hendricks, S. (1977). *J. Clin. Endocrinol. Metab.* **44**, 356.
3. Barron, J. L., Millar, R. P., and Searle, D. (1982). *J. Clin. Endocrinol. Metab.* **54**, 1169.
4. Karsch, F. J., *Physiologist* **28**, 23.
5. Knobil, E. (1980). *Recent Prog. Hormone Res.* **36**, 53.
6. Belchetz, P. E., Plant, T. M., Nakai, Y., Keogh, E. J., and Knobil, E. (1978). *Science* **202**, 631.
7. Wildt, L., Marshall, G., and Knobil, E. (1980). *Science* **207**, 1373.
8. Leyendecker, G., Wildt, L., and Hansmann, M. (1980). *J. Clin. Endocrinol. Metab.* **51**, 1214.
9. Crowley, W. F., and McArthur, J. W. (1980). *J. Clin. Endocrinol. Metab.* **51**, 173.
10. Hoffmann, A. R., and Crowley, W. F. (1982). *N. Engl. J. Med.* **307**, 1237.
11. Yen, S. S. C., Tsai, C. C., Naftolin, F., Vandenberg, G., and Ajabor, L. (1972). *J. Clin. Endocrinol. Metab.* **34**, 671.
12. Santen, R. J., and Bardin, C. W. (1973). *J. Clin. Invest.* **52**, 2617.
13. Filicori, M., Marseguerra, M., Mimmi, P., Bolelli, F., Franceschetti, F., Possati, G., and Flamigni, C. (1982). *In* "The Gonadotropins: Basic Science and Clinical Aspects in Females" (C. Flamigni and J. R. Givens, eds.), pp. 365–375. Academic Press, London.
14. Brody, S. A., McAtee, N. M., Wachter, K. W., Merriam, G. R., and Loriaux, D. L. (1982). *Clin. Res.* **30**, 684A.
15. Bachstrom, C. T., McNeilly, A. S., Leask, R. M., and Baird, D. T. (1982). *Clin. Endocrinol.* **17**, 29.
16. Liu, J. H., and Yen, S. S. C. (1983). *J. Clin. Endocrinol. Metab.* **57**, 797.
17. Carmel, P. W., Araki, S., and Ferin, M. (1976). *Endocrinology* **99**, 243.
18. Antunes, J. L., Carmel, P. W., Housepian, D. M., and Ferin, M. (1978). *J. Neurosurg.* **49**, 382.
19. Corley, K. P., Valk, T. M., Kelch, R. P., and Marshall, J. C. (1981). *Pediatr. Res.* **15**, 157.
20. Merriam, G. R., and Wachter, K. W. (1982). *Am. J. Physiol.* **243**, E310.

21. Kallmann, F. J., Schonfeld, W. A., and Barrora, S. E. (1944). *Am. J. Mental. Def.* **48**, 203.
22. Boyar, R. M., Finkelstein, J. W., Witkin, M., Kapen, S., Weitzman, E., and Hellman, L. (1973). *J. Clin. Endocrinol. Metab.* **36**, 64.
23. Santen, R. J., and Paulsen, C. A. (1973). *J. Clin. Endocrinol. Metab.* **36**, 55.
24. Boyar, R. M., Wu, R. H. K., Kapen, S., Hellman, L., Weitzman, E. D., and Finkelstein, J. W. (1976). *J. Clin. Endocrinol. Metab.* **43**, 1268.
25. Hamilton, C. R., Henkin, R. I., Weir, G., and Kliman, B. (1973). *Ann. Intern. Med.* **78**, 47.
26. Bell, J., Spitz, I., Slonim, A., Perlman, A., Segal, S., Palti, Z., and Rabinowitz, D. (1973). *J. Clin. Endocrinol. Metab.* **36**, 791.
27. Spitz, I., Rosen, C., Bell, J., Ben-David, M., Palishuk, W., and Rabinowitz, D. (1974). *N. Engl. J. Med.* **290**, 10.
28. Lieblich, J. M., Rogol, A. D., White, B. J., and Rosen, S. W. (1982). *Am. J. Med.* **73**, 506.
29. Santen, R. J., and Paulsen, C. A. (1973). *J. Clin. Endocrinol. Metab.* **36**, 47.
30. Ewer, R. W. (1968). *J. Clin. Endocrinol.* **28**, 783.
31. Boyar, R. M., Rosenfeld, R. S., Kapen, S. *et al.* (1974). *J. Clin. Invest.* **54**, 609.
32. Nankin, H. R., and Troen, P. (1971). *J. Clin. Endocrinol. Metab.* **33**, 558.
33. Matsumoto, A. M., and Bremner, W. J. (1984). *J. Clin. Endocrinol. Metab.* **58**, 609.
34. Winters, S. J., and Troen, P. A. (1983). *J. Clin. Endocrinol. Metab.* **57**, 432.
35. Kourides, I. A., Weintraub, B. C., Ridgway, E. C., and Maloof, F. (1975). *J. Clin. Endocrinol. Metab.* **40**, 842.
36. Kourides, I. A., Weintraub, B. C., Re, R. N., Ridgway, E. C., and Maloof, F. (1978). *Clin. Endocrinol.* **9**, 535.
37. Kourides, I. A., Re, R. N., Weintraub, B. D., Ridgway, E. C., and Maloof, F. (1977). *J. Clin. Invest.* **59**, 508.
38. Hagen, C., and McNeilly, A. S. (1975). *J. Clin. Endocrinol. Metab.* **41**, 455.
39. Edmonds, M., Molitch, M., Pierce, J. G., and Odell, W. D. (1975). *J. Clin. Endocrinol. Metab.* **41**, 551.
40. Sargent, D. W. (1963). *Am. J. Clin. Nutr.* **13**, 318.
41. Hoff, J. D., Quigley, M. E., and Yen, S. S. C. (1983). *J. Clin. Endocrinol. Metab.* **57**, 792.
42. Healy, D. L., Schenken, R. S., Lynch, A., Williams, R. F., and Hodgen, G. D. (1984). *Fertil. Steril.* **41**, 114.
43. Filicori, M., Butler, J., and Crowley, W. F. (1984). *J. Clin. Invest.* **73**, 1638.
44. Aono, T., Minagawa, J., Kinogasa, T., Miyake, A., and Kurachi, K. (1973). *Am. J. Obstet. Gynecol.* **119**, 740.
45. Kletzky, O. A., Davajan, V., Nakamura, R. M., and Mishell, D. R. (1975). *J. Clin. Endocrinol. Metab.* **41**, 660.
46. Shearman, R. P., and Frasier, I. S. (1977). *Lancet* **1**, 1195.
47. Shaw, R. W. (1982). *Clin. Reprod. Fertil.* **1**, 219.
48. Oelsner, G., Serr, D. M., Mashiach, S., Blankstein, J., Snyder, M., and Lunenfeld, B. (1978). *Fertil. Steril.* **30**, 538.

DISCUSSION

J. D. Veldhuis: That was an outstanding presentation and right on the cutting edge of this field. I wonder if I might make a comment and ask a somewhat related question. The increase in immunoactive LH pulse frequency and some of the changes in LH pulse amplitude that you've observed in relation to various stages of the menstrual cycle are, of course, also recognized in relation to bioactive luteinizing hormone, as assessed by Dr. Dufau, Beitins, and ourselves (Veldhuis, J. D., Beitins, I. Z., Johnson, M. L., Serabian, M. A., and Dufau, M. L. *J. Clin. Endocrinol. Metab.* **58,** 1050, 1984). I think this is somewhat important in that there are conditions under which there is some discrepancy between the immunoactive measurements and their bioactivity.

The question I have relates to the interesting problem you've raised about the possibility that "blocked pulses" exist. This is a particularly contemporary and timely question that is going to be a bit hard to resolve for the following couple of reasons about which I'd like your further comments.

First, it's unclear to me that there's adequate mathematical modeling at the moment to define the expected concordance when two series of endocrine pulses are being studied. In other words, what is the exact probability of a given degree of concordance between a series of pulses of hormone A and a second series of pulses of hormone B? The second problem which occurs in relation to understanding whether blocked pulses really occur is that we need some clear assessment of the exact type 1 and 2 statistical errors inherent in pulse analysis. That is under what condition are we missing pulses (false negatives) and identifying pulses inappropriately (false positives). Also, under what condition are we identifying them appropriately? The third issue relates to whether or not one is measuring the bioactive or immunoactive constituent in blood. It's conceivable that some of these ostensibly blocked pulses are really the failure of one assay system to corroborate a biological response.

W. F. Crowley: I think those are all excellent points. The methods which we've chosen to relate one series of endocrine events to another is time series and cross-correlation analysis. These techniques give you a rough idea if series A and series B are mathematically related. They also permit one to phase shift the temporal sequence and reanalyze their association repeatedly. This method appears to us to be the best currently available. I would also say that in relation to your third point, the bio versus immunoactive hormone, we have measured both in several of these circumstances, and confirm your results that there are changes in both assays across the menstrual cycle. Finally, I would agree that there are a lot of methodologic problems in this field. I think that is why we've taken the approach of attempting to restore the normal physiology with the data derived from our pulsatile analysis. It seems to us that this technique puts your methods to the most rigorous test. Then even though you may have some of those errors of pulse analysis enrolled in your program these can't be major if they can prove capable of restoring pituitary and gonadal function totally to normal.

M. Thorner: That was a beautiful presentation. I just have a couple of questions. The first relates to the LH and progesterone pulses during the luteal phase. Looking at the slides today, it seems that the really large progesterone pulses were concordant with such enormous LH pulses that do not require any programs to identify them and I really wonder whether you ever get those large LH pulses without a progesterone pulse. Second, you said that sometimes you thought the small LH pulses were correlated with the changes in progesterone but that at other times this was difficult to observe.

W. F. Crowley: First of all, almost all of what we call the major LH secretory episodes generally seemed to be associated with a shift in the progesterone level. However, we have examined only the representative patients at each stage of the luteal phase because we simply don't have enough sample volume to assay in many of the patients studied. However, most of the major secretory episodes appear to be translated at the level of the corpus luteum into episodes of progesterone secretion. From the point of view of the little pulses, their association with high ambient serum progesterone levels is only evident when you use cross-correlation analysis. It was this correlation, however, which first gave us the idea that the very high progesterone levels might well be blunting smaller GnRH boluses from the hypothalamus at the level of the pituitary. Initially, there were numerous other explanations, but that is why we went on to examine the pituitary responsiveness to constant and varied GnRH doses in the follicular and luteal phases with matched estrogens to show more clearly that progesterone does have a direct pituitary effect.

M. Thorner: The second question was to ask you to try to speculate. I was very impressed that when you gave the higher frequency of GnRH to the male patients you observed an increase in LH level and you tended to lose the pulsatility and yet the testosterone surprisingly seemed to be if anything higher. So if that is the case, what is the role of pulses of LH in the male?

W. F. Crowley: We have repeatedly observed that in certain circumstances where it is LH that is needed, it is pulsatile LH delivery which is required. However, at the level of the gonad this observation has yet to undergo rigorous testing. It is interesting that Dr. Payne's presentation gives some evidence in favor of an intermittency of hormone delivery at the gonadal level in that you need to clear out with cytochrome P-45 enzyme of all those false substrates for it to function properly. Thus this observation could support a gonadal requirement for pulsatility. On the other hand, hCG appears to cause a normal Leydig cell secretion of testosterone. I do wonder however if the mechanisms by which hCG or these continuous LHRH administrations resulted in normal testosterone secretion isn't really an exercise in desensitization, not only at the pituitary level which can clearly sustain an infeebled but present LH release but also at the gonadal level where testosterone secretion is being sustained but not by the normal physiologic mechanisms. You know that as you administer hCG, which is another way of sustaining LH secretion, the serum hCG levels remain very high and Leydig cell testosterone secretion occurs but testosterone levels eventually lag long before the serum hCG levels fall. Thus, I suspect that desensitization, or giving more and getting less, winds up being the explanation for the testosterone levels during these maneuvers but that is pure speculation—which is what you requested.

N. Samaan: In the family pedigree you showed with the male with Kallmann's syndrome, it seemd that all the affected members were males. Do you have any explanation why females were not affected?

W. F. Crowley: That is generally true of most of the previous genetic trees of Kallmann's syndrome that have been studied. It seems that a marked variability of phenotypic expression exists and that males generally tend to be more frequently affected than females. If one looks in the literature, you can find affected females in a Kallmann's family, but often it will be only a partial defect in that the patient will be anosmic but have normal fertility. On the other hand, if you look at the females who are completely affected, i.e., with total anosmia and primary amenorrhea, almost all of those case histories are isolated and appear to occur spontaneously without a positive family history. I have no explanation for the marked preference for the full-blown expression of this gene in males.

N. Samaan: In the female, did you find the anosmia as predominant as you find in the male, because I have two female patients but they don't have anosmia.

W. F. Crowley: I don't know what the significance of the anosmia is but I will bet that it is significant. There is some histochemical evidence showing that GnRH is present in the olfactory lobes as well as in other areas of the brain, so I suspect that the level of GnRH deficiency and anosmia may well be pointing to a more profound genetic defect in these anosmic patients. We've tried very carefully to reconstruct the temporal lobes by CT scanning to see if the correlation of anosmia and complete absence of the olfactory lobes is total but the resolution of our CT scanner was insufficient to permit this reconstruction.

K. Sterling: Obviously, in previous times, women afflicted with Kallmann's syndrome have rarely, if ever reproduced, which has an obvious effect on family trees. I want to give you a compliment; although I was fortunate to have known Franz Kallmann, Fuller Albright, Harry Klinefelter, and Robert Boyar, I never really understood the facts of life until now. One of the things I used to kid Boyar about concerned these LH pulses, particularly during sleep; I said Bob, it's because these pulses are evoked by erotic dreams. Now I noticed that your one woman with the very high sleep-related peaks woke up twice during maximal peaks. In all seriousness, do you think there could be a relation between LH peaks and dreams?

W. F. Crowley: I don't know any relationship between GnRH secretion and dreams. In previous studies correlating LH pulses with stages of sleep and rapid eye movement, there has been none. We have not performed electroencephalographic monitoring in any of our studies.

E. Knobil: Those are magnificent data, and I'm sure the best extant at the moment. We owe you a great debt of gratitude for them. My first comment relates to the rise in FSH during the latter portions of the luteal phase, and its underlying mechanisms. As you may recall we showed in our lesioned monkey model that reduction in the frequency of administered GnRH pulses to lesioned-castrated animals is associated with a rise in FSH and a fall in LH levels. Thus we thought here was the answer to the problem. However, on further study we found that in a series of cycles induced by an unvarying frequency of exogenous GnRH in either stalk-sectioned or hypothalamic lesion animals, we also saw the very same rise in FSH in the late luteal phase of the cycle in the absence of any change in GnRH pulse frequency. Clearly, this rise is unrelated to GnRH frequency, and thus we were forced to the conclusion that this is a result of some interaction between the ovary and the pituitary. Perhaps inhibin may play a role in this story.

My second comment relates to the results you obtained in IHH males when you increased the frequency of exogenous GnRH and found that the pituitary became "nervous" or "jittery." Again, we had a very similar experience in the female monkeys. We had shown that in ovariectomized animals, if you increase the frequency of exogenous GnRH from physiologic to even twice that (i.e., from one pulse per hour to two pulses per hour), then their production of FSH and LH would decline and a very clear desensitization of the pituitary became evident. When we increased the frequency of GnRH even further this became more dramatic and equal to the responses to continuous GnRH infusion. When we repeated these experiments in animals with intact ovaries, we were surprised to find that where we expected a fall in gonadotropins there was actually a rise, but this rise was very erratic. The results were crazy and we never published these findings because we couldn't fit them into any physiologic schema. It occurred to us that we were putting the GnRH into the peripheral circulation as you did with your patients rather than via the physiologic route of local application to the pituitary by way of the pituitary-portal circulation. Thus we may have created a situation where we desensitized the gonad by exposing it directly to huge quantities of GnRH which it normally never sees and that we were actually seeing the results of episodic ovariectomies. Lastly, I think you know that our studies in lesioned animals and stalk-sectioned rhesus monkeys have led us to the conclusion that the preovulatory LH surge is initiated by a direct action of the rising tide of estrogen associated with follicular maturation directly on the pituitary gland in a normal physiologic environment which demands adequate ambient levels and patterns of GnRH. You indicated in your interpretation of your own magnificent data that the LH surge is caused by a combination of increased amplitudes and increased frequency. I wonder if you could put this into some mechanistic context for me. Exactly what do you mean by that? How does that work?

W. F. Crowley: I think that your first point in terms of this FSH rise from mid to late luteal phase is very interesting. It's difficult to account for these changes just by frequency alone as it occurs even in the absence of any change in GnRH frequency during induced cycles. It's one of the most interesting examples of preferential secretion of FSH and my thoughts have evolved very similarly to yours. It must be related to the waning levels of gonadal secretions in the cycles where GnRH frequency is held constant. On the other hand, as the GnRH frequency is declining across the luteal phase of spontaneous cycles, the slowed GnRH stimulation may also play a role in the selective FSH rise observed in this setting.

In relation to your second question about pituitary desensitization, we've made the same observation in the human. If you attempt to induce pituitary desensitization in the absence of gonadal steroids, it's much easier to do and much more complete than when steroids are present. I don't know why that is, but some of the studies in lower animals would suggest that the concentration of GnRH receptors on the pituitary membrane may be affected by gonadal steroids. It may well be that in certain experimental settings you're dancing on the line of pituitary desensitization and when sex steroids are present it's a much more complex situation than when they're absent.

In relation to your third question that you asked in terms of frequency and amplitude of GnRH of the mid cycle, it's quite clear from your studies and from studies that we've done that one need not increase the frequency of administered GnRH at mid cycle to get an LH surge. We have induced ovulation in Kallmann's women with a fixed 2 hour frequency of GnRH administration. However, I'm not sure whether the normal LH surge in this setting may be due to the fact that the GnRH doses used are totally physiologic or slightly excessive, or that a small amount of endogenous GnRH is still present in very low quantities, but in the presence of a maximally sensitized pituitary either of these factors may account for the presence of the LH surge following discontinuation of exogenous GnRH. It's just that when you look at the amplitude of each pulse in the late follicular phase and you sum them, you don't equal the magnitude of an entire LH surge. Consequently, our feeling is there has to be something else operating to create the surge. Thus, I believe it's not only when you increase the LH amplitude, but also when you bring the individual LH pulses a little closer together that you get the additive effect that's present in the LH surge naturally. However, this added factor is clearly not necessary when you induce ovulation. You can achieve the same results in the induced cycles by a fixed frequency of GnRH in combination with a primed pituitary in that circumstance. Thus it's a fine line between the normal physiology of endogenous GnRH secretion and the phenomenology of the exogenous replacement schedule and these are very subtle differences.

E. Knobil: I would just like to press on a little further. By physiology, I understand mechanism. How does Mother Nature construct the control system so that it actually works? Have you or anyone else seen pulses superimposed upon the surge? I vaguely recall, but I can't quote the chapter and verse, unfortunately, that this finding has been described in experimental animals and in the human. Now if that is indeed true, if you can see pulses superimposed upon the surge, this would imply that the surge is not an accumulation of, or a piling up of individual pulses, and it would sort of support the idea that the pulses are there and superimposed upon a separate release mechanism where estrogen may be thought of as being gonadotropin-releasing factor in its own light in this physiologic circumstance.

W. F. Crowley: Actually, we'd like to sample a little more frequently at the mid cycle surge, but we haven't as yet.

J. Weisz: I would like if I may to shift the discussion from the role of GnRH in the adult to that in the developing organism. When you were at Hershey a few years ago we discussed the possibility of taking advantage of the male patients with isolated GnRH deficiency to study some important unresolved questions concerning sexual differentiation of the brain in the human. In experimental animals, masculinization and defeminization of the sexually dimorphic CNS-mediated functions occur after completion of masculinization of the urogenital ridge and at a time when the fetal testes have already come under the influence and have established a feedback relationship with the hypothalamic–pituitary axis. This is likely to be the case also in the human. Moreover, this period of approximately 100 days after birth in the human male when testosterone levels are markedly elevated, which presumably depends on GnRH-mediated LH release. The patients with isolated GnRH deficiency could therefore provide a unique opportunity, by nature's experiment, for finding out what the role of the testosterone secretion due to stimulation of fetal and neonatal testes by the developing organism might be in psychosexual differentiation. I wonder what success you have had and what progress you have made in this area?

W. F. Crowley: I worked with a neurologist, Dan Hier, evaluating spatial ability, which is one of the things that's been reported to be an index in the human of sexual differentiation of the brain. Initially, Dr. Hier noticed that our IHH men were very verbal, in that many of them could speak two or three languages. As this was an interesting occurrence and they were presumably GnRH deficient during the period you alluded to, we wondered about their spacial ability as an index of the masculinization of their cerebral cortex. We eventually studied 19 of these IHH men and chose appropriate controls. In other words the IHH patients who had not had the neonatal and pubertal surge of testosterone were compared to control subjects in whom only the pubertal surge of testosterone and not the neonatal surge was absent, i.e., craniopharyngioma and peripubertal pituitary tumors. The statistical differences between these groups was impressive and we published these findings (Hier, D. G., and Crowley, W., *N. Engl. J. Med.*). I have never received so much mail and negative comments, not about the data but about the highly charged area of sex steroids on the brain claiming that our markers were far too imprecise. As Dr. Hier has now relocated, we've not pursued this study any further but I was struck by how similar these findings were to yours and others who have examined the effects of early exposure of sex steroids upon the brain.

J. Weisz: I appreciate the difficulties you have had. This is a surprisingly emotionally charged subject. May I suggest, however, that you do not give up and perhaps enlist the help of some veterans in the field, such as for example Dr. Anka Erhardt? My second question relates to the male patient you have shown with the variable testosterone levels, the enuchoid habitat and with excellent breast development. Do you have any idea what the gynecomastia could be due to in that case? Could it be, perhaps, that there is excessive aromatization in the target cells, or in the breast tissue, and perhaps even in the CNS?

W. F. Crowley: The patient's estrogens were normal all the way through the studies and so we hypothesized that the excessive breast development in this patient is probably one of the clinical expressions of his abnormal androgen–estrogen ratios in that the estrogens by and large were normal while his testosterone levels varied from normal to low levels. If you pool the bloods from those studies the testosterone–estrogen ratio of this patient was low.

D. L. Vogel: From your description, it sounded as though at least one of your patients had the fertile eunuch variant of hypogonadotropic hypogonadism and I'm curious as to whether or not you looked at that subset specifically at pulsatility and responses to exogenous GnRH?

W. F. Crowley: By and large the group that had some endogenous LH pulses tended to have larger testes and represented the fertile eunuch end of the clinical spectrum of hypogonadotropic hypogonadism. They all responded quite briskly and completely to exogenous GnRH administration.

Neurohormones from Fish Tails: The Caudal Neurosecretory System
I. "Urophysiology" and the Caudal Neurosecretory System of Fishes

Howard A. Bern, David Pearson,* Brett A. Larson, and Richard S. Nishioka

*Department of Zoology and Cancer Research Laboratory, University of California, Berkeley, California, and *Department of Biology, California State University, Los Angeles, California*

I. Introduction

Although the existence of the terminal organ of the caudal neurosecretory system in teleosts—the urophysis—has been known for more than 150 years since Weber (1827) first identified the structure in the carp, it was not until the middle 1950s that Enami (1959) defined the system by recognizing the connection of secretory neurons in the caudal spinal cord of fishes (Speidel, 1919, 1922) with the urophysis, a neurohemal organ whose functional morphology is much like that of the neural lobe of the hypophysis (Fig. 1). In fact, Enami's concept of a caudal neurosecretory system followed closely upon Bargmann's concept of the hypothalamo-neurohypophysial neurosecretory system. A urophysis as such does not exist in fish groups other than teleosts, but ganoid and elasmobranch fishes possess diffuse neurohemal areas on the ventral surface of the posterior spinal cord to which large caudal neurosecretory neurons project (cf. Fridberg and Bern, 1968).

The caudal system in teleosts is heavily innervated, consistently by aminergic input and occasionally by cholinergic and peptidergic pathways from the brain (cf. Gauthier *et al.*, 1983; Kriebel *et al.*, 1985). Local synaptic circuitry is also indicated. The complexity and intensity of the innervation alone bespeak some important physiological role for this system; yet, it is surprising how difficult it has been to ascribe a definite functional contribution to the caudal system and its hormones—the urotensins. The urophysis contains and presumably releases a variety of substances:

533

1. Urotensin I—a 41-amino acid peptide which is homologous and analogous to mammalian CRFs (cf. Lederis *et al.*, this volume).

2. Urotensin II—a 12-amino acid peptide which is partially homologous and partially analogous to somatostatin-14 (Fig. 2).

3. Urotensin IV—indistinguishable from arginine vasotocin and present in only a few teleost species (Lacanilao and Bern, 1972).

4. Urophysins—putative carrier proteins, cysteine-free, analogous to the neurophysins and with unknown biogenetic relationships to the urotensins (Berlind *et al.*, 1972; Moore *et al.*, 1975; cf. Bern and Lederis, 1978).

5. Acetylcholine—the highest concentrations of this substance reported for any tissue but of unknown significance in this locale (Ichikawa, 1978).

There is no reason why additional principles may not exist in the caudal system, and from time to time experimental data indicating the possible existence of other urotensins emerge and in some cases are still being examined.

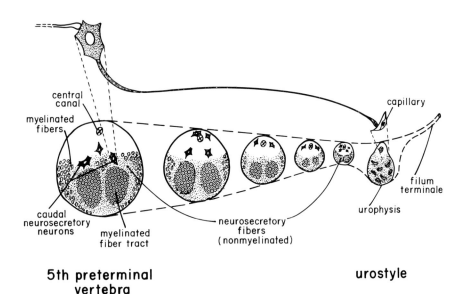

5th preterminal   **urostyle**
vertebra

FIG. 1. Diagram of caudal spinal cord and urophysis of the gobiid teleost *Gillichthys mirabilis* (long-jawed mudsucker), showing several transverse sections. The two types of caudal neurosecretory neurons (formerly called Dahlgren cells) are indicated (stippled, CRF/U_I reactive cells; solid, CRF/U_I and U_{II} reactive cells) (see Section III,B). Above the spinal cord is the diagram of a single caudal neurosecretory neuron showing its innervation from the brain and its axonal projection to a urophysial capillary.

Despite the elusiveness of the system to physiological delineation, the present paper and that by Lederis *et al.* in this volume attempt to describe some likely functions for the major caudal neurohormones: urotensins I and II.

II. Chemistry of Urotensin II

Urotensin II (U_{II}) was the first of the urophysial principles to be characterized biologically (Bern *et al.*, 1967) and sequenced (Pearson *et al.*, 1980). U_{II} is a dodecapeptide which is partially homologous to somatostatin-14, despite the different location and significance of the cysteinyl residues (Fig. 2). Disulfide bond reduction of somatostatin does not affect its biological activity, whereas it destroys the activity of U_{II} in the standard bioassays (trout bladder-contracting, trout posterior intestine-contracting) (cf. Lederis *et al.*, 1971). In somatostatin, the phenylalanyl residues apparently serve to maintain the central cyclic structure in the same fashion as is accomplished by the cysteinyl residues in urotensin II (Pearson *et al.*, 1980). U_{II} was isolated and sequenced from the urophysis of the gobiid teleost *Gillichthys mirabilis* (long-jawed mudsucker) (Pearson *et al.*, 1980); two different urotensins II are present in the teleost *Catosto-*

```
                                    5              1 0
SOMATOSTATIN-14  Ala-Gly-Cys-Lys-Asn-Phe-Phe-Trp-Lys-Thr-Phe-Thr-Ser-Cys
                                    - - - - - - - - - - - - -

GOBY   U II       Ala-Gly-Thr-Ala-Asp-Cys-Phe-Trp-Lys-Tyr-Cys-Val

SUCKER  U II_A    Gly-Ser-Gly-Ala-Asp-                      -Val

SUCKER  U II_B    Gly-Ser-Asn-Thr-Glu-                      -Val

CARP  U II_α      Gly-Gly-Gly-Ala-Asp-                      -Val

CARP  U II_β1     Gly-Gly-Asn-Thr-Glu-                      -Val

CARP  U II_β2     Gly-Ser-Asn-Thr-Glu-                      -Val

CARP  U II_γ      Gly-Gly-Gly-Ala-Asp-                      -Ile
```

FIG. 2. Amino acid sequences of somatostatin and urotensins II. Residues 6–10 are identical in all urotensins II so far sequenced [cf. Pearson *et al.* (1980); McMaster and Lederis (1983); Ichikawa *et al.* (1984)].

mus commersoni (white sucker) (McMaster and Lederis, 1983); four urotensins II are found in the teleost *Cyprinus carpio* (carp), one of which is
identical with one of the sucker urotensins II (Ichikawa *et al.*, 1984). This
represents a total of six different urotensins II from only three species of
teleost fish (Fig. 2). Interpretation of the significance of such molecular
diversity is challenging from both an evolutionary and a physiological
point of view.

All U_{II} molecules so far sequenced are cyclic dodecapeptides with six
identical residues in the disulfide-bonded ring. Substitutions occur at
other positions. The proposal (Ichikawa *et al.*, 1984) that there may be
two series of urotensin II peptides differing in biological activity: one with
Ala^4–Asp^5 and one with Asn^3–Thr^4–Glu^5, awaits adequate biological testing (cf. Ichikawa, 1985). *Gillichthys* U_{II} would belong to the former series.
It appears that all carp urotensins II occur in an individual urophysis
(Lederis, 1984).

III. Immunochemical Studies

A. DEVELOPMENT OF ANTISERA TO UROTENSIN II

Antisera to *Gillichthys* urotensin II were generated in male New
Zealand White rabbits using synthetic peptide (Clark *et al.*, 1982) coupled
to keyhole limpet hemocyanin. Inoculation was initiated with 10 intra-
dermal injections, each containing conjugate equivalent to 10 μg U_{II} in
Freund's complete adjuvant. Boosts of antigenic equivalent were given at
monthly intervals thereafter. Serum collected at monthly intervals was
screened for specific binding with iodinated synthetic U_{II}. In order to
assure high specific radioactivity of the tracer, HPLC purification was
used, in addition to chromatography on Sephadex G-10-120. This effectively removed all noniodinated U_{II} from the U_{II}. Specific binding of U_{II}
was observed in sera from 2 of 7 animals after 8 weeks, and in 4 of 7 after
12 weeks. The remaining rabbits did not respond after 5 months.

A radioimmunoassay (RIA) for urotensin II was developed using a
specific rabbit antiserum at a dilution of 1 : 12,000. Assays were carried
out in a total volume of 200 μl using 0.1 M phosphate buffer (pH 7.2) as
the diluent and 8,000 to 10,000 cpm of iodinated U_{II}. In order to minimize
adsorption of peptide to surfaces, 1 mg/ml bovine serum albumin was
added to all solutions. After equilibration for 24 hours at 4°C, unbound
peptide was precipitated with activated charcoal and centrifuged for 5
minutes at 15,000 g. The supernatant liquid was aspirated, and the charcoal pellets were counted.

The effective quantitative range of the RIA was 1 to 400 pg U_{II}/tube.

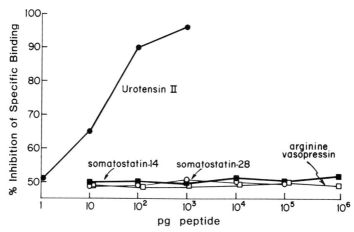

FIG. 3.   Specificity of antiserum (10-6/12) to synthetic *Gillichthys* urotensin II. Note lack of cross-reaction with somatostatins and arginine vasopressin (see text).

The following peptides were tested for cross-reactivity with U_{II} antisera (Fig. 3): somatostatin-14, somatostatin-28, arginine vasopressin, arginine vasotocin, oxytocin, neurotensin, substance P, vasoactive intestinal peptide, and corticotropin-releasing factor. None of these peptides showed competition for U_{II} binding when added in amounts as high as 1 μg. Figure 3 illustrates the specificity of the antiserum used in subsequent experiments and in immunocytochemical studies. It has not yet been possible to do RIA on blood samples because of the presence of an unknown interfering factor in the blood.

The RIA has been used to quantify the U_{II} content of tissues and of hormone released *in vitro*. In a preliminary experiment, the acetone-dried brain, anterior spinal cord, and posterior spinal cord from two *Gillichthys mirabilis* were homogenized in 0.25% acetic acid, heated in a boiling water bath for 3 minutes, and centrifuged for 5 minutes at 15,000 g. RIA of the supernatants showed 8 ng U_{II} in the posterior spinal cord, and no detectable amounts (i.e., <0.004 ng) in the anterior cord or brain. A series of experiments was carried out in which freshly dissected posterior spinal cord was assayed as individual vertebral segments. The samples were prepared as described for the acetone-dried tissues. Table I summarizes experiments in which tissues from 8 *Gillichthys* (BW 24 ± 1 g) were assayed individually in triplicate.

Release of U_{II} in response to potassium depolarization was measured in explants of the *Gillichthys* caudal neurosecretory complex which had been maintained in organ culture for 24 hours. Groups of three explants

TABLE I

Distribution of Urotensin II (U_{II}) in the Caudal Spinal Cord of Gillichthys (Radioimmunoassay)

Region	ng U_{II} (mean ± SEM)
Urophysis	3085 ± 531
Caudal spinal cord region	
Terminal vertebra (urostyle)	1.21 ± 0.15
1st preterminal vertebra	6.23 ± 0.48
2nd preterminal vertebra	4.31 ± 1.10
3rd preterminal vertebra	0.61 ± 0.19
4th preterminal vertebra	0.010 ± 0.002
5th preterminal vertebra	<0.004
Noncaudal spinal cord	<0.004
Brain	<0.004

were incubated for 5-minute periods in Dulbecco's modified Eagle's medium (DMEM) or in a similar medium in which sodium was replaced with potassium to a concentration of 56 mM. During incubation in normal DMEM, 4–7 ng U_{II} were released/explant/5-minute period. Incubation in medium containing depolarizing concentrations of K^+ resulted in a 5- to 7-fold increase in U_{II} released. After preincubation with calcium-free medium, a calcium-free potassium stimulus caused no significant increase in U_{II} release. Readdition of calcium restored potassium-stimulated release.

B. IMMUNOCYTOCHEMISTRY OF THE CAUDAL NEUROSECRETORY SYSTEM

The presence of at least two neurosecretory cell types in the fish caudal neurosecretory system has been postulated based on differential staining reactions, size and density of elementary granules in the axon terminals, electrophysiological responses to osmotic changes, and neural input (cf. Chan and Bern, 1976; Kriebel et al., 1985). It was assumed that one cell type might produce urotensin I (U_I) and the other U_{II}.

The first immunocytochemical localization of a peptide in the caudal neurosecretory system employed an antiserum to the frog skin peptide, sauvagine, that presumably cross-reacted with U_I (Renda et al., 1982). Sauvagine-like immunoreactivity was found in caudal neurons of various sizes, in axons, and in the urophysis. These results led to the prediction that sauvagine and U_I might have a similar structure which was later verified by an almost 50% sequence homology between the two peptides (cf. Lederis et al., this volume). Whether all neurosecretory cells were immunoreactive and the possibility of separate cell populations were not addressed, possibly because of variability in the extent of staining in individual fish.

Recent findings by Fisher *et al.* (1984) have cast doubt upon the two-cell hypothesis. Using a specific U_I antiserum for immunocytochemistry, all the neurons in the caudal neurosecretory system of the sucker (*Catostomus commersoni*) were U_I reactive. However, these investigators suggest that a separate functional subpopulation of U_I-reactive neurons composed of small bipolar cells dorsal to the urophysis may exist and feed back on the larger, more anteriorly located caudal cells. In contrast, employing an antiserum raised to ovine corticotropin-releasing factor (CRF) that cross-reacts with U_I in the catfish (*Ictalurus punctatus*), Onstott and Elde (1984) found that all caudal neurosecretory cells displayed immunofluorescence except for the majority of smaller, more rounded cells immediately rostral to the urophysis. These nonreactive cells could correspond to the subpopulation described by Fisher *et al.* (1984), and Onstott and Elde speculate that they may secrete U_{II}. Immunostaining with CRF antiserum has also been reported in the caudal neurosecretory system of poeciliids, but again the total extent of reactivity and the question of separate cell populations were not discussed (Kriebel *et al.*, 1985). The localization of U_{II} to particular cells has not been reported. Owada *et al.* (1985) have examined a series of fish with *Gillichthys* U_{II} antiserum; the carp and several other teleost species possess U_{II}-immunoreactive and U_{II}-immunonegative cells.

In an attempt to resolve the distribution of U_I and U_{II} cells, we used antisera to CRF (Immuno Nuclear, Stillwater MN) and to U_{II} (see above) and indirect immunofluorescence on the posterior spinal cord and urophysis of the goby (*Gillichthys mirabilis*) (Fig. 1). Tissues were fixed in 4% freshly depolymerized paraformaldehyde in phosphate buffer (0.13 M, pH 7.4) overnight. Serial cryostat sections (10 and 16 μm) were treated alternately with either an antiserum raised against synthetic *Gillichthys* U_{II} (1:50 and 1:200) or an antiserum to ovine CRF (1:100 and 1:500). Anti-CRF serum was used instead of antiserum to U_I owing to the ready availability of the former; the high degree of sequence similarity of the two peptides underlies the evident cross-reactivity.

All identifiable neurosecretory neurons, as well as nerve fibers and the urophysis, specifically reacted for CRF/U_I but with varied intensity (Figs. 1 and 4). Preabsorption of anti-CRF serum with 10 μM synthetic U_I or CRF eliminated the specific staining, whereas prior incubation with 10 μM sauvagine had no effect. Some CRF/U_I-positive neurons also stained for U_{II} (Fig. 4). The U_{II}-reactive cells were generally less reactive for CRF/U_I. The U_{II} staining was eliminated by prior incubation of anti-U_{II} serum with 10 μM *Gillichthys* U_{II}, but not with 10 μM somatostatin-14.

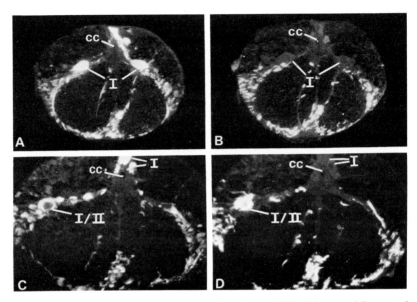

FIG. 4.   Indirect fluorescence immunocytochemistry of *Gillichthys mirabilis* posterior spinal cord. Serial cross-sections (10 μm) located in the central region of the caudal neurosecretory system at the level of approximately the third preterminal vertebra were incubated overnight with either anti-CRF or anti-U$_{II}$ followed by fluorescein-conjugated sheep antirabbit IgG (1 : 40) for 2 hours and were photographed using a Zeiss epifluorescence system. Dorsally located immunoreactive cell bodies and more ventrally situated fibers surrounding the bilateral bundles of myelinated fiber tracts are evident. A and B are a pair of consecutive sections: (A) treated with anti-CRF serum (1 : 100); (B) treated with anti-U$_{II}$ serum (1 : 50). Note the two CRF/U$_I$-immunoreactive cell bodies (I) in A which are not U$_{II}$-immunoreactive in B; these are examples of the CRF/U$_I$ neuron type. C and D are another pair of consecutive sections: (C) treated with anti-CRF serum (1 : 100); (D) treated with anti-U$_{II}$ serum (1 : 50). Note the cell (I/II) which stains with both antisera; this is an example of the CRF/U$_I$ and U$_{II}$ neuron type. I indicates portions of CRF/U$_I$ cell bodies nonreactive to anti-U$_{II}$ in D. cc, Central canal. A and B, ×115; C and D = ×160.

The U$_{II}$ immunostaining was present in cells and fibers at various locations anterior and dorsal to the urophysis and in both large and small neurons. The number of neurons with only CRF/U$_I$- like immunoreactivity exceeded those with both CRF/U$_I$- and U$_{II}$-like immunoreactivity. The existence of neurosecretory cells staining only for U$_{II}$ or for neither peptide has not been established.

To investigate further these possibilities and substantiate the results with serial sections, we have begun double immunofluorescence experiments on single sections. The IgG fraction of the anti-U$_{II}$ serum was purified and covalently linked to biotin (Wofsy, 1980). Biotinylated anti-U$_{II}$ (1:2) and anti-CRF serum (1:100) were applied simultaneously to *Gillichthys* spinal cord sections followed by a mixture of avidin conjugated to rhodamine isothiocyanate (12.5 μg/ml) and fluorescein-conjugated sheep anti-rabbit IgG (1:80). Neurons exhibiting only fluorescein fluorescence (indicating anti-CRF binding) as well as neurons showing both fluorescein and rhodamine fluorescence (CRF/U_I + U_{II} neurons) are present. A refinement of this technique using sequential application of the anti-CRF and anti-IgG fluorescein conjugate followed by the biotinylated anti-U_{II} and avidin conjugate eliminates cross-reactivity problems and yields the same results.

Thus, at least two populations of neurons exist in the *Gillichthys* caudal neurosecretory system: (1) CRF/U_I cells and (2) cells immunoreactive for both CRF/U_I and U_{II}. Although two neurosecretory cell types are present, the simple suggestion of separate U_I- and U_{II}-producing cells does not appear to be valid in this fish. Because of their differences in location and size, the U_{II}-positive cells in *Gillichthys* do not appear to correspond to the subpopulation described by Fisher *et al.* (1984) for *Catostomus*. It is difficult to assess whether there may be an additional analogous subpopulation in *Gillichthys*. The apparent variability in immunoreactivity of the caudal neurosecretory system in different species raises the specter of potential species differences. The resolution of this problem will require additional studies, with antisera specific for U_I as well as for U_{II}.

In the meantime, the presence of U_I-like material and U_{II}-like material in the same neuron raises the possibility that both of these bioactive neuropeptides could represent different fragments of the same preprohormone which may be processed differently in two neurosecretory neuron populations.

IV. Biological Activities of Urotensin II in Teleosts

A. VASOPRESSOR AND SPASMOGENIC EFFECTS

One of the earliest effects described for urotensin II was its vasoactivity in teleost fishes (Bern *et al.*, 1967; Chan *et al.*, 1969). Urotensin II is pressor and secondarily diuretic in teleosts (Chan, 1975). Vascular responses to this peptide, however, show both regional and species specificity (Muramatsu and Kobayashi, 1979). Furthermore, the vasoconstrictor action reflects a general spasmogenic activity of urotensin II, which has now been demonstrated for the urinary bladder (trout) (Lederis, 1970a), the posterior intestine (trout) (Zelnik and Lederis, 1973; Chan *et al.*, 1978), the oviduct and ovary (guppy) (Lederis, 1970b), the sperm duct (mudsucker) (Berlind, 1972), and the caudal lymph heart (eel) (Chan, 1971). In view of the existence of the system, and of urotensin II in elasmobranch and ganoid fishes (Bern *et al.*, 1973), it is surprising that we have no information on the actions of urotensin II on smooth muscle in these forms.

B. HYPOPHYSIOTROPIC EFFECTS

Using a partially purified preparation of *Gillichthys* urotensin II, Grau *et al.* (1982) demonstrated the comparable ability of urotensin II and of somatostatin-14 to inhibit prolactin secretion by tilapia prolactin cells [incubated rostral pars distalis (RPD) of the hypophysis] *in vitro*. Recently, evidence for two separate prolactins (20 and 24 kDa) has been obtained in tilapia (Specker *et al.*, 1985). Rivas *et al.* (1984) have demonstrated inhibition of both of these prolactins using synthetic urotensin II. Inasmuch as the tilapia pituitary lacks dopaminergic innervation of its prolactin cells, the nature of the inhibitory innervation to these cells remained unknown. Both somatostatin and its partial analogue urotensin II were candidate factors. Immunocytochemical studies indicate that the fibers projecting to the RPD in tilapia are somatostatinergic (Grau *et al.*, 1983), and that somatostatin, at least in this species, is a peptide prolactin-inhibitory factor (PIF). In the goby, which also lacks aminergic innervation of the RPD, the fibers are neither somatostatin-immunoreactive nor urotensin II-immunoreactive. However, both of these peptides remain as candidate PIFs for other species of fish, and conceivably for other vertebrates.

There is a need to investigate the action of U_{II} on the secretion of other hormones in teleost fish and in other vertebrates. In mammals, U_{II} apparently has no hypophysiotropic action (cf. Lederis, 1984).

C. OSMOREGULATORY EFFECTS

A persistent theme regarding the possible function of the caudal neurosecretory system concerns its relationship to osmo-ionoregulation (cf. Bern and Nishioka, 1979). The early data largely involved histological and cytological changes in the system as a result of osmotic stress or salinity transfer. In addition, changes in electrophysiological responses of the caudal neurons, in bioassayable hormone content, and in urophysin content measured after polyacrylamide gel electrophoresis, also indicated possible responses to alterations in hydromineral metabolism. In some species, urophysectomy leads to changes suggestive of osmoregulatory insufficiency, and administration of urophysial extracts/homogenates results in alterations in blood ion levels. Despite all this information (Bern

TABLE II

Effects of Urotensins on Transepithelial Transport in Teleost Fishes

Transport site	U_{II} Effect	U_1 Effect	Reference
Goby skin (SW)[a]	Inhibits active Cl efflux	Stimulates active Cl efflux	Marshall and Bern (1979, 1981)
Tilapia opercular membrane (a model for the gill) (SW)	Inhibits active Cl efflux	Inhibits active Cl efflux (?)	Foskett and Hubbard (1981); Loretz et al. (1982)
Goby urinary bladder (SW)	Stimulates active Na absorption	[Stimulates active Na absorption]	Loretz and Bern (1982); Loretz et al. (1982)
Tilapia anterior intestine	Stimulates water and NaCl absorption (SW)	Inhibits water and NaCl absorption (FW)	Mainoya and Bern (1982, 1984)
Goby posterior intestine (5% SW)	Stimulates active NaCl absorption		Loretz et al. (1983)

[a] SW, Seawater; FW, fresh water.

and Nishioka, 1979, Tables 1 and 2), albeit of varying degrees of reliability, until recently no convincing picture of a urophysis-osmoregulation relationship had emerged.

In updating and reassessing the potential role of urotensins in osmotic and ionic changes, it is necessary to recognize that there are at least three major ways in which these neuropeptides could intervene in a physiologically meaningful manner. First, by virtue of its vasopressor activity, urotensin II may regulate the blood flow to a variety of osmoregulatory surfaces and thus influence the rate in which ions and water can be absorbed or excreted. As indicated above, increase in glomerular filtration rate ensues as a consequence of vasoconstriction, leading to a secondary diuresis in fish injected with urotensin II.

Second, the hypophysiotropic effects of urotensins in fish are well established. Euryhaline teleosts are considered to depend primarily upon cortisol, the major secretory product of the adrenocortical homolog, the interrenal, for hyperosmotic regulation (adaptation to seawater), and upon prolactin for hypoosmotic regulation (adaptation to fresh water) (cf. Loretz and Bern, 1982). The inherent CRF activity of urotensin I makes its hypophysiotropic involvement a strong probability (Fryer and Lederis,

1985; Woo *et al.*, 1985; see Lederis *et al.*, this volume); the somatostatin-like inhibitory action of urotensin II on prolactin secretion makes its hypophysiotropic action at least a possibility.

Third, a series of studies indicate the ability of urotensins to modulate transepithelial transport directly across a variety of osmoregulatory surfaces. Active transport of Na^+ and of Cl^- and movement of water are altered by direct application of urotensins I and II to membranes maintained in Ussing chambers and studied by electrophysiological and isotope-flux methods and to incubated intestinal sacs studied gravimetrically and by absorption spectrophotometry of ions (cf. Loretz *et al.*, 1982).

Table II is a summary of the claims made for the direct effects of urotensins on transepithelial transport. Most of these studies were conducted with partially purified urotensin preparations; the effects of urotensin II have since been confirmed with synthetic *Gillichthys* urotensin II on the goby skin and bladder (C. Loretz, personal communication) and the current studies on the goby intestine (Loretz, 1985) involve only the synthetic peptide. Occasionally, the goby skin may prove refractory to urotensin II (J. Lindzey, unpublished data), raising questions about the possibility of seasonal variability and about the effects of prior environmental salinity changes on the responsiveness of this target organ. It is of great interest that the seawater goby urinary bladder initially shows high Na^+ transport activity; a period of around 4 hours is needed before this activity is reduced to baseline and the stimulatory effect of urotensin II can be demonstrated (cf. Loretz and Bern, 1981). Possibly this reflects strong binding of endogenous urotensin II to the bladder which must be dissociated before the effect of added urotensin II can be demonstrated.

An ability of U_I to act in the same manner as U_{II} on the goby urinary bladder is seen only when the amount of U_I used is ~ 100 times that of U_{II} (Loretz *et al.*, 1982). In any case, as there is no obvious chemical resemblance between U_{II} and U_I, this is a surprising finding. There is precedent for this action, however, inasmuch as U_I is also hypertensive (like U_{II}) in the eel when similarly high doses are administered (Chan, 1975). Like U_{II}, U_I may inhibit chloride extrusion across the tilapia opercular membrane, but not across the goby skin (cf. Loretz *et al.*, 1982; Marshall and Bern, 1981) where it acts oppositely to urotensin II and stimulates Cl excretion.

Figure 5 is an attempt to indicate the various pathways by which urotensins I and II may affect ion and water balance in various teleostean fishes. The urinary bladder as an extension of the collecting duct system of the kidney (it arises from the opisthonephric ducts) can be viewed as a membrane model of the kidney, and the opercular membrane, scaleless mucous membrane underlying the gill cover or operculum, as a model for the gill.

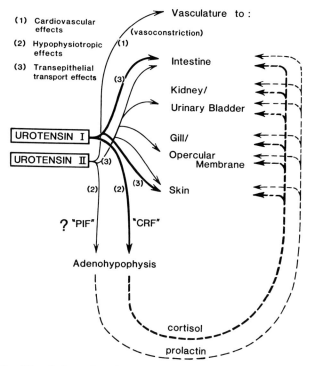

FIG. 5. Possible relations of caudal neurosecretory system to osmoregulation in teleost fishes. Effects of urotensins may be directly on transepithelial transport or indirectly through influences on vascular system and on adenohypophysial function.

D. OTHER PHYSIOLOGICAL EFFECTS

If urotensin I acts as a CRF in teleosts, then the cortisol which may be secreted as the result of stimulation of ACTH secretion, may have important metabolic effects related to gluconeogenesis (and hence to protein and fat metabolism). Other possible metabolic effects of urotensin I invite investigation. Urotensin II (and its partial analog somatostatin) both have lipolytic effects on the liver of coho salmon, resulting from increased triacylglycerol lipase activity and in increased nonesterified fatty acid release (Sheridan, *et al.*, 1985).

In the past (cf. Fridberg and Bern, 1968, Fig. 6), emphasis has been laid on the venous drainage of the urophysial region ultimately into the caudal vein and hence into the renal portal system. The implication that structures in the "renal field" would be the logical target organs for urotensin action suggested that the effects observed on intestine, gill, skin, and

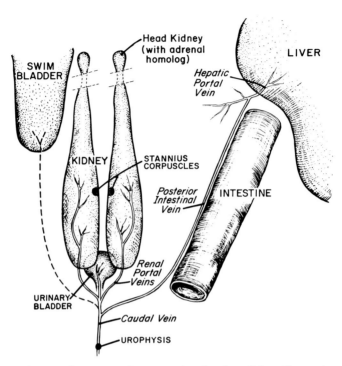

FIG. 6. Diagram of some vascular connections in teleost fishes. The renal portal veins carry urotensins to the "renal field" which includes the kidneys and the dorsum of the urinary bladder and possibly other tissues embedded in the kidney such as the calcium-regulating Stannius corpuscles and the juxtaglomerular cells. However, some branches of the caudal vein are known to bypass the kidneys and connect with the liver and probably the urinary bladder. Hemodynamic status of the posterior intestinal vein is such as to allow possible backflow of blood from the caudal vein into the intestinal wall. Hence, "direct" targets of urotensins could include the intestine, the liver, and the swim bladder, in addition to structures in the renal field.

pituitary might not have physiological meaning. However, information regarding branches from the renal portal system (caudal vein) to the liver via the posterior intestinal vein (Allen, 1905; Mott, 1950) and probably to the swim bladder of physoclist teleosts (Fänge, 1983) opens the possibility of relatively direct blood supply to targets other than those in the renal field. Figure 6 attempts to illustrate these possibilities, which include retrograde flow to the intestine via branches of the posterior intestinal vein (G. H. Satchell, personal communication). An occasional physiological observation may prove to be of more than heuristic significance as a consequence of recognizing these vascular pathways. Thus, the hyperglycemic effect of urophysial extracts in the snakehead fish (Woo *et al.*,

1980) could result from a direct effect on the liver (as well as a CRF-like action on the pituitary—see Lederis *et al.*, this volume). Roy (1975) has recorded a sensitization by urophysial extracts of swim bladder smooth muscle to acetylcholine.

The occurrence of specific binding of U_i and U_{II} to a variety of structures in the goldfish supports the possibility of various effects on metabolism and transport (Woo *et al.*, 1985; see Lederis *et al.*, this volume).

V.   Effects of Urotensin II in Mammals

The effects of urotensins in tetrapods have been reviewed recently (Larson *et al.*, 1985). In contrast to U_I, U_{II} has not been found to have much activity in mammalian systems (cf. Bern and Lederis, 1978; MacCannell and Lederis, 1983; Lederis, 1984). At least one report (Muramatsu *et al.*, 1979) has described a vasoconstrictor effect of U_{II} on the rat *in vivo* and on the rabbit dorsal aorta *in vitro*, but these results seemed to be contradicted by studies on rat blood vessels *in vitro* (Muramatsu *et al.*, 1981) and do not appear to have been pursued further. However, recently U_{II} has been found to be a potent relaxant of an unusual smooth muscle, the anococcygeus, in mice (Gibson *et al.*, 1984).

The anococcygeus muscle is a bilaterally paired, thin sheet of smooth muscle with a true tendinous origin on vertebral bone (cf. Gillespie, 1980). In the strains of mice examined by us, the major origin of the anococcygeus muscle was actually on the fused sacral vertebrae (Larson *et al.*, 1985). From these origins the muscle runs ventrocaudad around each side of the rectum to unite on its ventral aspect and insert close to the anal margin. Thus, a more appropriate name for the muscle, at least in these mice, is the *sacrorectal* muscle. Regardless of name, preparations of the anococcygeus muscle have been used extensively in pharmacological research, although the physiological function of the muscle remains unknown.

While searching for potential inhibitory neurotransmitters, three neuropeptides were found to relax carbachol-raised tone of isolated anococcygeus muscles (Gibson *et al.*, 1984): Vasoactive intestinal polypeptide (VIP) caused rapid, powerful relaxations; *Gillichthys* U_{II} was almost equipotent to VIP but produced weaker, more slowly developing relaxations; somatostatin-14 caused changes in tone similar to those of U_{II}, but was 1/20 to 1/50 less potent. U_{II} was also found to cause a long-lasting inhibition of twitches resulting from electrical stimulation of the sympathetic innervation (Larson *et al.*, 1985).

Immunofluorescence of mouse anococcygeus muscle sections with antisera to VIP, U_{II}, and somatostatin demonstrated the presence of immunoreactive VIP-specific nerve fibers only (Larson *et al.*, 1985). No fluorescent fibers were found using anti-U_{II} or anti-somatostatin sera even at dilutions as high as 1 : 50, while in the same sections U_{II}-specific caudal neurosecretory cells in *Gillichthys* posterior spinal cord and somatostatin-specific pancreatic islet and antral cells in the mouse were clearly reactive.

Inasmuch as VIP has been the candidate inhibitory peptide transmitter for the nonadrenergic, noncholinergic nerve fibers to the anococcygeus (Gibson and Tucker, 1982), the immunocytochemical findings bolster the likelihood of this role for VIP. However, an influence of a urotensin II-like peptide from the circulation remains a possibility. The remarkable sensitivity of the mammalian anococcygeus muscle to urotensin II suggests the desirability of further search for possible urotensin II targets in vertebrates other than fishes. The paucity of reported U_{II} effects in tetrapods may result from failure to examine appropriate systems rather than from an absence of U_{II} bioactivity in higher vertebrates.

VI. Somatostatin and Urotensin II: Partial Analogs

The primary structures of urotensin II and of somatostatin-14 (see Fig. 2) reveal some striking similarities and some striking differences. The antibodies against somatostatin used to date do not cross-react with *Gil-*

TABLE III

Comparison of Some Actions of Somatostatin-14 and Urotensin II

	Somatostatin	Urotensin II
Inhibition of prolactin secretion (tilapia pituitary *in vitro*)	++	++
Inhibition of growth hormone secretion (tilapia pituitary *in vitro*)	++	−?
Inhibition of Cl efflux across goby skin	++	++ (sometimes −)
Inhibition of Cl efflux across tilapia opercular membrane	+	+
Relaxation of mouse anococcygeus muscle	+	++
Stimulation of Na absorption across goby bladder	−	+
Contraction of trout posterior intestine	−	++
Stimulation of NaCl and water absorption across seawater tilapia anterior intestine	−	+
Inhibition of NaCl and water absorption across freshwater tilapia anterior intestine	+	−
Stimulation of NaCl absorption across "freshwater" goby posterior intestine	−	+
Inhibition of Cl secretion by rat colon	+	−

lichthys urotensin II and vice versa, and somatostatin has no action in the spasmogenic bioassays for urotensin II. Table III compares the effect of these two peptides in a variety of systems. Both peptides are equipotent in inhibiting prolactin secretion by the teleost pituitary (Grau *et al.*, 1982) and share an ability to inhibit chloride secretion by fish skin and opercular membrane (cf. Loretz *et al.*, 1982); however, in other systems, the peptides are clearly distinguishable in their actions. In regard to intestinal transport, urotensin II acts on the "freshwater" goby intestine in essentially the same manner as somatostatin acts on the rat colon (cf. Loretz *et al.*, 1983; Loretz, 1985); however, urotensin II has no effect on the rat colon, nor does somatostatin affect the goby intestine. The parallel action of the two peptides in two different classes of vertebrates: Osteichthyes and Mammalia, is a form of analogy with possible evolutionary significance insofar as receptor evolution is concerned. It would be of interest to learn if the mechanism of action of the two peptides is similar in the two sites.

In summary, although the analogy between somatostatin and urotensin II is by no means complete, the data supporting a partially analogous status are substantial.

VII. Concluding Remarks

In fishes, the urophysial neurohormones—the urotensins—may prove to have a much broader physiological influence than was anticipated. Binding studies, vascular pathways, and possible extraurophysial production all support the probability of major contributions of these peptides to fish physiology. In tetrapods generally and in mammals specifically, no clear evidence for the existence of urotensins as such exists, but the responses of specific vascular beds and of the pituitary to urotensin I, the occurrence of specific binding sites for urotensin I, and the response of the anococcygeus muscle to urotensin II, all support the possibility of a relevance of these peptides to mammalian physiology. Research on the caudal neurosecretory system has been impeded in the past by the limited number of investigators involved; with more extensive interest, new findings of general biological significance can be expected, along with an elucidation of both the physiological and the evolutionary significance of a neuroendocrine apparatus located at the tail end of the spinal cord.

ACKNOWLEDGMENTS

On this occasion, the acknowledgments include an appreciation. Support for research on the caudal neurosecretory system has come from its very initiation from the U.S. National

Science Foundation. Consistent aid to H.A.B. for 25 years has allowed a continuity of effort for which gratitude needs to be expressed. Beginning at a time when such research was both exploratory and of uncertain significance, NSF support has allowed the emergence of a field of endeavor relevant to modern neurobiology and neurochemistry with possible implications far beyond any originally conceived. Not only has the NSF covered the usual research expenditures but also it has provided much of the support of R.S.N. since the grant's inception in 1959, as well as support for the first year of urophysial research (at Berkeley in 1968) by Professor Karl Lederis, the contributor of the second paper on the urotensins in this volume. The NSF Program Directors for Regulatory Biology from David Tyler to Bruce Umminger (with no slight to those unnamed in between) have been valued counsellors as well as necessary administrators. The indispensable support of the National Science Foundation is deeply appreciated.

B.L. received support from NCI Grant CA-09041 and NIH fellowship NS-07260. A research grant to D.P. from the National Institutes of Health (NS-18863) is also gratefully acknowledged, especially for provision of the support of Ms. Marsha L. Davis whose expert technical assistance has been invaluable in the biochemical aspects of our studies. We are grateful to Michael Mackey for his assistance in preparing the biotinylated urotensin II, to John Underhill for the photography, to Phyllis Thompson for the diagrams, and to Peggy Moffett for manuscript preparation.

REFERENCES

Allen, W. F. (1905). *Proc. Wash. Acad. Sci.* **7,** 27–157.
Berlind, A. (1972). *J. Endocrinol.* **52,** 567–574.
Berlind, A., Lacanilao, F., and Bern, H. A. (1972). *Comp. Biochem. Physiol. A* **42,** 345–352.
Bern, H. A., and Lederis, K. (1978). *In* "Neurosecretion and Neuroendocrine Activity" (W. Bargmann *et al.,* eds.), pp. 341–349. Springer-Verlag, Berlin and New York.
Bern, H. A., and Nishioka, R. S. (1979). *Gunma Symp. Endocrinol.* **16,** 9–18.
Bern, H. A., Nishioka, R. S., Chester Jones, I., Chan, D. K. O., Rankin, J. C., and Ponniah, S. (1967). *J. Endocrinol.* **37,** xl–xli.
Bern, H. A., Gunther, R., Johnson, D. W., and Nishioka, R. S. (1973). *Acta Zool. (Stockholm)* **54,** 15–19.
Chan, D. K. O. (1971). *Mem. Soc. Endocrinol.* **19,** 391–412.
Chan, D. K. O. (1975). *Gen. Comp. Endocrinol.* **27,** 52–61.
Chan, D. K. O. and Bern, H. A. (1976). *Cell Tissue Res.* **174,** 339–354.
Chan, D. K. O., Chester Jones, I., and Ponniah, S. (1969). *J. Endocrinol.* **45,** 151–159.
Chan, D. K. O., Gunther, R., and Bern, H. A. (1978). *Gen. Comp. Endocrinol.* **34,** 347–359.
Clark, B. R., Dattilo, J., and Pearson, D. (1982). *Int. J. Peptide Protein Res.* **19,** 448–453.
Enami, M. (1959). *In* "Comparative Endocrinology" (A. Gorbman, ed.), pp. 697–724. Wiley, New York.
Fänge, R. (1983). *Rev. Physiol. Biochem. Pharmacol.* **97,** 112–158.
Fisher, A. W. F., Wong, K., Gill, V., and Lederis, K. (1984). *Cell Tissue Res.* **235,** 19–23.
Foskett, J. K., and Hubbard, G. (1981). *Ann. N.Y. Acad. Sci.* **372,** 643.
Fridberg, G., and Bern, H. A. (1968). *Biol. Rev.* **43,** 175–199.
Fryer, J., and Lederis, K. (1985). *In* "Neurosecretion and the Biology of Neuropeptides" (H. Kobayashi, H. A. Bern, and A. Urano, eds.). Japan Sci. Soc. Press, Tokyo, in press.
Gauthier, L., Audet, C., and Chevalier, C. (1983). *Can. J. Zool.* **12,** 2856–2867.
Gibson, A., and Tucker, J. F. (1982). *Br. J. Pharmacol.* **77,** 97–103.

Gibson, A., Bern, H. A., Ginsburg, M., and Botting, J. H. (1984). *Proc. Natl. Acad. Sci. U.S.A.* **81,** 625–629.

Gillespie, J. S. (1980). *Trends Pharmacol. Sci.* **1,** 453–457.

Grau, E. G., Nishioka, R. S., and Bern, H. A. (1982). *Endocrinology* **110,** 910–915.

Grau, E. G., Nishioka, R. S., Young, G., and Bern, H. A. (1983). *Am. Zool.* **23,** 883.

Ichikawa, T. (1978). *Gen. Comp. Endocrinol.* **35,** 226–233.

Ichikawa, T. (1985). *In* "Neurosecretion and the Biology of Neuropeptides" (H. Kobayashi, H. A. Bern, and A. Urano, eds). Japan Sci. Soc. Press, Tokyo, in press.

Ichikawa, T., Lederis, K., and Kobayashi, H. (1984). *Gen. Comp. Endocrinol.* **55,** 133–141.

Kriebel, R. M., Parsons, R. L., and Miller, K. E. (1985). *In* "Neurosecretion and the Biology of Neuropeptides" (H. Kobayashi, H. A. Bern, and A. Urano, eds.). Japan Sci. Soc. Press, Tokyo, in press.

Lacanilao, F., and Bern, H. A. (1972). *Proc. Soc. Exp. Biol. Med.* **140,** 1252–1253.

Larson, B., Gibson, A., and Bern, H. A. (1985). *In* "Neurosecretion and the Biology of Neuropeptides" (H. Kobayashi, H. A. Bern, and A. Urano, eds.). Japan Sci. Soc. Press, Tokyo, in press.

Lederis, K. (1970a). *Gen. Comp. Endocrinol.* **14,** 417–426.

Lederis, K. (1970b). *Mem. Soc. Endocrinol.* **18,** 465–484.

Lederis, K. (1984). *In* "Frontiers in Neuroendocrinology" (L. Martini and W. F. Ganong, eds.), Vol. 8, pp. 247–263. Raven, New York.

Lederis, K., Bern, H. A., Nishioka, R. S., and Geschwind, I. I. (1971). *Mem. Soc. Endocrinol.* **19,** 413–433.

Loretz, C. A. (1985). *In* "Neurosecretion and the Biology of Neuropeptides" (H. Kobayashi, H. A. Bern, and A. Urano, eds.). Japan Sci. Soc. Press, Tokyo, in press.

Loretz, C. A., and Bern, H. A. (1981). *Gen. Comp. Endocrinol.* **43,** 325–330.

Loretz, C. A., and Bern, H. A., (1982). *Neuroendocrinology* **35,** 292–304.

Loretz, C. A., Bern, H. A., Foskett, J. K., and Mainoya, J. R. (1982). *In* "Neurosecretion, Molecules, Cells, Systems" (D. S. Farner and K. Lederis, eds.), pp. 319–328. Plenum, New York.

Loretz, C. A., Freel, R. W., and Bern, H. A. (1983). *Gen. Comp. Endocrinol.* **52,** 198–206.

MacCannell, K. L., and Lederis, K. (1983). *Fed. Proc., Fed. Am. Soc. Exp. Biol.* **42,** 91–95.

McMaster, D., and Lederis, K. (1983). *Peptides* **4,** 367–373.

Mainoya, J. R., and Bern, H. A. (1982). *Gen. Comp. Endocrinol.* **47,** 54–58.

Mainoya, J. R., and Bern, H. A. (1984). *Zool. Sci.* **1,** 100–105.

Marshall, W. S., and Bern, H. A. (1979). *Science* **204,** 519–521.

Marshall, W. S., and Bern, H. A. (1981). *Gen. Comp. Endocrinol.* **43,** 484–491.

Moore, G., Burford, G., and Lederis, K. (1975). *Mol. Cell. Endocrinol.* **3,** 297–307.

Mott, J. C. (1950). *Proc. Zool. Soc. London* **120,** 503–518.

Muramatsu, I., and Kobayashi, Y. (1979). *Gunma Symp. Endocrinol.* **16,** 49–56.

Muramatsu, I., Fujiwara, M., Hidaka, H., and Akutagawa, H. (1979). *Gunma Symp. Endocrinol.* **16,** 39–48.

Muramatsu, I., Miura, A., Fujiwara, M., and Lederis, K. (1981). *Gen. Comp. Endocrinol.* **45,** 446–452.

Onstott, D., and Elde, R. (1984). *Neuroendocrinology* **39,** 503–509.

Owada, K., Kawata, M., Akaji, K., Takagi, A., Moriga, M., and Kobayashi, H. (1985). *Cell Tissue Res.* (in press).

Pearson, D., Shively, J. E., Clark, B. R., Geschwind, I. I., Barkley, M., Nishioka, R. S., and Bern, H. A. (1980). *Proc. Natl. Acad. Sci. U.S.A.* **77,** 5021–5024.

Renda, T., D'Este, L., Negri, L., and Lomanto, D. (1982). *Basic Appl. Histochem.* **26,** 89–98.

Rivas, R. J., Nishioka, R. S., Specker, J. L., and Bern, H. A. (1984). *Am. Zool.* **24,** 117A.

Roy, V. (1975). *Indian J. Exp. Biol.* **13,** 253–255.

Sheridan, M., Plisetskaya, E., Bern, H. A., and Gorbman, A. (1985). *Fed. Proc.* (in press).

Specker, J. L., King, D. S., Rivas, R. J., and Young, B. K. (1985). *Proc. Int. Congr. Prolactin; 4th* (in press).

Speidel, C. C. (1919). *Papers Dept. Mar. Biol. Carnegie Inst. Wash.* **13,** 1–31.

Speidel, C. C. (1922). *J. Comp. Neurol.* **34,** 303–317.

Weber, E. H. (1827). *Meckels Arch. Anat. Physiol.* **2,** 316–317.

Wofsy, L. (1980). *In* "Immunochemical Techniques, Part E" (J. J. Langone and H. Van Vunakis, eds.). Academic Press, New York.

Woo, N. Y. S., Tong, W. C. M., and Chan, E. L. P. (1980). *Gen. Comp. Endocrinol.* **41,** 458–466.

Woo, N. Y. S., Wong, K. L., Hontela, A., Fryer, J. N., Kobayashi, Y., and Lederis, K. (1985). *In* "Neurosecretion and the Biology of Neuropeptides" (H. Kobayashi, H. A. Bern, and A. Urano, eds.). Japan Sci. Soc. Press, Tokyo, in press.

Zelnik, P. R., and Lederis, K. (1973). *Gen. Comp. Endocrinol.* **20,** 392–400.

Neurohormones from Fish Tails
II: Actions of Urotensin I in Mammals and Fishes

K. Lederis, J. Fryer,* J. Rivier,† K. L. MacCannell,
Y. Kobayashi,[1] N. Woo,[2] and K. L. Wong

*Department of Pharmacology and Therapeutics, University of Calgary, Calgary, Alberta, Canada, * Department of Anatomy, University of Ottawa, Ottawa, Ontario, Canada, and † Peptide Biology Laboratory, The Salk Institute, La Jolla, California*

The search for factors from the brain that regulate the pituitary control of endocrine systems, including adrenocortical function, has continued since the postulation and subsequent classical experiments by Harris (1955) providing convincing evidence for such control. The recent determination of the structure and biological properties of a larger corticotropin-releasing factor (CRF) than other hypothalamic factors known at the time (Vale *et al.*, 1981) is one of the reasons it took more than 25 years of searching before the identity of a CRF was established.

The publication of the ovine hypothalamic CRF (oCRF) structure preceded by a few months the completion of final structural studies on the teleostean caudal neurosecretory peptide urotensin I (U_I), at which time an unexpected and a remarkably close structural homology between oCRF and U_I became apparent (Lederis *et al.*, 1982a,b).

It was realized at that time that another member of this "family" of peptides, sauvagine (SVG), had earlier been isolated from frog skin by Erspamer and his colleagues (Montecucci *et al.*, 1979; Erspamer *et al.*, 1980). Subsequent pharmacological studies revealed that the biological properties of the three peptides were even more similar than the structural homology (see below). On the basis of the phylogenetic time scale, U_I was considered a prototype of this family of peptides (Lederis, 1984). However, not knowing which one of at least two evolutionary processes, i.e., convergence (Grutter *et al.*, 1983) or evolutionary propensities (Popper, 1979), may have contributed to the existence of the closely related pep-

---

[1] Present address: Department of Pharmacology, Shimane Medical University, Shimane 693, Japan.

[2] Present Address: Department of Biology, Chinese University of Hong Kong, Shatin, NT, Hong Kong.

			5					10					15			

Cyprinus carpio
UROTENSIN I (U_{IC}) H - Asn - Asp - Asp - Pro - Pro - Ile - Ser - Ile - Asp - Leu - Thr - Phe - His - Leu - Leu - Arg - Asn - Met -

Catostomus commersoni
UROTENSIN I (U_{IS}) H - Asn - Asp - Asp - Pro - Pro - Ile - Ser - Ile - Asp - Leu - Thr - Phe - His - Leu - Leu - Arg - Asn - Met -

SAUVAGINE pGlu - Gly - Pro - Pro - Ile - Ser - Ile - Asp - Leu - Ser - Leu - Glu - Leu - Leu - Arg - Lys - Met -

oCRF H - Ser - Gln - Glu - Pro - Pro - Ile - Ser - Leu - Asp - Leu - Thr - Phe - His - Leu - Leu - Arg - Glu - Val -

	20					25					30			

Cyprinus carpio
UROTENSIN I Ile - Glu - Met - Ala - Arg - Asn - Glu - Asn - Gln - Arg - Glu - Gln - Ala - Gly - Leu -

Catostomus commersoni
UROTENSIN I Ile - Glu - Met - Ala - Arg - Ile - Glu - Asn - Glu - Arg - Glu - Gln - Ala - Gly - Leu -

SAUVAGINE Ile - Glu - Ile - Glu - Lys - Gln - Glu - Lys - Glu - Lys - Gln - Gln - Ala - Ala - Asn -

CRF Leu - Glu - Met - Thr - Lys - Ala - Asp - Gln - Leu - Ala - Gln - Gln - Ala - His - Ser -

	35					40		

Cyprinus carpio
UROTENSIN I Asn - Arg - Lys - Tyr - Leu - Asp - Glu - Val - NH$_2$

Catostomus commersoni
UROTENSIN I Asn - Arg - Lys - Tyr - Leu - Asp - Glu - Val - NH$_2$

SAUVAGINE Asn - Arg - Leu - Leu - Asp - Thr - Ile - NH$_2$

CRF Asn - Arg - Lys - Leu - Leu - Asp - Ile - Ala - NH$_2$

FIG. 1. Primary structures of carp (*Cyprinus carpio*) and sucker (*Catostomus commersoni*) U_1, sauvagine, and amunine (ovine hypothalamic CRF) peptides. Residues underlined in sauvagine and CRF are homologous with carp U_1 (from Ichikawa *et al.*, 1982). Note that the *Catostomus* U_1 peptide differs from the *Cyprinus* peptide only in positions 24 and 27 (Asn is replaced by Ile and Gln is replaced by Glu, respectively). Note further that rat (r)CRF differs from oCRF by the following substitutions: Glu[2], Ala[22], Arg[23], Glu[25], Met[38], Glu[39], and Ile[41] (Vale *et al.*, 1983), thus increasing the homology between U_1 and rCRF by further three residues (positions 22, 23, and 25) as compared with oCRF.

tides in widely divergent vertebrates (teleost fish, amphibian, mammal), the question of a prototype can not be meaningfully considered until such a time that the structures and the precursor forms of U_I (or CRF)-like peptides from more representative vertebrates (or even invertebrates!) have been identified.

The fact that the biological properties of this group of peptides have been more highly conserved during evolution than their primary structures (see Fig. 1), has indicated the need to establish and to compare their secondary and tertiary structures: an analysis of the secondary structures of the three peptides, oCRF, U_I, SVG, according to the method of Chou and Fasman (1978) by Pallai *et al.* (1983) has already shown that the overall structure of all three peptides is basically the same: all three peptides possess a long internal helix, extending to about 25 residues, which is connected by a turn region to a C-terminal structural element that is an α-helix in CRF and U_I, but is a β-sheet in SVG. The analysis of the pharmacological properties of U_I and the comparison of its actions with those of the other two peptides in subsequent sections will indicate some structure–function properties and peptide–receptor interactions, the latter implying different receptor classes or mechanisms for the mammalian vascular actions of U_I and the related peptides on the one hand and for the pituitary actions (i.e., stimulation of ACTH release) in mammals and fishes on the other.

I. Hemodynamic Actions of Urotensin I in Mammals

The early report by Kobayashi *et al.* (1968) of a hypotensive effect of urophysial extracts in the rat gave an impetus for detailed investigations of the vascular pharmacology of U_I and for an evaluation of *in vitro* and *in vivo* laboratory procedures in order to analyze the sites and mechanisms of the apparently unique vascular action of U_I in mammals (Lederis, 1973; Lederis and Medakovic, 1974a,b; MacCannell and Lederis, 1977; Muramatsu *et al.*, 1981).

In parallel with attempts to isolate U_I in a highly purified form (Lederis, 1977; Lederis *et al.*, 1981) and to determine its structure in two teleosteans (Ichikawa *et al.*, 1982; Lederis *et al.*, 1982a,b), the vascular actions of U_I were investigated in several mammalian species. In the conscious or the urethane anaesthetized rat U_I induced a marked, dose dependent, and a long lasting hypotensive effect, 20 minutes to 6 hours in duration after intravenous administration (Lederis and Medakovic, 1974a) and in excess of 24 hours after subcutaneous administration in spontaneously hypertensive rats (Medakovic *et al.*, 1975b). An investigation of the hypotensive-vasodilatory actions in different vascular regions revealed that in the rat,

TABLE I

Mesenteric Vasodilation upon Injection into Other Vascular Beds[a]

Injection site	Ovine CRF (1.25 µg)		Sauvagine (0.25 µg)		Urotensin I (0.25 µg)	
	Increase regional flow (%)	Increase mesenteric flow (%)	Increase regional flow (%)	Increase mesenteric flow (%)	Increase regional flow (%)	Increase mesenteric flow (%)
Femoral A	0	0.0 ± 0.0	0	20.5 ± 7.9	0	19.8 ± 8.9
Carotid A	0	8.0 ± 3.0	0	43.8 ± 19.1	0	29.8 ± 7.8
Coeliac A	0	2.5 ± 2.5	0	32.2 ± 11.0	0	30.0 ± 8.3
Renal A	0	5.0 ± 5.0	0	12.3 ± 12.3	0	8.3 ± 8.3

[a] MacCannell and Lederis (unpublished observations).

vasodilatation was most pronounced in the gastrointestinal region but it could be observed in most major vascular beds (Medakovic *et al.*, 1975a). *In vitro*, the rat mesenteric artery was the most sensitive preparation (Muramatsu *et al.*, 1981). In striking contrast to the rat, vasodilatation

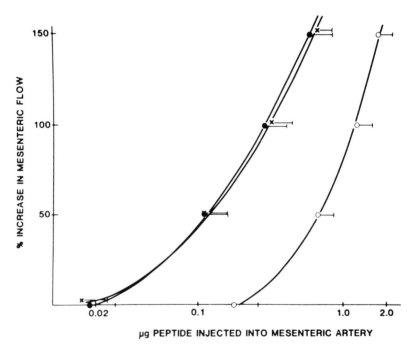

FIG. 2. Percentage increase in mesenteric flow in the anesthetized dog after close-arterial injection of urotensin I (●), sauvagine (×), or ovine hypothalamic CRF (○).

could only be detected in the superior mesenteric vascular bed of the anesthetized dog (MacCannell and Lederis, 1977). Table I shows that after close-arterial injection of U_I into various major arteries of the dog, vasodilatation (dose-related increase in blood flow) could only be detected in the superior (cephalic) mesenteric artery (MacCannell and Lederis, 1977).

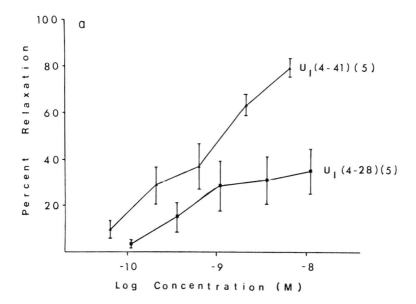

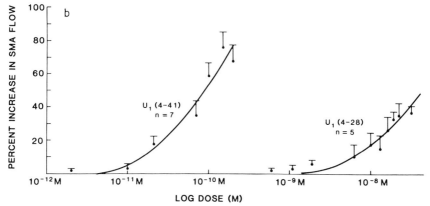

FIG. 3.   (a) The dose–response curves for the *in vitro* vasorelaxant activity for synthetic sucker $U_I(4–41)$ and (4–28). Numbers in parentheses show the number of experiments. (b) Comparison of *in vivo* dose–response curves in the anesthetized dog for urotensin I ($U_I(4–41)$) and the fragment $U_I(4–28)$ after intraarterial injection into superior mesenteric artery.

Comparison of the vasodilatory activities of the other two related peptides revealed that while the frog skin peptide (SVG) was equipotent with U_I both *in vivo* and *in vitro* in the rat and in the dog, the mammalian CRF had only about 1/20 of the activity, suggesting that for reasons not understood at present (perhaps phylogenetic propensity or a physiologic need for a decreased peripheral vasodilatory effects in mammals - or terrestrial vertebrates in general?) a pronounced decrease in vascular receptor affinity has occurred (see Fig. 2).

Interestingly, a part sequence of U_I, natural or synthetic $U_I(4-28)$ of the carp or sucker (Ichikawa *et al.*, 1982; Lederis *et al.*, 1982a) also retains about the same vasodilatory activity in the rat mesenteric artery *in vitro* as that of the intact oCRF (Fig. 3a), with at least one apparent pharmacological difference: while oCRF produces the same maximal response as U_I at appropriately increased concentration (the dose–response curve shifted to the right; see Fig. 2), maximal response could not be obtained with $U_I(4-28)$ at the peptide concentration used, suggesting decreased

TABLE II

Comparison of Natural and Synthetic U_1 (1–41) and Some Analogs from Carp and Sucker[a]

Peptides	Specific activity (%)	
Natural carp $U_I(1-41)$	111.3 ± 17.6[b]	(3)[c]
Synthetic carp $U_I(1-41)$	97.6 ± 1.8[b]	(3)
Synthetic sucker $U_I(1-41)$	94.7 ± 18.5[b]	(2)
Synthetic carp $U_I(4-41)$	113.4 ± 22.0[b]	(3)
Synthetic sucker $U_I(4-41)$	100	
Natural carp $U_I(4-28)$	≈ 4.0[d]	(2)
Synthetic sucker $U_I(4-28)$	8.1 ± 3.7[d]	(5)
Natural carp $U_I(29-41)$	< 0.8[d]	(5)
Natural carp $U_I(4-23)$	< 0.3[d]	(5)
Natural carp $U_I(24-28)$	< 0.3[d]	(6)
Natural carp $U_I(4-16)$	< 0.2[d]	(3)

[a] Y. Kobayashi, D. McMaster, and K. Lederis (unpublished observations).

[b] ED_{50} for peptides were compared with synthetic sucker $U_I(4-41)$ as standard and paired assays were done. No significant difference was observed among the peptides.

[c] Numbers in parentheses are number of paired assays.

[d] The relative value obtained from paired assays comparing synthetic $U_I(4-41)$ dose–response curve as standard.

intrinsic activity as well as receptor affinity (Fig. 3b). Various other tryptic fragments of U_I did not show residual vasodilatory activity (Table II).

II. Stimulation of Corticotropin Release by Urotensin I in Mammals and Fishes

Prior to the completion of sequence determination, highly purified natural *Catostomus c.* U_I appeared to have *in vitro* ACTH-releasing activity comparable to that of synthetic oCRF (W. Vale, personal communication). A more detailed analysis of ACTH secretion in the rat *in vivo* and *in vitro* (see Fig. 4) and of plasma corticosterone, using the synthetic urotensin peptide or its fully active (vasodilatation) acid hydrolysis product $U_I(4–41)$ showed that U_I was not significantly different from oCRF under all experimental conditions tested (Lederis *et al.*, 1982a,b; Rivier *et al.*, 1983); a somewhat longer duration of action by U_I, as compared to oCRF, was apparent in some of the *in vivo* experiments, however, the significance of this has not been determined (Rivier *et al.*, 1983).

Observations on ACTH release in a teleost fish have revealed that U_I, oCRF, and SVG stimulate cortisol secretion in dexamethasone-blocked goldfish (*Carassius auratus*) *in vivo* (Fryer *et al.*, 1983). In contrast to mammals, where all three related peptides have similar ACTH-releasing activity, as indicated above, U_I was significantly more potent than oCRF or SVG in stimulating the release of ACTH from cells of the goldfish anterior pituitary *in vitro* (Fryer *et al.*, 1983; Fig. 5). Furthermore, more recent *in vitro* investigations have shown that U_I is approximately twice as potent as oCRF or SVG in stimulating the concomitant release of ACTH and α-MSH from cells of the goldfish neurointermediate lobe (Tran, Fryer, Lederis, Rivier, and Vaudry, unpublished data). Although the identity of definitive (hypothalamic?) fish CRF(s) has not been determined nor investigated at the present time, a physiological role for U_I in the control of adrenocortical (i.e., interrenal) function in teleosts appears likely for several reasons:

1. U_I is highly potent in the stimulation of ACTH secretion *in vivo* and *in vitro* (Fryer *et al.*, 1983).

2. One week after urophysectomy, elevated plasma cortisol and increased immunoreactive U_I (IR-U_I) in goldfish *brain* have been determined (Woo *et al.*, 1984a).

3. Basal and U_I-stimulated ACTH release from perifused goldfish pituitary cells is suppressed in the presence of cortisol in the perfusing solution, suggesting that a "short loop" negative feedback mechanism may be operative *in vivo* in relation to U_I and ACTH secretion (Fryer *et al.*, 1984).

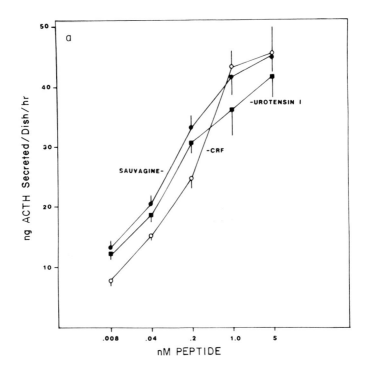

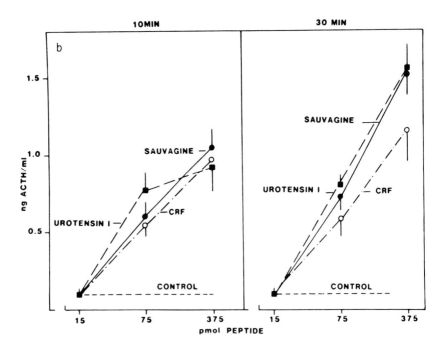

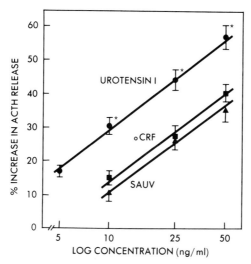

FIG. 5.   Comparison of the ACTH-releasing activity from dispersed perifused goldfish pituitary cells by urotensin I, CRF, and sauvagine. The percentage increase in ACTH release above background evoked by a 2-minute pulse of test peptide has been plotted from 14 goldfish pituitary cell columns. Each point represents the mean ± SEM of 6–10 stimulations. *Significantly greater ($p < 0.01$) than CRF or SVG. (From Fryer *et al.*, 1983.)

III.   Occurrence of Urotensin I in Fish Brain

It would not be unexpected for a peptide structurally homologous with CRF to have also homologous biological properties, with or without a physiological significance, or to be synthesized in a comparable locale of the brain. The observations summarized above, suggesting a possible physiological role for U_I in the brain–pituitary–interrenal axis, were extended to include the question for a possible occurrence of U_I in the brain and in other body systems of the fish. With the use of highly specific antisera to U_I, raised in rabbits against U_I conjugated to large proteins (Suess and Lederis, 1981) or against authentic synthetic U_I peptides without coupling to large proteins (D. Ko, J. Rivier, and K. Lederis, unpublished observations), employing radioimmunoassays (RIA) or immunocytochemistry [(IHC); immunostaining, or immunofluorescence], occurrence of IR-U_I was seen in many teleostean body systems, including

FIG. 4.   (a) Effect of ovine CRF, sauvagine, and urotensin I on ACTH secretion by cultured pituitary cells ($n = 3$ for all points, vertical bars represent SEM). (From Rivier *et al.*, 1983). (b) Effect of ovine CRF, sauvagine, and urotensin I on plasma ACTH levels measured 10 minutes after iv administration ($n = 6$ rats for each point; vertical bars represent SEM). (From Rivier *et al.*, 1983.)

the brain and pituitary. Thus, RIA showed higher concentrations of IR-U$_I$ in the *Catostomus* brain and pituitary, as compared with different parts of the digestive tract; the urophysis and caudal spinal cord having the expected high concentrations of U$_I$ (Kobayashi, Ishimura, Poulin, and Lederis, unpublished observations). Subsequent IHC investigations, using specific antisera to oCRF as well as U$_I$, indicated an intriguing situation whereby (1) oCRF-reacting cell bodies were seen in the preoptic nucleus, centripetal fibers running in the direction of the pituitary; intense immunostaining was present in the neurohypophysial area of the pituitary, (2) the presence of U$_I$ antiserum-reacting neurosecretory cell bodies in the preoptic nucleus was seen in some experiments but not in others, raising the question of the ultimate specificity of the antibodies used and thus making the interpretation of findings inconclusive. Again, in some experiments (but not in others, possibly depending on tissue fixation procedures) U$_I$-specific immunostaining was seen in the general area of the lateral tuberal nuclei. Numerous nerve fibers could be seen, apparently running from the tuberal region toward the preoptic area as well as the pituitary (Fisher *et al.*, 1984; Wong *et al.*, 1984). On the basis of these observations, together with the previously seen *increase* in IR-U$_I$ in the goldfish hypothalamus after urophysectomy (Woo *et al.*, 1984a,b) it may be tentatively suggested that (1) two closely related peptides (oCRF and U$_I$) may be synthesized in different neurosecretory cell groups of the fish hypothalamus, those cell groups being located in areas of the fish brain previously implicated in the control of pituitary-interrenal function (Fryer and Maler, 1982), and (2) if the above is proved unequivocally to be the case, an interesting physiological mechanism might be operative in teleost fishes—at least in the two species investigated—where two closely related, yet different, peptides are synthesized, by the same or different populations of nerve cells of the fish central nervous system, for the purpose of, possibly, exercising different inputs in the control of interrenal function. Could it be, for example, that one of the two peptides may regulate the basal, the other the "stimulated" (osmoregulation? stress response?) function of the fish interrenal system? If such a "dual" control system, possibly different from the mammalian pituitary–adrenocortical control, were operative, the involvement of the neurohypophysial peptides—which already at this time appear to be different in fishes—would need more detailed studies: recent experiments have shown that, in contrast to the "stimulatory" (i.e., potentiating) effects of vasopressin on the action of CRF in mammals, arginine vasotocin (AVT) per se may stimulate ACTH secretion from the goldfish pituitary; AVT or the other neurohypophysial peptides, including arginine vasopressin, do not potentiate the action of U_I (or oCRF) on the stimulation of ACTH secretion (Fryer *et al.*, 1984).

IV.   Distribution of Urotensin I-Specific Binding Sites in Mammals and Fishes

Using ^{125}I-labeled U_I—a process which preserves unchanged vascular activity of the labeled peptide (McMaster *et al.*, 1984)—the distribution and properties of U_I binding sites were investigated in the rat, dog, and goldfish, using receptor-enriched membrane preparations of different tissues as previously described (Wong and Lederis, 1982). In the rat, the distribution of U_I-specific binding sites could be determined in various major blood vessels, mainly arteries. Specific binding was also seen in the liver and kidney. Table III shows the presence of two classes of binding sites in some of the tissues but not others, as revealed by the analysis according to Scatchard (1949). All the binding sites indicated high affinity, but could be classified separately as shown in Table III into "high" or "higher" affinity sites, with equilibrium binding constants in the range of $0.1–4.5 \times 10^{-9}$ and $1–6 \times 10^{-11}$ M, respectively. In the rat mesenteric artery which shows the highest sensitivity to U_I *in vitro* (Muramatsu *et al.*, 1981) only one class of binding sites was present (see Table III).

TABLE III

Equilibrium Binding Constants Illustrating Two Classes of Binding Sites for Urotensin I in Rat and Dog Tissues[a]

Tissue and species	K_d (nM)	
	Class I	Class II
Rat		
Mesenteric artery	—	0.21
Mesenteric vein	0.026	
Celiac artery	0.034	
Descending aorta	0.010	0.14
Tail artery	0.047	0.28
Tain vein	0.059	
Liver	0.02	0.45
Kidney	0.01	0.32
Dog		
Mesenteric artery (proximal)	0.018	4.5
Mesenteric artery (distal)	0.026	0.35

[a] From Wong, Goren, and Lederis (1984, unpublished).

In contrast to the rat, significant high-capacity, high-affinity binding sites in the dog were only found in the mesenteric (superior, or cephalic) artery. Moreover, unlike the rat mesenteric artery (Fig. 6a), two classes of binding sites were present in the dog artery (see Table III and Fig. 6b). On the basis of the known sites of vasodilatory action in the rat and the dog (i.e., vasodilatation in most vascular beds in the rat, but only in the superior mesenteric region in the dog), it may be viewed that the distribution of the class II binding sites in the two species corresponds to a generalized and a highly selective vasodilatation, respectively. To take this argument further, it follows that "high" class II, rather than the "higher" affinity class I sites, are those at which the U_I binding has to occur in order to induce vasorelaxation–vasodilatation. Interestingly, relatively high-affinity U_I-binding sites seem to be present in the mammalian tissues as compared to the binding affinity for most other peptides (see Table III).

Binding sites for U_I have been demonstrated in the goldfish pituitary (Figs. 7 and 8): ^{125}I-labeled U_I was found to bind to dispersed cells of the anterior pituitary or neurointermediate lobe. The binding of ^{125}I-labeled U_I to cells of the anterior pituitary or neurointermediate lobe was completely inhibited by U_I, only partially inhibited by oCRF and SVG, supporting the view that ACTH-releasing or α-MSH-releasing activities of these peptides in the teleost pituitary are mediated by a common receptor (Fig. 7). Scatchard analysis of the binding of ^{125}I-labeled U_I to cells of the anterior pituitary or of neurointermediate lobe is consistent with a single class of U_I binding site (Fig. 8). The demonstration that arginine vasotocin, arginine vasopressin, and isotocin do not inhibit the binding of ^{125}I-labeled U_I to cells of the anterior pituitary indicates that the ACTH-releasing activities of U_I and of the neurohypophyseal peptides are mediated by different receptors. The rank order of pituitary receptor affinity i.e., $U_I > $ oCRF $ > $ SVG, reflects the relative potency of these peptides in stimulating ACTH and α-MSH release which suggests that differences in the potencies of these peptides may be attributable to differences in hypophyseal receptor affinity. The demonstration that the peptide fragment $U_I(4–28)$ is virtually equipotent with $U_I(4–41)$ in displacing ^{125}I-labeled U_I from the pituitary U_I binding site indicates that this region of the U_I molecule contains the binding site which is recognized by the pituitary U_I receptor.

Preliminary data suggest that $U_I(4–28)$ lacks ACTH-releasing activity in the goldfish (Tran, Fryer, Lederis, and Rivier, unpublished data) which suggests that $U_I(4–28)$ may be of considerable pharmacological significance as a competitive inhibitor of U_I- or CRF-induced ACTH release from the goldfish pituitary. In other experiments, U_I-specific binding sites of widely varying binding capacities were found in goldfish brain, intes-

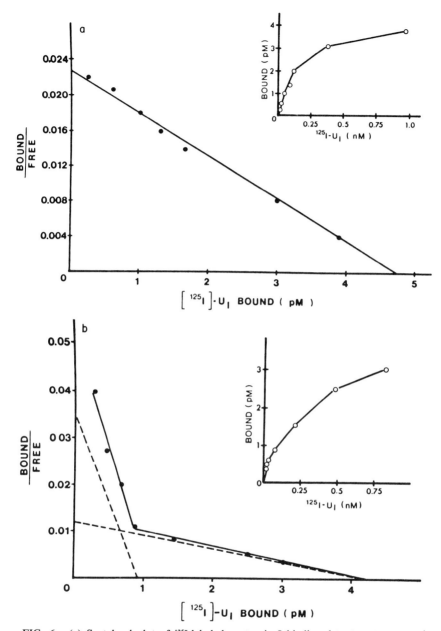

FIG. 6. (a) Scatchard plot of ^{125}I-labeled urotensin I binding data to rat mesenteric artery. Rat mesenteric artery plasma membrane fractions were mixed with different concentrations of ^{125}I-labeled U_I (inset = saturation curve showing means of two determinations) and after 60 minutes at room temperature, the reaction mixture was centrifuged. Radioactivity associated with membranes was determined. Nonspecific binding was the membrane-associated radioactivity in the presence of 0.8 μM U_I (Wong, Goren, and Lederis, unpublished observations). (b) Scatchard plot of ^{125}I-labeled urotensin I binding data to dog mesenteric (distal) artery. Details of the binding experiments are the same as for a.

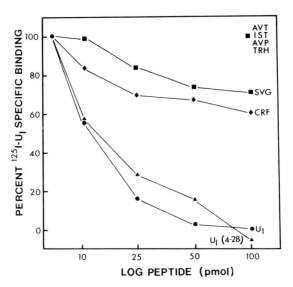

FIG. 7.   Binding of ^{125}I-labeled U$_I$ to dispersed cells of the goldfish anterior pituitary expressed as a percentage of the ^{125}I-labeled U$_I$ specific binding. Anterior pituitary cells were isolated (Fryer *et al.*, 1983) and incubated with ^{125}I-labeled U$_I$ for 10 minutes at 21°C in the presence of increasing concentrations of urotensin I (U$_I$), the U$_I$ fragment [U$_I$(4–28)], ovine corticotropin-releasing factor (oCRF), sauvagine (SVG), arginine vasotocin (AVT), arginine vasopressin (AVP), isotocin (IST), or thyrotropin-releasing hormone (TRH). Radioactivity associated with the cells was determined following centrifugation (Weld, Fryer, Lederis, and Rivier, unpublished data).

tine, liver, kidney, and gills, but not in the heart (myocardium) or skeletal (white) muscle. Moreover, adaptation of the fish to dilute sea water (14‰) caused a significant increase in U$_I$ binding in the brain and, especially, intestine (anterior) but not in other tissues (Fig. 9a). The discovery of this diverse tissue distribution of U$_I$ binding sites raises a number of questions, such as (1) what physiological implications, in terms of a systemic role of U$_I$, would be indicated by this observation and (2) could such a distribution pattern also be observed for the other known urophysial peptide—urotensin II (U$_{II}$). Samples of the same tissues that were used for binding studies or for RIA of IR-U$_I$ from both the fresh water- and the dilute seawater-adapted goldfish were also utilized for determination of U$_{II}$ binding sites (Woo *et al.*, 1984a,b; Fig. 9b). Several interesting differences between U$_I$ and U$_{II}$ binding were seen: (1) unlike the distribution of U$_I$ binding sites, significant and specific U$_{II}$ binding was observed in all tissues tested, including the heart and skeletal muscle, (2) more U$_{II}$ than U$_I$ was bound by all tissue preparations, i.e., 25–55 fmol/mg protein for

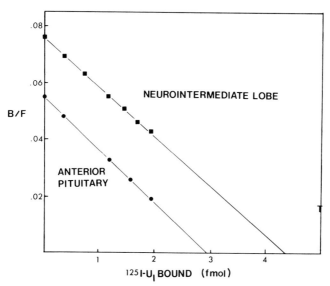

FIG. 8.   Scatchard plots of ^{125}I-labeled U_I binding to dispersed cells of the goldfish anterior pituitary or neurointermediate lobe. Pituitary cells were isolated and incubated in the presence of ^{125}I-labeled U_I and increasing concentrations of unlabeled U_I under the same conditions as Fig. 7. Binding to anterior pituitary cells revealed a K_a of $0.20 \times 10^{-9}\ M$ and a binding capacity of 4.7 fmol per 1.5×10^5 cells. Binding to neurointermediate lobe cells revealed a K_a of $0.19 \times 10^{-9}\ M$ and a binding capacity of 4.4 fmol per 1.0×10^5 cells (Weld, Fryer, Lederis, and Rivier, unpublished data).

U_{II} against <5–15 fmol/mg for U_I, and (3) whereas adaptation to dilute sea water caused significant increases of U_I binding in the brain and intestine, an increase in U_{II} binding occurred only in the kidney; significant *decreases* in U_{II} binding were measured in the gills and the myocardium. Figure 9a and b summarizes and compares the distribution of U_I and U_{II} binding, respectively.

The findings from these binding studies present further strong hints as to the possible physiology of the urophysial peptides, suggesting a probable importance of U_{II} in all tissues of the fish and, furthermore, adding further support to complex osmoregulatory roles for the urophysial peptides in bony fishes as demonstrated repeatedly by Bern and his colleagues (see Bern *et al.*, this volume).

One unexpected finding from competitive displacement studies was the ability of the vasoactive intestinal polypeptide (VIP) to displace U_I binding from the *mammalian and piscine* binding sites. In the rat mesenteric artery VIP had about 40% potency of that of the U_I peptide in displacing

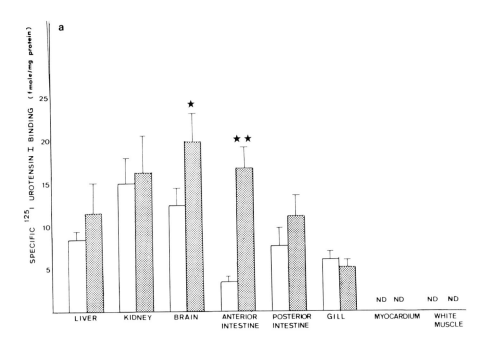

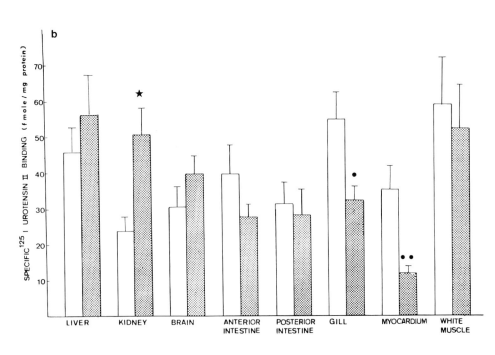

^{125}I-labeled U_I from its binding site(s), whereas SVG was equipotent with U_I and oCRF had only a very low competitive displacement capacity—similar to its relatively low vasodilatory activity (Fig. 10a). The findings of competitive displacement of U_I by VIP in the goldfish kidney membrane preparation are even more dramatic: VIP was by far more potent than even U_I in displacing ^{125}I-labeled U_I binding ($<200\%$ if unlabeled $U_I =$ 100%; Woo et al., 1984b). At first glance, these findings appear to be difficult to explain—the structural similarity between VIP and U_I being minimal. The extremely high U_I displacement capacity by VIP from the kidney receptors may even be interpreted that the "U_I-specific" binding sites are in actual fact VIP receptors. However, recent more detailed analysis of U_I binding sites in the rat mesenteric artery, with respect to the receptor recognition site of the U_I peptide (Wong, Goren, and Lederis, unpublished observations) which shows that the C-terminal region of the U_I peptide [$U_I(28-39)$] contributes about 50% of the U_I-receptor binding capacity, suggests that sufficient similarity exists in the C-terminal regions of the two peptides, between the part sequences of VIP(15–24) and $U_I(28-39)$: thus, VIP(15–19) (Lys-Gln-Met-Ala-Val) is quite similar to $U_I(28-32)$ (Arg-Glu-Gln-Ala-Gly) and VIP(19–24) (Val-Lys-Lys-Tyr-Leu-Asn) is similar to $U_I(34-39)$ (Asn-Arg-Lys-Tyr-Leu-Asp). In contrast to the above argument being of sufficient probability to explain the U_I–VIP interactions at the receptor site, the much greater sequence similarity and the predicted sameness of the secondary structures between U_I and oCRF (Pallai et al., 1983) do not suffice to explain the low receptor affinity and the very low competitive displacement potency of oCRF. A plausible explanation could be the localization, in the U_I receptor, of a charged residue at a place where, in the peptide, a neutral or an opposite-charge residue is normally present. Thus, position 32 of U_I (or sauvagine) is occupied by a neutral amino acid (Gly in U_I, Ala in SVG) and, therefore, the His-32 of oCRF may actually hinder CRF binding and may be sufficient to explain low competitive displacement potency, the low mamma-

---

FIG. 9. (a) Distribution of ^{125}I-labeled U_I binding sites in tissues of the freshwater and dilute seawater (14‰)-adapted goldfish. Open bars, specific binding to membranes prepared from freshwater adapted goldfish. Stippled bars, specific binding to membranes prepared from dilute seawater adapted goldfish. Each value (means ± SEM) represents the mean obtained from 8 to 10 membrane preparations from different fish. *Dilute seawater binding > freshwater binding ($p < 0.05$). **Dilute seawater binding > freshwater binding ($p < 0.001$). ND, Not detectable. (From Woo et al., 1984b.) (b) Distribution of ^{125}I-labeled U_{II} binding sites in tissues of the freshwater and dilute seawater (14‰)-adapted goldfish. All information given under a is the same for b except *dilute seawater binding > freshwater binding ($p < 0.02$); ●, dilute seawater binding < freshwater binding ($p < 0.02$); ●●, dilute seawater binding < freshwater binding ($p < 0.01$). (From Woo et al., 1984b.)

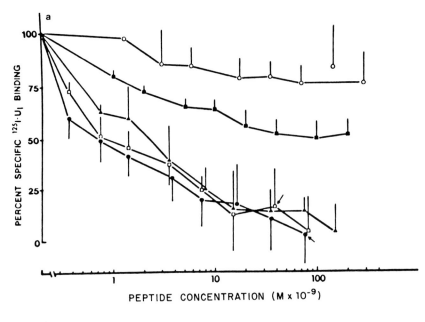

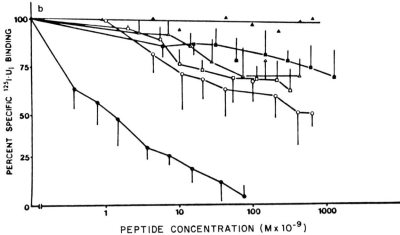

FIG. 10. (a) Competitive displacement of ^{125}I-labeled U_I from membrane preparations of rat mesenteric artery by increasing concentrations of unlabeled U_I and other peptides: natural sucker U_I (●), synthetic U_I (□), sauvagine (▲), vasoactive intestinal peptide, VIP (■), corticotrophin releasing factor, CRF (○), arginine vasopressin, AVP (*), oxytocin (◊), and insulin (△). Specific binding in the absence of unlabeled peptide was taken as 100%. Vertical bars represent SEM of 4 or 5 determinations (Wong, Goren, and Lederis, unpublished observations). (b) Competitive displacement of ^{125}I-labeled U_I from membrane preparations of rat mesenteric artery by increasing concentrations of U_I fragments: $U_I(4–16)$ (▲); $U_I(4–23)$ (△); $U_I(4–28)$ (□); $U_I(4–41)$ (●); $U_I(32–39)$ (■); and $U_I(29–41)$ (○). Specific binding in the absence of unlabeled peptide was taken as 100%. Vertical bars represent SEM of 3 or 4 determinations (Wong, Goren, and Lederis, unpublished observations).

lian vasodilatory activity, and the relatively low ACTH releasing activity from the goldfish pituitary.

The analysis of the N-terminal region of U_I, in terms of receptor binding and for structure–activity studies, may be even of greater significance in the understanding of the biological activity spectra and receptor mechanisms of U_I and of the closely related peptides oCRF and SVG. The fragment peptide $U_I(4–28)$ has been seen to be equipotent with the intact oCRF in inducing vasorelaxation *in vitro* and to induce a vasodilatation response *in vivo* (Lederis *et al.*, 1982a; Ichikawa *et al.*, 1982; Lederis, 1984), but to have only about 25% competitive displacement potency of U_I from its vascular receptor, as compared to $\approx 50\%$ for $U_I(28–39)$, the latter having no known biological activity (see Fig. 10b). In view of the need of an almost intact oCRF peptide for significant ACTH releasing activity (Vale *et al.*, 1981), the conclusion becomes attractive that separate receptors, or at least different receptor mechanisms, exist in mammals for the vascular and pituitary actions of U_I and its related peptides. The evidence in favor of the two receptor hypothesis can be summarized as follows: (1) the spectrum of the vascular order of potency in mammals (U_I, SVG $\rightarrow$ oCRF; 100:100:4) indicates a similar trend in the goldfish pituitary order of ACTH-releasing potency ($U_I \rightarrow$ SVG $\rightarrow$ CRF; 100:50:40; Fryer *et al.*, 1984), and (2) the fragment $U_I(4–28)$ is active upon interaction with the mammalian vascular receptors but not with pituitary receptors in the rat (i.e., does not stimulate ACTH release; C. Rivier, personal communication); furthermore, this fragment has high fish pituitary receptor binding capacity (see Fig. 7) and a strikingly similar receptor binding affinity to that of the high-affinity sites in the rat mesenteric artery. It is tempting to conclude, first, that the mammalian vascular receptors are different from those on the mammalian pituitary corticotrophes and, second, that the mammalian vascular and the fish pituitary receptors may be similar or even identical whereas the mammalian pituitary receptors are different (Table III and legend, Fig. 8). A further, hypothetical, extrapolation of this view is that the mammalian vascular and fish pituitary receptors represent a more ancient form of a receptor (and ligand!).

Assuming that the existence of U_I-specific binding sites in many tissues of the goldfish implies its physiological action at all these sites, many more experimental approaches will have to be applied to establish a clear understanding of the physiological importance of this peptide as well as of U_{II} and any other hormonal substances that may yet be discovered in the caudal neurosecretory system of fishes. Evidence available at present cannot even resolve the question of whether the stimulation of ACTH secretion by U_I is a separate phenomenon linked solely to the modulation of the level of interrenal activity—if indeed U_I is a physiological CRF in fishes—or whether the pituitary–interrenal effects of U_I represent only an indirect event that is linked to an overall osmoregulatory control.

REFERENCES

Chou, P. Y., and Fasman, G. D. (1978). *Annu. Rev. Biochem.* **47,** 231.
Erspamer, V., Falconieri Erspamer, G., Improta, G., Negri, L., and deCastiglione, R. (1980). *Naunyn-Schmiedebergs Arch. Pharmakol.* **312,** 265.
Fisher, A. W. F., Weng, K., Gill, U., and Lederis, K. (1984), *Cell Tissue Res.* **235,** 19.
Fryer, J. N., and Maler, L. (1982). *Brain Res.* **242,** 179.
Fryer, J., Lederis, K., and Rivier, J. (1983). *Endocrinology* **113,** 2308.
Fryer, J., Lederis, K., and Rivier, J. (1984). *Peptides,* **5,** 925.
Grutter, M. G. *et al.* (1983). *Nature (London)* **303,** 828.
Harris, G. W. (1955). "Neural Control of the Pituitary Gland." Arnold, London.
Ichikawa, T., McMaster, D., Lederis, K., and Kobayashi, H. (1982). *Peptides* **3,** 859.
Kobayashi, H., Matsui, T., Hirano, T., Iwata, T., and Ishii, S. (1968). *Annot. Zool. Jpn.* **41,** 154.
Lederis, K. (1973). *Am. Zool.* **13,** 771.
Lederis, K. (1977). *Am. Zool.* **17,** 823.
Lederis, K. (1984). "Frontiers of Neuroendocrinology." Raven, New York.
Lederis, K., and Medakovic, M. (1974a). *Br. J. Pharmacol.* **51,** 315.
Lederis, K., and Medakovic, M. (1974b). *Gen. Comp. Endocrinol.* **24,** 10.
Lederis, K., Ichikawa, T., and McMaster, D. (1981). "Neurosecretion. Molecules, Cells, Systems." Plenum, New York.
Lederis, K., Letter, A., McMaster, D., Moore, G., and Schlesinger, D. (1982a). *Science* **218,** 162.
Lederis, K., Vale, W., Rivier, J., MacCannell, K. L., McMaster, D., Kobayashi, Y., Suess, U., and Lawrence, J. (1982b). *Proc. West. Pharmacol. Soc.* **25,** 223.
MacCannell, K. L., and Lederis, K. (1977). *J. Pharmacol. Exp. Ther.* **203,** 38.
MacCannell, K. L., Lederis, K., Hamilton, P. C., and Rivier, J. (1982). *Pharmacology* **25,** 116.
McMaster, D., Rorstad, O. P., Suzuki, Y., and Lederis, K. (1984). *Proc. West. Pharmacol. Soc.* **27,** 237.
Medakovic, M., Chan, D. K. O., and Lederis, K. (1975a). *Pharmacology* **13,** 409.
Medakovic, M., Devlin, A., and Lederis, K. (1975b). *Proc. West. Pharmacol. Soc.* **18,** 384.
Montecucchi, P. C., Henschen, A., and Erspamer, V. (1979). *Hoppe-Seyler's Z. Physiol. Chem.* **360,** 1178.
Muramatsu, I., Miura, A., Fujiwara, M., and Lederis, K. (1981). *Gen. Comp. Endocrinol.* **45,** 446.
Pallai, P. V., Mabilia, M., Goodman, M., Vale, W., and Rivier, J. (1983). *Proc. Natl. Acad. Sci. U.S.A.* **80,** 6770.
Popper, K. R. (1979). "Objective Knowledge: An Evolutionary Approach." Clarendon, Oxford.
Rivier, C., Rivier, J., Lederis, K., and Vale, W. (1983). *Regul. Peptides* **5,** 139.
Scatchard, G. (1949). *Ann. N.Y. Acad. Sci.* **51,** 660.
Suess, U., and Lederis, K. (1981). *Proc. Can. Fed. Biol. Soc.* **24,** 524.
Vale, W., Spiess, J., Rivier, C., and Rivier, J. (1981). *Science* **213,** 1394.
Vale, W. *et al.* (1983). *Endocr. Soc. Abstr.* 730.

Wong, K. L., and Lederis, K. (1982). *Proc. West. Pharmacol. Soc.* **25,** 285.
Wong, K., Fisher, A., and Lederis, K. (1984). *Proc. Can. Fed. Biol. Soc.* **27,** PO 36.
Woo, N. Y. S., Hontela, A., Fryer, J. N., Kobayashi, Y., and Lederis, K. (1984a). *Am. J. Physiol.,* submitted.
Woo, N. Y. S., Wong, K. L., Hontela, A., Fryer, J. N., Kobayashi, Y., and Lederis, K. (1984b). *Int. Symp. Neurosecretion, 9th, Susono-shi, Japan,* in press.

DISCUSSION

P. Kelly: For a mammalian endocrinologist perhaps you can describe the short- and long-term pathophysiological effects of removing the urophysis?

H. A. Bern: I spent a year in Hawaii cauterizing urophyses in tilapia and finding that the fish appeared to do just as well without them as with them. In other species, removal of the urophysis may alter survival ability. There have been some chronic studies by Professor Gunnar Fridberg where urophysectomy of developing fish led to gross somatic abnormalities. One of the problems in tilapia is that urophysectomy still leaves the caudal neurons as a source of hormones. If you remove the entire posterior end of the vertebral column by tying off the tail, the caudal neurosecretory system re-forms anterior to the ligature. This does not happen in all species however.

G. T. Campbell: Professor Bern, I would like to ask you several questions with some reservation. The first time I met Professor Gorbman he gave me a lecture on the deficiency of my education in the biological sciences because I had absolutely no idea what a hagfish looked like. I'm glad to say that now I know what a long-gilled sucker looks like. With respect to the biological activities of urotensin II does it stimulate a chloride pump? There are very few chloride pumps that I know of. One exists in the avian salt gland. Also recent evidence indicates that the reabsorption of sodium in various parts of the kidney tubule is actually secondary to a chloride pump, and if I'm not mistaken I think there is some evidence which indicates that the problem in cystic fibrosis is alteration in chloride pumps. Do you have any idea whether your urotension II is present in avian species?

H. A. Bern: No, no evidence at all.

G. T. Campbell: Since I don't follow the biochemistry of all these peptides, do you have any idea whether there are any sequence similarities between urotensin II and perhaps one of the various forms of atrial natriuretic factor?

H. A. Bern: Not to my knowledge. Sodium pumps are also influenced by urotensin II: it is the sodium pump which is stimulated in the urinary bladder, for example, the chloride pump (in chloride cells) of fish gills (rather, opercular membrane) and fish skins is specifically inhibited, not stimulated, by urotensin II, and may be stimulated in the skin by urotensin I. In Dr. Chris Loretz's recent work active chloride reabsorption occurs across the posterior intestine of the mudsucker, which is stimulated by urotensin II.

G. T. Campbell: Do you have any idea whether the concentrations of urotensins differ, or the distribution of these substances differ in fish who have a particular vascular system, the rete mirabile, in which the veins and the arteries run together and in which control of vasoaction would be very important.

H. A. Bern: I know nothing about it. If you are referring to the structure associated with the swim bladder, this is one region that may be reached by urophyseal hormones.

D. Krieger: I have several questions specifically to ask. The first deals with regulation of the release of this particular hormone or the concentrations of this hormone. If you destroyed amonergic input to the urofices, is there more diminution and release?

H. A. Bern: I would like to refer that question to Dr. Pearson.

D. Pearson: I really don't have much to add in terms of the positive results. Our *in vitro* studies are fairly recent due to the fact that our sensitive radioimmunoassay has only recently been developed. We have not shown releasable U_{II} in response to a bank of neurotransmitters, and other peptides. We can clearly demonstrate calcium-sensitive, or calcium-dependent potassium release of the hormone, but we really at this point don't know anything about physiological release forms; we also are having a technical problem regarding measuring circulating levels of the hormone. We have not been able to do that with our antibody at the present time, so I think we can cross those technological hurdles.

D. Krieger: There was some mention of the effect of glucocorticoid on the action of eurotensin. Are there any effects of glucocorticoids on concentrations or immunocytochemical distribution of urotensin I?

K. Lederis: Unfortunately we have not looked so I cannot enlighten you.

D. Krieger: Is it feasible to obtain blood from this renal portal system and measure eurotension concentrations under various osmotic stimuli?

H. A. Bern: It would be quite feasible to get enough caudal blood on which to do RIA once a reliable RIA has been developed.

K. Lederis: Well perhaps we are more fortunate with our assays as far as we seem to have overcome one of the hurdles that still bugs Dr. Pearson's group, namely, we can assay both urotensins in plasma. At the present time we're applying our measurement systems in areas such as surveys of the distribution and occurrence of the urotensins in fishes and possibly other vertebrates.

D. Krieger: One of the things that is intriguing to me is that looking at extrapituitary sites of production we find things like CRS as well in the same tissues; the question is whether there is any evidence in the urofices of any ACTH-related peptides being present?

D. Pearson: Well, we have had urophyseal extracts analyzed for ACTH activity and found none.

H. A. Levey: I'd like to ask a question on urotensin I and a question on urotensin II. With respect to urotensin I, this may be an example of a fish hormone pointing to a putative activity in the mammal. I refer to the hypotensive effect of urotensin I which is analogous to the hypotensive action of CRF: The vasodilation and increased blood flow reminded me of the intense pituitary hyperemia and dilation of the portal circulation seen after thyroidectomy and to some degree after orchiectomy in the rat; and after long-standing hypothyroidism in the human. The latter was first reported at the turn of the century, only a few years after the initial anatomical description of the urophysis. Is it possible that there might be a hypothalamic influence on the pituitary portal circulation which would result in intense vasodilation with concomitant hyperemia of the adenohypophysis as is so readily demonstrated after thyroidectomy?

K. Lederis: I cannot answer your question directly because one of the places where we did not look for the vasodilatory action of urotensin I is the pituitary portal system. We know that urotensin does not affect the cerebral vasculature; if the pituitary portal system is part of cerebral blood flow, urotensin would not be expected to induce vasodilation. However, physiological implications of this unusual vasodilatory action of all these peptides, be it urotensin or CRF or sauvagine, cannot be excluded as an integral part of the adaptation syndrome or the stress response, for example, to increase gut blood flow during excessive sympathetic discharge. It may be of importance to recall that the ovine CRF has retained only a small proportion of the vasodilator activity of urotensin I. Both human and rat CRF are a few residues closer to urotensin I than is the ovine CRF, so it would be of interest to know the pharmacology of those other CRFs in terms of their vascular action and their physiological implication in modulation of flow in the process of the stress response.

H. A. Levey: To Dr. Bern: Do you have any ideas about the possible influence or adaptive role of urotensin II in osmoregulation in anadromous fish. I see that you did some work with coho salmon. Were they caught in the ocean, or were they on a spawning run from sea to fresh water, or had they been living in freshwater for some time? As an extension of this question, are there differences in concentration of urotensin II in the urophyses of exclusively freshwater and exclusively sea water teleosts—if, in fact, your methodology permits quantitative determination of tissue or blood levels of urotensin II?

H. A. Bern: We're not able to measure blood levels of urotensins in our laboratory yet, and that's something we badly need to do, especially on fish transferred from one salinity to another. In our euryhaline seawater fish (Gillichflup) we have tried to get some information relative to salinity and the content of urotensin II, measured by bioassay. There certainly are seasonal changes but we are not sure whether they are related to reproductive activity, or to seasonal rainfall and hence dilution of the environment or to temperature.

K. Lederis: Several years ago we sampled the sucker fish monthly for several years, and found a clear pattern of changing concentration of the urotensin peptides in the spinal cord and the urophysis, namely during the summer months very low amounts of peptides were present in the system whereas during the winter months (between September and May) very dramatically increased quantities were present. It remains to be determined using the more sensitive immunoassays available now if the photoperiod, temperature, or the reproductive cycle, or a combination of these, could be the cause or the result of the pronounced changes.

K. Sterling: For Dr. Bern: We were taught long, long ago about the adaptations to salt and freshwater getting rid of the hypertonic, seawater ingested through the gills and so on, and I would gather this has changed since the era of Homer Smith; I wonder if you could simply put it together in light of these hormones.

H. A. Bern: I am not sure I understand your question.

K. Sterling: The freshwater fish, of course has a higher tonicity than the water, and the saltwater fish has got a much lower one. The only one we understand fully, I think is the elasmobranch which has high urea. Do we know more now than we did when I studied what Homer Smith taught? Have these hormones contributed to our understanding? You were mentioning various sodium and chloride pumps; could you put them all together?

H. A. Bern: For euryhaline higher bony fish, prolactin is a freshwater-adapting hormone responsible for the ability of the fish to maintain a blood tonicity above that of its environment. Prolactin is sodium-retaining and reduces water entry into the body. In seawater cortisol facilitates the excretion of ions and the absorption and retention of water. Whatever urotensins do in osmoregulation would seem to be relatively minor compared with these major regulatory factors.

A. Barofsky: I was interested in the effect that Dr. Lederis showed on the displacement by VIP of urotensin I binding in goldfish kidney membranes. I was wondering if there are any similar data in mammalian systems. I would also like to ask a related question because of the known effect of VIP on prolactin release. Have you examined the effect of urotensin I on prolactin release?

K. Lederis: So far, we have not included studies on prolactin, but as to VIP in mammalian systems, I tried to indicate the problem we are facing: some kind of a close interaction between urotensin and VIP seems to exist in terms of receptor binding.

M. Selmanoff: I have a brief question related to prolactin. Have you studied the urotensins or sauvagine for PIF activity in any mammalian species?

K. Lederis: No, we have not and I believe Dr. Bern has not done so either. However, Dr. Wylie Vale's laboratory was unable to show any somatostatin like effects of urotensin II in terms of mammalian pituitary hormone release.

P. Donahoe: Question for Dr. Bern. Is there any correlation between the urophysis and the mesenephreson in the avian species?

H. A. Bern: Do you mean has anyone done any work with urotensins or is there caudal system in birds?

P. Donahoe: Is there a caudal system in birds?

H. A. Bern: There is none to my knowledge. There was a claim for an equivalent group of cells in the lumbar spinal cord. When these were examined ultrastructurally in my laboratory by Prof. Asok Ghosh some years back, these beautiful secretory neurons turned out to be loaded with virus-like particles.

S. Cohen: My question is: are there no neurohormones concerned with sexual activity of the animal?

H. A. Bern: What kind of activity, sir?

S. Cohen: Sex!

H. A. Bern: As Professor Lederis has indicated there may be correlations between levels of hormones and reproductive cycles. Urotensin II does have effects on the oviduct of the guppy, according to Lederis and on the sperm duct of the mudsucker, according to Dr. Allen Berlind. These could be meaningful reproductive actions of the caudal system.

I. Callard: Can you tell me if there is any indication of a caudal urophysial system in the caudate amphibia?

H. A. Bern: We have looked for both the cells and urotensin II activity in urodeles (salamanders) and in the tadpoles of anurans, and found neither.

K. Lederis: We have surveyed different organs of representative amphibian, reptilian, avian, and mammalian vertebrates, but could not show, convincingly, the occurrence of immunoreactive urotensin peptides.

L. Birnbaumer: With respect to the VIP effect on urotensin I binding did you look whether this is just a change in the K_D of the urotensin I or is there a change in the maximum number of binding sites?

K. Lederis: Again, no we have not analyzed this any further because we still are baffled as to why we found what we found. So if you know something that I don't know?

K. Birnbaumer: No, I do not have additional information. A second question for Dr. Bern: At one point you said you were looking at CRF and U_{II} and at another point you were saying that you were looking at U_I and U_{II}; you created some confusion in my mind. You were comparing the U_{II} and U_I localization, but at one point you said CRF and then the next time you said U_I.

H. A. Bern: That is because we have no evidence except positive that would indicate that the CRF antibody we are using appears to demonstrate urotensin I at least in the caudal spinal cord of our fish and so it is an anti-CRF which we just call anti-CRF urotensin I.

Glycosylation and Posttranslational Processing of Thyroid-Stimulating Hormone: Clinical Implications

Bruce D. Weintraub, Bethel S. Stannard, James A. Magner,
Catherine Ronin, Terry Taylor, Lata Joshi,
Robert B. Constant, M. Margarida Menezes-Ferreira,
Patricia Petrick, and Neil Gesundheit

*Molecular, Cellular and Nutritional Endocrinology Branch, National Institute of
Arthritis, Diabetes, and Digestive and Kidney Diseases, National Institutes of Health,
Bethesda, Maryland*

I. Introduction

Thyroid-stimulating hormone (TSH) is a glycoprotein hormone of molecular weight 28,000 which is composed of 2 noncovalently linked subunits, α and β. Bovine, porcine, and human pituitary TSH have been characterized in detail including the amino acid sequence and carbohydrate composition of each subunit (Pierce and Parsons, 1981). For bovine TSH, the α subunit has a molecular weight of 13,600, of which 10,800 is comprised of a protein core of 96 amino acid residues and 2800 (21%) represents two oligosaccharide units linked to asparagine residues. Bovine TSH-β has a molecular weight of 14,700 of which 13,100 is comprised of a protein core of 113 amino acid residues and 1600 (12%) represents one asparagine-linked oligosaccharide unit.

TSH is chemically related to the pituitary gonadotropins, luteinizing hormone (LH) and follicle-stimulating hormone (FSH), as well as to chorionic gonadotropin (CG). Within a single species, the α subunits from each of these glycoprotein hormones are virtually identical, while the β subunits are unique and confer immunologic and biologic specificity (Fig. 1). However, the free subunits are essentially devoid of receptor-binding and biologic activity.

Early observations of large-molecular-weight immunoreactive forms of TSH and gonadotropins raised the possibility that these hormones were synthesized from a common prohormone (Table I) containing both α and β subunits, analogous to proinsulin (Prentice and Ryan, 1975). However, it now seems clear that these large forms represent aggregated or bound material whose physiological significance remains unknown. We have

577

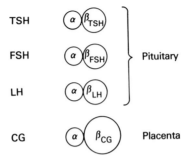

FIG. 1. Structure of pituitary and placental glycoprotein hormones, thyroid-stimulating hormone (TSH), follicle-stimulating hormone (FSH), luteinizing hormone (LH), and chorionic gonadotropin (CG). Within a single species, each hormone contains an α subunit identical in polypeptide but not carbohydrate structure. The noncovalently bound β subunits are unique, but both α and β subunits are necessary for receptor-binding and biological activity.

shown that such glycoprotein hormone or subunits aggregates may be very resistant to dissociation unless complete reduction is performed in the presence of denaturants (Weintraub et al., 1976), conditions that destroy TSH biological and immunological activity (Kourides et al., 1978).

Other observations had instead suggested that the α and β subunits of TSH and related glycoprotein hormones were separately synthesized. We and others had observed many instances of highly unbalanced or even isolated production of α or β subunits both in vivo and in vitro (Tashjian et al., 1973; Weintraub and Rosen, 1973; Rosen and Weintraub, 1974). In the normal pituitary gland, there is a molar excess of free α subunits compared to complete glycoprotein hormones and only small concentrations of free β subunits (Kourides et al., 1975, 1980; Hagen and McNeilly, 1975).

TABLE I

Polypeptide Hormone Precursors and Processing Mechanisms

Pre-pro-hormone
    Cotranslational and posttranslational peptide cleavages with or without glycosylation
        (insulin, parathyroid hormone, hypothalamic releasing hormones, and other
        hormones of molecular weight $\ll 15,000$)
Pre-hormone
    Cotranslational peptide cleavage
        (growth hormone, prolactin, placental lactogen—20,000 to 22,000 MW)
Presubunit
    Cotranslational peptide cleavage and posttranslational subunit combination that is
        dependent on conformation induced by glycosylation
        (thyrotropin and gonadotropins—28,000 to 38,000 MW)

II.   TSH Biosynthesis: Cell-Free Translation Studies

The normal pituitary gland is not an ideal tissue for the study of TSH biosynthesis since it contains only a small percentage of thyrotrophs, as well as gonadotrophs which synthesize α subunits indistinguishable from those in TSH. Therefore, we and others have primarily utilized various strains of mouse pituitary thyrotropic tumors originally developed by Jacob Furth (Furth *et al.*, 1973) for such biosynthesis studies. These transplantable tumors synthesize and secrete large amounts of TSH, and most variants do not synthesize gonadotropins, growth hormone, prolactin, or other pituitary hormones (Blackman *et al.*, 1978; Giudice *et al.*, 1979). We have shown that TSH and its precursor forms synthesized by these tumors are similar if not identical to those synthesized by the nonneoplastic mouse pituitary gland. However, certain of these thyrotropic tumors may show quantitative differences from normal thyrotrophs, including a larger than normal excess of α subunit production and a decreased response to certain regulatory agents (Blackman *et al.*, 1978).

Messenger RNA has been extracted from thyrotropic tumors and translated in wheat germ or reticulocyte lysate cell-free systems that are devoid of enzymes necessary for the proteolytic cleavage of polypeptide precursors or for carbohydrate attachment (Chin *et al.*, 1978; Kourides and Weintraub, 1979; Giudice *et al.*, 1979; Kourides *et al.*, 1979; Giudice and Weintraub, 1979). The major cell-free translation product, representing 25–50% of the total [^{35}S]methionine-labeled proteins synthesized had an apparent molecular weight of 14,000–17,000, depending upon the conditions of the sodium dodecyl sulfate (SDS) gel electrophoresis. It is likely, from other lines of evidence that the true molecular weight of this protein is close to 14,000. This protein was shown to be closely related to standard TSH-α on the basis of immunoprecipitation and tryptic peptide analysis. It apparently did not contain carbohydrate although its molecular weight was at least 3000 greater than the protein core of the α subunit (10,000). These data were consistent with a "pre" or "signal" peptide extension as has been shown for other secretory proteins, and hence this precursor was termed "pre-α." Pre-α could be cleaved of the signal peptide and glycosylated by the translation of messenger RNA in intact frog oocytes or by the addition of homologous or heterologous microsomal membranes during translation in cell-free systems.

Mouse thyrotropic tumor pre-α was purified from translation mixtures and characterized by labeled microsequence analysis using automated Edman degradation (Giudice *et al.*, 1979). Although present in smaller amounts, pre-α's synthesized from normal mouse and bovine pituitary mRNA were also purified and analyzed. The partial amino-terminal analy-

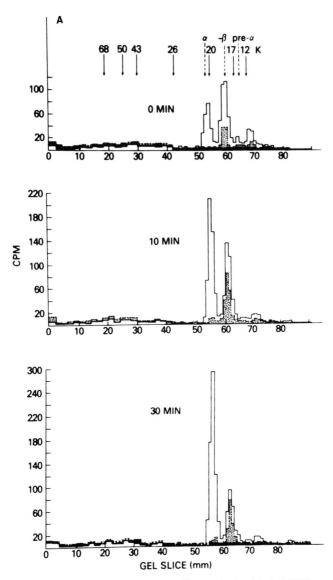

FIG. 2. (A, B, C) Immunoprecipitation of [³⁵S]methionine-labeled TSH-α and TSH-β synthesized by mouse thyrotropic tumor cells during pulse-chase study. (A, B) Cell lysate (intracellular) radioactivity; (C) medium (extracellular) radioactivity. Analysis was by SDS–gradient polyacrylamide slab gels having a 1-cm stacking and 9-cm resolving gel. At each time, cells had been exposed to a constant 10-minute pulse of [³⁵S]methionine followed by a chase of 30,000-fold excess unlabeled methionine for the various times indicated (0 to 240 minutes). Solid lines, unshaded bars (anti-bLH-α); dashed lines, shaded bars (anti-bTSH-β); crossed lines (nonimmune serum). Internal molecular weight markers identified by Coomassie brilliant blue stain were included in each lane of slab gels and used to align figures. Also indicated are the apparent M_r of standard rat LH-α and TSH-β as well as that of mouse

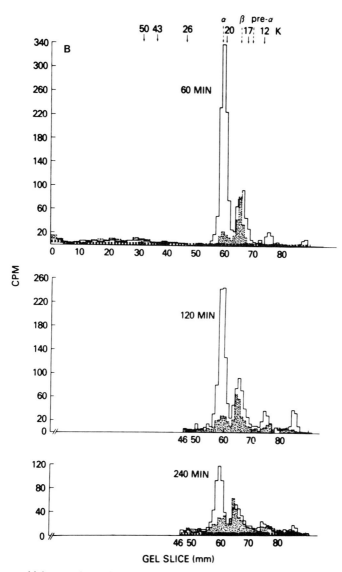

tumor pre-α which were determined in separate experiments (Weintraub *et al.,* 1980). (D) Model of TSH biosynthesis. The initial translation products of separate α and β messenger RNA are presubunits containing an amino-terminal "pre" or signal peptide. Cotranslationally the prepeptide is cleaved and one asparagine-linked carbohydrate unit [CHO (N)] is added to each subunit. Posttranslationally the α subunit only has the addition of a second such carbohydrate unit, which is necessary for α and β subunit combination. There is usually excess production of α subunits, and uncombined α has the addition of a third threonine-linked carbohydrate unit [CHO (O)]. TSH and uncombined α subunits, but virtually no uncombined β subunits, are secreted. Further details of carbohydrate processing and subcellular localization are shown in Fig. 6D.

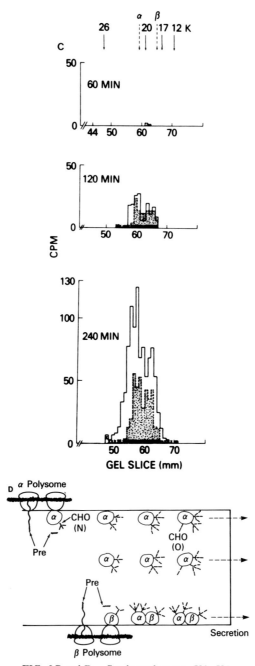

FIG. 2C and D.   See legend on pp. 580–581.

sis of these proteins was compared to the partial sequence analysis of human placental pre-α. As expected for initial translation products, each protein shows a methionine residue in position 1. In addition, there are at least 7 other homologies in the signal peptides from the various species including tyrosines at positions 3, 4, and 7 as well as leucines at positions 12, 15, 19, and 22. Multiple leucine residues are characteristically found in the central hydrophobic regions of signal peptides. Their strict conservation in pre-α derived from various species and tissues may signify an essential role in the attachment and subsequent translocation of nascent chains through the membranes of the endoplasmic reticulum.

The identification of pre-TSH-β in cell-free translation mixtures of mouse tumor mRNA proved more difficult. This difficulty arose in part because of the decreased amounts of [^{35}S]methionine-labeled pre-β synthesized compared to pre-α, as well as its poor immunoreactivity with antisera raised against standard glycosylated β. Direct immunologic identification of pre-β required the use of an antiserum directed at determinants in the primary structure of denatured, reduced, carboxymethyl-TSH-β (Giudice and Weintraub, 1979). The relationship of the cell-free product to standard β was also confirmed by tryptic peptide analysis. Under the conditions of SDS gel electrophoresis where pre-β was well resolved from pre-α, it had an apparent molecular weight of 15,500, or 2500 greater than the protein core of standard TSH-β (13,000). Addition of homologous or heterologous microsomal membranes during translation in cell-free systems caused conversion of pre-β to a glycosylated form similar to standard β.

Recently the methodology of molecular genetics has confirmed and greatly extended the concepts of independent TSH subunits biosynthesis derived from cell-free translation studies. The complete nucleotide sequence of mouse pre-α (Chin et al., 1981a), mouse and bovine pre-TSH-β (Gurr et al., 1983; Maurer et al., 1984) has been determined, permitting deduction of the complete amino acid sequence. In addition, the genes for α and TSH-β have been assigned to different mouse chromosomes (Kourides et al., 1984a). Finally the regulation of TSH subunit messenger RNA levels by thyroid hormone has been studied (Gurr and Kourides, 1983; Shupnik et al., 1983). These data were described in detail in the last volume of the series (Kourides et al., 1984b) and will not be covered here.

III. Posttranslational TSH Processing in Intact Cell Systems

The cell-free studies have been important to define the initial precursor forms of TSH subunits since these forms may be rapidly processed *in vivo* even before release of the nascent subunits from the ribosomes. How-

ever, biosynthetic studies in intact TSH-producing cells are also necessary to elucidate the physiologic mechanisms of posttranslational processing including proteolytic cleavage of signal peptides, glycosylation
and combination of subunits, as well as secretion of TSH and subunits.
Initial studies of TSH biosynthesis in primary cultures of dispersed mouse
thyrotropic tumor cells used gel chromatography under nondenaturing
conditions to distinguish the intact hormone from free subunits (Weintraub and Stannard, 1978). In labeling studies with [^{35}S]methionine, the
earliest α form identified intracellularly during a 10-minute pulse was
smaller than standard α but was converted to higher molecular weight α
forms during a 60-minute chase period with excess unlabeled methionine,
and only this higher molecular weight form of α has been found in intact
TSH. TSH and excess free α, but not free β, appeared in the media
between 60 and 120 minutes of the chase period and were larger than the
respective intracellular forms. There was no evidence in these or the cell-
free studies of *pro*-subunit forms containing trypsin-sensitive amino acids
that might be cleaved after translation (Table I).

Subsequently TSH biosynthesis was studied in these cells using immunoprecipitation combined with sodium dodecyl sulfate gradient gel
electrophoresis under reducing conditions (Weintraub et al., 1980) (Fig.
2). During a 10-minute pulse, the predominant ^{35}S-labeled α form was of
apparent molecular weight 18,000 with a second component of 21,000.
When the labeled pulse was followed by variable chase periods with excess unlabeled methionine, the 18,000 α form was converted progressively to the 21,000 form, implying a precursor–product relationship between the two. The ^{35}S-labeled β form of 18,000 began to combine
selectively with the excess α form (21,000) within 10 to 30 minutes of the
chase period. TSH and excess free α (23,000), but not free β, were secreted between 60 to 240 minutes of the chase. During continuous labeling, the ratio of the two intracellular α forms remained relatively constant.
The [^{35}S]methionine α/β ratio was 4.0 and the molar α/β ratio was estimated to be 2.7; there was no significant degradation of either labeled
subunit for up to 240 minutes. After 120 minutes of continuous labeling,
the intracellular α forms of molecular weight 21,000 and 18,000 showed
different relative incorporations of various ^{3}H-labeled carbohydrates, suggesting that posttranslational processing included modifications of carbohydrate structures. At early labeling times, the α precursors of apparent
molecular weight 18,000 and 21,000 were both converted by endoglycosi-
dase-H treatment to a form of apparent weight 11,000 (Magner and Weintraub, 1982; Weintraub et al., 1983), consistent with the weight of nonglycosylated α also cleaved of the signal peptide. This evidence, plus the
quantal nature of the reaction, have led us to believe that α precursors of
molecular weight 18,000 have had one asparagine-linked high-mannose

carbohydrate unit added, whereas the forms of molecular weight 21,000 have had a second such unit added (see below).

IV. TSH Glycosylation and Carbohydrate Processing

Until 1970 it was believed that the complicated branching carbohydrate moieties of glycoproteins were constructed in the microsomes by the slow accretion of one residue after another. In that year, Behrens and Leloir at the University of Buenos Aires demonstrated that animal cells contain lipid-linked oligosaccharides which serve as intermediates in glycoprotein biosynthesis (Behrens and Leloir, 1970). The oligosaccharide (glucose)$_3$(mannose)$_9$(N-acetylglucosamine)$_2$ is preassembled in rough microsomes linked by phosphates at the reducing terminus to a long organic molecule containing approximately 20 isoprene units, the dolichol phosphate carrier (Fig. 3). Asparagine residues of nascent chains destined to become glycosylated in an N-linked fashion are always present in the sequence (asparagine)-(X)-(serine or threonine). Various lines of evidence suggest that an enzyme, oligosaccharyl transferase, facilitates the co-translational *en bloc* transfer of the oligosaccharide from the dolichol carrier to the asparagine of the nascent chain; for glycoproteins within chick embryo fibroblasts, this step is followed by rapid cleavage of the first two glucoses within about 5 minutes, and then cleavage of the third glucose by 30 to 60 minutes (Hubbard and Robbins, 1979). In order to form so-called "complex" carbohydrate moieties, mannose residues are

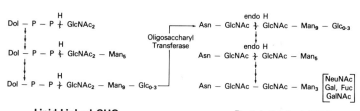

Lipid-Linked CHO   **Protein-Linked CHO**

FIG. 3. Carbohydrate (CHO) chain assembly, transfer, and processing. The oligosaccharide (glucose)$_3$(mannose)$_9$(N-acetylglucosamine)$_2$ is preassembled on a lipid carrier, dolichol pyrophosphate. The enzyme oligosaccharyl transferase facilitates the transfer of the chain to asparagine residues that are followed by any amino acid and then a serine or threonine. Subsequently the protein-linked carbohydrate chains undergo various processing steps: all glucose (Glc) and 6 mannose (Man) residues are removed, and various other sugars are added sequentially to the 3 remaining core mannose residues. Hydrogen ion (H) is used to release carbohydrate chains from lipid, and endoglycosidase H (endo H) is used to release high mannose chains from proteins for analytical studies. The final complex carbohydrate chain may contain N-acetyglucosamine (Glc NAc), N-acetylgalactosamine (Gal NAc), galactose (Gal), fucose (Fuc), sialic acid (Neu NAc), as well as sulfate (see text).

progressively cleaved until a "core" unit of the two N-acetylgluco-samines and 3 mannoses remain, and various residues such as galactose, N-acetylglucosamine, sialic acid, and possibly sulfate or other species, are then added (Fig. 3).

In contrast to the rapid processing of membrane glycoproteins to final complex carbohydrates, we found a much slower processing of secretory TSH carbohydrate (Magner *et al.*, 1984; Ronin *et al.*, 1984). Using thyrotropic tumor cells and a pulse-chase technique we observed (Weintraub *et al.*, 1983) that, during an 11-minute pulse, most α and β subunit precursors were of the high mannose type or endoglycosidase H-sensitive. However only a small amount (approximately 19%) of endoglycosidase H-resistant α forms was present in cells by 30 minutes of chase. Although the percentage of these resistant forms increased progressively with various chase time, they did not comprise the majority (76%) of intracellular α forms until 18 hours of chase. There was also a progressive and apparently more rapid increase in β forms resistant to endoglycosidase H. At all time points media forms were predominantly resistant to endoglycosidase H, reflecting processing to complex carbohydrate.

Recent studies from our laboratory (Ronin *et al.*, 1984) have indicated that the mechanisms and kinetics of the addition and processing of the carbohydrate of TSH subunit precursors within mouse thyrotropic tumor cells differ in some important respects from those of membrane glycoproteins in fibroblasts or viral-infected cells studied by others. Moreover, the rates of carbohydrate processing on TSH-α and β subunits appear to differ.

Thyroid-stimulating hormone (TSH) subunit glycosylation was compared to that of total cell glycoproteins in mouse thyrotropic tumors (Fig. 4). Lipid-linked oligosaccharides, total cell glycoproteins and TSH subunits were labeled either with [^{3}H]mannose, [^{3}H]galactose, or [^{3}H]glucose in pulse and pulse-chase experiments. The various oligosaccharides were isolated, respectively, by lipid extraction and mild acid hydrolysis, selective immunoprecipitation, or acid precipitation followed by trypsin and endoglycosidase H treatment. The nature of the oligosaccharides was assessed by their migration in paper chromatography, their relative incorporation of different precursors, as well as their resistance to α-mannosidase. At 60 minutes, lipid-linked oligosaccharides were found to be composed of $Glc_{3-2}Man_9GlcNAc_2$, $Man_{9-8}GlcNAc_2$, and $Man_5GlcNAc_2$. At 10 or 60 minutes of labeling, total cell proteins contained $Glc_3Man_9GlcNAc_2$, $Glc_1Man_9GlcNAc_2$, $Man_9GlcNAc_2$, $Glc_1Man_8GlcNAc_2$, $Man_8GlcNAc_2$, and $Man_7GlcNAc_2$. The largest oligosaccharide, $Glc_3Man_9GlcNAC_2$, had an unusually long half-life of about 2 hours. In contrast, no $Glc_3Man_9GlcNAc_2$ was found on either TSH + α, or free α subunits either

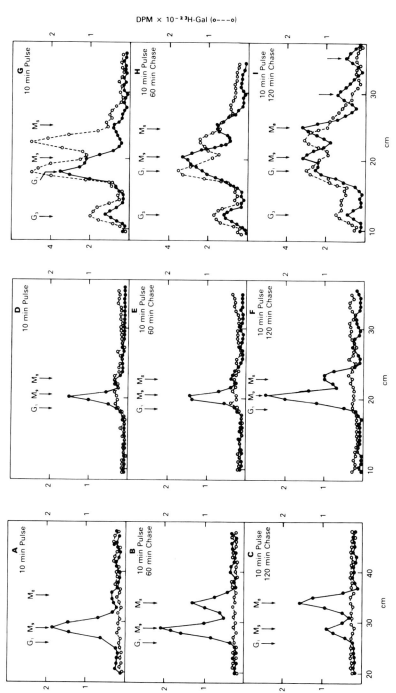

FIG. 4. Paper chromatography of endo-H-released oligosaccharides from TSH + α (left panel), free β (middle panel), and total proteins (right panel). Tumor minces were pulsed for 10 minutes (A,D,G) with [³H]mannose or [³H]galactose and chased for either 60 minutes (B,E,H) or 120 minutes (C,F,I). The chromatogram was developed for 48 hours. The standards are Glc₃Man₉GlcNAc(G₃), Glc₁Man₉GlcNac(G₁), Man₉GlcNAc(M₉), Man₈GlcNAc(M₈), Man₇GlcNAc(M₇), and Man₆GlcNAc(M₆) (Ronin et al., 1984).

isolated by immunoprecipitation or sodium dodecyl sulfate gel electrophoresis. Instead, primarily $Man_9GlcNAc_2$ was found after a 10-minute
pulse on both TSH + α, and β subunits. When the pulse was followed by a
chase up to 2 hours, there was progressive increase in $Man_8GlcNAc_2$ in
higher amount on TSH + α carbohydrate chains than on β. In addition,
when the chase was performed in the presence of hypothyroid serum, a
species comigrating with $Glc_1Man_9GlcNAc_2$ was detected primarily on
TSH + α subunits. These data suggest a differential carbohydrate processing rate for secretory TSH subunits compared to certain cell nonse-
cretory glycoproteins and also demonstrate a differential processing rate
between TSH + α compared to free β subunits. The detailed structures of
the final complex oligosaccharides of TSH remain unknown, and these
studies do not preclude the possibility that other posttranslational modification may take place. Parsons and Pierce (1980) found that the oligosaccharide moieties of some glycoprotein hormone subunits, including the
terminal amino sugars in bovine TSH-α, bovine LH-α and human LH (but
not in human chorionic gonadotropin) are sulfated (Fig. 5). They speculated that the negatively charged sulfate in pituitary glycoprotein hor-

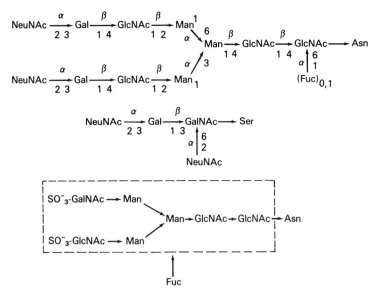

FIG. 5. Representative carbohydrate structures of glycoprotein hormones. The upper
and middle structures have been identified in human CG (Bahl *et al.*, 1978) while the lower
structure has been found in bovine TSH and LH (Parsons and Pierce, 1980). There is great
heterogeneity of carbohydrate structure that appears to be hormonally regulated and has
major implications for function (see text).

mones may play some functional role in the molecule comparable to negatively charged sialic acid in chorionic gonadotropin. Human TSH is probably partly sialylated and partly sulfated. Hortin *et al.* (1981) have demonstrated incorporation of [^{35}S]sulfate into the oligosaccharides of the α and β subunits of bovine and rat lutropin.

Various lines of evidence had suggested that secreted free TSH-α subunit had a slightly higher molecular weight than those α forms combined with β (Weintraub *et al.*, 1980). Parsons *et al.* (1983) have recently reported that the free α subunit derived from bovine pituitaries is glycosylated at an additional site, the threonine at position 43. In recent studies (Weintraub *et al.*, 1983) using mouse thyrotropic tumor cells, endoglycosidase H treatment of TSH- α precursors resulted in the appearance of a component of $M_r = 13,000$ in addition to the form of $M_r = 11,000$ that is usually detected. The amount of the $M_r = 13,000$ form appeared to increase progressively with chase periods of 30 minutes to 18 hours after an 11-minute pulse, and might represent a form of α subunit that had undergone some type of posttranslational addition to the protein or to the asparagine-linked *N*-acetylglucosamine, such as glycosylation at threonine 43.

V. Subcellular Location of TSH Subunit Combination and Processing

The application of subcellular fractionation techniques has recently provided new insight into the intracellular sites of carbohydrate processing, subunit combination, and the relationship of these events (Magner and Weintraub, 1982; Magner *et al.*, 1984); the enzyme endoglycosidase H, which cleaves between the two proximal *N*-acetylglucosamines of precursor high-mannose oligosaccharides but not of complex oligosaccharides, was used to characterize the carbohydrate moieties of both combined and uncombined subunits from various subcellular fractions. Recently, endoglycosidase H has been used to release [^{3}H]mannose-labeled carbohydrate moieties from TSH subunit precursors, and analyses of carbohydrate structure have been performed (Magner *et al.*, 1984; Ronin *et al.*, 1984).

As shown in Fig. 6, separate α and β subunit precursors were rapidly and probably cotranslationally glycosylated with one high-mannose unit in the rough endoplasmic reticulum (RER). This initial glycosylation probably occurred at asparagine 56 in α, and asparagine 23 in β, producing subunit precursors of $M_r = 18,000$. An oligosaccharide presumably containing two *N*-acetylglucosamines, nine mannoses, and three glucoses was transferred *en bloc* to each nascent chain after preassembly on a dolichol phosphate carrier, although recent data suggest that transfer of a

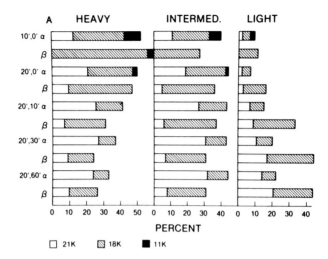

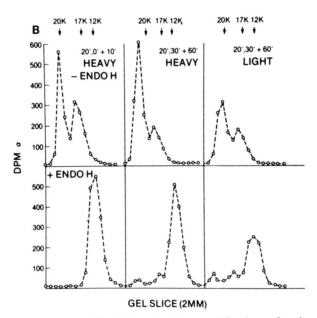

FIG. 6. (A) Percentage of distribution in microsomal fractions of various molecular weight varieties of TSH-α and TSH-β. The sum of radioactivity of TSH-α or TSH-β subunits in the three microsomal fractions at a given labeling time was normalized to 100%. The first time designation (10 or 20 minutes) indicates the minutes that tumor minces were pulse-labeled. The second time designation indicates the chase incubation time with excess unlabeled methionine. The species of $M_r = 21,000$ precipitated by anti-β is TSH-α originally in

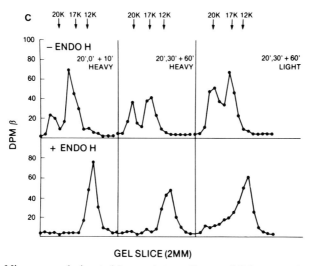

GEL SLICE (2MM)

intact TSH. Microsomes designated heavy, intermediate, and light are enriched in rough endoplasmic reticulum, proximal Golgi, and distal Golgi, respectively (Magner and Weintraub, 1982). (B) Endoglycosidase H sensitivity of TSH-α subunits. [^{35}S]Methionine-labeled TSH-α subunits were immunoprecipitated from sucrose gradient fractions and several specimens were pooled to ensure adequate substrate; the designation Light 20',30'+60' indicates that subunits immunoprecipitated by anti-bovine LH-α from the gradient fraction near the 0.86 m/0.6 m sucrose interface (enriched in smooth ER/Golgi) after tumor slices had been pulse-labeled for 20 minutes followed by a chase incubation of 30 minutes, were pooled with subunits from that gradient fraction after a 20-minute pulse and 60-minute chase. Each of the three specimens was equally divided, and incubated either with (bottom) or without (top) endoglycosidase H (ENDO H). Incubation products were then analyzed by SDS–polyacrylamide gel electrophoresis (Magner and Weintraub, 1982). (C) Endoglycosidase H sensitivity of TSH subunits immunoprecipitated from microsomal fractions by anti-bovine TSH-β. [^{35}S]Methionine-labeled subunits of TSH were immunoprecipitated from sucrose gradient fractions by anti-bovine TSH-β. Specimens were pooled in the same manner as described for B, equally divided, and incubated with (bottom) or without (top) endoglycosidase H (ENDO H). Incubation products were then analyzed by SDS–polyacrylamide gel electrophoresis (Magner and Weintraub, 1982). (D) Model of TSH subunit combination and carbohydrate processing in subcellular compartments. The rough endoplasmic reticulum (ER), proximal Golgi, distal Golgi, and secretory granules of a thyrotroph cell, as well as the extracellular space, are depicted. Boldface α and β represent the respective polypeptide chains, and $\sim$ represents the respective signal sequences. The carbohydrate moieties of precursors sensitive to endoglycosidase H have been indicated with N, N-acetylglucosamine; M, mannose; and G, glucose. Moieties resistant to cleavage by this enzyme are designated C or C', and presumably have a so-called complex carbohydrate structure. The X on certain free α subunits represents an O-linked carbohydrate moiety at threonine 43. The cotranslational transfer of (glucose)$_3$ species is indicated in this figure by analogy to studies of the biosynthesis of membrane glycoproteins; studies at early times show TSH subunit precursors to contain (glucose)$_1$ but not (glucose)$_3$ species, suggesting either a different transfer mechanism or rapid trimming of the glucose residues. See text for details (Magner et $al.$, 1984; Magner and Weintraub, 1984).

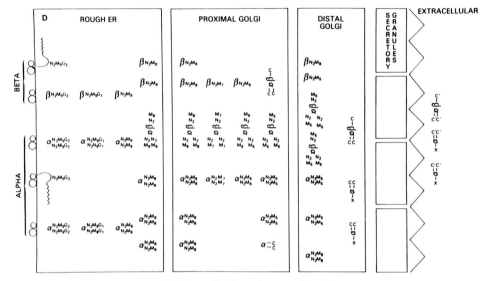

FIG. 6D. See legend on pp. 590–591.

(glucose)$_1$ containing species may occur, or that glucose residues may be rapidly cleaved. Cotranslational glycosylation, i.e., covalent addition of carbohydrate to nascent proteins still attached to ribosomes, was likely since studies of unfractionated thyrotrophs demonstrated that precursors of M_r = 18,000 predominated after pulse times as short as 1 minute. Small amounts of α and β precursors of M_r = 11,000 also were detected in RER fractions at 10 minutes, and likely represented a few early precursors that were not glycosylated since in other experiments forms of M_r = 11,000 predominated in whole cell lysates and media when thyrotrophs were incubated with tunicamycin, an antibiotic which prevents the *en bloc* glycosylation of proteins at asparagine sites (Weintraub *et al.*, 1980, 1983). Moreover, precursors of M_r = 18,000 were converted to forms of M_r = 11,000–12,000 by treatment with endoglycosidase H (Magner and Weintraub, 1982; Weintraub *et al.*, 1983).

The RER was also the site of the co- or posttranslational addition of a second high-mannose unit to the α subunit precursor of M_r = 18,000; this glycosylation, probably at the asparagine at position 82 near the carboxyl-terminus, resulted in an endoglycosidase H sensitive α form of M_r = 21,000. A quantal precursor–product relationship between α forms of M_r = 18,000 and 21,000 has been well demonstrated by pulse-chase techniques both in our laboratory (Weintraub *et al.*, 1980, 1983), and by others (Chin *et al.*, 1981b). In studies of unfractionated cells, there was a gradual

TABLE II

Calculated Percentages of Limiting TSH-β Subunit Combined with α in Microsomal Subfractions of Mouse Thyrotropin Tumor Cells[a]

Microsomes	Percentage of TSH-β combined with α				
	10 min, 0 min	20 min, 0 min	20 min, 10 min	20 min, 30 min	20 min, 60 min
Heavy	0	19	21	42	43
Intermediate	0	12	13	19	24
Light	0	18	24	41	61

[a] Cells were pulse labeled with [^{35}S]methionine for either 10 or 20 minutes, and then chased with excess unlabeled methionine for 0 to 60 minutes. Microsomes were subfractionated on sucrose gradients into heavy, intermediate, and light density fractions, enriched in rough endoplasmic reticulum, proximal Golgi, and distal Golgi elements, respectively. TSH subunit combination was measured by methods described in the text. [Modified from Magner and Weintraub (1982).]

predominance of the heavy form during 5- to 10-minute chase periods after a brief pulse. This identification of α subunit precursors of $M_r = 18,000$ as being glycosylated at one site, and α precursors of $M_r = 21,000$ as being glycosylated at two sites is also consistent with the finding that both forms reverted to apparently the same form of $M_r = 11,000–12,000$ after incubation with endoglycosidase H, a weight consistent with that of the protein core subunit plus one or two N-acetylglucosamine residues.

The molar ratio of $α:β$ subunits in the RER at early times was approximately 7:1, based on experiments done in our laboratory (Magner and Weintraub, 1982). The synthesis of excess α subunit might be analogous to excess light chain synthesis during immunoglobulin biosynthesis (Tartakoff and Vassalli, 1979).

Combination of high-mannose forms of α of $M_r = 21,000$ with β of $M_r = 18,000$ began in the RER and continued in the smooth endoplasmic reticulum (SER), Golgi, and post-Golgi compartments, where carbohydrate processing was completed; attainment of endoglycosidase H resistance (i.e., processed complex-type carbohydrate) is not a prerequisite for subunit combination. Approximately 19% of limiting β subunits in the RER were combined with α at 20 minutes of pulse labeling; after an additional 60 minutes of chase, a Golgi fraction was highly enriched in combined subunits, with 61% of β combined (Table II). The rate of combination of subunits in intact cells was much faster than observed rates *in vitro* (Ingham *et al.*, 1974). Alpha precursors of $M_r = 11,000$ and 18,000 were not observed to combine with β; the α species of $M_r = 11,000$ was also not found in intact TSH. Finally, virtually all of the secreted TSH and free α was processed to complex forms.

Subfractionation techniques have also provided insight into the intracellular transport of newly synthesized subunits. After a 20 minute pulse with [^{35}S]methionine, subunits declined in the RER and increased in SER/Golgi fractions during chase incubations of up to 60 minutes. Free and combined β subunit precursors moved from the RER to a light density SER/Golgi fraction faster than free α subunit precursors. We speculated that the interaction of membrane-bound glycosylating enzymes with free α subunit precursors at the time of their second glycosylation retards the exit of α precursors from the RER as compared to β precursors. However, total [^{35}S]methionine-labeled proteins moved at about the same rate as α, suggesting that transport of α was not retarded, but that transport of β was in fact accelerated. Moreover, those few subunits that combined in the RER appeared to move to the light density SER/Golgi fraction more rapidly than uncombined subunits (Magner and Weintraub, 1982).

With respect to cotranslational glycosylation and subsequent processing of carbohydrate moieties, our current model of TSH biosynthesis (Fig. 6) while being consistent with the general scheme proposed by others for other glycoproteins (Hubbard and Robbins, 1979) presents some interesting new features. Nascent chains destined to acquire asparagine-linked carbohydrate have been shown in other systems to undergo cotranslational *en bloc* addition of the oligosaccharide (glucose)$_3$(mannose)$_9$(N-acetylglucosamine)$_2$, or $G_3M_9N_2$. However, as described above, although $G_3M_9N_2$ has been noted on thyrotropic membrane proteins at early pulse times, no species longer than $G_1M_9N_2$ has been noted on TSH subunits, implying either a different transfer mechanism or more rapid trimming of glucose residues (Ronin *et al.*, 1984). During posttranslational processing, glucose and mannose residues are progressively trimmed away, followed by addition of a variety of sugar residues to produce so-called "complex," endoglycosidase H-resistant forms.

Recent mannose-labeling experiments in our laboratory (Magner *et al.*, 1984) enabled the assignment of structures for the α subunit carbohydrate as the precursor was transported through various subcellular compartments. In the RER of cells pulsed for 180 minutes, 65% of the mannose label was in $G_1M_9N_1$, M_9N_1, and M_8N_1. Only 6% was in endoglycosidase H-resistant forms and small amounts of M_7N_1, M_6N_1, and M_5N_1 were detected, perhaps attributable to cross-contamination during subcellular fractionation. In a low density sucrose fraction believed to be enriched in distal Golgi elements, 42% of the label was in M_8N_1, 17% in M_5N_1, and 19% in endoglycosidase H-resistant forms. On a molar basis, most of the α carbohydrate units in the RER were M_8N_1, whereas in the distal Golgi endoglycosidase H-resistant forms predominated. TSH and free α subunit secreted into media were > 95% endoglycosidase H-resistant. Pulse-chase techniques confirmed that the glucose and first mannose were cleaved in the RER, and again demonstrated accumulation of M_8N_1 and M_5N_1 species, which may be rate limiting steps in processing.

Our studies (Ronin *et al.*, 1984) with unfractionated thyrotrophs have also demonstrated an accumulation of TSH-α and β precursors having oligosaccharides containing eight mannoses. The accumulation of units having eight mannoses has also been reported by others studying the biosynthesis of hCG-α (Ruddon *et al.*, 1981) and certain other glycoproteins (Hubbard and Robbins, 1979) in unfractionated cells, and has been attributed to a possible rate-limiting transport of M_8 forms to the Golgi. In contrast our direct subcellular fractionation studies demonstrated substantial amounts of M_8 forms of TSH-α in Golgi, weighing against a transport block, and suggesting instead that an alternative mechanism perhaps a conformational change in the protein, may allow processing beyond M_8. The substantial accumulation of M_5 intermediates has not generally been observed in other systems and may be related to the different nature of the mannosyl linkages of the inner five mannoses as compared to the outer mannoses. We suspect that α precursors having units containing eight mannoses begin to combine with β to form TSH in the RER because α subunits isolated from unfractionated cells after a 60-minute pulse can combine *in vitro* with α; at that time α precursors with two high mannose units predominated.

VI. Role of Glycosylation in TSH Biosynthesis, Bioactivity, and Metabolic Clearance

The carbohydrate of TSH appears to play multiple roles in the assembly of the hormone and in its action (Table III). These conclusions have been reached by observing the effects of inhibition of subunit glycosylation during biosynthesis, the effects of chemical deglycosylation of TSH as

TABLE III

Roles of Carbohydrate in TSH Synthesis and Action

High mannose precursor carbohydrate
    Induction of conformation necessary for α-β subunit combination
    Protection from intracellular proteolysis and aggregation
Complex final carbohydrate
    Intrinsic biologic activity
    Metabolic clearance rate

well as the bioactivity and clearance of naturally occurring TSH forms differing in carbohydrate content.

Tunicamycin is an antibiotic that inhibits the formation of the oligosaccharide-lipid intermediates involved in glycosylation at asparagine residues. Since all oligosaccharides in TSH are linked to asparagine, we expected that this agent could totally inhibit subunit glycosylation. Indeed, tunicamycin in doses of 1–5 μg/ml caused the appearance of a new molecular weight α form of 11,000 and a new molecular weight β form of 12,000 (Weintraub et al., 1980, 1983). These forms incorporated [^{35}S]methionine but did not incorporate [^{3}H]glucosamine, confirming the fact that glycosylation had been fully inhibited. Moreover, the molecular weight of these subunit forms corresponded to that of the α and β protein cores. The nonglycosylated subunits produced by tunicamycin treatment showed a high degree of aggregation, especially after heating at 37°C under nonreducing conditions. Unlike glycosylated subunits, which were not degraded, nonglycosylated subunits were 50–65% degraded intracellularly before secretion; the degradation caused by tunicamycin was specific for TSH subunits and not noted for other ^{35}S-labeled proteins. Incubation of various ^{35}S-labeled α forms with excess unlabeled TSH-β showed high combining activity for intracellular α with two high mannose units, intermediate activity for media α with two complex units, and low activity for intracellular α with one high mannose unit or nonglycosylated media α. These data suggest that the initial glycosylation with high mannose carbohydrate units prevents intracellular aggregation and degradation of TSH subunits and enhances attainment of the conformation necessary for α and β subunit combination.

Specific carbohydrate processing also appears necessary for the expression of TSH biologic activity (Joshi and Weintraub, 1983). We have examined the interaction of certain forms of mouse (m) tumor and bovine (b) pituitary TSH with standard bTSH on the activation of adenylate cyclase in human thyroid membranes. Tumor extract, serum for tumor-bearing mice, culture medium from dispersed cell incubations, and two preparations of purified bTSH (Sigma and Pierce) were fractionated on Sephadex G-100 (1.2 × 200 cm). For each fraction, TSH bioactivity was measured by stimulation of adenylate cyclase activity in human thyroid membranes, and immunoactivity was determined by radioimmunoassay. On G-100, Pierce bTSH and multiple immunoactive components with partition coefficients (K_{av}) of 0.28–0.32 and ratios of biological over immunological activity (B/I) of 0.59–1.42. Sigma bTSH, mouse tumor, serum, and medium were even more heterogeneous (K_{av} = 0.23–0.32), with a lower range of B/I (0.04–1.01). When single doses (125–2000 ng) of those fractions with the highest K_{av} (0.30–0.32) and lowest B/I (0.04 =

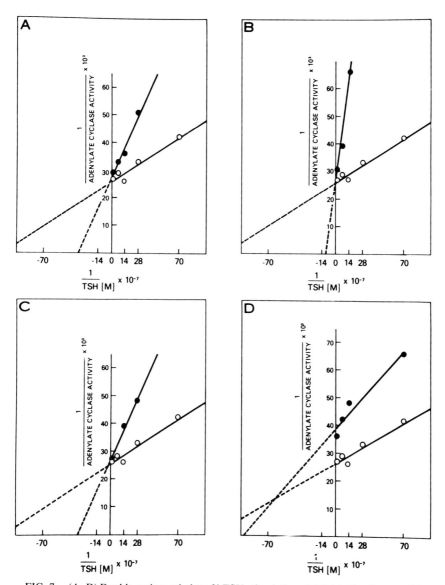

FIG. 7. (A–D) Double reciprocal plot of bTSH stimulation of ACA in the absence (○) or presence (●) of bTSH (Sigma) fraction 116 with $K_{av} = 0.30$ (A), mouse tumor fraction 116 with $K_{av} = 0.32$ (B), mouse serum fraction 115 with $K_{av} = 0.32$ (C), mouse tumor medium fraction 115 with $K_{av} = 0.31$ (D). Arbitrary concentrations of inhibitors (10^{-3} dilution of the column fraction = 125–2000 ng rTSH) were mixed with various concentrations (200–10,000 μU) of bTSH (Armour), and the standard adenylate cyclase assay was performed. Each point is a mean of three observations. A, B, and C show the competitive type of inhibition, i.e., no statistically significant difference in ordinate intercepts ($p > 0.05$). D shows mixed type of inhibition, i.e., significant differences in ordinate intercepts ($p < 0.05$). The slopes of the two lines with and without inhibitor were significantly different in all cases ($p < 0.05$) (Joshi and Weintraub, 1983).

0.51) were mixed with multiple doses (200–10,000 μU) of Armour TSH standard (B/I = 1), there was 30–56% inhibition of adenylate cyclase activity stimulation. Double reciprocal plots (Fig. 7) showed competitive inhibition for the low B/I forms from all sources, except for a medium form which showed mixed inhibition. The medium form had the highest inhibitory activity. There were no inhibitors in G-100 fractions from the K_{av} regions devoid of TSH immunoactivity or from the same K_{av} regions of normal mouse serum. To determine the chemical differences between different forms, affinity chromatography on concanavalin A, wheat germ agglutinin, and soybean agglutinin was employed. Compared with the apparent higher molecular weight form with higher B/I, the apparent lower molecular weight form with lower B/I contained decreased amounts or availability of α-mannose and increased amounts or availability of N-acetyl-D-galactosamine and/or β-galactose; both forms appear to contain similar β-N-acetyl-D-glucosamine residues, presumably in the inner core.

Recently it has been shown that bovine TSH chemically deglycosylated with anhydrous hydrogen fluoride showed markedly diminished bioactivity despite normal or enhanced receptor-binding activity (Amir et al., 1984). This deglycosylated TSH demonstrated a competitive inhibition of normal TSH bioactivity, similar to certain naturally occurring antagonists described above (Amr et al., unpublished data). Finally, the chemically deglycosylated TSH showed a more rapid metabolic clearance than normal TSH when injected intravenously into euthyroid rats (Constant and Weintraub, 1984). These data suggest that carbohydrate is necessary for both the intrinsic bioactivity of TSH as well as for protection from metabolic clearance in vivo.

VII. Regulation of TSH Biosynthesis and Glycosylation

We have shown that thyroid hormone deficiency caused increases in both TSH apoprotein and carbohydrate biosynthesis in cultured rat pituitaries (Taylor and Weintraub, 1985a). In hypothyroid pituitaries plus media [^{14}C]alanine incorporation in combined and free β subunits was 26 times normal and considerably greater than the 3.4-fold increase seen in total protein; combined and free α showed no specific increase in apoprotein synthesis. [^{3}H]Glucosamine incorporation in combined α and β subunits in hypothyroid samples was 13 and 21 times normal, respectively, and was greater than the 1.9-fold increase seen in total protein; free α subunit showed no specific increase in carbohydrate synthesis (Fig. 8). The GlcN/ Ala ratio, reflecting relative glycosylation of newly synthesized molecules, was increased in hypothyroidism for combined α but not for combined β, free α subunits or total proteins.

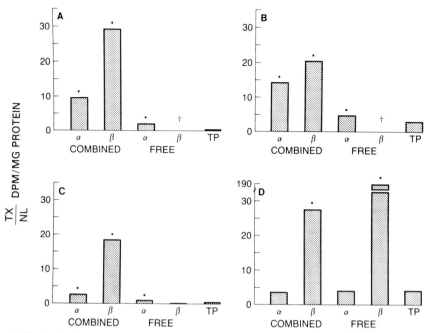

FIG. 8. Ratio of hypothyroid to normal labeled precursor incorporation in TSH subunits and total proteins. Shown is the hypothyroid (TX) to normal (NL) ratio for [³H]glucosamine incorporation present in the media (A) and the pituitary (B) and for [¹⁴C]alanine incorporation present in the media (C) and the pituitary (D). Free β subunit carbohydrate content could not be determined by the methods used in these experiments and is illustrated by †. Significant differences in the ratios between total protein and TSH subunits were determined by Wilcoxon signed rank sum test (*$p < 0.05$) (Taylor and Weintraub, 1985a).

In summary, short-term hypothyroidism selectively stimulated TSH β subunit apoprotein synthesis and carbohydrate synthesis of combined α and β subunits. Hypothyroidism also increased the relative glycosylation of combined α subunit. Thus, thyroid hormone deficiency appears to alter the rate-limiting step in TSH assembly (i.e., β subunit synthesis) as well as the carbohydrate structure of TSH, which may play important roles in its biologic function.

In contrast early biosynthetic studies had suggested that thyrotropin-releasing hormone (TRH) caused a selective stimulation of TSH glycosylation (Wilber, 1971; Ponsin and Mornex, 1983). Using subunit-specific analytic methods, we have recently shown (Taylor and Weintraub, 1985b) that normal rat pituitaries stimulated with TRH for 24 hours showed a 3-fold stimulation of labeled glucosamine incorporation into secreted TSH

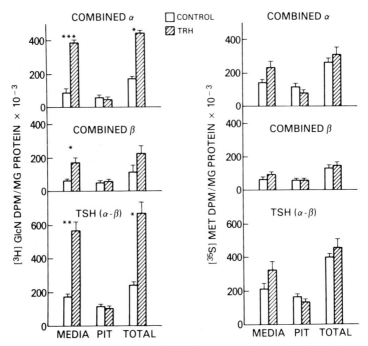

FIG. 9.   TSH subunit incorporation of labeled precursors in normal pituitary incubates at 24 hours ± 1 ng/ml TRH. Demonstrated is [³H]glucosamine (left panels) and [³⁵S]methionine (right panels) incorporation in combined α (upper panels), combined β (middle panels), and intact TSH (lower panels). Significant differences between control and TRH treated samples are demonstrated by *$p < 0.05$, **$p < 0.01$, ***$p < 0.001$ (Taylor and Weintraub, 1985b).

but no change in labeled alanine incorporation (Fig. 9). The increased glycosylation was noted in both combined α and β subunits but not in the free α subunit. Preliminary lectin analysis of TSH glycopeptides after TRH treatment of hypothyroid mouse pituitaries revealed increased glucosamine incorporation into biantennary carbohydrate chains (Gesundheit and Weintraub, unpublished data). Moreover, the increased glycosylation of secreted TSH caused by TRH was shown to enhance its intrinsic bioactivity (Menezes-Ferreira and Weintraub, 1984).

VIII.   Clinical Implications

Elevated serum α/TSH ratios have been described in patients with TSH-secreting pituitary tumors (Kourides *et al.*, 1976). The excess α production from such tumors has been of value in differentiating patients with neoplastic from nonneoplastic causes of TSH-induced hyperthyroidism (Weintraub *et al.*, 1981). In addition, we have demonstrated isolated production of α subunit, without concomitant production of TSH or gonadotropins, by certain pituitary adenomas (Kourides *et al.*, 1976) as well as certain other malignant tumors (Rosen and Weintraub, 1974). Elevated serum TSH-β/TSH ratios have been described in two patients, one with an enlarged thyroid and one with an enlarged pituitary (Kourides *et al.*, 1978). The TSH-β in both cases had an apparently large molecular weight (160,000–200,000), displayed immunologic properties different from standard TSH-β, and was unresponsive to TRH. Although this unusual form of TSH-β has been partially characterized, its significance remains unknown.

We have also described unusual forms of human TSH with decreased bioactivity. One apparently normal subject was found to have a high-molecular-weight form of TSH with normal receptor-binding properties but decreased bioactivity (Spitz *et al.*, 1981). Such forms may result from aggregated or protein-bound TSH caused by abnormalities of glycosylation, similar to those noted after tunicamycin treatment (see above).

Early studies had suggested that certain cases of idiopathic central hypothyroidism might result from the secretion of biologically inactive TSH (Faglia *et al.*, 1979). To investigate this possibility and to define the mechanism of defective hormone action, we measured the adenylate cyclase-stimulating bioactivity (B) and receptor-binding (R) activity of immunoreactive (I) TSH which was affinity purified from the serum of seven selected patients with central hypothyroidism (Beck-Peccoz *et al.*, 1985). We found a strikingly decreased ratio of R/I (<0.15) in patients compared to controls (0.6–2.7), and a similarly decreased B/I (<0.2 vs 2.8–5.6). After actue TRH injection (200 μg iv), the ratio of R/I increased in two of three patients while the B/I normalized in only one patient. After chronic TRH administration (40 mg/day po for 20 days), both ratios normalized in all but one patient who showed apparent desensitization. The increased bioactivity of the secreted TSH after chronic TRH therapy resulted in increased secretion of serum thyroid hormones in all patients studied, with restoration of clinical euthyroidism. We conclude that, in certain cases of central hypothyroidism, the secreted TSH lacks biological activity because of imparied binding to its receptor; TRH treatment can correct both TSH defects. These data imply that TRH regulates not only TSH secretion, but also its specific molecular and conformational features required for hormone action. In view of the results presented above showing that TRH causes a selective increase in TSH glycosylation, it seems likely that these conformational changes result from alterations in carbohydrate structure. However other alterations in apoprotein structure or unknown posttranslational modifications cannot be excluded.

IX. Conclusions

The glycosylation and posttranslational processing of TSH subunits are important for hormone assembly, bioactivity, and metabolic clearance. Endocrine factors may specifically regulate TSH carbohydrate structure, resulting in heterogeneous forms with different physicochemical and functional properties. Certain human diseases may be associated with unbalanced production of TSH subunits or abnormal forms of hormone with reduced bioactivity.

REFERENCES

Amir, S., Keutmann, H. T., Randall, M. F., and Kubota, K. (1984). *Program Annu. Meet. Am. Thyroid Assoc., 60th* T-24 (Abstr.).

Bahl, O. P., Marz, L., and Kessler, M. J. (1978). *Biochem. Biophys. Res. Commun.* **84**, 667.

Beck-Peccoz, P., Amir, S., Menezes-Ferreira, M. M., Faglia, G., and Weintraub, B. D. (1985). *N. Engl. J. Med.,* in press.

Behrens, N. H., and Leloir, L. F. (1970). *Proc. Natl. Acad. Sci. U.S.A.* **66**, 153.

Blackman, M. R., Gershengorn, M. C., and Weintraub, B. D. (1978). *Endocrinology* **102**, 499.

Chin, W. W., Habener, J. F., Kieffer, J. D., and Maloof, F. (1978). *J. Biol. Chem.* **253**, 7985.

Chin, W. W., Kronenberg, H. M., Dee, P. C., Maloof, F., and Habener, J. F. (1981a). *Proc. Natl. Acad. Sci. U.S.A.* **78**, 5329.

Chin, W. W., Maloof, F., and Habener, J. F. (1981b). *J. Biol. Chem.* **256**, 3059.

Constant, R. B., and Weintraub, B. D. (1984). *Clin. Res.* **32**, 483 (Abstr.).

Faglia, G., Bitensky, L., Pinchera, A., Ferrari, C., Paracchi, A., Beck-Peccoz, P., Ambrosi, B., and Spada, A. (1979). *J. Clin. Endocrinol. Metab.* **48**, 989.

Furth, J., Moy, P., Hershman, J., and Ueda, G. (1973). *Arch. Pathol.* **96**, 217.

Giudice, L. C., and Weintraub, B. D. (1979). *J. Biol. Chem.* **254**, 12679.

Giudice, L. C., Waxdal, M. J., and Weintraub, B. D. (1979). *Proc. Natl. Acad. Sci. U.S.A.* **76**, 4798.

Gurr, J. A., and Kourides, I. A. (1983). *J. Biol. Chem.* **258**, 10208.

Gurr, J. A., Catterall, J. F., and Kourides, I. A. (1983). *Proc. Natl. Acad. Sci. U.S.A.* **80**, 2122.

Hagen, C., and McNeilly, A. S. (1975). *J. Endocrinol.* **67**, 49.

Hortin, G., Natowicz, M., Pierce, J., Baenizer, J., Parsons, T., and Boime, I. (1981). *Proc. Natl. Acad. Sci. U.S.A.* **78**, 7468.

Hubbard, S. C., and Robbins, P. W. (1979). *J. Biol. Chem.* **254**, 4568.

Ingham, K. C., Aloj, S. M., and Edelhoch, H. (1974). *Arch. Biochem. Biophys.* **163**, 589.

Joshi, L. R., and Weintraub, B. D. (1983). *Endocrinology* **113**, 2145.

Kourides, I. A., and Weintraub, B. D. (1979). *Proc. Natl. Acad. Sci. U.S.A.* **76**, 298.

Kourides, I. A., Weintraub, B. D., Ridgway, E. C., and Maloof, F. (1975). *J. Clin. Endocrinol. Metab.* **40**, 872.

Kourides, I. A., Weintraub, B. D., Rosen, S. W., Ridgway, E. C., Kliman, B., and Maloof, F. (1976). *J. Clin. Endocrinol. Metab.* **43**, 97.

Kourides, I. A., Weintraub, B. D., and Maloof, F. (1978). *J. Clin. Endocrinol. Metab.* **47**, 24.

Kourides, I. A., Vamvakopoulos, N. C., and Maniatis, G. M. (1979). *J. Biol. Chem.* **254,** 11106.

Kourides, I. A., Landon, M. B., Hoffman, B. J., and Weintraub, B. D. (1980). *Clin. Endocrinol.* **12,** 407.

Kourides, I. A., Barker, P. E., Gurr, J. A., Pravtcheva, D. D., and Ruddle, F. H. (1984a). *Proc. Natl. Acad. Sci. U.S.A.* **81,** 517.

Kourides, I. A., Gurr, J. A., and Wolf, O. (1984b). *Recent Prog. Horm. Res.* **40,** 79.

Magner, J. A., and Weintraub, B. D. (1982). *J. Biol. Chem.* **257,** 6709.

Magner, J. A., and Weintraub, B. D. (1985). *In* "The Thyroid" (S. H. Ingbar and L. E. .Braverman, eds.), Harper, New York, in press.

Magner, J. A., Ronin, C., and Weintraub, B. D. (1984). *Endocrinology* **115,** 1019.

Maurer, R. A., Croyle, M. L., and Donelson, J. E. (1984). *J. Biol. Chem.* **259,** 5024.

Menezes-Ferreira, M. M., and Weintraub, B. D. (1984). *Program Annu. Meet. Am. Thyroid Assoc. 60th,* T-33 (Abstr.).

Parsons, T. F., and Pierce, J. G. (1980). *Proc. Natl. Acad. Sci. U.S.A.* **77,** 7089.

Parsons, T. F., Bloomfield, G. A., and Pierce, J. G. (1983). *J. Biol. Chem.* **258,** 240.

Pierce, J. G., and Parsons, T. F. (1981). *Annu. Rev. Biochem.* **50,** 465.

Ponsin, G., and Mornex, R. (1983). *Endocrinology* **113,** 549.

Prentice, L. G., and Ryan, R. J. (1975). *J. Clin. Endocrinol. Metab.* **40,** 303.

Ronin, C., Stannard, B. S., Rosenbloom, I. L., Manger, J. A., and Weintraub, B. D. (1984). *Biochemistry* **23,** 4503.

Rosen, S. W., and Weintraub, B. D. (1974). *N. Engl. J. Med.* **290,** 1441.

Ruddon, R. W., Bryan, A. H., Hanson, C. A., Perini, F., Ceccorulli, L. M., and Peters, B. P. (1981). *J. Biol. Chem.* **256,** 5189.

Shupnik, M. A., Chin, W. W., Ross, D. S., Downing, M. F., Habener, J. F., and Ridgway, E. C. (1983). *J. Biol. Chem.* **258,** 15120.

Spitz, I. M., LeRoith, D., Hirsch, H., Carayon, P., Pekonen, F., Liel, Y., Sobel, R., Chorer, Z., and Weintraub, B. D. (1981). *N. Engl. J. Med.* **304,** 278.

Tartakoff, A., and Vassalli, P. (1979). *J. Cell Biol.* **83,** 284.

Tashjian, A. H., Jr., Weintraub, B. D., Barowsky, N. J., Rabson, A. S., and Rosen, S. W. (1973). *Proc. Natl. Acad. Sci. U.S.A.* **70,** 1419.

Taylor, T., and Weintraub, B. D. (1985a). *Endocrinology* **116,** 1535.

Taylor, T., and Weintraub, B. D. (1985b). *Endocrinology* **116,** 1968.

Weintraub, B. D., and Rosen, S. W. (1973). *J. Clin. Invest.* **52,** 3135.

Weintraub, B. D., and Stannard, B. S., (1978). *FEBS Lett.* **92,** 303.

Weintraub, B. D., Krauth, G., Rosen, S. W., and Rabson, A. S. (1976). *J. Clin. Invest.* **56,** 1043.

Weintraub, B. D., Stannard, B. S., Linnekin, D., and Marshall, M. (1980). *J. Biol. Chem.* **255,** 5715.

Weintraub, B. D., Gershengorn, M. C., Kourides, I. A., and Fein, H. (1981). *Ann. Intern. Med.* **95,** 339.

Weintraub, B. D., Stannard, B. S., and Meyers, L. (1983). *Endocrinology* **112,** 1331.

Wilber, J. F. (1971). *Endocrinology* **89,** 873.

DISCUSSION

J. Robbins: There's beginning evidence that carbohydrates not only exert their own function in terms of receptor interactions, etc. but may actually have an effect on the conformation of the polypeptide chain. We've just begun to develop such evidence for the thyroxin-binding globulin. I wonder if you know anything about this in respect to TSH, or have any general comments on this.

B. Weintraub: Yes, it's a very important comment. Early work in glycoprotein biochemistry did not show major conformational changes and it led to the view that carbohydrates didn't play much of a role in conformation. However, as Dr. Robbins mentioned, nowadays using more sensitive techniques such as NMR, one can clearly demonstrate that carbohydrates induce at least local changes in conformation. Indeed, for the glycoprotein hormone there is such evidence. Our group [Giudice, L. C., and Weintraub, B. D. (1979). *J. Biol. Chem.* **254,** 12679] and then more recently Pierce's group (Strickland, T. W., and Pierce, J. G. (1983). *J. Biol. Chem.* **258,** 5927] have shown that certain of the nonglycosylated forms of subunits have a different conformation when probed by conformation-dependent antisera.

H. E. Grotjan: S. Chappel's lab has recently shown that the charge microheterogeneity of pituitary FSH is largely due to neuraminic acid residues. I think it is possible that there is a difference in general carbohydrate structure between FSH-like hormones and TSH or LH which presumably have sulfated carbohydrates. Why do you think there is such a difference in structure and how do you think that the processing might be different. Second, you said that you had seen forms of TSH which contained sialic acid; are those in an $\alpha\beta$ dimer or are those just on the free subunits?

B. Weintraub: These are very preliminary studies mostly conducted by Dr. James Magner, and the subunit specificity has not yet been well characterized. I would say more generally that one should not take any of the published data on carbohydrate structures as dogma. There is enormous heterogeneity of glycoproteins and the proper way to do carbohydrate chemistry is to first separate microheterogeneous forms and then do an individual structure of each form. I think that we will find that there are both sulfated and sialylated forms of FSH, LH, and TSH, but we're not yet at that level.

B. F. Rice: From the historical perspective, it seems to me I recall the late Frank Engel postulating that there might be abnormal forms of pituitary hormones; I think he was thinking more on the genetic basis than acquired basis. The second question has to do with the fact that in some patients, the few that I've seen that have had pituitary hyperthyroidism assoicated with a tumor or without an obvious tumor, I've been impressed with how severe the hyperthyroidism can be and how relatively low their TSH levels can be. You've apparently shown low biological activity in some of these molecules. I wonder if you've entertained the notion that there might be high biological activity in some of the TSH molecules.

B. Weintraub: Yes, we've been very intrigued by the same finding. Early studies done in collaboration with Ione Kourides showed that many of the patients with TSH-induced hyperthyroidism and levels of TSH that were within the normal range would be associated with very high levels of thyroid hormone. Now one could postulate some abnormal sensitivity of thyroid in those patients, but there was no evidence to support that. Currently we are measuring the biologic activity of such TSH and do expect to find forms with high activity.

L. Birnbaumer: In view of the extreme difficulty in characterizing chemically the nanogram quantities that you have of TSH, I was wondering whether there is any work going on attempting to tackle the problem from the other side. That is, if a different type of carbohydrate moiety of TSH is made, there must be enzymes that are making it. A correlate to this is that the complement of the enzymes in the cells must be changing with chronic TRH treatment and this may be another way to analyze for the TRH effect.

B. Weintraub: Yes, that's a very good point, and we hope to measure these enzymes. Obviously, the previous question relating to why there might be more sulfate or more sialic acid could be addressed directly by looking at the respective transferring enzymes.

M. O. Thorner: I was interested in the apparent discrepancy between on the one hand deglycosylated TSH and on the other TSH from patients with hypothalamic hyperthyroidism. You also mentioned that within the extracts of pituitaries, presumably deglycosylated TSH forms are found. There seems to be a major discrepancy between the findings on the hypothalamic hypothyroidism because in the former situation, what you told us was that there was actually increased binding and decreased biological activity while in the latter the biological activity was still lost, but the binding was decreased too?

B. Weintraub: I do not mean to imply that the hypothalamic forms are equivalent to deglycosylated forms. They are not and, in fact, they do bind to lectin columns showing they have carbohydrates. Their low activity appears to be related to a qualitative difference in carbohydrate structure.

M. O. Thorner: Is there any evidence that there are naturally occurring forms of TSH which fulfill the same criteria as found in the hypothalamic hypothyroidism?

B. Weintraub: Yes, certain of the heterogeneous components in pituitary TSH appear to have similar properties, but they have not been fully characterized [Joshi, L. R., and Weintraub, B. D. (1983). *Endocrinology* 113, 2145].

H. E. Grotjan: I believe you showed some data from patients in which TSH has B:I ratios of about 5. We've observed the same thing with regard to rat LH using an *in vitro* bioassay, that rLH consistently yields B:I ratios of about 5. Similarly Scott Chappel observes B:I ratios of about 3 to 5 for rat and hamster FSH. Why do you think one obtains B:I ratios greater than one? At least theoretically wouldn't you expect to see B:I ratios distributed around 1?

B. Weintraub: Not at all. It is just a historic artifact that hormones have been purified from the glandular source instead of what's in the circulation. The glandular source has hormones in all states of processing, including early high mannose precursor forms that may have relatively low activity as well as the very late forms that we feel are the best agonists.

J. Meites: I don't know whether you follow the literature on the endocrinology of aging, but it's very interesting that in old rats, we and others have reported that TSH levels are normal but T_3 and T_4 are definitely reduced. Klug and Adelman (*Biochem. Biophys. Res. Commun.* **77**, 1431, 1977) have reported that much of the TSH in the circulation appears to be biologically inactive, which could account for the reduced T_3 and T_4. I was wondering whether you would care to comment on this.

B. Weintraub: I have followed that literature, and it is very interesting. In fact, Mornex and others have even shown by gel filtration that much of the TSH is of a very high molecular weight. This form was originally speculated to be a precursor but we now know from the biosynthetic and the molecular genetic studies that it is not a precursor. There appears to be some posttranslational change that leads to high molecular weight, either by aggregation or by protein binding. When we inhibit glycosylation with tunicamycin we see that the nonglycosylated subunits have a tendency to aggregate. Thus, I would speculate that in aging there might be derangements of glycosyltransferases that cause these effects.

S. Cohen: I was surprised that your cases of hypothalamic, hypothyroidism had an abnormal TSH but when you gave TRH it was no longer abnormal. Isn't that a peculiar function for an RH hormone to also alter the chemistry?

B. Weintraub: The history of these hypothalamic hormones has been an increasing array of activities and functions as general neurotransmitters and even outside the central nervous system. Thus it is not surprising to me to find that TRH may regulate qualitative changes in the TSH molecules. Further, LHRH has been shown to regulate the bioactivity of LH under certain conditions.

S. Cohen: My second question concerns the carbohydrate: do you think it might be possible by altering the carbohydrate to form agonists and antagonists of the hormone?

B. Weintraub: Yes, and in fact, as I showed you, one can produce competitive antagonists by deglycosylation of TSH. Beside giving us insight into the mechanism of hormone action, such antagonists may have therapeutic uses. For example, a competitive antagonist of TSH might be useful in certain resistant forms of Graves' disease or thyrotropin-induced hyperthyroidism. In any case, these should be very useful tools for studying hormone action.

C. W. Bardin: Would you summarize the data suggesting that carbohydrate additions are necessary for peptide folding and disulfide bond formation?

B. Weintraub: These are data published by Strickland and Pierce (*J. Biol. Chem.* **258,** 5927, 1983). They, following our studies of tunicamycin treatment of intact cells producing nonglycosylated forms, were able to use a cell-free system plus membranes that were pretreated with tunicamycin to produce nonglycosylated subunits. They were able to compare the nonglycosylated subunits to native subunits in folding by using conformation-dependent antisera, and by performing subunit combination studies. By both criteria the nonglycosylated subunits were not properly folded. However, the actual disulfide bond alignments have not been determined.

Thyrotropin-Releasing Hormone Action: Mechanism of Calcium-Mediated Stimulation of Prolactin Secretion

MARVIN C. GERSHENGORN

Division of Endocrinology and Metabolism, Department of Medicine, Cornell University Medical College and The New York Hospital, New York, New York

I. Introduction

It is generally agreed that an elevation of cytoplasmic free calcium ion concentration ($[Ca^{2+}]_i$)[1] serves to couple the interaction of many hormones and neurotransmitters with plasma membrane receptors to the stimulation of a variety of cellular processes (Campbell, 1983). The elevation of $[Ca^{2+}]_i$ induced by these stimulants may be caused by mobilization (or redistribution) of cellular calcium or enhancement of influx of extracellular Ca^{2+}, or both (Douglas, 1978). It has been demonstrated that in some of these cells a very rapid effect after stimulant–receptor interaction is enhanced hydrolysis of phosphatidylinositol 4,5-bisphosphate [PtdIns(4,5)P$_2$] by a phospholipase C (or phosphodiesterase) to yield diacylglycerol and inositol 1,4,5-trisphosphate (InsP$_3$) (Downes and Michell, 1982). Furthermore, it has been proposed that both diacylglycerol (Nishizuka *et al.*, 1984) and InsP$_3$ (Berridge, 1983) may serve as intracellular mediators (or second messengers) to transduce and amplify the signal leading to stimulation of the physiologic response(s). Diacylglycerol appears to exert its effect, at least in part, by enhancing the activity of a calcium- and phospholipid-dependent protein kinase (protein kinase C) by an action that does not depend on an elevation of $[Ca^{2+}]_i$. InsP$_3$ appears to act to mobilize calcium from an intracellular pool to elevate $[Ca^{2+}]_i$ and thereby activate the biologic response. The molecular mechanism(s) by which influx of extracellular calcium may be enhanced by hormones and neurotransmitters to elevate $[Ca^{2+}]_i$ is not known.

[1] Abbreviations: TRH, thyrotropin-releasing hormone; $[Ca^{2+}]_i$, cytoplasmic free calcium ion (Ca^{2+}) concentration; PtdIns(4,5)P$_2$, phosphatidylinositol 4,5-bisphosphate (formerly triphosphoinositide or TPI); PtdIns4P, phosphatidylinositol 4-phosphate (formerly diphosphoinositide or DPI); PtdIns (or PI), phosphatidylinositol; PtdA (or PA), phosphatidic acid; DG, diacylglycerol; [^{32}P]P$_i$, [^{32}P]orthophosphate; InsP$_3$, inositoltrisphosphate; InsP$_2$, inositolbisphosphate; InsP, inositolmonophosphate; Ins, inositol; EGTA, ethylene glycol bis(β-aminoethyl ether)-N,N,N',N'-tetraacetic acid; CCCP, carbonylcyanide m-chlorophenylhydrazone; 1799, bis(hexafluoroacetonyl)acetone.

Thyrotropin-releasing hormone (TRH; thyroliberin) is a secretagogue that is released from hypothalamic neurons and binds to receptor sites on the surface of prolactin- and thyrotropin-producing cells in the anterior pituitary gland. Because the interaction of TRH with its receptor induces alterations in cellular phosphoinositide and calcium homeostasis it was suggested that an elevation of $[Ca^{2+}]_i$ in pituitary cells serves to couple, at least in part, stimulation by TRH to secretion (for review, see Gershengorn, 1982) in a manner similar to that described above. Recently, this hypothesis was supported by the direct demonstration, employing intracellularly trapped fluorescent and luminescent probes of Ca^{2+}, that TRH stimulates a rapid elevation of $[Ca^{2+}]_i$ in GH cells, a prolactin-secreting rat pituitary tumor cell line (Gershengorn and Thaw, 1983; Snowdowne and Borle, 1984; Albert and Tashjian, 1984; Kruskal *et al.*, 1984). In this article, I will describe studies mainly from my laboratory that attempt to define the intracellular events that couple TRH–receptor interaction to the elevation of $[Ca^{2+}]_i$ in GH$_3$ cells.

In order to understand the molecular mechanisms that mediate the elevation of $[Ca^{2+}]_i$, it was important to identify both the potential mediator(s) of this effect and the pool(s) of calcium that contribute to the increase in $[Ca^{2+}]_i$. For our investigations, we have utilized GH$_3$ cells, a cloned cell line that is widely employed as a model to study the physiology of pituitary mammotropic cells (Martin and Tashjian, 1977). I will present evidence from our studies in GH$_3$ cells that (1) TRH stimulates an elevation of $[Ca^{2+}]_i$ in part by mobilizing calcium from an intracellular, nonmitochondrial pool; (2) TRH stimulates the rapid, phospholipase C-mediated hydrolysis of PtdIns(4,5)P$_2$, a minor plasma membrane phospholipid, to yield InsP$_3$; and (3) InsP$_3$ is capable of rapidly mobilizing calcium from an intracellular, nonmitochondrial pool. Based on these observations, I propose that TRH stimulates the hydrolysis of PtdIns(4,5)P$_2$ to InsP$_3$ that, in turn, mobilizes calcium from a nonmitochondrial pool(s) leading to elevation of $[Ca^{2+}]_i$ then to activation of exocytosis and to stimulated prolactin secretion.

II. TRH and Calcium: Initial Studies

TRH stimulation of prolactin secretion from GH cells is dependent on calcium. The calcium dependency of TRH action was initially demonstrated in experiments in which GH cells were incubated in medium to which the Ca^{2+} chelator EGTA was added. The usual effect of TRH to stimulate prolactin secretion was abolished under these conditions (Tashjian *et al.*, 1978). Further, these investigators showed that this inhibition was completely reversed by adding Ca^{2+} to the medium in a concentration in excess of that of EGTA. Other investigators, based on similar findings (Ostlund *et al.*, 1978; Gautvik *et al.*, 1980), suggested that influx of extracellular Ca^{2+} caused by TRH was essential for simulated prolactin secretion. We (Gershengorn *et al.*, 1981) and others (Moriarty and Leuschen, 1981) found that exposure of GH_3 cells to medium without added Ca^{2+} or medium containing Ca^{2+} chelators, such as EGTA, causes a marked loss of cellular calcium. Hence, it cannot be concluded from experiments of this design that TRH action is dependent on extracellular Ca^{2+} but only that Ca^{2+} is required for TRH stimulation of prolactin secretion. It was proposed, moreover, that the lack of response to TRH in pituitary cells incubated in medium without added Ca^{2+} or in the presence of Ca^{2+} chelators may have been due to loss of Ca^{2+} from a critical cell-associated pool(s). The important determination as to the source(s) of Ca^{2+} required for TRH stimulation of prolactin secretion will be discussed in detail.

Indirect evidence in support of the notion that TRH may acutely stimulate prolactin secretion by affecting cellular Ca^{2+} metabolism came initially from studies demonstrating that TRH enhances ^{45}Ca efflux from prelabeled cells (Vale *et al.*, 1976; Gershengorn *et al.*, 1981; Gautvik *et al.*, 1980). Furthermore, I demonstrated that there was no measurable lag period between exposure of the cells to TRH and the effect to stimulate ^{45}Ca efflux. These indirect data suggested, therefore, that the effect of TRH on cellular calcium homeostasis is a very early event in the sequence leading to acute stimulation of prolactin secretion.

As described above, the demonstration that TRH stimulation of prolactin secretion was abolished from cells incubated for prolonged periods in medium to which no Ca^{2+} was added or in medium containing Ca^{2+} chelators does not prove that extracellular Ca^{2+} is required for the TRH effect because these conditions deplete cellular Ca^{2+}. However, important insights can be obtained from studies in which TRH-induced prolactin secretion is measured from cells which are incubated in medium with varying Ca^{2+} concentrations for short periods of time prior to TRH addition. Clearly, if TRH were to stimulate prolactin secretion from cells incubated in medium with very low Ca^{2+} concentrations, that is, under conditions of a Ca^{2+} gradient favoring outward flow of Ca^{2+}, it would strongly suggest that influx of extracellular Ca^{2+} was not required for stimulated release to occur. This experimental design, therefore, would permit valuable conclusions to be drawn. It is important to point out the inaccuracy in the common usage of the term "Ca^{2+}-free" in describing medium to which no Ca^{2+} is added. It has been amply demonstrated that medium prepared without added Ca^{2+} usually contains about 10 μM Ca^{2+} due to contamination from the other constituents. For example, in my laboratory, the balanced salt solution used in many of our studies is prepared so as to avoid Ca^{2+} contamination but contains 3.0 ± 0.2 μM Ca^{2+} as measured by colorimetric titration with arsenazo III dye (Gershengorn *et al.*, 1981). Although this concentration is only approximately 0.2% of the physiologic extracellular Ca^{2+} level, it is still 30-fold higher than the $[Ca^{2+}]_i$ (see below) and may still present a significant gradient for Ca^{2+} to flow into the cell. Medium containing lower concentrations of ionized Ca^{2+} can be prepared by using chelators of Ca^{2+}. With these buffers, the free or unbound Ca^{2+} concentration in the medium can be lowered to below the $[Ca^{2+}]_i$ and, thereby, reverse the concentration gradient and favor Ca^{2+} efflux rather than influx.

My colleagues and I studied the effect of varying the extracellular Ca^{2+} concentration on TRH-induced ^{45}Ca efflux and prolactin secretion from GH_3 cells. In the first study, we (Gershengorn *et al.*, 1981) compared the effect of TRH to that of a depolarizing concentration of K^+ (50 mM), because stimulation of prolactin secretion by K^+ depolarization appears to be due solely to influx of extracellular Ca^{2+}. Figure 1 illustrates the results of the critical experiment in this study. In this experiment, we examined the effects of lowering the extracellular Ca^{2+} concentration to

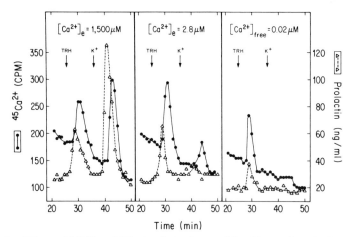

FIG. 1.   Effects of TRH and K^+ depolarization on ^{45}Ca efflux and prolactin secretion from GH_3 cells incubated in medium with 1500 and 2.8 μM Ca^{2+} and 0.02 μM free Ca^{2+}. Cells were preincubated with $^{45}Ca^{2+}$ (2 $\mu Ci/ml$) for 16 hours. Medium containing 0.02 μM free Ca^{2+} ($[Ca^{2+}]_{free}$) was prepared by adding 33 μM EGTA to medium with no added Ca^{2+}. There was a marked efflux of ^{45}Ca from cells incubated in medium containing 2.8 μM Ca^{2+} and 0.02 μM free Ca^{2+} between 10 and 15 minutes. TRH (1 μM) and 50 mM K^+ were added for 1 minute at 25 and 36 minutes, respectively. The appearance of the prolactin peaks before the peaks of ^{45}Ca is an artifact of the perfusion system due to partial exclusion of prolactin and inclusion of ^{45}Ca by the polyacrylamide beads onto which the cells are adsorbed in the column. (Reproduced from Gershengorn *et al.*, 1981.)

below that present free in the cell cytoplasm on ^{45}Ca efflux and prolactin secretion elicited by TRH. The effects of a 1-minute pulse of 1 μM TRH and 50 mM K$^+$ were compared in perifusion medium containing 1500 and 2.8 μM Ca^{2+} and in medium in which the concentration of unbound or free Ca^{2+} was lowered to 0.02 μM by adding 33 μM EGTA to medium without added Ca^{2+}. Between 10 and 15 minutes after beginning perifusion with the low Ca^{2+} mediums, there was a transient, marked increment in efflux of ^{45}Ca from the cells, not shown in Fig. 1, which most likely represented loss of cellular Ca^{2+} caused by the abrupt decrease in extracellular Ca^{2+} concentration. We found that the increment in prolactin secretion elicited by 50 mM K$^+$ in medium with 2.8 μM Ca^{2+} was less than 3% of that in medium with 1500 μM Ca^{2+} and there was no detectable increment in prolactin secretion in medium with 0.02 μM free Ca^{2+}. In contrast, TRH enhanced prolactin secretion under all conditions; prolactin secretion stimulated by TRH was 50 and 35% of control (medium with 1500 μM Ca^{2+}) in medium with 2.8 μM Ca^{2+} and 0.02 μM free Ca^{2+}, respectively. These suboptimal responses, however, may have been due to loss of Ca^{2+} from a critical cellular pool(s) induced by the low Ca^{2+} medium. Hence, extracellular Ca^{2+} was necessary for K$^+$-stimulated secretion but it was not required for TRH-stimulated prolactin secretion. Similar results were reported by Tan and Tashjian (1981) who found that TRH stimulates release of prolactin from GH$_4$C$_1$ cells incubated in medium containing approximately 1 μM Ca^{2+}.

In a second study (Gershengorn et al., 1983), we measured prolactin secretion stimulated by TRH from GH$_3$ cells incubated in medium containing 120 mM K$^+$ and 2 mM EGTA; these conditions were employed to abolish both the electrical and Ca^{2+} concentration gradients that usually promote influx of extracellular Ca^{2+}. TRH still caused prolactin secretion and ^{45}Ca efflux from cells incubated under these conditions. In static incubations, TRH stimulated accumulation of prolactin in the medium from 11±1.2 to 19±1.8 ng/ml/20 minutes in control incubations and from 3.2±0.6 to 6.2±0.8 ng/ml/20 minutes from cells incubated in medium with 120 mM K$^+$ and 2 mM EGTA.

In a third study (Rebecchi et al., 1982), we measured loss and uptake of nonradioactive Ca^{2+} by GH$_3$ cells during TRH action using the metallochromic indicator arsenazo III. Figure 2 illustrates an experiment in which cells were perifused in medium initially containing 2.8 μM Ca^{2+}; nonradioactive (or stable) Ca^{2+}, ^{45}Ca, and prolactin were measured in the perifusion effluent. Under these conditions, there was a sustained loss of calcium from the cells for at least 30 minutes. TRH caused a transient, marked increase in the amount of nonradioactive Ca^{2+} released into the medium that occurred in parallel with enhancement of ^{45}Ca efflux and

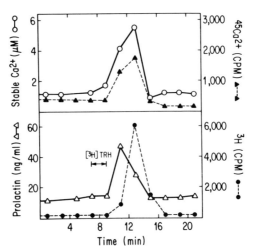

FIG. 2.   Effects of TRH on nonradioactive (or stable) Ca^{2+}, ^{45}Ca and prolactin secretion into the medium during perifusion of GH_3 cells. Cells were incubated in growth medium supplemented with $^{45}Ca^{2+}$ (8 $\mu Ci/ml$). After 20 hours, 40×10^6 cells were placed in a column and perifused with medium at 23°C. After 30 minutes, collection of the perifusate effluent was begun. At 7 minutes, 1 μM [^3H]TRH was added to the medium for 2 minutes. Stable Ca^{2+} concentration represents the difference between the amount in the effluent minus that in the original medium. (Reproduced from Rebecchi *et al.*, 1982.)

stimulation of prolactin secretion. There was no measurable decrease in the concentration of Ca^{2+} in the medium at the onset of the TRH effect that would have been consistent with Ca^{2+} influx into the cells. In static incubations performed in parallel, TRH caused a decrease in total cell calcium content of $23\pm5\%$. These data provided direct evidence that, under certain conditions, TRH causes loss of calcium from GH_3 cells without causing measurable Ca^{2+} uptake. Hence, the results from this series of studies strongly supported the contention that TRH acts, at least in part, to mobilize calcium from an intracellular pool(s) and suggested that this action was sufficient to stimulate prolactin secretion.

To determine whether TRH stimulation of prolactin secretion was in part dependent on influx of extracellular Ca^{2+}, several groups of investigators have employed organic Ca^{2+} channel blocking agents, in particular, verapamil and its methoxy derivative D600. These agents appear to act primarily at the plasma membrane to inhibit Ca^{2+} influx and are, for example, potent inhibitors of Ca^{2+} influx into and prolactin secretion from GH_3 cells stimulated by K^+ depolarization (Geras *et al.*, 1982); however, there appear to be effects of these agents on intracellular calcium pools also (see below). The effects of verapamil and D600 have been inconsistent. Some investigators (Moriarty and Leuschen, 1981; Geras *et al.*, 1982) have reported that these organic channel blocking agents have no effect of TRH stimulation of prolactin secretion while others (Murayama *et al.*, 1981; Ozawa and Kimura, 1982; Tan and Tashjian, 1984) have found that these agents partially to completely inhibit stimulation of prolactin secretion elicited by TRH in GH cells. Although a definitive explanation to account for these contradictory findings is not apparent, it may be that the different conditions used to prepare the cells for the experiments may have allowed for variable effects of verapamil and D600 on intracellular calcium pools (see below). Hence, these agents have not provided insight into whether enhanced Ca^{2+} influx is needed for optimal TRH stimulation of prolactin secretion.

Another approach employed by some investigators in an apparent attempt to probe whether TRH stimulation of prolactin secretion required Ca^{2+} influx was to determine the effect of cobalt ion (Co^{2+}) (Tashjian *et al.*, 1978; Ozawa and Kimura, 1979; Tan and Tashjian, 1981). Co^{2+} is a potent inhibitor of both Ca^{2+} influx into excitable cells through voltage-dependent channels in the plasma membrane and a potent inhibitor of Ca^{2+}-mediated secretion from these cells. Furthermore, because it has not been possible to measure Co^{2+} influx through voltage-dependent channels, some investigators have assumed that Co^{2+} binds to the external surface of cells and exerts its Ca^{2+} antagonistic effects only by blocking influx of extracellular Ca^{2+}. Because, in GH cells, Co^{2+} was found to abolish Ca^{2+}-dependent action potentials (Ozawa and Kimura, 1979) and to inhibit TRH-stimulated prolactin secretion (Tashjian *et al.*, 1978; Ozawa and Kimura, 1979; Tan and Tashjian, 1981), these investigators concluded that TRH-enhanced Ca^{2+} influx was necessary for stimulated prolactin secretion. My colleagues and I (Thaw *et al.*, 1984) have recently presented evidence that Co^{2+} enters within GH_3 cells and have suggested that at least part of the action of Co^{2+} may occur at an intracellular locus. We have concluded, therefore, that inhibition by Co^{2+} should not be interpreted as demonstrating a requirement for Ca^{2+} influx in stimulated prolactin secretion. This conclusion is based on the following observations. When cells were incubated in medium containing 3 μM Ca^{2+} to inhibit Ca^{2+} influx, K^+ depolarization-induced prolactin secretion was abolished but Co^{2+} still inhibited basal and TRH-stimulated prolactin secretion. Co^{2+} also inhibited prolactin secretion stimulated by 1-methyl-3-isobutylxanthine, dibutyryl adenosine 3′,5′-cyclic monophosphate (cyclic AMP), and vasoactive intestinal peptide, three secretagogues that act to elevate intracellular cyclic AMP, a mechanism that appears not to involve enhanced Ca^{2+} influx.

Most importantly, we demonstrated that Co^{2+} enters within GH_3 cells.

We found that Co^{2+} quenches the fluorescence of Quin 2, a chelator of divalent cations, that had been trapped within the cytoplasm of intact cells. To demonstrate directly that Co^{2+} had entered the cells and bound to the intracellularly trapped Quin 2, the cells were washed extensively, placed in Ca^{2+}-free buffer, and then lysed (Fig. 3). There was a concentration-dependent decrease in Quin 2 fluorescence in the lysate of cells exposed to Co^{2+} when they were intact. When 1 mM EGTA was added to the lysate of control cells (cells not previously exposed to Co^{2+}), there was a marked decrease in the Quin 2 fluorescence intensity as Ca^{2+} dissociated from the Quin 2–Ca^{2+} complex and was bound by EGTA. A similar effect was observed in lysates from cells exposed to 0.5, 1, and 2 mM Co^{2+}. In contrast, in the lysates of cells exposed to 6 mM Co^{2+}, addition

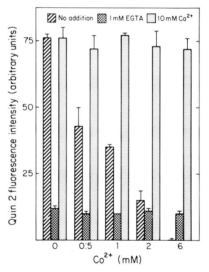

FIG. 3.   Effect of incubation of intact GH$_3$ cells with cobalt ion (Co^{2+}) on the intensity of fluorescence of Quin 2 in the cell lysates. Cells were loaded with Quin 2, washed, and resuspended in fresh medium without Quin 2 acetoxymethylester and with or without Co^{2+}. The Quin 2 fluorescence signal in the intact cells decreased after Co^{2+} addition. After 5 minutes, the cells were washed extensively to remove extracellular Co^{2+} and resuspended in fresh "Ca-free" medium without Co^{2+}. The cells were then lysed either by addition of 0.1% Triton X-100 or by sonication, centrifuged at 25,000 g for 15 minutes to remove debris and the fluorescence measured. Thereafter, 1 mM EGTA and then 10 mM Ca^{2+} were added and the fluorescence intensity measured after each addition. The intrinsic fluorescence of the cell lysate from cells not loaded with Quin 2 was subtracted from the total fluorescence to yield Quin 2 fluorescence. The bars represent mean±SD of duplicate determinations in 2 experiments. (Reproduced from Thaw *et al.*, 1984.)

of EGTA caused an increase in Quin 2 fluorescence intensity, presumably as the previously bound Co^{2+} dissociated from the Quin 2–Co^{2+} complexes and was bound by EGTA; that is, EGTA reversed the Co^{2+}-induced quenching of Quin 2 fluorescence. Moreover, under all conditions, when excess Ca^{2+} was added to the lysate the same maximum intensity of Quin 2 fluorescence was attained, demonstrating that the initial decrease was secondary to quenching and not to loss of Quin 2 from the cells. Hence, these data demonstrated that Co^{2+} enters within GH_3 cells, that its inhibition of prolactin secretion may be caused by a Ca^{2+} antagonistic action at an intracellular locus (or loci), and, therefore, that inhibition by Co^{2+} may not be used to suggest a role for stimulated Ca^{2+} influx in prolactin secretion.

To demonstrate an effect of TRH on Ca^{2+} within intracellular pools in intact GH cells more directly, my colleagues and I (Gershengorn *et al.*, 1981; Thaw *et al.*, 1982) utilized chlortetracycline, a fluorescent probe of Ca^{2+} in lipid domains. This probe has been used successfully to monitor changes in membrane-associated Ca^{2+} in several intact cells. In GH_3 cells, we found that the fluorescence emission spectrum indicates that chlortetracycline was complexed with Ca^{2+} and Mg^{2+} but that the intensity of fluorescence varied directly with the extracellular Ca^{2+} concentration. We compared the effects of TRH to those elicited by K^+ depolarization-induced influx of extracellular Ca^{2+}. In these experiments, the cells were incubated in medium with chlortetracycline for 10 minutes and then resuspended in medium without chlortetracycline prior to addition of secretagogue. Figure 4 illustrates the effects of TRH and of 50 mM K^+ on chlortetracycline fluorescence of GH_3 cells incubated in medium containing 3.5 or 13.5 μM Ca^{2+}. Under these conditions, K^+ depolarization caused a small increase in the rate of fluorescence loss which persisted for at least 10 minutes. TRH also increased the rate of loss of chlortetracycline fluorescence but this differed from that induced by 50 mM K^+ in two ways. First, the effect of TRH was transient, lasting less than 1.5 minutes. Second, the magnitude of the decrease in fluorescence achieved within the first 0.5 minute after addition of TRH was much greater than after exposure to 50 mM K^+. Further evidence supporting the contention that the loss of chlortetracycline fluorescence induced by TRH was caused by mobilization of cellular Ca^{2+} and not related to influx of extracellular Ca^{2+} was provided by the finding that the response to TRH was observed even in cells that had been incubated in medium with 50 mM K^+. Although other factors could have affected chlortetracycline fluorescence, the very close parallels between the effects of TRH on ^{45}Ca efflux (see above) and fluorescence suggested that the decrease in cell-associated chlortetracycline fluorescence caused by TRH was best explained by displacement of

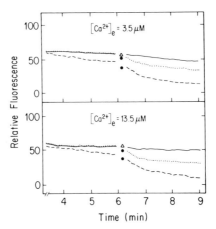

FIG. 4. Effect of TRH and K$^+$ depolarization on chlortetracycline fluorescence associated with GH$_3$ cells. Cells were loaded with chlortetracycline in medium containing 3.5 or 13 μM Ca^{2+}. Cells were washed and resuspended in medium without chlortetracycline and diluted with 0.5 vol of medium (solid and dotted lines) or buffer with 150 mM KCl instead of NaCl (final concentration of 50 mM K$^+$, dotted line). After 6 minutes, 1 μM TRH was added where indicated (0). (Reproduced from Gershengorn et al., 1981.)

cellular membrane-bound Ca^{2+} as has been concluded for other secretagogues in other cell types.

We also used chlortetracycline in conjunction with a series of agents with local anesthetic activity, which are known to displace Ca^{2+} from biologic membranes, to demonstrate more rigorously that TRH mobilized Ca^{2+} from membranes within GH$_3$ cells. Specifically, it is known that agents with local anesthetic activity intercalate into biological membranes and compete with and displace Ca^{2+} from negatively charged sites. In particular, procaine-like anesthetics, such as tetracaine, and other drugs such as trifluoperazine and propranolol at high doses have been shown to displace Ca^{2+} complexed with the acidic headgroups of phospholipids within membranes. We demonstrated that these agents caused a decrease in cellular ^{45}Ca content and cell-associated chlortetracycline fluorescence intensity, and markedly inhibited TRH-stimulated loss of chlortetracycline fluorescence (Fig. 5) and prolactin secretion. We concluded that the loss of cellular Ca^{2+} was due to displacement of Ca^{2+} from membrane binding sites and that inhibition of TRH action by these agents may have been secondary to depletion of membrane-associated Ca^{2+}. These observations that TRH may be affecting Ca^{2+} bound to negatively charged sites within membranes, for example, to acidic phospholipids, suggested that

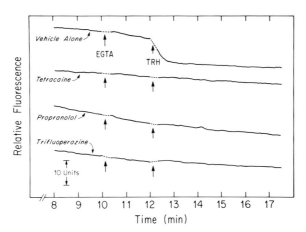

FIG. 5. Effects of tetracaine, propranolol, and trifluoperazine on the decrease in chlorte-tracycline fluorescence associated with GH₃ cells elicited by TRH. After loading with chlor-tetracycline, cells were resuspended in medium without chlortetracycline containing 1 mM tetracaine, 1 mM propranolol, or 0.03 mM trifluoperazine which decreased fluorescence to 75 ± 3, 87 ± 4, and $88 \pm 1\%$, respectively, or vehicle alone. After an additional 10 minutes, 0.01 mM EGTA was added and after 12 minutes, 1 μM TRH was added. Similar results were obtained in experiments without EGTA. (Reproduced from Thaw *et al.*, 1982.)

TRH may affect phosphoinositide metabolism in GH₃ cells (see Section IV).

We (Gershengorn *et al.*, 1984) next addressed the question of which membrane-delimited cellular calcium pool(s) was mobilized during TRH action in GH₃ cells. In two previously reported studies (Ronning *et al.*, 1982; Leuschen *et al.*, 1983) evidence was presented that TRH mobilizes calcium from mitochondria; Ronning *et al.* (1982) also reported loss of calcium from endoplasmic reticulum. However, both groups of investigators employed methods that require disruption or permeabilization of the plasma membrane which has been associated in other cell types with a redistribution of calcium. We used a technique, originally developed for hepatocytes (Bellomo *et al.*, 1982; Joseph and Williamson, 1983), to monitor cellular calcium pools in intact cells that does not require permeabilization of the plasma membrane. This method, therefore, minimized artifactual redistribution of calcium. We showed that depletion of mitochondrial calcium with the "classical" proton ionophore uncouplers, carbonylcyanide *m*-chlorophenylhydrazone (CCCP) and bis(hexafluoroacetonyl) acetone (1799), did not affect TRH-induced loss of ⁴⁵Ca from cells prelabeled to isotopic equilibrium. For this analysis, cells were incubated overnight in suspension in growth medium supplemented with

$^{45}Ca^{2+}$; these cells contained 2.5 ± 0.2 nmol $^{45}Ca/10^6$ cells. The cells were suspended in "Ca-free" medium which led to the rapid loss of $48\pm1.2\%$ of total cell ^{45}Ca after 3 minutes; this level remained unchanged for at least an additional 20 minutes. Cells incubated in "Ca-free" medium contained 1.5 ± 0.10 nmol calcium/10^6 cells as measured with arsenazo III dye and 1.3 ± 0.093 nmol $^{45}Ca/10^6$ cells; thus, under the conditions of overnight incubation, an isotopic equilibrium had been attained. The effects of TRH, CCCP, 1799, and the Ca^{2+} ionophore, A23187, to release ^{45}Ca from intact cells are illustrated in Fig. 6. As we had shown previously (Rebecchi *et al.*, 1982), TRH caused a loss of cellular calcium. Under the conditions of these experiments in which the cells were incubated in "Ca-free" medium, this loss amounted to $16\pm2.7\%$ of cell ^{45}Ca. CCCP and 1799 released 36 ± 2.3 and $36\pm1.5\%$ of cellular ^{45}Ca, respectively. When TRH was added simultaneously with CCCP or 1799, or 3 or 7 minutes after the addition of the mitochondrial uncouplers, it caused the loss of an additional 13 ± 2.0 or $19\pm0.69\%$ of cell ^{45}Ca. Hence, the effect of TRH to

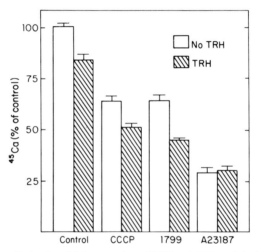

FIG. 6.   Effects of mitochondrial uncouplers, CCCP and 1799, and the ionophore A23187 on TRH-induced loss of ^{45}Ca from intact GH$_3$ cells. Cells were loaded with ^{45}Ca by incubation overnight in culture medium containing 5 μCi/ml $^{45}Ca^{2+}$. The cells were separated from the medium and resuspended in a "Ca-free" medium (control) or medium containing 5 μM carbonyl *m*-chlorophenylhydrazone (CCCP), 30 μM bis(hexafluoroacetonyl)acetone (1799), or 10 μM A23187 without or with 1 μM TRH at 23°C. After 5 minutes, the cells were washed twice with ice-cold medium and the residual cell-associated ^{45}Ca measured by liquid scintillation counting after solubilization of the cell pellet with Triton X-100. Each bar represents the mean$\pm$SE of triplicate determinations from 4 experiments. (Reproduced from Gershengorn *et al.*, 1984.)

release cellular calcium was not affected by CCCP or 1799. In contrast, the ionophore A23187 caused the release of $61\pm1.4\%$ of cell ^{45}Ca and TRH caused no additional loss when added with the ionophore. The residual 30% of cell calcium not released by A23187 may represent calcium bound to proteins in the cytoplasm or to membrane-bound proteins or phospholipids. Because the action of TRH to release cellular calcium was not affected by CCCP or 1799, it appeared that TRH caused loss of calcium from a nonmitochondrial pool(s). However, because almost 50% of total cell calcium was lost when the cells were resuspended in "Ca-free" BSS, it was possible that a portion of the calcium released by incubation in low Ca^{2+} buffer was from a TRH-responsive, mitochondrial pool and that under physiological conditions release of calcium induced by TRH from this pool could be measured; this possibility was explored in experiments in which $[Ca^{2+}]_i$ was measured directly (see Section III). Our data suggested that TRH does not mobilize calcium from mitochondria but only from a nonmitochondrial pool(s). Although it is likely that the nonmitochondrial pool from which calcium is mobilized by TRH in intact GH_3 cells is within the endoplasmic reticulum, it is possible that TRH may release plasma membrane-bound Ca^{2+} (Tan and Tashjian, 1981; Thaw *et al.*, 1982), or it may affect both of these calcium pools.

Hence, the data reviewed in this Section demonstrated that TRH rapidly affects calcium homeostasis in GH_3 cells by in part mobilizing calcium from an intracellular, nonmitochondrial pool(s). A role for enhanced influx of extracellular Ca^{2+} was neither established nor refuted. More importantly, the findings provided only indirect evidence that TRH stimulation of prolactin secretion depended upon an elevation of $[Ca^{2+}]_i$.

III. TRH and Cytoplasmic-Free Calcium

Based upon the observations reviewed in the preceding Section and results from other investigators, it was suggested that an elevation of the concentration of calcium ion free in the cytoplasm ($[Ca^{2+}]_i$) of GH cells served to couple stimulation by TRH to secretion of prolactin in accord with the mechanism proposed in the stimulus-secretion coupling hypothesis of Douglas (1978). Recently, this hypothesis was supported by direct demonstrations employing an intracellularly trapped fluorescent probe of Ca^{2+}, Quin 2 (Tsien, 1980), and an intracellularly trapped photoprotein, aequorin, that TRH stimulates a rapid elevation of $[Ca^{2+}]_i$ in GH cells (Gershengorn and Thaw, 1983, 1985; Snowdowne and Borle, 1984; Albert and Tashjian, 1984; Kruskal *et al.*, 1984; Gershengorn *et al.*, 1984). In these studies, basal $[Ca^{2+}]_i$ was reported to be 37 nM (Kruskal *et al.*, 1984), 100 nM (Snowdowne and Borle, 1984, and personal communication), 118 nM (Gershengorn and Thaw, 1983), 127 nM (Gershengorn *et al.*, 1984), 148 nM (Gershengorn and Thaw, 1985), and 350 nM (Albert and Tashjian, 1984). It appears, from the majority of reports, that in agreement with measurements in other cell types, that the basal (or resting) $[Ca^{2+}]_i$ in GH cells is about 100 nM.

TRH stimulates an immediate several-fold elevation of $[Ca^{2+}]_i$ followed by a more prolonged secondary increase, that is, a biphasic elevation of $[Ca^{2+}]_i$. Figure 7 illustrates the effects of TRH on $[Ca^{2+}]_i$ within and prolactin secretion from GH$_3$ cells. After inspection of a series of tracings, the "first phase" was defined as occurring during the first 1.5 minutes after TRH addition and the "second phase" after 1.5 minutes. TRH stimulated a rapid increase in $[Ca^{2+}]_i$ which reached a peak of 517±29 nM at less than 10 seconds, followed by a decline over 1.5 minutes. This was followed by a sustained elevation of $[Ca^{2+}]_i$ to 261±14 nM that lasted for at least 12 minutes ("second phase"). It is important to note, that the absolute magnitude of the increment in $[Ca^{2+}]_i$ is almost certainly an underestimation of what occurs in control cells that are not loaded with Quin 2 because Quin 2 behaves like a large capacity, high affinity buffer

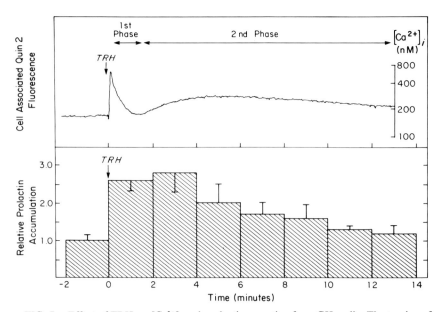

FIG. 7.   Effect of TRH on $[Ca^{2+}]_i$ and prolactin secretion from GH$_3$ cells. The tracing of Quin 2 fluorescence intensity is representative of 35 tracings from control incubations of GH$_3$ cells. The bars represent the mean±SE of prolactin accumulation in the medium of 5 perifusion experiments. (Reproduced from Gershengorn and Thaw, 1985.)

for Ca^{2+}. TRH stimulation of prolactin secretion was measured in parallel experiments from cells in a perifusion column. The basal rate of prolactin accumulation in the medium ranged between 0.85 and 5.0 ng/ml/2 minutes. In 5 experiments, TRH stimulated an increase in the rate of accumulation of prolactin in the perifusate to $270\pm27\%$ of control during the first 4 minutes of its effect. This was followed by a progressive decline in the rate of prolactin accumulation until 10 minutes after TRH addition, but the rate of accumulation was still $130\pm1.3\%$ of control between 12 and 22 minutes after TRH (data between 14 and 22 minutes are not shown).

We (Gershengorn and Thaw, 1983) initially reported that lowering extracellular free Ca^{2+} by chelation with EGTA did not abolish the "first phase" elevation of $[Ca^{2+}]_i$ induced by TRH and concluded that this rapid elevation of $[Ca^{2+}]_i$ was due predominantly to mobilization of cellular calcium. Albert and Tashjian (1984) concluded from experiments in which they also lowered extracellular free Ca^{2+} concentration with EGTA that the first phase elevation or "spike" caused by TRH is "dependent primarily on redistribution of intracellular Ca^{2+} stores" and that the sustained second phase elevation or "plateau" is "dependent on influx of extracellular Ca^{2+}." In a subsequent study, we (Gershengorn and Thaw, 1985) confirmed and extended these observations. We used two experimental approaches in attempts to assess the relative contributions of mobilization of cellular calcium and influx of extracellular Ca^{2+} to the elevation of $[Ca^{2+}]_i$ caused by TRH in each of the two phases. In both designs, we compared the effect of the manipulation on TRH-induced elevation of $[Ca^{2+}]_i$ to that caused by K^+ depolarization-induced Ca^{2+} influx. The effects of lowering the concentration of Ca^{2+} in the medium to 0.1 and 0.01 mM on the elevations of $[Ca^{2+}]_i$ caused by TRH and by depolarization of the plasma membrane with 50 mM K^+ are illustrated in Fig. 8. Resting $[Ca^{2+}]_i$ was lowered to 114 ± 3.4 and 110 ± 11 nM in cells incubated in medium containing 0.1 and 0.01 mM Ca^{2+}, respectively. These levels are significantly lower ($p<0.001$) than the resting $[Ca^{2+}]_i$ in cells incubated in medium with 1.5 mM Ca^{2+} (control), but are not different from each other. The peak elevation of $[Ca^{2+}]_i$ caused by 50 mM K^+ in cells incubated in medium containing 1.5 mM Ca^{2+} was 780 ± 12 nM (control); this value is an underestimation because all values of 800 nM or greater were recorded as 800 nM as measurements using Quin 2 are not accurate above this level. The peak elevation of $[Ca^{2+}]_i$ caused by 50 mM K^+ was lowered to 30 ± 3.9 and $7.3\pm2.0\%$ of control in cells in medium with 0.1 and 0.01 mM Ca^{2+}, respectively. The peak second phase elevation of $[Ca^{2+}]_i$ caused by TRH was lowered to 33 ± 2.8 and $16\pm5.6\%$ of control, respectively, but the peak first phase elevation was lowered only to 79 ± 5.5 and $52\pm10\%$ of control, respectively. In experiments in which the extracellu-

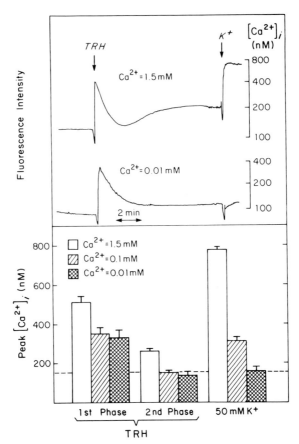

FIG. 8. Effects of lowering extracellular Ca^{2+} from 1.5 to 0.1, and 0.01 mM on the elevations of $[Ca^{2+}]_i$ caused by TRH and 50 mM K^+ in GH$_3$ cells. Upper panel: Representative tracings of GH$_3$ cells incubated in medium containing 1.5 or 0.01 mM Ca^{2+}. Cells loaded with Quin 2 were incubated in medium containing 1.5, 0.1, or 0.01 mM Ca^{2+} for 5 minutes prior to TRH addition. Lower panel: Peak $[Ca^{2+}]_i$ attained during first and second phases of TRH effect and during K^+ depolarization. The dotted line indicates the resting $[Ca^{2+}]_i$ in cells incubated in medium with 1.5 mM Ca^{2+}; calculation of responses was performed by subtracting the resting level from the stimulated level. The bars represent mean±SE of replicate determinations in 3 to 9 experiments. (Reproduced from Gershengorn and Thaw, 1985.)

lar free Ca^{2+} was lowered to less than 1 μM by adding EGTA, the second phase elevation of $[Ca^{2+}]_i$ caused by TRH and that induced by K^+ depolarization were abolished, whereas the first phase increase stimulated by TRH was inhibited by only 40 to 60%; the extent of this inhibition was dependent on the duration of incubation in medium containing EGTA.

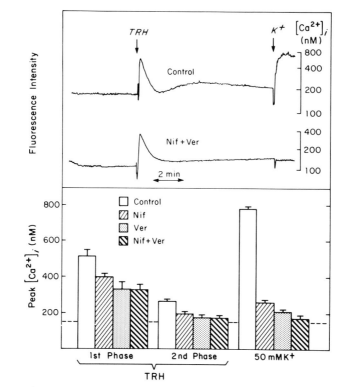

FIG. 9.   Effects of nifedipine (Nif), verapamil (Ver), and Nif plus Ver on the elevations of
$[Ca^{2+}]_i$ caused by TRH and 50 mM K^+ in GH_3 cells. Upper panel: Representative tracings of
GH_3 cells incubated in medium with 1.5 mM Ca^{2+} (control) and medium with 1.5 mM Ca^{2+}
containing 2 μM nifedipine and 75 μM verapamil. Cells loaded with Quin 2 were incubated
in medium containing Nif, Ver, or Nif plus Ver for 5 minutes prior to TRH addition. Lower
panel: Peak $[Ca^{2+}]_i$ attained during first and second phases of TRH effect and during K^+
depolarization. The dotted line indicates the resting $[Ca^{2+}]_i$ in cells incubated in medium with
1.5 mM Ca^{2+}; calculation of responses was performed by subtracting the resting level from
the stimulated level. The bars represent mean±SE of replicate determinations in 3 to 7
experiments. (Reproduced from Gershengorn and Thaw, 1985.)

Because lowering extracellular Ca^{2+} concentration is known to cause
depletion of intracellular calcium stores (see Section II), we monitored
TRH-induced elevation of $[Ca^{2+}]_i$ in cells incubated in medium with physiologic Ca^{2+} levels (1.5 mM) in which Ca^{2+} influx was inhibited with organic channel blocking agents. The effects of nifedipine and verapamil on
the elevations of $[Ca^{2+}]_i$ caused by TRH and K^+ depolarization are illustrated in Fig. 9. There was no effect on resting $[Ca^{2+}]_i$ in cells incubated in
medium with 1.5 mM Ca^{2+} (control) containing 2 μM nifedipine, 75 μM

verapamil, or both. These concentrations of nifedipine and verapamil are maximally effective and did not interfere significantly with binding of TRH. Nifedipine, verapamil, and nifedipine plus verapamil lowered the elevation of $[Ca^{2+}]_i$ caused by K^+ depolarization to 22 ± 2.6, 7.1 ± 2.5, and $6.5\pm1.0\%$ of control, respectively. The peak second phase elevation of $[Ca^{2+}]_i$ caused by TRH was lowered to 46 ± 4.7, 35 ± 3.0, and $28\pm4.3\%$ of control, respectively, but the peak first phase elevation was lowered only to 72 ± 3.3, 66 ± 4.0, and $64\pm3.7\%$, respectively. Moreover, in separate experiments, we showed that the partial inhibition of the TRH-stimulated first phase elevation of $[Ca^{2+}]_i$ caused by nifedipine plus verapamil may have been due to partial depletion of an intracellular calcium pool. This conclusion is based on the finding that cells incubated in medium containing nifedipine plus verapamil lost 15% of cell-associated ^{45}Ca from the nonmitochondrial pool; this represented approximately one-half of the TRH-responsive pool of ^{45}Ca (see Section II). We cannot determine from these data whether the effect of the channel blockers to deplete partially

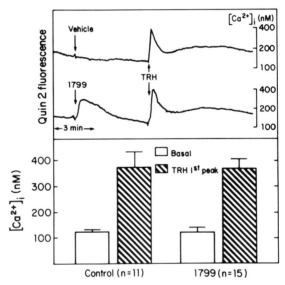

FIG. 10. Effect of the mitochondrial uncoupler 1799 on TRH-induced elevation of $[Ca^{2+}]_i$ in intact GH$_3$ cells. Top: Fluorescence tracings of cells loaded with Quin 2 and resuspended in medium containing 1.5 mM Ca^{2+}. After 5 minutes, vehicle alone (control) or 30 μM bis(hexafluoroacetonyl)acetone (1799) was added followed by 1 μM TRH after 10 minutes. These tracings are representative of tracings from 7 experiments. Bottom: Measurement of the effect of 1799 on the "first phase" peak elevation of $[Ca^{2+}]_i$ induced by TRH. The bars represent mean$\pm$SE of determinations in 7 experiments. (Reproduced from Gershengorn *et al.*, 1984.)

the nonmitochondrial pool of calcium requires that they enter within GH_3 cells or whether this effect is secondary to their known interaction with plasma membrane sites.

To confirm that TRH caused release of cellular calcium only from a nonmitochondrial pool to cause the first phase elevation of $[Ca^{2+}]_i$, we used the mitochondrial uncouping agent 1799 (Gershengorn et al., 1984). Figure 10 illustrates the effects of 1799 and TRH on $[Ca^{2+}]_i$. The effect of 1799, which was used in these experiments because it neither fluoresces nor quenches fluorescence, was to cause a transient elevation of $[Ca^{2+}]_i$ which reached a peak of 218 ± 21 nM at 0.5 minute and returned to the basal level within 5 minutes. When TRH was added after 1799, it still caused a first phase peak elevation of $[Ca^{2+}]_i$ that was indistinguishable from that in control cells. It may be concluded, therefore, that the first phase elevation of $[Ca^{2+}]_i$ caused by TRH, like the loss of cellular ^{45}Ca (see Section II), was not inhibited by depleting the mitochondrial pool of calcium and that TRH mobilizes calcium from a nonmitochondrial pool(s) in GH_3 cells.

Hence, we conclude that the first phase elevation of $[Ca^{2+}]_i$ caused by TRH is due predominantly, if not exclusively, to mobilization of cellular calcium, whereas the second phase elevation is caused mainly, if not solely, by stimulated influx of extracellular Ca^{2+}.

IV. TRH and Phosphoinositides

Michell (1975) proposed the hypothesis that stimulation of phosphatidyl-inositol (PtdIns) metabolism may couple receptor occupation to generation of an intracelluar calcium signal. He recognized that ligands that stimulated PtdIns and phosphatidic acid (PtdA) metabolism also induced changes in cellular calcium homeostasis. Michell postulated that formation of the ligand–receptor complex activated lipid metabolism by directly stimulating the hydrolysis of PtdIns to diacylglycerol (DG) and inositolmonophosphate (InsP) and that the fall in PtdIns concentration at the cell surface acted to increase the conductance of plasma membrane Ca^{2+} channels, thus stimulating influx of extracellular Ca^{2+}. He further suggested that the inositol sugar product of this reaction may act as an intracellular signal. More recently, Michell (Michell et al., 1981; Michell, 1982) and Berridge (Berridge, 1981, 1984) have revised this hypothesis to suggest that the initial enzymic reaction stimulated by this class of ligands is the phospholipase C (or phosphodiesterase)-mediated hydrolysis of phosphatidylinositol 4,5-bisphosphate [PtdIns(4,5)P$_2$] to yield DG and inositoltrisphosphate (InsP$_3$) and that the more commonly observed decrease in PtdIns is secondary to increased conversion of PtdIns to phosphatidylinositol 4-phosphate (PtdIns4P) and then to PtdIns(4,5)P$_2$. [In this article, I will employ the term phosphoinositides when referring to PtdIns, PtdIns4P, and PtdIns(4,5)P$_2$. The structures of these lipids and related sugars and their complex interconversions are illustrated in Figs. 11 and 12.] This hypothesis was proposed to explain stimulus activation of Ca^{2+} conductance and of mobilization of intracellular Ca^{2+}. Berridge (1983) has further suggested that InsP$_3$ is the intracellular messenger that mediates mobilization of calcium from cellular stores. Whether there is any direct interaction between PtdIns(4,5)P$_2$, PtdIns4P, and/or PtdIns and the calcium channel in the plasma membrane remains unknown. I will present evidence from my own studies and from those of other investigators that strongly supports the concept that in GH cells TRH acts to stimulate the hydrolysis of PtdIns(4,5)P$_2$ to yield InsP$_3$ and that this may be the initial step in the sequence of intracellular events leading to the first phase elevation of [Ca^{2+}]$_i$.

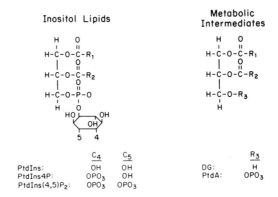

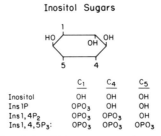

FIG. 11.   Structures of the phosphoinositides, sugars, and metabolic intermediates. R$_1$ and R$_2$ are fatty acyl moieties. The inositol sugar ring is represented schematically. In both the free and the phospholipid form the inositol ring assumes a stable chair conformation with all substituents oriented equatorially to the ring except the 2-position which is axial.

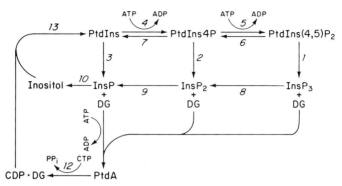

FIG. 12.   Pathways of phosphoinositide metabolism. Enzymes: (1) PtdIns(4,5)P$_2$ phospholipase C; (2) PtdIns4P phospholipase C; (3) PtdIns phospholipase C; (4) PtdIns kinase; (5) PtdIns4P kinase; (6) PtdIns(4,5)P$_2$ phosphomonoesterase; (7) PtdIns4P phosphomonoesterase; (8) InsP$_3$ phosphatase; (9) InsP$_2$ phosphatase; (10) InsP phosphatase; (11) DG kinase; (12) cytidine diphosphate-DG-synthetase; (13) cytidine diphosphate-DG:inositol transferase.

In order to study the effects of TRH on the metabolism of the phosphoinositides in GH$_3$ cells, we first measured the effects of TRH on labeling of these minor lipids with inorganic [^{32}P]phosphate ([^{32}P]P$_i$) (Rebecchi *et al.*, 1981, 1983; Rebecchi and Gershengorn, 1983). In one experiment, ^{32}P labeling of PtdIns(4,5)P$_2$ and PtdIns4P was measured in cells incubated with [^{32}P]P$_i$ under conditions in which phospholipids are not labeled to isotopic steady-state. Figure 13 illustrates the time course of the effect of

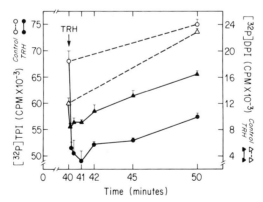

FIG. 13.   Effect of TRH on [^{32}P]PtdIns(4,5)P$_2$ ([^{32}P]TPI) and [^{32}P]PtdIns4P ([^{32}P]DPI) in GH$_3$ cells. Cells were incubated in medium containing 0.5 mCi/ml inorganic [^{32}P]phosphate for 40 minutes and then incubated for various times in medium without (control) or with 1 μM TRH (filled symbols). The points represent mean±SD of triplicate determinations in 3 experiments. (Reproduced from Rebecchi and Gershengorn, 1983.)

TRH on [^{32}P]PtdIns(4,5)P$_2$ and [^{32}P]PtdIns4P in GH$_3$ cells labeled with [^{32}P]P$_i$ for 40 minutes. TRH caused a rapid decrease in the levels of [^{32}P]PtdIns(4,5)P$_2$ and [^{32}P]PtdIns4P to 76 and 71% of control, respectively. The decreases in ^{32}P labeling of PtdIns(4,5)P$_2$ and PtdIns4P likely reflected decreases in the mass of these two lipids even though phospholipids were not labeled to constant specific activity in these experiments because the 4 position phosphate of PtdIns4P and the 4- and 5-position phosphates of PtdIns(4,5)P$_2$ reach isotopic equilibrium with cellular ATP pools within 60 minutes. By contrast, TRH increased [^{32}P]P$_i$ incorporation into PtdA and PtdIns. However, the time course of effect of TRH to stimulate [^{32}P]P$_i$ incorporation into PtdA and to decrease [^{32}P]PtdIns(4,5)P$_2$ and [^{32}P]PtdIns4P was similar but was very different from its effect to stimulate labeling of PtdIns. Figure 14 illustrates the effects of TRH, added after 31 minutes, on [^{32}P]P$_i$ labeling of PtdA and PtdIns. There was a slow, constant rate of incorporation into PtdA and PtdIns in control cells. Upon addition of TRH, a rapid increase in incorporation of [^{32}P]P$_i$ into PtdA was observed. The levels obtained at 5, 10, and 15 seconds after TRH addition demonstrated a progressive increase in [^{32}P]PtdA. A steady-state level of [^{32}P]PtdA, 5-fold greater than control, was attained after 2 minutes. By contrast, [^{32}P]P$_i$ labeling of PtdIns did not increase until approximately 1 minute after TRH addition. The effects of TRH on ^{32}P labeling of PtdIns and PtdA did not necessarily reflect changes in the mass of these lipids. The major cellular phospholipids,

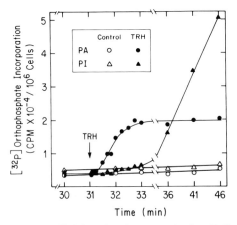

FIG. 14.   Effects of TRH on [^{32}P]phosphate incorporation into PtdIns (PI) and PtdA (PA) in GH$_3$ cells. Cells were incubated in medium containing 0.4 mCi/ml inorganic [^{32}P]phosphate for 31 minutes and then 1 μM TRH was added. (Reproduced from Rebecchi *et al.*, 1981.)

such as phosphatidylcholine and phosphatidylethanolamine, were not affected. Thus, TRH appeared to stimulate specifically the metabolism of the phosphoinositides and PtdA.

The effect of TRH on phosphoinositides labeled to isotopic steady-state with [^{3}H]inositol was determined; in these experiments, changes in the levels of ^{3}H-labeled lipids reflected changes in their masses. The relative content of inositol lipids in cells prelabeled with [^{3}H]inositol was PtdIns(4,5)P$_2$, 2.5%; PtdIns4P, 2.8%; lysoPtdIns, 6.2%; PtdIns, 88%; PtdIns comprises only 9% of total cellular phospholipid content. As illustrated in Fig. 15, TRH caused a marked fall in the levels of [^{3}H]PtdIns(4,5)P$_2$, [^{3}H]PtdIns4P, and [^{3}H]PtdIns. TRH stimulated rapid loss by 15 seconds of [^{3}H]PtdIns(4,5)P$_2$ and [^{3}H]PtdIns4P to 60 and 65% of control, respectively; the nadirs in the levels of [^{3}H]PtdIns(4,5)P$_2$ and [^{3}H]PtdIns4P occurred at 45 and 60 seconds, respectively. After 1 minute in the continued presence of TRH, the levels of [^{3}H]PtdIns(4,5)P$_2$ and [^{3}H]PtdIns4P increased but remained below control for at least 5 minutes. TRH also caused a decrease in [^{3}H]PtdIns to 86% of control by 2 minutes; there was no measurable change in the level of [^{3}H]lysoPtdIns. The percentage rate of decrease of [^{3}H]PtdIns was slower than that of [^{3}H]PtdIns(4,5)P$_2$ and [^{3}H]PtdIns4P.

The decrease in the level of [^{3}H]PtdIns(4,5)P$_2$ was similar in time course and in magnitude to that observed in the experiments in which

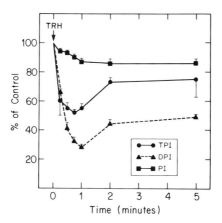

FIG. 15.   Effect of TRH on the levels of [^{3}H]PtdIns(4,5)P$_2$ (TPI), [^{3}H]PtdIns4P (DPI), and [^{3}H]PtdIns (PI) in GH$_3$ cells. Cells were incubated in growth medium containing 1 μCi/ml [^{3}H]inositol for 48 hours. Cells were resuspended in medium without [^{3}H]inositol and TRH was added at time zero. The data are mean±SE of triplicate determinations and are expressed as percentages of the levels in control cells. (Reproduced from Rebecchi and Gershengorn, 1983.)

PtdIns(4,5)P$_2$ was labeled with ^{32}P. However, the fall in the level of [^{3}H]PtdIns4P was far greater than the fall observed in the [^{32}P]PtdIns4P. Thus, during TRH stimulation there appeared to be a rapid increase in the ^{32}P specific radioactivity of PtdIns4P. This increase may have been due either to enhanced conversion of PtdIns to PtdIns4P or to increased metabolism of a pool of PtdIns4P which was unlabeled under the conditions of the experiments with ^{32}P. The former interpretation seems more likely and supports the notion that TRH-induced loss of PtdIns may be caused, at least in part, by enhanced conversion of PtdIns to PtdIns4P and PtdIns(4,5)P$_2$ by inositol lipid kinases.

The effect of TRH to decrease [^{3}H]PtdIns(4,5)P$_2$ and [^{3}H]PtdIns was concentration-dependent; half-maximal effect occurred with approximately 5 nM TRH, a concentration similar to that needed for half-maximal occupancy of the TRH receptor. These results suggest that stimulation of phosphoinositide metabolism is closely linked to the association of TRH with its plasma membrane receptor.

When the cellular content of the various phosphoinositides were compared, it was found that PtdIns(4,5)P$_2$ and PtdIns4P were present in much lower amounts than PtdIns (see above). Despite the very low levels of PtdIns(4,5)P$_2$ and PtdIns4P found in many tissues, these lipids appear to be concentrated in the plasma membrane. We have found that both PtdIns and PtdIns4P kinases, the enzymes which convert PtdIns to PtdIns4P and PtdIns(4,5)P$_2$, respectively, were highly enriched in the plasma membrane fraction isolated from GH$_3$ cells (unpublished observations). This is important because the subcellular compartment in which these enzymes are concentrated may indicate where PtdIns(4,5)P$_2$ and PtdIns4P are located in the intact cell. We estimated that the capacity of the plasma membrane fraction to synthesize polyphosphoinositides from PtdIns was large when compared to the total cellular PtdIns(4,5)P$_2$ and PtdIns4P present in unstimulated GH$_3$ cells. From the specific activity of the PtdIns4P kinase in the plasma membrane fraction, the plasma membrane marker and protein recovery data, and assuming that the enzyme activities measured *in vitro* are accurate reflections of activities *in vivo*, it could be calculated that plasma membranes of GH$_3$ cells have the capacity to synthesize the entire cellular content of PtdIns(4,5)P$_2$ and PtdIns4P each minute. Hence, in GH$_3$ cells, the plasma membrane has potential to be a major cellular reservoir of PtdIns(4,5)P$_2$ and PtdIns4P. Therefore, it is possible that the PtdIns(4,5)P$_2$ and PtdIns4P metabolized during TRH stimulation are located at the cell surface.

We have also measured the level of DG, the lipid product of phospholipase C-mediated hydrolysis of phosphoinositides and the immediate precursor of PtdA. Figure 16 shows the effects of TRH on the level of [^{3}H]DG in cells labeled to an isotopic steady state with [^{3}H]arachidonic

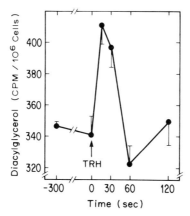

FIG. 16.   Effect of TRH on the level of diacylglycerol (DG) in GH_3 cells prelabeled with [^{3}H]arachidonic acid. Cells were incubated in growth medium containing 0.1 μCi/ml [^{3}H]arachidonic acid for 48 hours. Cells were resuspended in medium without [^{3}H]arachidonic acid and TRH was added at time zero. Each point represents mean $\pm$ SE of triplicate determinations. (Reproduced from Rebecchi *et al.*, 1983.)

acid. We observed that the level of DG increased to 120% of control within 15 to 30 seconds of TRH addition and returned to control levels by 1 minute after TRH addition. The increase in the level of DG observed during TRH stimulation was consistent with the notion that TRH stimulated a phospholipase C activity. However, because DG could have been formed by hydrolysis of any phosphoinositide, this finding did not prove conclusively which phospholipid was hydrolyzed.

The results described so far demonstrate that TRH affects the metabolism of PtdIns(4,5)P_2, PtdIns4P, and PtdIns. Moreover, the increase in DG revealed that activation of a phospholipase C was involved. However, these data alone could not be used to identify the initial reaction stimulated by TRH, because, although the increase in DG could have been due to phospholipase C-mediated hydrolysis of PtdIns, it was also possible that it resulted from hydrolysis of one or both of the polyphosphoinositides. Therefore, in order to identify the initial reaction activated by TRH it was important to monitor the levels of all the inositol sugars during TRH stimulation. In particular, InsP$_3$ was measured because it is the only sugar that is a specific reaction product in the metabolism of the phosphoinositides; that is, InsP$_3$ appears only to be formed by hydrolysis of PtdIns(4,5)P_2 in animal cells.

We measured inositol sugars in cells prelabeled to isotopic steady-state with [^{3}H]inositol. The labeled sugars were separated by anion exchange chromatography. In unstimulated cells, the relative content of the inositol sugars was [³H]InsP₃, 1.3%; [³H]InsP₂, 3.9%; [³H]InsP, 16%; [³H]inositol, 78%. The time course of the effect of TRH on the levels of ³H-labeled inositol sugars is illustrated in Fig. 17. Addition of TRH induced a rapid, transient increase in [³H]InsP₃ to 410% of control at 15 seconds; the level declined after 15 seconds but was still above control after 5 minutes. The level of [³H]InsP₂ was also increased by 15 seconds and attained its highest level of 450% of control at 30 seconds after TRH addition; its level declined after 30 seconds but was above control at 5 minutes. In contrast, [³H]InsP and [³H]inositol were not elevated until 30 and 60 seconds after TRH addition, respectively. In four experiments, the effects of TRH on the levels of [³H]inositol sugars after 30 seconds, expressed as percentages of unstimulated levels (mean ± SE) were [³H]InsP₃, 246 ± 19%; [³H]InsP₂, 316 ± 21%; [³H]InsP, 138 ± 7%; and [³H]inositol, 100 ± 3%.

Because the levels of InsP₃ and InsP₂ preceded the elevation in InsP and free inositol, it appears that TRH stimulates the phospholipase C-mediated hydrolysis of PtdIns(4,5)P₂ prior to any direct hydrolysis of PtdIns. Moreover, the demonstration of an increase in the concentration of InsP₃ during TRH stimulation proves that a phospholipase C that hydrolyzes PtdIns(4,5)P₂ was activated. The TRH-induced increase in InsP₂ and InsP may have resulted from dephosphorylation of InsP₃ by a phosphatase(s) [or phosphomonoesterase(s)] rather than increased hydrolysis of PtdIns4P or PtdIns, respectively. The transient nature of the accumulation of inositol phosphates and the delayed, but linear increase in free

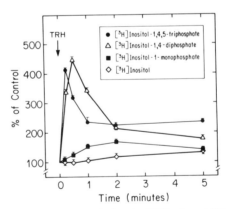

FIG. 17.   Effect of TRH on [³H]InsP₃, [³H]InsP₂, [³H]InsP, and [³H]inositol in GH₃ cells. Cells were incubated in growth medium containing 1 μCi/ml [³H]inositol for 48 hours. Cells were resuspended in medium without [³H]inositol and TRH was added at time zero. The data are mean ± SE of triplicate determinations and are expressed as percentages of the levels in control cells. (Reproduced from Rebecchi and Gershengorn, 1983.)

inositol suggests that these phosphatases may be stimulated subsequent to the initial increase in the levels of the inositol phosphates. Similar findings of the effects of TRH on phosphoinositide metabolism in GH cells have been obtained by several other laboratories (Drummond and MacPhee, 1981, 1984; Schlegel et al., 1981, 1984; Sutton and Martin, 1982; Martin, 1983; Drummond et al., 1984).

The evidence presented above strongly supports the notion that the initial reaction in TRH-stimulated phosphoinositide metabolism is hydrolysis of PtdIns(4,5)P$_2$ to InsP$_3$ and DG. Is there any evidence that the fall in the levels of PtdIns and PtdIns4P are linked to PtdIns(4,5)P$_2$ hydrolysis? We have obtained some data that strongly suggest that the fall in PtdIns may be due in large part to its conversion to PtdIns4P and then to PtdIns(4,5)P$_2$. In GH$_3$ cells, we observed that during the first 15 seconds of TRH stimulation there is no significant increase in [^{3}H]InsP despite the fall in PtdIns. The increase in [^{3}H]InsP$_3$ caused by TRH at 15 seconds was 615 cpm/5 × 10^6 cells, whereas the fall in [^{3}H]PtdIns(4,5)P$_2$ was only 182 cpm/5 × 10^6 cells. This means that about three times as much InsP$_3$ was produced than PtdIns(4,5)P$_2$ was lost. These results suggest that TRH enhanced the conversion of PtdIns to PtdIns4P and PtdIns(4,5)P$_2$ by PtdIns and PtdIns4P kinases, respectively. This notion is also supported by the increase in PtdIns4P specific ^{32}P radioactivity observed during TRH stimulation as described above.

The results discussed so far demonstrate that TRH-stimulated hydrolysis of PtdIns(4,5)P$_2$ to InsP$_3$ and DG is a very early event in TRH action and that the fall in the levels of PtdIns and PtdIns4P may be accounted for, at least in part, by their rapid conversion to PtdIns(4,5)P$_2$. These events occur over a time course very similar to the elevation of [Ca^{2+}]$_i$ induced by TRH (see Section III). Moreover, the close association between the binding of TRH to its receptor and enhanced phosphoinositide metabolism suggests that the hydrolysis of PtdIns(4,5)P$_2$ to InsP$_3$ and DG is closely linked to the initial ligand receptor interaction and that this event may not require amplification of the TRH signal. Therefore, it seemed possible that hormone-stimulated phosphoinositide metabolism is one of the first steps in a sequence of events that alters cellular Ca^{2+} homeostasis leading to the elevation of [Ca^{2+}]$_i$. The remainder of my discussion will concern the experiments which have been performed to test this hypothesis.

V. Phosphoinositides or Calcium: Horse or Cart?

An important question regarding TRH-stimulated phosphoinositide metabolism in GH$_3$ cells was whether the initial enzyme reaction induced by

TRH is dependent on (or caused by) an elevation of $[Ca^{2+}]_i$. If stimulated phosphoinositide metabolism were secondary to an increase in $[Ca^{2+}]_i$ it could not be the initial event after ligand–receptor interaction. Because it appeared likely that the primary effect of TRH on phosphoinositides was to stimulate phospholipase C-mediated hydrolysis of $PtdIns(4,5)P_2$, I attempted to determine whether TRH-stimulated $PtdIns(4,5)P_2$ hydrolysis could be caused by an elevation of $[Ca^{2+}]_i$ that is sufficient to stimulate several other cellular responses including prolactin secretion.

To study whether hydrolysis of $PtdIns(4,5)P_2$ induced by TRH may have been caused by an elevation of $[Ca^{2+}]_i$, TRH-stimulated changes in phosphoinositides were initially compared with the effects of K^+ depolarization that elevates $[Ca^{2+}]_i$ leading to a marked enhancement of phosphorylation of several proteins (Drust and Martin, 1982) and of prolactin secretion (Gershengorn, 1982). The effects of TRH on inositol sugar levels were compared with those of depolarization by 50 mM K^+ after 30 seconds in cells prelabeled with $[^3H]$inositol. As illustrated in Fig. 18, TRH markedly increased the levels of $[^3H]InsP_3$ and $[^3H]InsP_2$, and minimally increased $[^3H]InsP$. In contrast, 50 mM K^+ had no effect on the levels of $[^3H]InsP_3$, $[^3H]InsP_2$, or $[^3H]$inositol. Also, in contrast with TRH, 50 mM K^+ did not measurably change the levels of any of the ^3H-labeled inositol lipids. To determine whether the lack of measurable increases in $[^3H]InsP_3$ and $[^3H]InsP_2$ was caused by accelerated dephosphorylation of these sugars to $[^3H]InsP$ induced by 50 mM K^+, cells were exposed to TRH and 50 mM K^+ simultaneously. There was no effect of 50 mM K^+ on TRH-stimulated increases in $[^3H]InsP_3$ or $[^3H]InsP_2$, nor did 50 mM K^+ have any effects on the TRH-induced fall in the levels of $PtdIns(4,5)P_2$, PtdIns4P, and PtdIns. Hence, the elevation of $[Ca^{2+}]_i$ induced by K^+ depolarization that is comparable in magnitude and longer in duration than that induced by TRH (Gershengorn and Thaw, 1983) and is sufficient to cause phosphorylation of several proteins (Drust and Martin, 1982) and stimulate prolactin secretion (Gershengorn, 1982) does not cause hydrolysis of $PtdIns(4,5)P_2$ to $InsP_3$. These results were consistent with the notion that TRH-stimulated $PtdIns(4,5)P_2$ hydrolysis by a phospholipase C is *not* caused by an elevation of $[Ca^{2+}]_i$ but instead may lead to Ca^{2+} mobilization.

Further evidence in favor of this hypothesis was obtained by incubating GH_3 cells in Ca^{2+}-free buffer (Fig. 18). Under these conditions, TRH stimulated an increase in the levels of $[^3H]InsP_3$, $[^3H]InsP_2$, and $[^3H]InsP$ which was almost identical to that in cells stimulated by TRH in medium with 1.5 mM Ca^{2+}. Incubation of cells in medium with no added Ca^{2+} also did not interfere with the TRH-stimulated decrease in $[^3H]PtdIns(4,5)P_2$, $[^3H]PtdIns4P$, or $[^3H]PtdIns$. Thus, TRH-stimulated $PtdIns(4,5)P_2$ hydro-

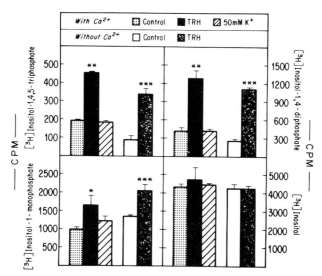

FIG. 18.   Effects of TRH, in medium without or with added Ca^{2+}, and 50 mM K^+, in medium with Ca^{2+}, on the levels of [³H]InsP₃, [³H]InsP₂, [³H]InsP, and [³H]inositol after 30 seconds in GH₃ cells. Cells were incubated in growth medium containing 1 μCi/ml [³H]inositol for 48 hours. Cells were resuspended in medium without [³H]inositol and the cells were harvested 30 seconds after TRH addition. The data are mean±SE of triplicate determinations and are expressed as percentages of the levels in control cells. (Reproduced from Rebecchi and Gershengorn, 1983.)

lysis was not affected by a low Ca^{2+} concentration in the medium which is known to lead to depletion of cellular Ca^{2+} and to prevent influx of extracellular Ca^{2+} into GH₃ cells (Gershengorn, 1982). This provided further indirect evidence that TRH-induced PtdIns(4,5)P₂ hydrolysis is not dependent on an increased $[Ca^{2+}]_i$.

Another approach which has been used to determine whether hormone-stimulated phosphoinositide metabolism is dependent on an elevation of $[Ca^{2+}]_i$ involves the use of Ca^{2+} ionophores. Ionophores act to transport Ca^{2+} rapidly down electrochemical gradients across the plasma membrane and intracellular, membrane-delimited compartments and, thereby, elevate markedly $[Ca^{2+}]_i$. We (Kolesnick and Gershengorn, 1984) have demonstrated that the Ca^{2+}] ionophores, A23187 and ionomycin, affect phosphoinositide metabolism in GH₃ cells in a manner that is quite different from TRH. We found, in cells prelabeled to isotopic steady-state with [³H]inositol, that A23187 caused small, but significant decreases in [³H]PtdIns(4,5)P₂, [³H]PtdIns4P, and [³H]PtdIns to 76, 64, and 88% of control, respectively after 5 minutes. Although these effects were qualita-

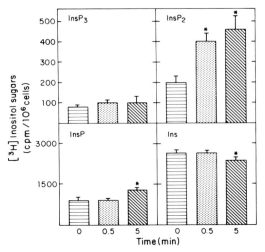

FIG. 19.   Effect of ionophore A23187 on [³H]InsP₃, [³H]InsP₂, [³H]InsP, and [³H]inositol after 0.5 and 5 minutes in GH₃ cells. The experiment was performed and analyzed as in the legend to Fig. 18. Levels in unstimulated cells did not change during the incubation. These data represent triplicate determinations from 9 experiments and are presented as percent of zero time control (mean±SE). (Reproduced from Kolesnick and Gershengorn, 1984.)

tively similar to those induced by TRH, the rate of the A23187-induced fall in the levels of these lipids was much slower. Figure 19 illustrates the effects of A23187 on the levels of inositol sugars. At 0.5 minute, A23187 caused an increase in the level of [³H]InsP₂ to 200±20% of control; there were no significant changes in the levels of [³H]InsP₃ [³H]InsP, and [³H]Inositol. At 5 minutes, [³H]InsP₂ was 230±30% of control and [³H]InsP was elevated to 140±10%, and free [³H]inositol was lowered to 89±6%; [³H]InsP₃ remained unchanged. Similarly, at 0.5 minute, 50 μM ionomycin caused an increase in the level of [³H]InsP₂ to 415% of control after 0.5 minute while the other inositol sugars were unchanged. These results were very different from those obtained during TRH stimulation (compare to Fig. 17). In particular, the Ca²⁺ ionophores did not stimulate the phospholipase C-mediated hydrolysis of PtdIns(4,5)P₂ as reflected by the unchanged level of InsP₃. Because it was possible that the inability to measure an increase in [³H]InsP₃ was due to rapid conversion to InsP₂ by dephosphorylation, the effects of A23187 and TRH added simultaneously on the levels of inositol lipids and sugars (Fig. 20) were studied. A23187 did not affect TRH-induced decreases in phosphoinositides or TRH-induced increases in inositol sugars. These data again demonstrated that in GH₃ cells phospholipase C-mediated hydrolysis of PtdIns(4,5)P₂ is not

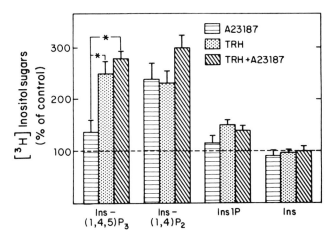

FIG. 20. Effects of ionophore A23187, TRH, and A23187 plus TRH at 30 seconds on [³H]InsP₃, [³H]InsP₂, [³H]InsP, and [³H]inositol in GH₃ cells. A23187 (10 μM), TRH (1 μM), or both were added at time zero and the effects measured at 30 seconds; otherwise studies were performed as described in the legend to Fig. 18. These data (mean±SE) represent triplicate determinations from 3 separate experiments. (Reproduced from Kolesnick and Gershengorn, 1984.)

stimulated by an elevation of $[Ca^{2+}]_i$. It appeared that, in contrast, phospholipase C-mediated hydrolysis of PtdIns4P to InsP₂ and DG is stimulated by an elevation of $[Ca^{2+}]_i$ caused by ionophores. The relatively slow decrease in the level of PtdIns(4,5)P₂ may be explained by its dephosphorylation to PtdIns4P by an ionophore-stimulated phosphomonoesterase. The fall in the level of PtdIns is likely due, in part, to its conversion to PtdIns4P by PtdIns kinase. Hence, the stimulation of phosphoinositide metabolism by Ca^{2+} ionophores appears to be via pathways which are different than those affected by TRH.

These findings also suggest that two different phospholipase C activities to hydrolyze phosphoinositides exist in GH₃ cells. One enzyme appears to be specific for PtdIns(4,5)P₂ and is stimulated by the TRH–receptor interaction. The second appears to be specific for PtdIns4P and is activated by a marked elevation of $[Ca^{2+}]_i$. In accordance with this notion, we have obtained preliminary evidence that the distribution of two phospholipase C activities, one which favors the hydrolysis of PtdIns(4,5)P₂ and another which more efficiently hydrolyzes PtdIns4P were differentially distributed in subcellular fractions isolated from GH₃ cells (unpublished observations). It can be suggested from these data that *in situ* TRH–receptor interaction initially stimulates the hydrolysis of PtdInd(4,5)P₂ that leads to an elevation of $[Ca^{2+}]_i$ (see Section VI). Thereafter, a second phospholipase C may be activated by the increase in $[Ca^{2+}]_i$ that serves to limit the amount of $InsP_3$ generated by hydrolyzing PtdIns4P and, thereby, inhibiting its conversion to $PtdIns(4,5)P_2$.

Hence, the effects of elevating $[Ca^{2+}]_i$ on phosphoinositide metabolism are *not* similar to those induced by TRH; that is, the elevation of $[Ca^{2+}]_i$ caused by ionophores does not stimulate hydrolysis of $PtdIns(4,5)P_2$ to $InsP_3$. These results support the hypothesis that phospholipase C-mediated hydrolysis of $PtdIns(4,5)P_2$ induced by TRH is not secondary to an elevation of $[Ca^{2+}]_i$ but rather may be an early event in the sequence leading to an elevation of $[Ca^{2+}]_i$.

VI. InsP₃ as Intracellular Messenger

Berridge (1983,1984) proposed that $InsP_3$ may function as an intracellular messenger to mobilize Ca^{2+} from a pool(s) within cells. This hypothesis has been supported by observations that $InsP_3$ releases Ca^{2+} from a nonmitochondrial pool(s) in "leaky" rat pancreatic acinar cells (Streb *et al.*, 1983), in saponin-permeabilized rat and guinea pig hepatocytes (Joseph *et al.*, 1984; Burgess *et al.*, 1984) and in rat insulinoma cells (Prentki *et al.*, 1984). To determine whether $InsP_3$ may serve as a mediator of the TRH-induced release of Ca^{2+} from an intracellular pool(s), a preparation of saponin-permeabilized GH_3 cells was developed (Gershengorn *et al.*, 1984). It was first necessary to demonstrate that this preparation retained the ability to sequester Ca^{2+} as in the intact cell. Figure 21 illustrates ^{45}Ca uptake by saponin-permeabilized cells. ^{45}Ca uptake was time and ATP dependent. In the presence of 5 mM ATP, permeabilized cells accumulated 6- to 10-fold more ^{45}Ca than similarly prepared, permeabilized cells incubated in the absence of ATP or in the presence of both ATP and the ionophore A23187. Because A23187 releases all intravesicular ^{45}Ca, ^{45}Ca not released by ionophore, as in intact cells, likely represents calcium bound to cytoplasmic proteins or to membrane-bound proteins or phospholipids, or perhaps ^{45}Ca in the extracellular buffer trapped in the pellet. The uptake of ^{45}Ca by saponin-treated cells in the presence of ATP was half-maximal within 2 minutes and reached a steady-state level by 5 minutes that remained unchanged for at least 40 minutes. When saponin-treated cells which had taken up ^{45}Ca for 10 minutes in the presence of ATP were exposed to A23187, there was an immediate release of the accumulated ^{45}Ca. This observation provides further evidence that the ^{45}Ca accumulation was an active process into vesicular pools. In other experiments, we showed that this preparation retained the ability to sequester Ca^{2+} within separate mitochondrial and nonmitochondrial pools. My colleagues and I showed that the nonmitochondrial pool had a high

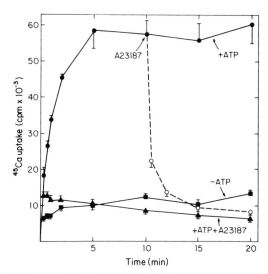

FIG. 21. Effects of ATP and ionophore A23187 on the uptake of ^{45}Ca by saponin-permeabilized GH$_3$ cells. Cells were suspended in a cytosol-like buffer containing 5 μM Quin 2 to yield free Ca^{2+} concentration of 60 nM and permeabilized by incubation with 100 μg/ml saponin for 60 seconds at 24°C. The cells were separated from the buffer and resuspended in the same buffer without saponin and with or without ATP or with ATP and 10 μM A23187. ^{45}Ca^{2+} (1 μCi/ml) was added at time zero. To one series of tubes of permeabilized cells incubating in buffer with ATP, 10 μM A23187 was added after 10 minutes. At the times indicated, the permeabilized cells were separated from the buffer by centrifugation through silicone oil and ^{45}Ca was measured in the pellet after solubilization. The points represent the mean±SE of triplicate determinations in 2 experiments. (Reproduced from Gershengorn *et al.*, 1984.)

affinity for Ca^{2+}, maximal uptake occurred with less than 200 nM [Ca^{2+}]$_{free}$, and that it was saturable. By contrast, the mitochondrial pool exhibited a lower affinity for Ca^{2+}, but a greater capacity for calcium accumulation which was not fully saturated at free Ca^{2+} concentrations up to 1000 nM. We also demonstrated that when permeabilized cells were incubated in buffer with a [Ca^{2+}]$_{free}$ initially between 200 and 1000 nM, [Ca^{2+}]$_{free}$ was buffered to 129 nM, mainly by the mitochondrial pool. Because the [Ca^{2+}]$_i$ in intact cells is maintained at approximately 130 nM, these findings suggested that the mitochondria serve a primary role in intact cells to buffer [Ca^{2+}]$_i$. It is important to remember, however, that a major role in the intact cell to buffer [Ca^{2+}]$_i$ may also be performed by the plasma membrane via the Ca^{2+}, Mg^{2+}-ATPase ("Ca^{2+} pump") or Na$^+$– Ca^{2+} exchange mechanisms (Kaczorowski *et al.*, 1984; Barros and Kaczorowski, 1984) that cannot be analyzed in permeabilized cells. Hence, a

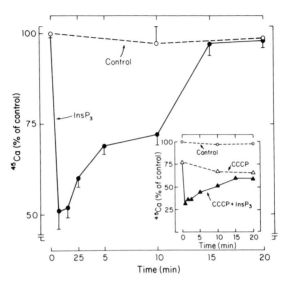

FIG. 22.   Effect of InsP₃ on ⁴⁵Ca accumulated by saponin-permeabilized GH₃ cells in the absence or presence of CCCP. Permeabilized cells were loaded with ⁴⁵Ca²⁺ as in Fig. 21. After 15 minutes, 10 μM InsP₃ or vehicle (control) was added and the permeabilized cell-associated ⁴⁵Ca was measured. Inset: CCCP (5 μM) was added to the cell suspension after 10 minutes of incubation with ⁴⁵Ca²⁺ and InsP₃ was added after 15 minutes. The points represent the mean±SE of triplicate determinations from 3 experiments. (Reproduced from Gershengorn *et al.*, 1984.)

definitive conclusion regarding the relative contributions of these various mechanisms in buffering [Ca²⁺]ᵢ in intact cells can not be made from our studies.

Having established that saponin-permeabilized GH₃ cells retained at least some of the mechanisms that appear to regulate calcium homeostasis in intact cells, we proceeded to test the effect of InsP₃ on Ca²⁺ accumulation by intracellular pools. Figure 22 illustrates the effect of InsP₃ on ⁴⁵Ca that had accumulated to a steady-state level in permeabilized cells incubated in cytosol-like buffer containing ATP and 75 nM [Ca²⁺]free. InsP₃ caused a very rapid loss of ⁴⁵Ca from saponin-treated cells followed by a slow reuptake to the original steady-state level. In 11 experiments in which permeabilized cells were incubated in cytosol-like buffer containing 66±2.0 nM [Ca²⁺]free, 3 μM or greater concentrations of InsP₃ caused a transient loss of 35±4% of accumulated ⁴⁵Ca at between 0.5 and 2.5 minutes. In permeabilized cells incubated in buffer containing the mitochondrial uncoupler CCCP to prevent mitochondrial accumulation of calcium, InsP₃ still caused release of ⁴⁵Ca which was indistinguishable in

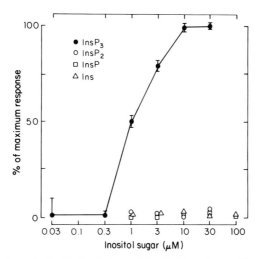

FIG. 23. Effects of InsP$_3$, InsP$_2$, InsP, and inositol to release ^{45}Ca from saponin-permeabilized GH$_3$ cells. Permeabilized cells were loaded with ^{45}Ca^{2+} as in Fig. 21. After 15 minutes, various concentrations of InsP$_3$, InsP$_2$, InsP, or inositol (Ins) were added and the permeabilized cells were separated from the medium after an additional 2.5 minutes. The points represent the mean±SE of triplicate determinations in 2 experiments. (Reproduced from Gershengorn *et al.*, 1984.)

amount from that released in control saponin-treated cells; the reuptake of released ^{45}Ca was also not impaired. These data are most easily interpreted as demonstrating that InsP$_3$ releases calcium specifically from a nonmitochondrial pool(s).

Figure 23 illustrates the concentration dependency of the effect of InsP$_3$ and the specificity of the ^{45}Ca release response. InsP$_3$-induced release of ^{45}Ca from a pool within permeabilized cells was half-maximal at approximately 1 μM and was maximal with concentrations of 10 μM or greater. The effect of InsP$_3$ was specific because InsP$_2$, InsP, and inositol had no effect on ^{45}Ca accumulated by saponin-treated cells at similar or even higher concentrations.

An important characteristic of the InsP$_3$ effect was that the rapid release of calcium was followed by its reuptake. This is similar to the transient nature of the TRH-stimulated "first phase" elevation of [Ca^{2+}]$_i$ in intact GH$_3$ cells that appears to be caused primarily by the release of calcium from an intracellular pool(s) (see Section III). It has been suggested that at least part of the reversal of the calcium release response in permeabilized cells, that is, the reuptake, is due to InsP$_3$ degradation; however, an autoregulation or desensitization may also occur. Also, because the release and reuptake phases induced by InsP$_3$ are present in preparations in which mitochondrial calcium accumulation is blocked, it appears that a nonmitochondrial calcium pool(s) may be involved in both the release and the reuptake of Ca^{2+}, at least under certain circumstances. However, under physiologic conditions *in situ,* the elevation of cytoplasmic free Ca^{2+} in intact cells may be reversed by reuptake into the nonmitochondrial pool(s), but also by extrusion from the cells and even by uptake into mitochondria.

The concentration of InsP₃ that causes a half-maximal release of nonmitochondrial calcium is approximately 1 μM and maximal release occurs with 10 μM InsP₃ in permeabilized GH₃ cells. These concentrations are lower than the concentration of InsP₃ that we calculate (50–75 μM) from our measurements of InsP₃ in intact GH₃ cells 15 seconds after TRH addition (Rebecchi and Gershengorn, 1983). However, it should be remembered that such a calculation is a very rough estimate of the concentration of InsP₃ that may be biologically active because the portion of intracellular InsP₃ which is bound to protein or other cellular sites is unknown. Furthermore, the quantity of active InsP₃ isomer, that is, inositol 1,4,5-trisphosphate, present in the cell or in the InsP₃ preparations are unknown. Thus, it is not yet possible to make quantitative comparisons of InsP₃ action in intact and permeabilized cells. Nevertheless, these data are compatible with a role for InsP₃ in transducing the signal of TRH-receptor interaction into mobilization of Ca^{2+} from an intracellular pool(s).

VII.   TRH Action: A Model

Based on the observations of my colleagues and I, and those reported by others, I propose the following as the sequence of intracellular events involved in the mechanism of TRH stimulation of prolactin secretion from GH₃ cells (see Fig. 24). The binding of TRH to its plasma membrane

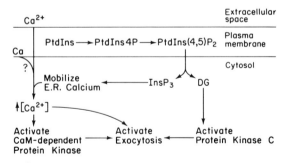

FIG. 24.   Model of TRH action. See text for discussion.

receptor stimulates, by an as yet undefined mechanism, the hydrolysis of PtdIns(4,5)P_2 to yield InsP$_3$ and DG. The fall in the level of plasma membrane PtdIns(4,5)P_2 enhances the conversion of PtdIns4P and PtdIns to PtdIns(4,5)P_2. Thus, these three phosphoinositides contribute to the formation of InsP$_3$ and DG, both of which serve subsequent mediator functions. InsP$_3$, the water-soluble product of PtdIns(4,5)P_2 hydrolysis, diffuses from the plasma membrane to an intracellular, nonmitochondrial, membrane-delimited pool of calcium, perhaps the endoplasmic reticulum. Because of the unique conformation of its phosphate groups, InsP$_3$ may associate specifically with intracellular receptors which control the release of calcium and thereby mobilize Ca^{2+} from these sites. The movement of Ca^{2+} from a cellular pool(s) into the cytoplasm results in the first phase elevation of [Ca^{2+}]$_i$ which couples, in part, stimulus to secretion. The elevation of [Ca^{2+}]$_i$ is extended by a delayed, but prolonged, TRH-induced enhancement of influx of extracellular Ca^{2+}, most likely through voltage-dependent channels; the molecular events that mediate enhanced Ca^{2+} influx are not known though phosphorylation of channel proteins may be involved. The elevation of [Ca^{2+}]$_i$ may activate exocytosis directly and/or through phosphorylation of proteins involved in the exocytotic process via activation of a calmodulin-dependent protein kinase(s).

Concomitant with the effects of InsP$_3$, phosphorylation of proteins involved in the exocytotic process may be stimulated through DG activation of the phospholipid- and Ca^{2+}-dependent protein kinase (protein kinase C) (Nishizuka *et al.,* 1984). Although the role of DG formed during TRH-stimulated phosphoinositide metabolism is less certain, it has been proposed that the increased concentration of DG stimulates protein phosphorylations which may act synergistically with Ca^{2+} to stimulate secretion. In this regard, phorbol esters have been found to increase the phosphorylation of some of the same proteins as TRH and also to stimulate prolactin secretion (Osborne and Tashjian, 1981; Sobel and Tashjian, 1983), apparently through activation of protein kinase C. Therefore, it is possible that the TRH-stimulated increase in DG caused by phospholipase C-mediated hydrolysis of PtdIns(4,5)P_2 may increase the activity of protein kinase C and so increase protein phosphorylation. These phosphoproteins may, in addition to activating exocytosis, mediate other aspects of the actions of TRH, for example, the increase in plasma membrane Ca^{2+} permeability. Hence, in this hypothesis, optimal stimulation of prolactin secretion by TRH requires the synergistic effects of an elevation of [Ca^{2+}]$_i$ and specific protein phosphorylation.

Although the model I have proposed appears well-founded, many of the essential features remain undefined. Neither the molecular events which underlie the coupling of the TRH-receptor complex to hydrolysis of Ptd-

Ins(4,5)P$_2$ nor the mechanism by which InsP$_3$ mobilizes calcium are known. In fact, the localization of the hormone-sensitive pool(s) of phosphoinositides to the cell surface can only be inferred from very indirect evidence. Furthermore, the link between TRH-stimulated phosphoinositide metabolism and elevation of [Ca^{2+}]$_i$ has not been rigorously demonstrated and the activation of protein phosphorylation and its role in activation of exocytosis is speculative. Moreover, in GH$_3$ cells, none of the proteins which are phosphorylated have been identified and their role in stimulated prolactin secretion is unknown. Hence, it must be emphasized that the model I propose is intended to serve mainly to guide further investigation into the molecular events that couple TRH-receptor interaction at the cell surface to the transduction and amplification of intracellular signals. Although this model was developed to explain the mechanism of TRH stimulation of prolactin secretion from GH cells, it is consistent with observations that have been made in a variety of cells and I believe is generally applicable to stimulus–response coupling in many cell types.

ACKNOWLEDGMENTS

I gratefully thank my colleagues, especially E. Geras, R. N. Kolesnick, C. Thaw, and M. J. Rebecchi, for their enormous contributions to the work described in this article. This research was supported by grants from the National Institutes of Health (AM-33468 and AM-33469).

REFERENCES

Albert, P. R., and Tashjian, A. H., Jr. (1984). *J. Biol. Chem.* **259,** 5827–5832.

Barros, F., and Kaczorowski, G. J. (1984). *J. Biol. Chem.* **259,** 9404–9410.

Bellomo, G., Jewell, S. A., Thor, H., and Orrenius, S. (1982). *Proc. Natl. Acad. Sci. U.S.A.* **79,** 6842–6846.

Berridge, M. J. (1981). *Mol. Cell. Endocrinol.* **24,** 115–140.

Berridge, M. J. (1983). *Biochem. J.* **212,** 849–858.

Berridge, M. J. (1984). *Biochem. J.* **220,** 345–360.

Burgess, G. M., Godfrey, P. O., McKinney, J. S., Berridge, M. J., Irvine, R. F., and Putney, J. W., Jr. (1984). *Nature (London)* **309,** 63–66.

Campbell, A. K. (1983). "Intracellular Calcium, Its Universal Role as Regulator." Wiley, New York.

Douglas, W. W. (1978). *Ciba Found. Symp.* **54,** 61–90.

Downes, C. P., and Michell, R. H. (1982). *Cell Calcium* **3,** 467–502.

Drummond, A. H., and MacPhee, C. H. (1981). *Br. J. Pharmacol.* **74,** 967P–968P.

Drummond, A. H., and MacPhee, C. H. (1984). *Mol. Pharmacol.* **25,** 193–200.

Drummond, A. H., Bushfield, M., and MacPhee, C. H. (1984). *Mol. Pharmacol.* **25,** 201–208.

Drust, D. S., and Martin, T. F. J. (1982). *J. Biol. Chem.* **257,** 7566–7573.

Gautvik, K. M., Iversen, J. G., and Sand, O. (1980). *Life Sci.* **26,** 995–1005.

Geras, E., Rebecchi, M. J., and Gershengorn, M. C. (1982). *Endocrinology* **110,** 901–906.

Gershengorn, M. C. (1980). *J. Biol. Chem.* **255,** 1801–1803.

Gershengorn, M. C. (1982). *Mol. Cell. Biochem.* **45,** 163–179.

Gershengorn, M. C., and Thaw, C. (1983). *Endocrinology* **113,** 1522–1524.

Gershengorn, M. C., and Thaw, C. (1985). *Endocrinology,* **116,** 591–596.

Gershengorn, M. C., Hoffstein, S. T., Rebecchi, M. J., Geras, E., and Rubin, B. G. (1981). *J. Clin. Invest.* **67,** 1769–1776.

Gershengorn, M. C., Thaw, C., and Gerry, R. H. (1983). *Cell Calcium* **4,** 117–124.

Gershengorn, M. C., Geras, E., Spina Purrello, V., and Rebecchi, M. J. (1984). *J. Biol. Chem.* **259,** 10675–10681.

Joseph, S. K., and Williamson, J. R. (1983). *J. Biol. Chem.* **258,** 10425–10432.

Joseph, S. K., Thomas, A. P., Williams, R. J., Irvine, R. F., and Williamson, J. R. (1984). *J. Biol. Chem.* **259,** 3077–3081.

Kaczorowski, G. J., Costello, L., Dethmers, J., Trumble, M. J., and Vandlen, R. L. (1984). *J. Biol. Chem.* **259.** 9395–9403.

Kolesnick, R. N., and Gershengorn, M. C. (1984). *J. Biol. Chem.* **259,** 9514–9519.

Kruskal, B. A., Keith, C. H., and Maxfield, F. R. (1984). *J. Cell Biol.* **99,** 1167–1172.

Leuschen, M. P., Moriarty, C. M., and Sampson, H. W. (1983). *Histochemistry* **77,** 85–97.

MacPhee, C. H., and Drummond, A. H. (1984). *Mol. Pharmacol.* **25,** 193–200.

Martin, T. F. J. (1983). *J. Biol. Chem.* **258,** 14816–14822.

Martin, T. F. J, and Tashjian, A. H., Jr. (1977). *In* "Biochemical Actions of Hormones" (G. Litwack, ed.), pp. 269–312. Academic Press, New York.

Michell, R. H. (1975). *Biochim. Biophys. Acta* **415,** 81–147.

Michell, R. H. (1982). *Nature (London)* **296,** 492–493.

Michell, R. H., Kirk, C. J., Jones, L. M., Downes, C. P., and Creba, J. A. (1981). *Philos. Trans. R. Soc. London Ser. B* **296,** 123–137.

Moriarty, C. M., and Leuschen, M. P. (1981). *Am. J. Physiol.* **240,** E705–E711.

Murayama, T., Shiino, M., and Rennels, E. G. (1981). *Neuroendocrinology* **32,** 28–32.

Nishizuka, Y., Takai, Y., Kishimoto, A., Kikkawa, U., and Kaibuchi, K. (1984). *Recent Prog. Horm. Res.* **40,** 301–346.

Osborne, R., and Tashjian, A. H., Jr. (1981). *Endocrinology* **108,** 1164–1170.

Ostlund, E. R., Jr., Leung, J. R., Vaerewyck, H., Winokur, T., and Melman, M. (1978). *Endocrinology* **103,** 1245–1252.

Ozawa, S., and Kimura, N. (1979). *Proc. Natl. Acad. Sci. U.S.A.* **76,** 6017–6020.

Ozawa, S., and Kimura, N. (1982). *Am. J. Physiol.* **243** (*Endocrinol. Metab.* **6**), E68–E73.

Prentki, M., Biden, T. J., Janjic, D., Irvine, R. F., Berridge, M. J., and Wollheim, C. B. (1984). *Nature (London)* **309,** 562–564.

Rebecchi, M. J., and Gershengorn, M. C. (1983). *Biochem. J.* **216,** 287–294.

Rebecchi, M. J., Monaco, M. E., and Gershengorn, M. C. (1981). *Biochem. Biophys. Res. Commun.* **101,** 124–130.

Rebecchi, M. J., Gerry, R. H., and Gershengorn, M. C. (1982). *J. Biol. Chem.* **257,** 2751–2753.

Rebecchi, M. J., Kolesnick, R. N., and Gershengorn, M. C. (1983). *J. Biol. Chem.* **258,** 227–234.

Ronning, S. A., Heatley, G. A., and Martin, T. F. J. (1982). *Proc. Natl. Acad. Sci. U.S.A.* **79,** 6294–6298.

Schlegel, W., Roduit, C., and Zahnd, G. (1981). *FEBS Lett.* **134,** 47–49.

Schlegel, W., Roduit, C., and Zahnd, G. R. (1984). *FEBS Lett.* **168,** 54–60.

Snowdowne, K. W., and Borle, A. B. (1984). *Am. J. Physiol.* **246,** E198–E201.

Sobel, A., and Tashjian, A. H., Jr. (1983). *J. Biol. Chem.* **258,** 10312–10324.

Streb, H., Irvine, R. F., Berridge, M. J., and Schulz, I. (1983). *Nature (London)* **306,** 67–69.

Sutton, C. A., and Martin, T. F. J. (1982). *Endocrinology* **110**, 1273–1280.

Tan, K. N., and Tashjian, A. H., Jr. (1981). *J. Biol. Chem.* **256**, 8994–9002.

Tan, K. N., and Tashjian, A. H., Jr. (1984). *J. Biol. Chem.* **259**, 427–434.

Tashjian, A. H., Jr., Lomedico, M. E., and Maina, D. (1978). *Biochem. Biophys. Res. Commun.* **81**, 798–806.

Thaw, C., Wittlin, S. D., and Gershengorn, M. C. (1982). *Endocrinology* **111**, 2138–2140.

Thaw, C., Geras Raaka, E., and Gershengorn, M. C. (1984). *Am. J. Physiol.* **247** (*Cell. Physiol.* **16**), C150–C155.

Tsien, R. Y. (1980). *Biochemistry* **19**, 2396–2403.

Vale, W., Rivier, C., Brown, M., Chan, L., Ling, N., and Rivier, J. (1976). *In* "Hypothalamus and Endocrine Functions" (F. Labrie, J. Meites, and G. Pelletier, eds.), pp. 397–429.

DISCUSSION

L. Birnbaumer: With respect to your last data slide where you showed that only the IP$_3$ is effective in mobilizing calcium stores and none of the other inositol phosphates is, did you try combinations of these phosphates to see whether there could be a modulation?

M. C. Gershengorn: As I think was evident from our data showing the kinetics of the InsP$_3$ elevation after TRH, degradation might be a very important turn-off signal for InsP$_3$ effect. It was, therefore, very likely that some of the lesser phosphorylated sugars might be antagonists or turn off signals. We performed those mixing experiments in which the effect of InsP$_3$ was monitored in the presence of, for example, InsP$_2$, unfortunately the effect of InsP$_3$ was not at all interfered with by InsP$_2$ or inositol monophosphate or inositol.

L. Birnbaumer: Have you been able to isolate membrane vesicles with calcium stores and perform the same type of calcium release experiment in a cell-free system?

M. C. Gershengorn: Clearly that is one of the major avenues that we are now pursuing, that is, to try to demonstrate conclusively the intracellular vesicular pool from which InsP$_3$ is releasing calcium. We will then obtain this membrane fraction to perform biochemical studies so as to understand better the way InsP$_3$ releases calcium from inside the cell. We have only very preliminary evidence that at least in a subcellular fraction markedly enriched in endoplasmic reticulum that InsP$_3$ does have its effect. The data, however, that have already been published are the data alluded to using a rat insulinoma model [Prentki, M., Biden, T. J., Janjic, D., Irvine, R. F., Berridge, M. J., and Wollheim, C. B. (1984). *Nature* (*London*) **309**, 562–564]. In microsomes derived from the rat insulinoma, InsP$_3$ caused release of preaccumulated calcium only from a fraction enriched in endoplasmic reticulum. Our data aren't quite as well along as those yet.

L. Birnbaumer: Do you know whether people are making analogs to IP$_3$? What sort of structure–activity relationships exist?

M. C. Gershengorn: That's a very important question, and I was careful, I think to call our preparation InsP$_3$ or inositol trisphate. Although, as on the schematic I showed you, I think it's the 1,4,5-triphosphorylated sugar. I don't know that. It is important to mention that InsP$_3$ is not available commercially, so you end up making it yourself, and most laboratories, including the three or four laboratories to which I've alluded already who have performed similar studies in different tissues, have received their InsP$_3$ from Robin Irvine's group in Great Britain. The initial production of that InsP$_3$ was by enzymatic hydrolysis of PtdIns(4,5)P$_2$ in erythrocyte membranes; more recently, they have switched over to enzymatic hydrolysis in bovine brain membranes. Everyone has avoided using acid hydrolysis of PtdIns(4,5)P$_2$ because it is well known that during exposure to strong acids to cleave the diester linkage there is rearrangement of the other phosphates on the myoinositol ring. We have taken another approach. We have shown in other studies that there is a phospholipase C activity or activities within the cytosol fraction of GH_3 cells. We used this as a source of our enzyme to specifically cleave $PtdIns(4,5)P_2$, purified from that available commercially. We believe, therefore, that the conformation of the $InsP_3$ is 1,4,5-triphosphate because it's been generated by enzyme cleavage; however, we have not shown that. So my guess is that although we might have several different isomers of the $InsP_3$ molecule in our preparation, I think most of it is the 1,4,5-triphosphate. Moreover, I do think that the positions of the phosphate groups are very important.

L. Birnbaumer: This brings me to the initial reaction of TRH and the stimulation of the phospholipase C activity. Could you give us a short update of where the research stands in terms of the biochemistry of the lipases?

M. C. Gershengorn: First of all, it's almost impossible to give a short update because there have been many different laboratories working with phospholipase C enzymes from many different tissue sources. One of the problems in this field, at least in the first 25 years, was that I think investigators were concentrating on the wrong enzyme. They were studying phospholipases C that hydrolyze phosphatidylinositol (PtdIns); the concept that PtdIns4P and $PtIns(4,5)P_2$ are the more important lipids involved in stimulation was really not appreciated. This is not in any way to denigrate what had been done previously because much very important information may be gleaned from those studies.

$PtdIns(4,5)P_2$ and PtdIns4P were avoided because these lipids are (1) minor components, (2) terribly labile, and (3) because of their high charge density were very difficult to separate on thin layer chromatographic systems. It was only until recently, when the idea of using systems that would chelate calcium away from the lipid so as to allow it to migrate on thin layer systems, that these lipids have been more readily analyzed. One of the problems in the literature is that it is stated that phospholipases C require calcium for stimulability. If that were true, then you would worry that the first effect after a ligand that stimulates this activity interacts with its receptor might raise cytoplasmic free calcium, and that the lipase C activity follows this. I think it's fair to summarize those data now to suggest that calcium is important for activation *in vitro*; however, in the physiologic, that is, micromolar or submicromolar, range calcium per se is not a very strong activator of lipase C activity. Clearly if you achieve millimolar calcium concentration in a test tube you get a profound stimulation of lipase C activity. *In vivo*, however, an elevation of cytoplasmic calcium does not precede enzyme activation.

A second problem and I think the major one, that we have no direct evidence for or against, is which lipase C and, more importantly, in which subcellular site is the lipase C that is stimulated by ligand. Clearly, the majority of the phospholipase C activity in intact cells resides in a soluble fraction, but also there is about 5% within the plasma membrane. My prejudice, as shown in my model of TRH action, is that TRH stimulates a phospholipase C specific for $PtdIns(4,5)P_2$, that is within the plasma membrane. The next more interesting question, especially to someone like yourself, is how does TRH–receptor interaction turn on even a plasma membrane localized phospholipase C. Unfortunately, I can't give you any definitive answers to that, but I can describe the major areas of research at the present time. The potential molecular mechanisms by which the TRH–receptor complex might stimulate a plasma membrane localized enzyme include the following. TRH–receptor interaction may affect a conformational change that increases accessibility of the $PtdIns(4,5)P_2$ molecule to the enzyme or vice versa. In fact, that there are major changes in the conformation of plasma membranes in GH_3 cells upon TRH receptor interaction was shown quite clearly by monitoring tryptophan fluoresence [Imae, T., Fasman, G. D., and Tashjian, A. H., Jr. (1979). *Biochim. Biophys. Acta* **552**, 103–113]. Hence, it is possible that the enzyme itself is not activated but that the substrate and enzyme are brought into contact. A second possibility, one that we are very interested in and hope to pursue, is that, by analogy to the growth factor receptors having an intrinsic tyrosine kinase activity, the TRH receptor possesses intrinsic phospholipase C activity directed specifically against PtdIns(4,5)P$_2$. This is very appealing to me, but we have no data so far.

A third possibility that we have pursued, by analogy to the adenylate cyclase system, is that there is a coupling protein between receptor and lipase C analogous to the guanine nucleotide binding protein that has been so elegantly demonstrated for the cyclase system. There is some indirect evidence that there is a guanine nucleotide binding protein involved in the TRH receptor interaction. Hinkle and Kinsella [Hinkle, P. M., and Kinsella, P. A. (1984). *J. Biol. Chem.* **259**, 3445–3449] have shown that GTP decreased receptor affinity for TRH in GH cell plasma membranes and Hinkle and Phillips [Hinkle, P. M., and Phillips, W. J. (1984). *Proc. Natl. Acad. Sci. U.S.A.*, in press) showed that TRH stimulated a GTPase activity associated with plasma membranes derived from GH cells. Whether this binding protein for guanine nucleotides is involved with coupling TRH–receptor interaction to the lipase C is not known. We have performed a study using Bordetella pertussis toxin in GH$_3$ cells; pertussis is known to ADP-ribosylate the inhibitor, guanine nucleotide binding protein of the adenylate cyclase system (N$_1$) and inactivate it. We reasoned that if a N$_i$-like protein were involved in TRH–receptor stimulation of phospholipase C pertussis toxin treatment might inhibit TRH response. P. M. Hinkle, E. L. Hewlett, and I found that there was no effect of intoxication with pertussis toxin on TRH-induced changes in cytoplasmic free calcium, phospholipid metabolism and prolactin secretion in GH cells. Hence, if a guanine nucleotide-binding protein is involved in TRH it's one that either isn't ADP-ribosylated by pertussis toxin or ADP-ribosylation does not affect its biological activity.

G. D. Aurbach: In your permealized cell preparation would it be possible to introduce inositol triphosphate, and determine whether secretion is affected? What is known about the mechanism of action of potassium which, of course, can release a variety of pituitary, pancreatic, and other hormones? What is the connection between potassium and intracellular calcium? Are intracellular kinases activated by potassium?

M. C. Gershengorn: Unfortunately, in the detergent-permeabilized GH$_3$ cell, TRH–receptor interaction is abolished. This is an interesting finding because I think it suggests that the lipid environment within which the TRH–receptor resides in the plasma membrane is important for its binding activity as we did not observe release of receptor into the medium. We are trying other ways of permeabilizing cells to circumvent this difficulty. We have started to use a method of hypotonic shock, described by Borle and Snowdowne [Borle, A. B., and Snowdowne, K. W. (1982). *Science* **217**, 252–254]. GH$_3$ cells permeabilized by this method will reseal and are still responsive to TRH stimulation [Snowdowne, K. W., and Borle, A. B. (1984). *Am. J. Physiol.* **246** (*Endocrinol. Metab.* 9), E198–E201]. We have not as yet performed experiments with this preparation. For completeness, another method to permeabilize cells involves exposure to very transient high voltage fields [Baker, P. F., and Knight, D. E. (1978). *Nature (London)* **276**, 620–622]. We have not used this method.

As far as potassium depolarization is concerned, if I take the stance of giving you the majority opinion it's quite simple: namely, that depolarization induced by high extracellular potassium opens calcium gates by changing the membrane potential difference, and that the only effect of potassium depolarization is to allow for influx of extracellular calcium. This is easy to substantiate because if you take calcium out of the extracellular buffer and then try to stimulate cells with depolarization by potassium in the majority of instances you abolish the biological response. I'm not certain, however, whether there isn't an additional effect of the depolarization process per se on other aspects of cellular calcium homeostasis. This notion comes from data in a paper we published about 1 year ago [Gershengorn, M. C., Thaw, C., and Gerry, R. H. (1983). *Cell Calcium* **4**, 117–124]. When we depolarized GH$_3$ cells in the presence of EGTA, we still found stimulation of ^{45}Ca efflux and a small release of prolactin. We have not gone back and performed experiments to determine the site of calcium release. Is this due to mobilization of intracellular stores of calcium? I don't know. Is this due to release of calcium that might have been bound to the cytoplasmic side or extracellular side of the plasma membrane which is released as you dissipate the potential gradient across the membrane? I can't tell you. And is this the mechanism by which that small stimulation of prolactin secretion occurred? I can't tell you that either. However, I do think there may be other effects of depolarization by high extracellular potassium in addition to stimulating calcium influx by opening voltage-dependent channels.

K. A. Gregerson: I have a question that may relate to this subject of potassium-induced depolarization. Depolarization should activate sodium channels, allowing an influx of sodium ions down their electrochemical gradient. The resulting elevation in intracellular sodium can, in turn, mobilize intracellular stores of calcium. It would be a small effect that may account for the small biological response you have just described. My question is: have you at any time examined the transport of sodium during TRH-induced prolactin release or have you tried blocking the sodium channels with something like tetrodotoxin to see if this has an effect on the initial phase of the Quin 2 response? The reason I ask this is that experiments on the electrophysiological response of lactotrophs to TRH demonstrate an initial hyperpolarization which would be concurrent with the initial rise in cytosolic calcium as measured by Quin 2. This current appears to be carried by potassium ions and, indeed, looks very much like calcium-activated potassium channels. However, I believe it is *not* dependent on external calcium but *is* dependent on external *sodium*. What I'm getting at is that if there is an influx of sodium during the TRH stimulus, as during a potassium depolarization, the sodium may mobilize intracellular stores of calcium, accounting for the observations I just mentioned and at least contributing to the initial rise of cytosolic calcium.

M. C. Gershengorn: First of all, for those not familiar with what Dr. Gregerson was alluding to, I think I showed schematically that there are at least two mechanisms to exclude calcium from cells: (1) sodium–calcium exchange and (2) the Ca^{2+},Mg^{2+}-ATPase or calcium "pump" at the plasma membrane. In normal secretory cells, it is not known which one of these is predominant under physiological circumstances. It is possible that these two mechanisms, which can act in concert, can act to variable extents under different conditions. You may be aware that there are two recent publications in the *Journal of Biological Chemistry* [Kaczorowski, G. J., Costello, L., Dethmers, J., Trumble, M. J., and Vandlen, R. L. (1984). *J. Biol. Chem.* **259**, 9395–9403; Barros, F., and Kaczorowski, G. J. (1984). *J. Biol. Chem.* **259**, 9404–9410] which have demonstrated in plasma membrane vesicles from GH$_3$ cells both the sodium–calcium exchanger and the Ca^{2+},Mg^{2+}-ATPase, and we have data that are very similar to those as well. So, clearly, both of those mechanisms may be active. Our biological data, however, demonstrate that if we deplete the extracellular space of sodium by substituting choline chloride from sodium chloride, we still find an optimal TRH-induced prolactin secretory response. Hence, at least from that point of view, I don't think that sodium influx is necessary. Your idea that the transient hyperpolarization after TRH binding may be due to sodium is something that we have not tested directly. We are not electrophysiologists, therefore, I can't answer that. We have not looked either at the effect of TRH on sodium flux, either uptake or release, although we have looked at the effect of TRH on ^{86}Rb efflux which is the usual way of monitoring what is believed to be potassium fluxes. As you would predict, concomitant with the rise in cytoplasmic free calcium there's also an efflux of ^{86}Rb suggesting that the potassium channels in the GH$_3$ cell behave like other potassium channels and are most likely activated by the rise in cytoplasmic free calcium.

Hence, I can't describe any data that point to a requirement for sodium in TRH action, at least at this level. Moreover, the sodium channel blocking agents, such as tetrodotoxin, have no effect on TRH-induced prolactin secretion either, or on the rise of cytoplasmic free calcium.

K. A. Gregerson: You're saying that it has no effect when you're looking at the biological response in prolactin, but is that during that initial phase.

M. C. Gershengorn: I think it's not only on prolactin secretion but also on the initial rise in cytoplasmic free calcium.

V. Ramirez: I would like to comment, and to present some data that we have published in the *Journal of Neuroscience* last year in relation with the effect of potassium on our *in vitro* hypothalamic preparations; this work was done in collaboration with Dr. Zamora an expert in electron microscopy at Marseille, and there we found that potassium produces marked changes in the ultrastructural morphology of the mitochondria, that reveal to us that perhaps the increase in intracellular calcium induced by the mechanism that you mentioned only alters phosphorylation of a specific protein, but may, as you know, modify in a very dramatic way, the metabolism of calcium at the level of the mitochondria; so my question to you, because I was really shocked when you said that IP3 was acting through mobilization of calcium from other cell system on mitochondria: Have you tried to check these at the EN, or have you had a chance and possibility to examine this phenomenon at the EN in your GH$_3$ cells?

M. C. Gershengorn: Let me try to answer that with a brief historical introduction. It was believed for many years up to about 3 or 4 years ago that the majority of intracellular calcium was present within the mitochondria, not in other nonmitochondrial pools. That conclusion was drawn exclusively from studies employing subcellular fractionation. I think most workers in the field now believe that those very high levels of calcium measured in mitochondria are artifactual. I think those experiments really showed that if you preturb the plasma membrane in any way and allow for increased influx of extracellular calcium, the majority, if not the entirety, of that calcium ends up in mitochondria. Hence, I'm not surprised by the findings of the photomicrographic studies that you describe, because if you increase the entry of calcium in this unphysiological way, for example, by depolarization with 45 to 50 mM potassium, which represents a change in membrane potential difference from about -50 to -5 mV, you produce much more influx of extracellular calcium than would ever occur during physiological stimulation. Moreover, we have data that confirms your findings. When we depolarize GH$_3$ cells, the additional calcium has gone almost exclusively into the mitochondrial pool. However, physiologically, the important differences between the mitochondrial and the nonmitochondrial pool are 2-fold. The nonmitochondrial pool, as I think I tried to show on one of the slides, has a low-capacity, high-affinity calcium sequestration mechanism that is almost fully saturated at cytoplasmic free calcium levels of 100 nM. In contrast, the mitochondrial uptake mechanism is of much lower affinity but its capacity, at least under our experimental conditions, appears unlimited. Specifically, we have not fully saturated the mitochondrial pool of GH$_3$ cells, when permeabilized cells were incubated in medium with up to 2–3 μM free calcium; I'm certain that in medium with millimolar calcium you'll do it, but we don't believe that that's physiologically relevant.

D. A. Leong: I'm curious about how prolactin cells, stimulated with TRH, turn off, when TRH is withdrawn. Have you withdrawn TRH, or antagonized the action of TRH, during the second phase of the increase in calcium in order to see if calcium then falls?

M. C. Gershengorn: That is a very important question and the answer is easy. At present, there are no TRH antagonists that will rapidly displace TRH from the plasma membrane receptor under physiological conditions. When you try to dilute and wash the TRH out, the $t_{\frac{1}{2}}$ for receptor binding in the intact cell, even at 37°C, is greater than 20–30 minutes, so we cannot, at present, rapidly turn off that effect. When we try to block the second phase response, by, for example, adding a calcium channel blocking agent 3–4 minutes into the TRH stimulation, we do affect two changes: (1) we lower the cytoplasmic free calcium level from 220 back down to 120 nM and partially, but not totally, inhibit the prolongation of the prolactin secretory response. That finding has been taken by others to suggest that part of the more prolonged secretory response, the one after 2 minutes if you will, is being generated simultaneously by a small rise in cytoplasmic calcium acting in concert with diacylglycerol stimulation of protein kinase C. We have not performed those experiments so that I can't confirm that interpretation

J. Meites: First of all, I concur with Dr. Robbins' initial statement and want to congratulate you on your clear presentation. However, I wonder when studying the mechanisms controlling prolactin secretion, about your model and parameters. You used a tumor cell, the GH$_3$ cell, that secretes both prolactin and growth hormone. What about using a normal cell? Second, you used TRH, and there is a serious question as to whether it is the physiological releasor of prolactin. Ever since Tashjian in 1971 came out with the evidence showing the TRH will release prolactin in these cells, there's been reason to question whether TRH is a physiological releasor of prolactin. You know that in most physiological situations when you get prolactin release, TSH is not necessarily released at the same time, and may even go in the opposite direction. On the other hand, estrogen is a prolactin releasor that can act directly on the prolactin cell to release prolactin, as we and others have shown. Also VIP appears to be a good candidate as a direct releasor of prolactin and may be the prolactin releasing factor (PRF) of the hypothalamus. Finally I'd like to ask you how a substance like dopamine acts directly on the prolactin cell to inhibit prolactin secretion.

M. C. Gershengorn: First of all, I agree wholeheartedly with you that the major physiological regulation of prolactin secretion does not appear to be via TRH, and I didn't mean to imply that TRH acting on GH$_3$ cells was analogous to the physiological secretagogue acting in the intact animal. I don't think TRH is. The second point relates to the cell model, that is, can you use a neoplastic cell as a model for study of normal physiological regulation? I think the answer to that is most certainly yes. The conclusion is based on many studies in which a comparison between the action of various stimulants has been compared in neoplastic and nonneoplastic cells—the effects in the majority of instances are similar. We were concerned initially with using these neoplastic cells as models, and in our initial studies of secretion, where possible, compared the effects with GH cells with those observed in cells derived from the nonneoplastic rat pituitary. For example, in one study, we compared the effects of verapamil, an organic calcium channel blocking agent, on TRH stimulation of prolactin and TSH secretion. Our model for prolactin secretion was GH$_3$ cells and for TSH secretion was TtT cells, cells in primary culture derived from mouse pituitary tumors [Gershengorn, M. C. (1983). In "Molecular Basis of Thyroid Hormone Action" (J. H. Oppenheimer and H. H. Samuels, eds.), pp. 387–412. Academic Press, New York]. Verapamil had no effect on TRH stimulation of prolactin secretion from the neoplastic or nonneoplastic cells but partially inhibited, by about 50%, TRH stimulated TSH secretion from both neoplastic and nonneoplastic cells [Geras, E., Rebecchi, M. J., and Gershengorn, M. C. (1982). *Endocrinology* **110,** 901–906]. Of note are the similar findings in human subjects given verapamil intravenously, namely, that verapamil had no effect on TRH stimulation of prolactin secretion but that it inhibited TRH stimulation of TSH secretion by about 70% [Barbarino, A., and Demarinis, L. (1980). *J. Clin. Endocrinol. Metab.* **51,** 749–753]. Hence, these neoplastic cells appear to be very good models for the study of intracellular mechanisms because of the great advantage of being a homogeneous population of cells. I think this advantage overwhelms the potential disadvantage especially for the biochemical studies that we are involved in.

As far as dopamine is concerned, unfortunately, the GH_3 cell is not a model for dopamine inhibition of prolactin secretion. As a matter of fact, I think the consensus opinion is that bona fide dopamine receptor is not present on GH_3 cell membranes. However, we as well as several other groups have shown inhibitory effects of dopamine and dopamine analogs in GH_3 cells but only at a micromolar concentration for which we have preliminary data to suggest is via a nonspecific local anesthetic like action. That's quite different from the specific effect which occurs with nanomolar concentrations of dopamine, as seen in the normal pituitary. So I don't think GH_3 cells are a model in which to study dopamine action.

The effect of TRH on phospholipid turnover has been studied in pituitary cells derived from normal rats but only be measuring [^{32}P]phosphate labeling of lipids [Leung, P. C. K., Raymond, V., and Labrie, F. (1982). *Life Sci.* **31**, 3037–3041]. As I mentioned before, it is a sensitive way of monitoring phospholipid turnover, but I think a limited way because it tells you nothing about changes in mass of the lipids or the enzymes being stimulated. It was observed that TRH stimulated ^{32}P incorporation into phosphatidylinositol and phosphatadic acid in those cells, suggesting that if you look further to the polyphosphorylated derivatives you'd see the same effects I showed you today. There is evidence that dopamine may partially inhibit ^{32}P incorporation into phosphatidylinositol [Canonico, P. L., Valdenegro, C. A., and MacLeod (1983). *Endocrinology* **113**, 7–14]; however, I hasten to add that Brown's group in Great Britain has found no effect of dopamine to inhibit TRH-induced hydrolysis of PtdIns(4,5)P_2. My notion regarding how dopamine acts is similar to my feeling about how somatostatin acts in these cells. Namely, that we may see as with somatostatin-induced partial inhibition of VIP-stimulated adenylate cyclase activity as a good example, that with dopamine you might see a partial inhibition of phospholipid turnover but that cannot be the only mechanism whereby these two inhibitors act, because they also inhibit stimulated secretion induced by other ligands that do not act by either of these mechanisms. Hence, I believe that there's a more distal site of action for somatostatin and for dopamine also.

J. Robbins: There are partially successful procedures for separating normal pituitary cells. Do you think there's any possibility that you could move in that direction?

M. C. Gershengorn: I'm glad you said "partially successful" because the best that has been accomplished is an enrichment of one cell type over another; there has been no method reported that I'm aware of that has produced populations of even 80% of a single cell type in any of these separation methods. I think, therefore, that is a possible way to proceed and one that is being pursued actively in several laboratories.

M. O. Thorner: I wanted to come back to Dr. Leong's question and I don't really have any experience with TRH but we have quite a lot of experience with GnRH on our pituitary cell columns, and I'm really disturbed at the concept that after withdrawal of the hypothalamic hormone, you continue to have an effect that goes on for 20 or 30 minutes because on LH secretion with GnRH as soon as we withdraw it, within a minute, or within the time frame of the elution from the column we see a reduction in LH. I wonder whether the 20 minute time frame you described might be an "artifact," a characteristic of the system of using primary cultured cells where it is very difficult to really remove the hormone that you are dealing with.

M. C. Gershengorn: I don't think so. And the reasons are several. (1) We've performed similar experiments with nonneoplastic and neoplastic cells in perifusion columns; similar to those which you are referring to with GnRH. When we administer TRH in a pulsatile fashion to either one of these cell systems, we see a secretory response which persists, in the majority of experiments, for 20 minutes. Of note also, are the findings that brief TRH exposure will induce a prolactin synthetic response 24–48 hours later [Murdoch, G. H., Franco, R., Evans, R. M., and Rosenfeld, M. G. (1983). *Biol. Chem.* **258**, 15329–15335].

Hence, withdrawing the releasing factor need not lead to obliteration of the biologic response.

M. O. Thorner: To answer the other question you bring up; I think that we really do not know. First of all the effects that they showed were on messenger RNAs. I think one has to be very cautious of extrapolating messenger RNA changes necessarily to change in ultimate synthesis of the protein. It may be true, it may not be true, that changes of messenger RNA always lead to changes in protein synthesis. To my knowledge it is not established. I think that the question that Dr. Leong was asking was that if you withdraw the hormone without the complexities of artificial systems, what happens? Let us just take the *in vivo* situation in man where you give an infusion of a hypothalamic hormone and stop the infusion. You see that within the time frame of the half-life of the hormone almost instantly the infusion is stopped, if you're giving low doses, the hormone secretion stops. And I think that that problem needs to be addressed.

M. C. Gershengorn: I'm sorry if I implied that we were able to perform the experiment that you are suggesting. We have not been able to rapidly displace TRH from its receptor during static incubations. Unfortunately, when you perform this experiment in the perifusion columns you have different conditions, namely, cells that are adsorbed to polyacrylamide beads in a perfusion chamber; this set of conditions may yield results that are somewhat different than cells in static incubations in suspension.

M. Selmanoff: I'd like to come back to one of Dr. Meites' questions. I believe you have done some work using VIP in the GH$_3$ cells. Could you relate to us any differences you have discovered regarding intracellular effects of VIP versus TRH?

M. C. Gershengorn: To be honest, the work I'll restate is not my own, it is mainly from two laboratories, Martin's in Wisconsin and Tashjian's in Boston [Drust, D. S., Sutton, C. A., and Martin, T. F. J. (1982). *J. Biol. Chem.* **257,** 3306–3312; Sobel, A., and Tashjian, A. H., Jr. (1983). *J. Biol. Chem.* **258,** 10312–10324]. It appears that vasoactive intestinal polypeptide (VIP) interacts with receptors on the GH$_3$ cell surface to directly stimulate, in a guanine nucleotide-dependent way, adenylate cyclase activity. In contrast, and these are our data, VIP has no effect to turn over polyphosphoinositides. The effect of VIP can be partially inhibited by somatostatin and by, in other studies using membranes derived from normal rat pituitaries, dopamine. One apparent mode of action of somatostatin and dopamine is to directly antagonize the stimulation of adenylate cyclase. I think that although TRH and VIP acutely stimulate prolactin release, they act in GH$_3$ cells by independent pathways. For example, different protein phosphorylations are stimulated by TRH versus VIP. VIP, cyclic AMP analogs, and cyclic AMP phosphodiesterase inhibitors stimulate the phosphorylation of a given subset of soluble proteins within GH$_3$ cells. Cell depolarization with potassium causes a transient rise in cytoplasmic free calcium concentration, and stimulates phosphorylation of a separate subset of soluble proteins in GH$_3$ cells. There is no apparent overlap between the cyclic AMP- nor the high potassium depolarization-induced phosphorylations. Phorbol esters, which appear to act by stimulating protein kinase C, stimulate the phosphorylation of a third subset of cytosolic proteins. TRH, on the other hand, stimulates two out of those three subclasses, those affected by phorbol esters and by high potassium but TRH does not affect the cyclic AMP-stimulated class. In contrast, VIP does not affect proteins phosphorylated by phorbol esters nor high potassium but only those affected by elevating intracellular cyclic AMP. Hence, I think there are clearly two separate actions, one mediated by cyclic AMP, the other one mediated by a rise in cytoplasmic free calcium in concert with stimulation of protein kinase C that yields in the GH$_3$ cell a coordinate stimulation of the biological response, namely prolactin secretion.

INDEX

A

A23187, 144, 635–639
Acetylcholine
  interaction with somatostatin, 342–343
  in teleosts, 534
ACTH, *see* Adrenocorticotropic hormone
Actin, cholesterol transport and, 7–12, 14,
  15, 28, 37
Actinomycin D, 6
Adenosine triphosphate, calcium uptake,
  638–640
Adenylyl cyclase system, *see also* C unit;
  N_i protein; N_s protein
  dual regulation by subunits of, 59
  fluoride ion and, 82–84
  forskolin and, 84–85
  hormonal regulation of, 61–70
    inhibitory, 66–67
    parameter affected, 61–62
    stimulatory, 62–66
  structure, 43–46
Adrenal gland, glucocorticoid resistance
  and, 221
Adrenocorticotropic hormone
  cell rounding and, 7, 32, 36
  cholesterol transport studies, 4–29
  high levels, 244
  mechanism of action, 149–150
  plasma levels, 218–219
  release, urotensin I and, 559–561
  side-chain cleavage and, 2–6
  steroidogenesis and, 1–39
Aldosterone
  plasma levels, 232
  urinary, 203–204
Aldosterone receptor, 230, 233
Aldosterone resistance, 237
α subunit, 577
Alzheimer's disease, 366–367
Aminoglutethimide, 4–5, 8, 11, 15, 16, 17,
  23, 24, 26, 168–169, 186–188
Amphetamine, in dopamine release studies, 425, 426, 427, 428, 429, 430
Androgen receptor, 236, 261
Androgen resistance, 237, 241

Δ^4-Androstenedione, 153, 170, 201, 202
Anti-actin antibodies, 9–12, 34
Antibody, to steroid receptors, 264, 266–
  268
Antiestrogen, in cancer therapy, 254–258
Antipain, 279
Antiprogestin agents, *see* R5020; RU38 486
Arcuate nucleus, 411, 423
Ascorbic acid depletion, 34–35

B

Bacterial toxins, 44, 46, *see also* Cholera
  toxin; Pertussis toxin
Bis(hexafluoroacetonyl) acetone, 617–619,
  624–625
Brain-specific proteins, 347–357, *see also*
  1B236
Breast cancer, *see also* Mammary tumors,
  experimental
  progestin and treatment of, 253–258

C

Cadmium ion, gene transcription and, 321–
  322
Calcium ion
  cholesterol transport and, 21–22, 32–33,
    35, 38–39
  cytoplasmic-free, TRH and, 619–625
  steroid synthesis and, 19–22, 32–33, 35–
    36
  TRH and, 608–625, 633–638, 642–644
  versus phosphoinositides, 633–638
Calmodulin, steroid synthesis and, 19–22,
  32–33, 38–39
cAMP
  effect on Leydig cell steroidogenesis,
    153–154, 169–178, 180–190
  LHRH secretion and, 452–457
  receptor types affecting formation of, 42
  steroidogenesis and, 1–39
Carbohydrate processing
  conformational changes and, 603–604,
    606
  of TSH, 585–595, 603–604